SOIL MANAGEMENT IN TROPICAL AMERICA

ŚOIL MANAGEMENT IN TROPICAL AMERICA

Edited by:

Elemer Bornemisza

and

Alfredo Alvarado

Proceedings of a Seminar held at CIAT, Cali, Colombia
February 10 - 14, 1974

Co-sponsored by:

University Consortium on Soils of the Tropics
Centro Internacional de Agricultura Tropical
U. S. Agency for International Development
Sociedad Colombiana de la Ciencia del Suelo
Sociedad Latinoamericana de la Ciencia del Suelo

Published on behalf of the University Consortium on
Soils of the Tropics by the Soil Science Department
North Carolina State University
Raleigh, N. C.   27607, USA

1975

SEMINAR STEERING COMMITTEE

Fernando Fernández

Tejpal S. Gill

Luiz Alfredo León

Rafael Pietri

James M. Spain

Pedro A. Sánchez, Chairman

Editors:

Elemer Bornemisza

Alfredo Alvarado

Supported by Grant AID/TA-G-1058 of the U. S. Agency for International Development to North Carolina State University

This book is also published in Spanish

CONTENTS

Chapter 5.—Land Use Classification in the Lowlands of Bolivia

T. T. Cochrane

Chapter 6.—Soil Fertility Capability Classification

S. W. Boul, P. A. Sánchez
R. B. Cate Jr. and M. A. Granger

SECTION II.—SOIL-PLANT-WATER RELATIONS

Chapter 7.—Soil-Water Relations in Oxisols from Puerto Rico and Brazil

J. M. Wolf

Chapter 17.—Residual Effects of Liming a Latosol in São Paulo, Brazil

L. M. M. de Freitas and B. Van Raij

Chapter 18.—Differential Species and Varietal Tolerance to Soil Acidity in Tropical Crops and Pastures

J. M. Spain, C. A. Francis,
R. H. Howeler and F. Calvo

Chapter 19.—Micronutrient Limitations in Tropical Acid Rice Soils

F. N. Ponnamperuma

SECTION V.—SOIL MANAGEMENT SYSTEMS

Chapter 20.—Management Implications of Soil Mineralogy in Latin America

G. Uehara and J. Keng

SECTION VI.—SOIL FERTILITY EVALUATION

Chapter 25.—The Soil Fertility Evaluation Program in Guatemala

J. A. Palencia, J. L. Walker

and L. Estrada L.

Chapter 26.—New Techniques and Equipment for Routine Soil Plant Analytical Procedures

A. H. Hunter

Chapter 27.—New Concepts of Biological and Economical Interpretation of Fertilizer Response

D. L. Waugh, R. B. Cate, Jr.,

L. A. Nelson and A. Manzano

Chapter 28—Adequate Use of Fertilizers on Perennial and Annual Crops in Ecuador

W. Bejarano, J. Laínez

and S. S. Portch

FOREWORD

The Seminar on Soil Management and the Development Process in Tropical America was held with the objective of bringing together soil scientists and administrators to discuss relevant research advances on the application of soil science to this region. This is the second major regional seminar organized by the University Consortium on Soils of the Tropics and the first in Latin America.

The planning phase was conducted in cooperation with the four cosponsoring institutions. A Steering Committee was organized with representatives of each institution. They were responsible for the selection of the topics and speakers. Emphasis was given to invite outstanding working soil scientists from tropical America. In order not to lose worldwide perspective, speakers from other areas reported on research relevant to Tropical America.

The Centro Internacional de Agricultura Tropical offered to host the Seminar and kindly provided their excellent facilities and logistical support. The U. S. Agency for International Development awarded North Carolina State University, on behalf of the Consortium, a special grant (AID/TA-G-1058) to cover the travel of some participants as well as the publication of these proceedings in English and Spanish. A total of 209 representatives of 23 countries participated in the event.

A total of 33 papers were presented to the Seminar and are published in these proceedings. They are grouped in seven sections which focus on specific components of soil management.

Valuable new data in soil properties from the interior of South America are presented in the first section, as well as ways to correlate the different classification systems and interpret them in terms of land use and fertility limitations.

The usually ignored relationships between soils, plants and water are covered in the second section.

Studies on nitrogen sources, both symbiotic and inorganic, are the topics for the third section. The management of acid soils occupy a prominent place because of the vast extensions of such soils in Tropical America. Critical aspects such as liming requirements, residual effects and varietal and species tolerance to soil acidity are discussed in the fourth section.

The fifth section deals with the theoretical and practical aspects of soil management in savannas and rainforests. The sixth section covers the advances in soil fertility evaluation which have had a significant impact in the region. The last section describes the suggested mechanisms for closer collaboration and the development of a research network in tropical soils.

The Steering Committee is grateful for the leadership provided by the session chairmen: Waldemar Moura Filho (Brazil), Juan A. Comerma (Venezuela), Idelfonso Plá (Venezuela), Elemer Bornemisza (Costa Rica), Miguel Menéndez (El Salvador), James M. Spain (Colombia), Jaime Lotero (Colombia), and Carlos Valverde (Perú).

It is obvious that no single publication can include all the recent relevant research that is presently being conducted in Tropical America. Many broad topics, such as phosphorus management were not discussed in depth due to recent symposia on the subject. This collection of papers, however, gives ample indication of the quality and maturity of tropical soil science in the region.

The Seminar was followed by a 10-day tour to cover ongoing research in various regions of Tropical America. These included the Carimagua Experiment Station in the Llanos Orientales of Colombia, the Vista Florida Experiments Station in the Lambayeque Valley on the northern coastal desert of Perú, the Yurimaguas Experiment Station in the Amazon Jungle of Perú and a 1000 km journey from Campinas to Brasília covering the State of São Paulo and the Campo Cerrado of Brazil. The logistical support of the following institutions is greatly acknowledged for the success of the field trips: Instituto Colombiano Agropecuario and CIAT in Colombia; Ministerio de Agricultura and Sociedad Peruana de la Ciencia del Suelo in Perú; Empresa Brasilera de Pesquisas Agropecuarias and Instituto Agronômico de Campinas in Brazil.

The Steering Committee is grateful for the efforts of the editors Elemer Bornemisza and Alfredo Alvarado for months of dedicated hard work in producing this book.

PEDRO A. SANCHEZ, CHAIRMAN
EXECUTIVE COMMITTEE
UNIVERSITY CONSORTIUM ON SOILS OF THE TROPICS
MAY, 1975.

PREFACE

This volume contains the papers presented at the Seminar on Soil Management and the Development Process in Tropical America. The papers present the experimental results and the points of view of 63 authors. The individual opinions of these authors were highly respected even accepting the risk of including in the present volume contradictory material. Many real and apparent contradictions are expected when new problems are tackled in variable conditions as is the case with soil science in Latin America.

It is evident that in spite of the rapid gain in knowledge in the field, the areas which remain to be explored are enormous and will require hard work for many years, until a coherent model of the soil systems of Latin America is obtained.

This Seminar intended to examine the recent findings in terms of both their scientific relevance as well as their implications to the development of the countries in this area.

It was felt that the Seminar has shown that the research carried out is aimed toward the solution of significant problems which limit agricultural production. It appears, that these problems can only be solved through the efficient collaboration of the specialists in the different branches of soil science and through the cooperation between soil scientists and researchers in the other agricultural sciences.

The editors appreciate the collaboration received from the authors, during the review process. Evidently, they are not responsible for the imperfections of the present volume, for which the editors are responsible. Comments to improve the volume will be much appreciated.

Special thanks are also due to the Chairman of the Steering Committee, Dr. P. A. Sanchez, for his effective help and continuous support during the edition of these proceedings. The assitance of several members of the Soil Science Department of North Carolina State University is also most appreciated as they were ready to solve the many problems which occurred during the final phase of the preparation of this manuscript.

The editors want to express their appreciation to the translators whose effort contributed to the usefullness of the present volume.

ELEMER BORNEMISZA, EDITOR
PROFESSOR OF SOIL SCIENCE
UNIVERSITY OF COSTA RICA -
IICA CONTRACT.

ALFREDO ALVARADO, EDITOR
ASSISTANT PROFESOR OF SOIL SCIENCE
UNIVERSITY OF COSTA RICA.

CONTRIBUTORS, EDITORS AND ORGANIZERS

FERNANDO ABRUÑA, Soil Scientist, Agricultural Research Service, USDA, Río Piedras, Puerto Rico.

ALFREDO ALVARADO, Profesor Asistente de Suelos, Universidad de Costa Rica, San José, Costa Rica.

NELSON DE BARROS, Subsecretario, Ministerio de Agricultura y Ganadería, Asunción, Paraguay.

RUFO BAZAN, Edafólogo, Centro Agronómico Tropical de Investigación y Enseñanza, Turrialba, Costa Rica.

FRIEDRICH H. BEINROTH, Profesor Asociado de Suelos, Universidad de Puerto Rico, Mayagüez, Puerto Rico.

WASHINGTON BEJARANO, Jefe, Departamento de Suelos, Estación Experimental de Santa Catalina, Instituto Nacional de Investigaciones Agropecuarias, Quito, Ecuador.

A. ALVIN BISHOP, Senior Water Management Specialist, Agency for Internacional Development, Washington, D. C., USA.

ELEMER BORNEMISZA, Profesor de Suelos, Universidad de Costa Rica - IICA, San José, Costa Rica.

STANLEY W. BUOL, Profesor of Soil Science, North Carolina State University, Raleigh, North Carolina, USA.

FABIO CALVO, Asistente de Investigación, Centro Internacional de Agricultura Tropical, Cali, Colombia.

MARCELO N. CAMARGO, Centro de Pesquisas Pedológicas, EMBRAPA, Ruã Jardim Botânico, Río de Janeiro, Brasil.

ROBERT B. CATE, Jr. Regional Director ISFEI, Soil Science Department, North Carolina State University, c/o USAID, Bogotá, Colombia.

THOMAS T. COCHRANE, Asesores Británicos en Agricultura Tropical, Santa Cruz, Bolivia.

ALVARO CORDERO V., Jefe Sección Fertilidad de Suelos, Ministerio de Agricultura y Ganadería, San José, Costa Rica.

JOHN M. DAY, Rothamstead Experimental Station, Harpenden, England.

S. K. DE DATTA, Head, Department of Agronomy, International Rice Research Institute, Los Baños, Philippines.

JOHANNA DÖBEREINER, Instituto de Pesquisas Agropecuarias do Centro Sul, EMBRAPA, Km 47, Campo Grande, G. B., Brasil.

LUIS ESTRADA L., Investigador Asistente, Instituto de Ciencias y Tecnología Agrícola, Guatemala.

ITALO C. FALESI, Director, Instituto de Pesquisas Agropecuarias do Norte, EMBRAPA, Belén, Pará, Brasil.

F. G. FAYE, Research Scholar, International Rice Research Institute. Los Baños, Philippines.

FERNANDO FERNANDEZ de C., Training Director, Centro Internacional de Agricultura Tropical, Cali, Colombia.

WARREN M. FORSYTHE, Soil Physicist, Centro Agronómico Tropical de Investigación y Enseñanza, Turrialba, Costa Rica.

CHARLES A. FRANCIS, Plant Breeder, Centro Internacional de Agricultura Tropical, Cali, Colombia.

LUIZ M. M. DE FREITAS, SERINCO Planejamiento Agropecuario, Matão, S.P., Brasil.

TEJPAL S. GILL, Senior Soil Scientist, U. S. Agency for International Development, Washington, D. C., USA.

ENRIQUE GONZALEZ E., Graduate Assistant, Soil Science Department, North Carolina State University, Raleigh, N. C., USA.

PETER H. GRAHAM, Soil Microbiologist, Centro Internacional de Agricultura Tropical, Cali, Colombia.

MICHAEL A. GRANGER, Research Associate, Soil Science Department, North Carolina State University, Raleigh, N. C., USA.

RAMIRO GUERRERO M., Director Regional, Instituto Colombiano Agropecuario, Bogotá, Colombia.

JAMES E. HAWES, U. S. Agency for International Development, Washington, D. C.

REINHARDT, H. HOWELER, Soil Scientist, Centro Internacional de Agricultura Tropical, Cali, Colombia.

DAVID H. HUBBELL, University of Florida, Gainesville, Fla., USA.

ARVEL H. HUNTER, Associate Professor North Carolina State University, Raleigh, N. C., USA.

ANTHONY S. R. JUO, Soil Chemist, International Institute for Tropical Agriculture, Ibadan, Nigeria.

B. T. KANG, Soil Fertility Specialist, International Institute for Tropical Agriculture, Ibadan, Nigeria.

OMER J. KELLEY, Director, Office of Agriculture, Agency for International Development, Washington, D. C., USA.

JOHNNY KENG, Graduate Assistant, Agronomy Department, Cornell University, Ithaca, New York, USA.

JOSE LAINEZ, Instituto Nacional de Investigaciones Agropecuarias, Quito, Ecuador.

RATTAN LAL, Soil Physicist, International Institute for Tropical Agriculture, Ibadan, Nigeria.

LUIS ALFREDO LEON, Director del Programa Nacional de Suelos, Instituto Colombiano Agropecuario, Palmira, Valle, Colombia.

EDSON LOBATO, Soil Scientist, EMBRAPA, Brasilia, Brasil.

R. N. MALIK, Research Scholar, International Rice Research Institute, Los Baños, Philippines.

AMADO MANZANO, Jefe, Programa Nacional de Evaluación de Fertilidad de Suelo. Ministerio de Agricultura, La Paz, Bolivia.

A. COLIN McCLUNG, Associate Director, Rockefeller Foundation, New York, N. Y., USA.

GORDON S. MINER, Assistant Professor of Soil Science, North Carolina State University, Raleigh, N. C., USA.

JAMES C. MOOMAW, Assistant Director, International Institute for Tropical Agriculture, Ibadan, Nigeria.

FRANK R. MOORMANN, Pedologist, International Institute for Tropical Agriculture, Ibadan, Nigeria.

GEORGE C. NADERMAN, Jr., Research Associate, Cornell University, Ithaca, New York, USA.

LARRY A. NELSON. Research Associate. ISFEI Soil Science Department, Raleigh, N. C., USA.

J. ANIBAL PALENCIA, Investigador Principal, Instituto de Ciencias y Tecnología Agrícolas, Guatemala.

ROBERT W. PEARSON, Soil Scientist, USDA, Agricultural Research Service, Auburn, Alabama, USA.

RAUL PEREZ-ESCOLAR, Soil Scientist, Agricultural Experiment Station, University of Puerto Rico, Río Piedras, Puerto Rico.

CARLOS PEREZ Y., Técnico Agropecuario, Centro Regional de Investigación Agraria del Norte, Chiclayo, Perú.

RAFAEL PIETRI O., Profesor de Suelos, Universidad de Puerto Rico, Mayagüez, Puerto Rico.

FELIX N. PONNAMPERUMA, Soil Chemist, International Rice Research Institute, Los Baños, Philippines.

SAM S. PORTCH, Regional Director ISFEI, Soil Science Department, North Carolina State University, c/o USAID, Balboa, Panamá.

GUILLERMO E. RAMIREZ, Especialista de Suelos, Centro Regional de Investigación Agraria del Norte, Chiclayo, Perú.

PEDRO A. SANCHEZ, Associate Professor of Soil Science, North Carolina State University, Raleigh, N. C., USA.

K. SANTHIRASEGARAM, FAO, Instituto Veterinario de Investigaciones Tropicales y de Altura, Pucallpa, Perú.

WILSON V. SOARES, Chefe, Estação Experimental de Brasilia, EMBRAPA, Brasilia, Brasil.

JAMES M. SPAIN, Soil Scientist, Centro Internacional de Agricultura Tropical, Cali, Colombia.

GORO UEHARA, Professor of Soil Science, University of Hawaii, Honolulu, Hawaii.

BERNARDO VAN RAIJ, Soil Scientist, Instituto Agronômico de Campinas, S. P., Brasil.

ARMAND VAN WAMBEKE, Geology Institute, University of Ghent, Belgium.

JOSE VICENTE-CHANDLER, Soil Scientist, Agricultural Research Service, USDA, Agricultural Experiment Station, Río Piedras, Puerto Rico.

JAMES L. WALKER, Regional Director ISFEI, Soil Science Department, North Carolina State University, c/o ROCAP-USAID, Guatemala.

DONOVAN L. WAUGH, Soil Science Department, North Carolina State University, Raleigh, N. C., USA.

JAMES M. WOLF, Graduate Assistant, Agricultural Engineering Department, Cornell University, Ithaca, N. Y., USA.

CARLOS ZAMORA J., Director de Estudios Integrados, Oficina Nacional de Evaluación de Recursos Naturales, Lima, Perú.

SECTION I

SOIL CHARACTERIZATION AND CLASSIFICATION

1 Soils of the Central Plateau and Transamazonic Highway of Brasil

MARCELO N. CAMARGO and ITALO C. FALESI

I CENTRAL PLATEAU

In the Brazilian highlands, the Planalto Central is usually understood as a vast area occupying the broad drainage divide and the upper valleys of tributaries diverging, N, NE, SW to Amazon, São Francisco and Paraná Basins. It is located approximately between 14° and 20° latitude and 46° and 54° longitude.

Environment

The region consists of a core of Pre-Cambrian crystalline rocks exposed or overlain by Palezoic to Mesozoic sediments. Most of the area was subjected to uplifts and polycyclic geomorphic evolution, evidences being remarkably well expressed around the Federal District as the results of successive planations and dissections.

This core area is typified by dominance of sizeable undissected remnants of ancient erosion surfaces, forming nearly level to gently sloping high plateau *(chapadas)* sometimes bound by escarpments. The oldest planation reaching about 1200 m is believed to date from the low-Terciary.

Outwards, upper reaches of major rivers are often deeply entrenched. *Chapadas* form mostly the main divides. These chapadas gradually decline in elevation, narrow and finally remain as hilly relicts, as they give way to younger encroached outer sections of land forms with progressively wider valleys dominating the landscape.

Two main vegetation formations are found in the Planalto a *cerrado* (various forms) and mesophytic forest (mainly semideciduous). The inner part of the region is currently considered as the *cerrado* core area. *Cerrados* dominate the *chapadas* plus very large extensions comprising gentle landforms on lower erosion surfaces and steep sloping dissected areas. Besides minor strips of riparian and marshy forest, there are occasional patches and a few sizeable areas of semi deciduous forests. They are to be found in some valleys, steep slopes of uprising hilly and few mountainous areas, but seldom as large extensions on younger erosion surfaces of gentle topography. Further north in the valley they merge with Amazon gallery forests.

The climate is characterized by moderate temperatures and a sub-humid moisture regime —ustic isoyhperthermic and sometimes isothermic— the latter confined to both high elevations and latitudes in small areas to the southeast. Rainfall is concentrated in the summer with a long dry season (4 to 6 months) in the winter. In most of the region the *Aw* Köppen climate prevails. Higher areas northward are under Cwa and southard under Cwb. Mean annual temperature range from 23.6 to 19.8°C, and annual rainfall from 1920 to 1340 mm.

Soils

The existing knowledge about the soils of the Planalto has been acquired through field studies, some soil surveys, experiments on soil fertility, observations on land use and crop behavior, and farming experience. The information obtained about the kinds of soil, their behavior and mode of occurence would indicate that the nature of the soils is far more related to variations in geomorphic landforms than to kind of underlying rocks, which merely underlie a "drift" mantle, pseudo-autochthonous or allochthonous.

As a rule, old, strongly weathered soil materials practically devoid of weatherable minerals mantle the *chapadas* and gentle landforms, while younger, less weathered and sometimes rich soil materials are found to occur on youthful landform areas or more recent erosion surfaces where landscape dissection has been more active.

Concretionary laterite formations and even plinthite are only locally important. They occur more often in the edges of *chapada* or as colluvial debris.

In these *chapadas* is where the most strongly weathered Brazilian tropical soils are found (see soil varieties pH H_2O < KCl in Table 1). They occur on the oldest and most stable land surfaces.

The occurence of eutrophic soils is related to incision of streams, dissection giving rise to younger landforms on basic rocks (crystalline ultrabasic, basic, intermediate till granodioritic, limestone and calcareous sediments) favorable to the formation of rich parent materials under the present environment on these soils semideciduous or deciduous forests develop.

Except for the marginal strips at the boundary of forest and forest openings induced by fire, *cerrados* are found on soils of very to extremely low natural fertility. Without fertilizer and lime, yields even of low demanding crops, are negligible at the very outset of farming, and subsequent crops invariably fail. Thus, limited grazing has been the only land use until recently.

Forests are virtually absent in the higher flat surfaces. Outside of these *chapadas,* they coexist with *cerrados* on dystrophic soils and dominate on eutrophic soils, these being more often associated with semideciduous or drier forests of the less humid parts of the region.

The main soils identified in the region are briefly described below. Condensed analytical data are given in Tables 1 and 2.

Latosols

Latosols are by far the predominant soils in the region, comprising mainly Haplustox, few Haplorthox and rare Umbriorthox, either under *cerrados* or forest, Acrustox and few Acrorthox, both chiefly under *cerrados,* rarely under forest, and not many Eutrustox, always under forest.

The kinds distinguished are: DarkRed Latosols —including dystrophic varieties (plus endodystrophic∼eutrophic epipedon), eutrophic, clayey, loamy, intergrade to Red Yellow Podzolic and to Quartz Sands. Dusky Red Latosol clayey— are derived from basic rocks and include dystrophic varieties (plus endodystrophic), eutrophic, clayey, loamy, inter-grade to Red Yellow Podzolic and to Quartz Sands, and shallow soils.

The Latosols with pH $H_2O < 1$ N KCl as in Table 1 pertain to Acrustox or Acrorthox. Eutrophic Latosols are mostly of the Dusky Red kind. Eutrophic loamy Red-Yellow Latosols have not been found in the Central Plateau.

Lithosols

Actually this heading includes various soils, mainly: Dystropept, Ustropept, Ustorthent plus lithic subgroups and shallow skeletal varieties of some Ultisols, Oxisols, Alfisols and Mollisols.

Such assemblage of soils is associated to rougher landforms and escarpments, sometimes affecting large extensions of the landscape. The soils are thin or not much developed beyond the Lithosol stage, their nature being quite conditioned to parent rocks themselves.

Quartz Sands (dystrophic)

They correspond to Quartzipsamments and usually include inter-grades to Latosols and to Red Yellow Podzolics. They are related to quartzose sandstones or their detritus capping high or low surfaces.

These soils occupy sizeable extensions and occur usually associated with gentle landforms. They are predominantly covered by *cerrados,* rarely under forest.

Red Yellow Podzolics

These are comprese mainly of Paleustult, some Haplustults, few Plinthustults. Udults might occasionally occur in the southeast. Varieties are: clayey, loamy/clayey, loamy, sandy/loamy, intergarde to Latosol, abruptic, seldom endodystrophic, and plinthic. As a constant the epipedons are ochric and CEC values are low (< 24 meq/100g clay).

These soils are chiefly related to younger dissected surfaces —rolling to hilly landforms— and to the more acid gneisses and similar rocks. Loamy and sandy/loamy varieties are derived from argillaceous sandstones on gently topography. Their overall occurence is not great and they are to be found more towards the less dry parts of the region. Natural vegetation is mostly forest with *cerrados* being scarce.

Red-Yellow Podzolic, eutrophic equivalent

Comprises mainly Paleustalfs and some Haplustalfs. Udalfs might occasionally be found in the southeast. Varieties are: clayey, loamy/clayey, loamy, sandy/loamy, intergrade to Latosol, abruptic, seldom with mollic epipedon (~Mollisol). In general, the epipedon is ochric and CEC values are low.

Their relation to landform pattern is similar to the Red Yellow Podzolics, nevertheless, they occur in areas where rocks are more favorable to their formation —less acid to intermediate gneisses and related crystalline rocks, calcareous sandstones— being mainly associated to dry parts of the region, hence drier forests.

Reddish Brunizems, clayey

They correspond to rhodic high CEC (>24 meq/100g clay) Argioustolls. Varieties are : intergrade to *Terra Roxa Estruturada*, lithic and vertic.

These soils are of small extent and strictly related to steep sloping areas on basic rock or limestone. Natural vegetation is deciduous forest.

Terra Roxa Estruturada

These are also known as Reddish Brown Lateritic eutrophic, clayey. They correspond to rhodic low CEC varieties of Paleoustalfs, Rhodustalfs and Argiustolls. Varieties are: intergrade to Latosol, to Red Yellow Podzolic Eutrophic equivalent, shallow (~intergrade to Red Brunizem), and with mollic epipedon.

They are confined to basic parent rocks and related to gently undulating to rolling topography and sub-deciduous forest, mostly the drier ones.

Undifferentiated Concretionary Soils, dystrophic

This generical heading gathers diverse soil kinds in which lateritic concretions are the dominating constituent. It includes mainly clayey, loamy/claley —all skeletal— varieties of Acrustox, Haplustox and Ustults. Udalfs have not been found in the Planalto. Their total extent is not great, yet locally important and a striking feature in the inner Planalto.

The soils are low CEC, epipedon is ochric or umbric, and predominant vegetation is *cerrado*. Forest and endodystrophic soils occur occasionally. This collection of soils is obviously useless for agriculture and range, but their material is of considerable value for construction.

Upland Ground-Water Laterite, clayey

These are mainly Plinthaquults, Plinthaquoxs and occasionally Plinth-aqualfs. Varieties are: with or without argillic horizon, clayey, loamy/clayey, abruptic. Usually the epipedon is ochric, CEC and base saturation are low, and drainage is imperfect to moderate.

They are to be found more to the north on gentle relief and predominantly covered by *cerrados*.

In most of the entire Planalto the low to extremely low inherent fertility of the predominant dystrophic soils has undoubtly been the outstanding limiting factor hampering effective utilization of soil resources.

This unfavorable plant nutrient status of most of the soils is portrayed in Table 1 and 2.

In terms of present agriculture possibilities under traditional farming system —depending on natural fertility of the soils— suitable lands for continuous cropping are almost all confined to small areas of eutrophic Dusky Red Latosol, *Terra Roxa Estructurada* and Red Yellow Podzolic Eutrophic Equivalent. The topography might be somewhat steep, however, this is of minor importance for primative agricultural systems.

From an advanced farming system standpoint —intensive farming operations involving high inputs of fertilizers, lime, and also water control, the region offers a remarkably higher overall potential for agricultural development. Areas of very suitable topography are quite extensive, physical attributes of many soils are not adverse, and climate is not actually unfavorable, despite the pronounced dry season.

This set of potentially favorable conditions for agricultural development is inherent to Latosols on nearly level to gentle landforms found mostly on *chapadas* with dystrophic soils.

II TRANSAMAZÓNICA HIGHWAY

The exposition that follows refers to the first segment of the road with an extension of about 1300 km. It begins at the Tocantins River and runs northwest traversing the valleys of the Araguaia, and Xingu Rivers and then turns southwest reaching the Tapajos River.

Environment

Diversification of environmental conditions is slight. Variation in vegetation and climate is less than variation in relief and lithology. General distinctions found along the route from east to west are:

Vegetation

Three main types of vegetation are traversed by the road. The first section 130 km long is distinguished by the domain of *cerrados* with gallery forests and occasional patches of mesophytic forests (semideciduous). Km 130 to 220 pertains to the transitional forest belt bordering the Amazon forests and merging with *cerrados* south and eastward.

The most important section occupies the remaining 1100 km, covered by the Amazon hygrophilous evergreen and sub-evergreen forests. Cipoalic variations, hydrophilous and marshy forests are of minor extent. Despite the differences in structure and composition, Amazon forests present a uniform aspect. Large biomass, intense bio-cycling, thin litter mantle, poor undergrowth and heterogenous composition are inherent features of the forests.

Table 1.—Summary of selected analytical data for kinds of soil and their varieties most common in Planalto Central - Mean and standard deviations.

Horiz.[1]	Nº of Sites[2]	pH H₂O (range)	pH 1N KCl (range)	Sand %	Silt %	Clay Total %	Clay Water Disp. %	Organic Carbon %	Exch. Bases[3] me/100 g	CEC[4] me/100 g	Base Sat. %	Al Sat. %	SiO₂/Al₂O₃[5] (Ki)
							DARK RED LATOSOL dystrophic clayey forest						
A	12	4.2–5.8	3.6–4.6	40±5	13±2	47±4	23±3	2.1±0.2	2.3±1.0	11.0±0.9	18±5	43±9	1.41±0.11
B	12	4.7–6.0	3.9–5.5	35±3	12±2	53±3	1±1	0.5±0.1	0.4±0.1	3.6±0.5	13±2	27±11	1.31±0.11
							IDEM dystrophic clayey *cerrado*						
A	11	4.3–5.2	3.5–4.3	28±5	13±2	59±5	21±3	2.2±0.2	0.7±0.1	10.1±1.1	7±1	72±2	1.23±0.10
B	11	4.6–6.1	3.9–5.7	24±4	11±2	65±4	1±1	0.6±0.1	0.4±0.1	4.0±0.5	10±1	38±10	1.19±0.09
							IDEM dystrophic clayey *cerrado*, pH H₂O < 1N KCl						
A	8	4.5–5.5	4.3–4.9	22±5	21±3	57±6	16±4	2.3±0.2	1.2±0.3	8.8±0.7	14±3	37±7	0.64±0.09
B	8	4.9–6.2	5.6–6.7	20±5	15±2	65±6	11±2	0.6±0.1	0.5±0.1	1.9±0.3	32±5	0±0	0.55±0.09
							IDEM dystrophic loamy forest						
A	8	4.1–5.2	3.7–4.7	78±3	7±1	15±3	10±3	0.9±0.1	1.8±0.3	6.2±0.5	29±5	35±7	2.03±0.07
B	8	4.4–4.9	3.6–4.1	73±3	7±1	20±2	10±2	0.3±0.0	0.3±0.1	3.0±0.2	10±2	80±3	1.95±0.05
							IDEM dystrophic loamy *cerrado*						
A	11	4.5–5.3	3.7–4.3	79±2	6±1	15±1	9±1	0.9±0.1	0.7±0.1	4.6±0.7	16±2	59±5	1.87±0.10
B	11	4.4–5.5	3.8–4.6	73±2	7±1	20±2	5±2	0.2±0.0	0.3±0.1	2.1±0.2	16±3	70±4	1.82±0.03
							IDEM eutrophic clayey forest						
A	3	5.9–7.2	4.9–6.7	30±16	20±3	50±10	26±14	2.8±0.4	14.0±3.0	17.1±3.8	79±12	0±0	1.77±0.07
B	3	5.8–6.3	5.0–6.1	30±10	11±3	59±8	1±1	0.6±0.1	4.8±0.3	7.1±1.1	70±8	2±2	1.65±0.25
							DUSKY RED LATOSOL dystrophic clayey forest						
A	6	5.3–6.2	4.5–5.6	21±3	19±1	60±3	32±7	3.0±0.2	9.6±1.4	16.2±1.6	58±5	1±1	1.57±0.22
B	6	4.9–6.1	4.1–5.9	17±3	13±1	70±3	0±0	0.0±0.0	1.1±0.2	5.2±0.6	24±5	35±16	1.47±0.19
							IDEM dystrophic clayey *cerrado*						
A	3	4.9–5.2	3.9–4.6	26±7	15±4	59±4	33±8	1.5±0.1	1.5±0.5	8.1±1.3	17±5	46±4	1.43±0.32
B	3	5.3–5.9	4.0–5.5	23±6	14±4	63±3	0±0	0.5±0.1	0.4±0.1	3.8±0.7	10±1	50±23	1.37±0.35

TABLE 1.—(Continued).

Horiz.[1]	Nº of Sites[2]	pH (range)		Sand %	Silt %	Clay		Organic Carbon %	Exch. Bases[3] me/100 g	CEC[4] me/100 g	Base Sat. %	Al Sat. %	SiO_2[5] / Al_2O_3 (Ki)
		H_2O	1N KCl			Total %	Water Disp. %						
DUSKY RED LATOSOL dystrophic clayey *cerrado*, pH < H_2O 1N KCl													
A	3	4.6—5.2	4.3—4.5	31±4	18±2	51±2	17±7	1.9±0.2	0.7±0.1	8.4±0.8	8±1	49±1	0.35±0.04
B	3	5.4—5.9	5.7—6.1	24±1	16±1	60±1	10±9	0.6±0.2	0.6±0.1	2.8±0.4	22±8	0±0	0.35±0.05
IDEM eutrophic clayey forest													
A	5	5.2—6.7	5.0—6.1	19±3	21±2	60±3	28±9	3.0±0.3	15.3±1.8	18.7±1.4	81±5	0±0	1.79±0.24
B	5	5.2—6.8	4.5—6.3	15±2	15±2	70±3	0±0	0.5±0.0	4.8±0.7	7.1±0.6	66±9	6±4	1.60±0.22
RED-YELLOW LATOSOL dystrophic clayey forest													
A	1	4.4	3.7	51	9	40	17	2.0	0.7	4.6	8	58	1.23
B	1	5.3	4.8	34	17	49	0	0.5	0.3	2.4	14	40	1.20
IDEM dystrophic clayey *cerrado*													
A	5	4.3—5.5	3.5—4.4	46±7	9±3	45±5	17±4	1.8±0.2	0.7±0.2	7.8±1.7	10±3	62±3	1.24±0.18
B	5	5.2—6.2	3.9—5.5	38±6	9±2	53±4	0±0	0.5±0.1	0.4±0.1	2.7±0.4	13±0	42±9	1.18±0.18
IDEM dystrophic clayey *cerrado*, pH H_2O < 1N KCl													
A	1	4.7	4.1	19	9	72	13	2.6	0.8	9.5	8	86	0.38
B	1	5.1	5.4	14	13	73	0	1.1	0.4	4.6	10		0.33
IDEM dystrophic loamy *cerrado*													
A	3	4.9—5.2	4.1—4.2	71±1	7±3	22±2	7±3	1.0±0.2	0.5±0.1	4.5±0.3	10±3	58±12	0.65±0.07
B	3	5.0—5.9	4.5—5.3	64±2	7±2	26±1	2±2	0.4±0.1	0.3±0.1	2.0±0.3	16±2	42±8	0.64±0.06
IDEM dystrophic loamy *cerrado*, pH H_2O < 1N KCl													
A	1	4.6	4.6	67	6	27	6	0.8	0.4	3.3	12	47	0.49
B	1	4.9	5.7	60	5	35	10	0.5	0.4	1.6	28	0	0.42
LITHOLIC SOILS dystrophic *cerrado*													
A	10	4.4—5.7	3.7—4.8	50±7	27±4	23±3	9±2	1.3±0.4	1.4±0.3	6.7±0.5	19±3	47±1	1.74±0.23
LITHOLIC SOILS eutrophic forest													
A	8	5.6—7.0	4.6—6.0	37±6	31±3	33±3	22±2	3.2±0.5	16.8±3.7	20.9±2.1	74±7	1±1	2.78±0.36
QUARTZ SANDS dystrophic *cerrado*													
A	7	4.0—5.4	3.9—4.3	87±1	5±0	8±1	3±1	0.8±0.2	0.6±0.2	4.7±0.9	13±3	59±5	1.32±0.25
B	7	5.1—5.9	4.2—4.7	85±1	4±1	11±1	5±1	0.2±0.0	0.2±0.0	1.7±0.2	14±2	60±3	1.38±0.28

TABLE 1.—(Continued).

Horiz.[1]	N.o of Sites[2]	pH H2O	1N KCl (range)	Clay Sand %	Silt %	Total %	Water Disp. %	Organic Carbon %	Exch. Bases[3] me/100 g	CEC[4] me/100 g	Base Sat. %	Al Sat. %	$\frac{SiO_2[5]}{Al_2O_3}$ (Ki)
RED-YELLOW PODZOLIC clayey forest													
A	5	5.0—5.8	3.8—4.9	42±10	29±6	30±5	18±4	2.1±0.3	3.5±0.8	9.7±0.9	36±7	21±12	2.00±0.06
B	5	5.1—5.4	4.0—4.3	23±6	23±3	52±4	0±0	0.5±0.1	1.0±0.1	4.9±0.6	21±3	48±10	1.84±0.20
IDEM loamy _cerrado_													
A	3	4.7—5.4	4.2—4.4	81±7	10±3	9±1	6±1	0.7±0.1	2.3±0.2	4.8±0.5	45±4	22±7	2.46±0.27
B	3	5.0—5.3	3.9—4.0	67±2	13±2	20±3	14±4	0.2±0.0	0.9±0.3	5.0±0.3	18±4	74±7	2.37±0.19
RED-YELLOW PODZOLIC EQUIVALENT eutrophic clayey forest													
A	8	5.5—6.3	4.4—5.7	38±8	34±4	28±4	16±3	2.0±0.3	9.2±1.8	12.9±2.0	71±6	1±1	2.19±0.18
B	8	5.3—6.8	4.0—5.8	23±5	26±4	51±3	12±6	0.4±0.1	6.4±1.2	8.5±3.6	72±6	3±3	2.06±0.14
IDEM eutrophic loamy forest													
A	4	5.9—6.3	4.8—5.5	72±6	16±3	12±4	7±2	1.2±0.4	5.0±1.1	7.0±1.4	72±3	1±1	2.47±0.23
B	4	4.8—5.8	3.6—4.6	57±4	15±2	28±1	24±1	0.3±0.1	3.4±0.1	5.9±0.7	57±5	20±8	2.18±0.09
REDDISH BRUNIZEM clayey forest													
A	3	5.9—7.9	5.3—6.9	24±4	44±3	32±1	17±3	3.1±1.1	24.3±3.7	26.1±2.8	92±5	0±0	2.94±0.58
B	3	6.1—8.1	5.0—7.0	14±2	32±2	54±6	34±6	0.6±0.1	19.8±3.2	21.3±2.5	92±4	0±0	2.43±0.31
TERRA ROXA ESTRUTURADA (REDDISH BROWN LATERITIC) eutrophic clayey forest													
A	8	5.0—6.8	4.4—6.3	25±5	30±3	45±3	24±4	2.6±0.3	8.7±1.1	13.8±1.4	62±5	0±0	2.15±0.16
B	8	5.7—6.3	4.8—6.1	21±5	23±1	56±3	10±5	0.6±0.1	4.8±0.5	7.1±0.5	68±3	0±0	1.97±0.13
UNDIFFERENTIATED CONCRETIONARY SOILS dystrophic _cerrado_													
A	4	4.5—5.7	4.0—5.0	51±7	23±5	26±6	14±6	2.9±0.7	3.2±1.2	12.7±3.0	27±9	33±19	1.82±0.36
B	4	5.2—5.6	4.1—5.1	30±4	30±4	48±7	2±1	0.4±0.1	0.6±0.2	3.6±0.3	16±3	61±4	1.68±0.35

1/ Depth of B or C ranging from 80 to 140 cm.

2/ Not necessarily proportional to geographic extension of soil kinds or their varieties.

3/ Sum of bases - comparable to NH_4OAC pH 7.0.

4/ Sum of bases plus extractable acidity by $Ca(OAC)_2$ pH 7.0.

5/ Attack by H_2SO_4 (d=1.47) - comparable to composition of clay fraction.

Table 2.—Summary of some chemical data indicative of the fertility status of the soil kinds and their varieties most common in Planalto Central - Mean and standard deviations.

Horiz. or Depth[1]	N⁰ of Sites[2]	pH H₂O (range)	Exchangeable			"Available" P[4] ppm
			Al[3] meq/100 g	Ca + Mg[3] meq/100 g	K[4] meq/100 g	
DARK RED LATOSOL dystrophic clayey forest						
Surf.	20	4.2—5.8	0.7±0.1	1.2±0.2	0.16±0.02	1.9±0.4
Subsurf.	11	4.7—6.0	0.0±0.0	0.6±0.1	0.07±0.01	0.6±0.1
IDEM dystrophic clayey cerrado[5]						
Surf.	141	4.0—5.7	0.0±0.0	0.5±0.0	0.11±0.01	1.1±0.7
Subsurf.	32	4.1—6.1	0.2±0.0	0.3±0.1	0.03±0.00	0.8±0.1
IDEM dystrophic loamy forest						
Surf.	36	4.0—6.0	0.7±0.1	1.0±0.1	0.08±0.01	3.7±0.3
Subsurf.	21	4.1—4.9	1.0±0.1	0.4±0.1	0.03±0.01	0.8±0.1
IDEM dystrophic loamy cerrado[5]						
Surf.	157	4.0—5.6	0.7±0.0	0.6±0.0	0.07±0.00	1.3±0.1
Subsurf.	71	4.2—5.7	0.5±0.0	0.3±0.0	0.02±0.00	0.5±0.0
IDEM eutrophic clayey forest						
Surf.	28	5.4—7.2	0.0±0.0	6.2±0.5	0.27±0.03	4.8±2.7
Subsurf.	7	5.4—6.6	0.0±0.0	3.3±0.4	0.23±0.05	0.7±0.1
IDEM dystrophic loamy forest						
Surf.	15	5.3—6.5	0.0±0.0	4.2±0.4	0.19±0.08	10.8±3.8
Subsurf.	3	6.0—6.8	0.0±0.0	3.2±0.5	0.14±0.04	3.5±2.8
DUSKY RED LATOSOL dystrophic clayey forest						
Surf.	36	4.2—6.2	0.9±0.1	2.5±0.3	0.20±0.03	2.7±0.8
Subsurf.	20	4.4—6.1	0.2±0.2	1.1±0.2	0.09±0.03	0.6±0.0
IDEM dystrophic clayey cerrado[5]						
Surf.	88	4.1—6.0	1.0±0.1	1.4±0.3	0.11±0.01	1.4±0.3
Subsurf.	25	4.0—5.9	0.2±0.1	0.3±0.0	0.03±0.01	0.6±0.0
IDEM eutrophic clayey forest						
Surf.	33	4.5—7.2	0.3±0.1	7.0±0.6	0.33±0.02	6.1±1.6
Subsurf.	19	5.2—6.8	0.1±0.0	4.4±0.6	0.17±0.02	2.3±1.5
RED-YELLOW LATOSOL dystrophic clayey forest						
Surf.	23	4.4—6.1	1.1±0.2	1.7±0.4	0.18±0.02	1.9±0.3
Subsurf.	8	4.3—6.0	0.2±0.1	0.4±0.2	0.04±0.01	0.5±0.1
IDEM dystrophic clayey cerrado[5]						
Surf.	96	4.0—5.7	0.8±0.1	0.4±0.0	0.12±0.01	0.8±0.1
Subsurf.	20	4.1—6.2	0.2±0.1	0.3±0.0	0.04±0.01	0.7±0.1
IDEM dystrophic loamy cerrado[5]						
Surf.	25	4.1—5.7	0.6±0.0	0.5±0.1	0.07±0.01	1.3±0.2
Subsurf.	9	4.3—5.9	0.1±0.0	0.3±0.0	0.03±0.00	0.9±0.3

TABLE 2.—(Continued).

Horiz. or Depth[1]	N° of Sites[2]	pH H₂O (range)	Exchangeable			"Available" P[4] ppm
			Al[3] meq/100 g	Ca + Mg[3] meq/100 g	K[4] meq/100 g	
IDEM eutrophic clayey forest (or endodystrophic)						
Surf.	9	5.3—6.5	0.0±0.0	4.8±1.0	0.25±0.04	1.5±0.3
LITHOLIC SOILS dystrophic *cerrado*						
Surf.	30	4.4—5.7	1.2±0.1	0.7±0.1	0.17±0.02	1.1±0.2
IDEM eutrophic forest						
Surf.	11	5.4—7.6	0.0±0.0	12.5±2.4	0.43±0.04	13.5±5.6
QUARTZ SANDS dystrophic *cerrado*						
Surf.	17	5.0—5.9	0.6±0.2	2.7±0.3	0.24±0.03	1.3±0.2
Subsurf.	8	4.5—5.9	0.5±0.1	0.2±0.0	0.01±0.00	0.9±0.1
RED-YELLOW PODZOLIC clayey forest						
Surf.	7	4.5—5.4	0.6±0.1	1.3±0.1	0.14±0.01	1.1±0.2
Subsurf.	12	4.9—5.8	0.6±0.2	1.0±0.2	0.14±0.02	0.6±0.0
IDEM clayey *cerrado*						
Surf.	9	4.1—5.6	0.8±0.2	1.3±0.3	0.13±0.02	1.8±0.2
Subsurf.	3	4.7—5.0	1.8±0.5	0.8±0.5	0.07±0.01	0.7±0.2
IDEM loamy *cerrado*						
Surf.	39	4.9—7.4	0.0±0.0	7.4±0.6	0.28±0.02	7.8±1.8
Subsurf.	4	5.0—5.4	2.1±0.4	0.6±0.2	0.07±0.02	0.9±0.1
RED-YELLOW PODZOLIC EQUIVALENT eutrophic clayey forest						
Surf.	25	5.4—6.7	0.1±0.0	3.1±0.2	0.18±0.01	3.4±1.6
Subsurf.	15	5.2—6.8	0.3±0.2	4.5±0.7	0.13±0.02	1.8±0.5
IDEM eutrophic loamy forest						
Surf.	59	4.0—5.7	0.7±0.0	0.3±0.0	0.06±0.01	1.4±0.1
Subsurf.	8	5.0—6.6	0.5±0.3	2.9±0.3	0.10±0.07	0.8±0.1
REDDISH BRUNIZEM clayey forest						
Surf.	10	5.7—7.9	0.0±0.0	9.6±0.5	0.40±0.03	5.5±3.7
TERRA ROXA ESTRUTURADA (REDDISH BROWN LATERITIC) eutrophic clayey forest						
Surf.	16	5.0—7.1	0.0±0.0	10.0±0.9	0.28±0.05	15.2±5.5
Subsurf.	12	5.7—6.6	0.0±0.0	6.3±1.0	0.30±0.07	7.3±4.2
UNDIFFERENTIATED CONCRETIONARY SOILS dystrophic *cerrado*						
Surf.	28	4.5—5.7	0.9±0.1	0.5±0.1	0.16±0.04	0.8±0.0
Subsurf.	4	5.2—5.6	0.8±0.4	0.5±0.2	0.07±0.02	0.8±0.1
UPLAND GROUND-WATER LATERITE clayey *cerrado*						
Surf.	19	4.8—5.5	1.0±0.2	0.6±0.2	0.12±0.02	1.6±0.3

1/ Surface soil 0-20 cm, subsurface soil ranging from 80 to 120 cm.
2/ Not necessarily proportional to geographic extension of soil kinds or their varieties.
3/ 1N KCl extraction.
4/ Mixed acids (0.05 N HCl and 0,025 N H₂SO₄) extraction.
5/ Regardless of pH > or < KCl.

Climate

Temperatures are high with very small seasonal variations —isohyperthermic— and yearly rainfall distribution is the main cause of climatic differences, actually small, encompassing udic and ustic regimes.
In the first 300 km, the Aw (Köppen) climate prevails. Mean annual temperature is 25.5 to 26.4°C, annual rainfall 1590 to 1430 mm, with about 3-months dry season. There is no specific information for the following 450 km, that probably constitutes a section under Amw' climate. In the next 150 km Aw climate prevails. Mean annual temperature is 26°C, annual rainfall 1690 mm with 1 to 2 dry months. The fourth section, 400 km long, is under Amw' climate with a very weak dry season. Mean annual temperature is 26.6°C and annual rainfall is 1790 mm.

Physiography

Most of the area has been subjected to intense denudation and dissection in a variable degree, possibly relative to Pliocenic pediplanation. Fair land form distinctions, modest elevations, and several varieties of rocks are the main landscape features. Some sections can be identified:
1. Sedimentary Plateau of Maranhão Basin. Occupies the first 130 km of low tablelands of the drainage divide between the Tocantins and Araguaia Rivers. It comprise sedimentary sequences (Devonian to Cretaceous) in which sandstones predominant with occasional intercal of basalt and melaphyre flows. Topography is nearly level to gently undulating, elevations range from 150 to 250 meters.
2. Quaternary Alluvial Plains. Low river terraces are scarce and narrow, except for the most noticeable being found along the Araguaia River. The low river terraces consist mainly of argillaceous sand deposits about 10 m above the streams, elevations range from 70 to 40 meters above sea level.
3. Denudation Surface, Slightly Dissected. These surfaces occupy most of the area along the road from km 140 to 310, km 735 to 860, km 960 to 1150 and km 1165 on where the road cuts across crystalline and younger sedimentary rocks. Topography is mostly gently undulating, seldom rolling. Elevations range from 100 to 150 m, seldom reaching 200 meters above sea level.
The first tract comprises sedimentary sequences of Maranhão Basin (Devonian to Cretaceous) consisting mainly of sandstones with few interbedded silstones, shales that are seldom calcareous. In the central part of this tract, Pre-Cambrian schists and phyllites (muscovite, chlorite, sericite) with thin quartzite veins are found.
The remainingare a is composed of Silurian to Devonian sedimentary formations of the Amazon Basin consisting mostly of argillaceous and micaceous sandstones with few shale interbeddings. Diabase intrusions are scarce, except from km 790 to km 820.
4. Dissected Denudation Surface. This surface constitutes the section from km 310 to 735 and represents the low northern extension of the Brazilian shield. It consists of crystalline rocks that have been worn

— 35 —

away by erosion with later incision of streams, resulting in rough relief. Topography is mostly rolling, with elevations ranging 80-150 m. To the west topography is more gentle and elevations range from 40 to 80 meters. Dominant rocks are gneiss and migmatites of granitic and granodioritic composition with few granites and scarce intrusions of diabase.

5. Intrusions and Flows of Basic Rocks. From km 860 to 910 there occurs a distinctive section consisting of diabase and basalt referred to as Triassic. Topography is mainly gently undulating and seldom rolling. Elevations range from 100 to 150 meters.

This section is of prime importance because of the fertile soils formed from the rocks mentioned above. They are the main lands readily suitable to successful permanent agriculture.

6. Dissected Hilly Range. Detached from km 1150 to 1165 there is an area of strongly dissected landscape comprising crystalline rocks especially granites with elevations ranging from 200 to 300 m, protunding from the low adjoining plateaus at elevations of 100 to 120 meters.

Despite the variety of rocks along the route, sapric residues are far less diversified than would be expected in such relief variations. This would be expected because of the intensity factors role in the weathering rate. At the same time, landforms clearly evidence past intensive denudations, implying transportation and mixing of weathered residues.

Soils

The available soil information results from surveys of a few areas and studies throughout the road. The main soil kinds and varieties are briefly specified below along with their general relation to environment as described earlier. Condensed analytical data are given in Table 3.

Cambisols, dystrophic loamy or clayey

These soils are mainly Oxic Dystropepts. Minor varieties are: intergrade to Red Yellow Podzolic, plinthic, Imperfectly drained, and low CEC (<24 meq/100g clay).

These soils dominate the denudated areas of schists and phyllites of the third physiographic section and are found under forest vegetation, udic environment, and gentle relief. Scarce occurences to the west are related to shales exposed at steeper sloping dissected tracts.

Dusky Red Latosol, eutrophic

These soils correspond to Eutrorthox. Subordinate varieties are: intergrade to *Terra Roxa Estruturada*, seldom with mollic epipedon.

They are confined to areas of gentler topography within the fifth physiographic section, i.e., basic parent rocks and udic environment forests.

Red-Yellow Latosol, dystrophic clayey

These soils are mainly Haplorthox. Atypical varieties are: intergrade to Red Yellow Podzolic, not very deep, and seldom concretionary.

They are related to udic environment forests, and fairly dissected areas of granite and gneisses. They dominate the hilly sixth physiographic section, being quite frequent to the east of the fourth section, associated with Red Yellow Podzolics.

Yellow Latosols, dystrophic clayey or loamy

These soils are mainly Haplorthox. Subordinate varieties are: intergrade to Red Yellow Podzolic, concretionary, seldom plinthic and with umbric epipedons.

This is the second most extensive soil kind along the transect. It occurs under udic forest environment and occupies long stretches to the west of the third hpysiographic section plus the low terrace of the Araguaia River.

They are closely related to subdued landforms and to highly weathered residues derived from overlain sedimentary sequences of the Amazon Basin.

Quartz Sands, dystrophic

These soils closely correspond to Quartzipsamments and usually include intergrades to latosols and Red Yellow Podzolics.

They are strictly related to quartzose sandstones plus adjacent shifted detritus and to very gently topography. They dominate the first section under ustic *cerrado* environment, occuring in a small area of transitional forest in the third section and occasionaly in the remainder of the road forest udic environment to the west.

Red-Yellow Podzolic

These soils are mainly Pale, Tropo and Plinthic great groups of Udults and Ustults. Varieties are: clayey, loamy, loamy/clayey, sandy/clayey, sandy/loamy, concrecionary, plinthic, abruptic, imperfectly drained and intergrade to Latosols. The epipedon is always ochric and the CEC is low ($<$ 24 meq/100g clay).

Their occurence is largely linked to somewhat dissected areas —rolling to gently undulating— chiefly of gneissic bedrock. Forest udic environment is prevalent, except for small stretches under forest ustic environment to the east.

They are the most extensive soils along the road, being of importance in some areas of the third physiographic section, while in the fourth section they are remarkably frequent, continuously or associated to Red Yellow Latosol or Ground Water Laterite.

Red Yellow Podzolic, eutrophic equivalent

These soils are Tropudals and Paleustalfs. Epipedons are ochric with low CEC. Varieties are: clayey, loamy/clayey, abruptic and intergrade to *Terra Roxa Estructurada*.

Minor occurences were found in the fourth physiographic section under udic forest environment, and related to hilly and rolling granodioritic areas.

Reddish Brunizem, clayey

Corresponds to Rhodic, high CEC varieties or Argioustolls, Argiudolls, and Paleudolls. Varieties are Vertic and Lithic.

This soil is of very limited distribution and strictly related to steeper sloping areas and basic parent rocks. Small stretches occur both under sub-deciduous forests in ustic environments in the first section and udic rain forest environments in the fifth section. They are rarely found in the remaining physiographic sections.

Terra Roxa Estructurada (Reddish Brown Lateritic), dystrophic[1]/ and eutrophic clayey

These soils correspond to Rhodic, low CEC soils of Pale and Tropo great groups of Udults[1]/, Udalfs, Ustalfs, Udolls[1]/ and of Argioustolls[1]/. Varieties are: intergrade to Latosol, to Red Yellow Podzolic, to Red Brunizem, plinthic[1]/ and with mollic epipedon[1]/.

These soils are closely related to basic parent rocks and gently undulating to rolling topography. They are confined to the fifth physiographic section, occuring on occasional outcrops of those rocks elsewhere. Their major part is under udic forest environment and seldom found under ustic environments to the east.

Upland and Lowland Ground Water Laterite, dystrophic

These soils are mainly Plinthaquults and Plinthaquox. Varieties are: with or without argillic horizon, clayey, loamy, loamy/clayey, sandy/clayey, sandy/loamy, abruptic, concretionary, imperfectly and poorly plus very poorly drained. Epipedons are ochric and CEC values are low.

They are important soils associated with Red Yellow Podzolics to the west of the fourth section. In the remainder, they occur in scattered areas either under forest udic environments in gentle to steep sloping gneissic or sedimentary tracts with variably related to seeping, or in bottom lands[2]/ uncer hydrophilous or marshy forest.

Vertisols

These soils have mollic epipedons and are lithic varieties of Pellusterts. They are confined to very small gently sloping areas of basic rocks plus their colluvium-alluvium under ustic environments at the extreme eastern end of the transect. As for other varieties there are minor occurences of Low Humic Gley, Humic Gley and Alluvial Soils virtually all dystrophic, Podzol, and Litholic Soils plus Cambisols both eutrophic, related to basic bedrock.

1/ Scarce to few occurences.
2/ In general, bottom lands are scarce along the route.

Fertility Status Estimate and Agricultural Potential of the Soils

Information obtained by investigations carried out along the route, makes possible an evaluation of the agricultural potential of the soils.

Available data on soil pH values, Al, base and P contents that express the supply of available plant nutrients are summarized in Table 4. This may serve as an inventory of the natural fertility status of the soils that have been identified. These data together with the ones in Table 3 indicate that most of the soils are of rather low inherent chemical fertility, except for those derived from basic rocks, namely Eutrophic *Terra Roxa Estruturada*, Dusky Red Latosol, Red Brunizem and Vertisol, that except for Vertisols, have a remarkably higher agricultural potential.

The low plant nutrient status expressed by the analytical data, herein presented, are in conformity with experiments on soil fertility and with observation on land use and crop behavior. In addition to, experience has been gained trying to farm correlated soils elsewhere in Low and Middle Amazon Regions under traditional agricultural system.

According to actual knowledge about the udic tropical environment here considered essentially concordant with others in the world, —it is quite evident that the low inherent chemical fertility of the predominant dystrophic soils is per se one of the most, if not the decisive, limiting factor to agricultural development, despite the climate and often the physical attributes of the soils and topography being favorable.

In view of the low inmediate potential of soil resource the occurences of rich soils acquire anoutmost importance, because they are quite capable of readily supporting successful permanent agriculture settlements. The existence of given soils is subordinated to particular combinations of parent rocks (composition & mode of occurence) and geomorphic settling, where the dynamic of the soil system ensures preservation of the elements of fertility inherited from rich parent materials, formed from very favorable rock source-diabase, basalt and melaphyre.

In summary, the potential for agricultural use offered by the soil resources throughout the road, can be roughly estimated as follows:

Good suitability to permanent agriculture under traditional farming systems i.e., depending on natural fertility of the soils, is about 100 km straight as 8% of the total extent and being 50 km in a continuous segment. Practically this only comprises the Eutrophic *Terra Roxa Estructurada*, on gentle topography and udic moisture regime.

Good suitability to permanent agriculture under advanced (intensive) farming system, i.e., high technology and capital inputs to improve and maintain soil conditions —about 570 km straight or 44% of the extent. These include the above plus extensive segments of Dystrophic Yellow Latosols on gentle topography and udic moisture regime.

Table 3.—Summary of selected analytical data for kinds of soil and their varieties identified in Transamazonica. Mean and standard deviations.

Horiz.[1]	N° of Sites[2]	pH H2O	pH 1N KCl (range)	Sand %	Silt %	Clay Total %	Clay Water Disp. %	Organic Carbon %	Exch. Bases[3] me/100 g	CEC[4] me/100 g	Base Sat. %	Al Sat. %	SiO_2[5]/Al_2O_3 (Ki)
CAMBISOL dystrophic loamy or clayey forest													
A	8	4.2—4.7	3.1—3.7	25±3	47±1	27±4	17±4	1.5±0.3	1.7±0.3	10.8±0.7	16±3	70±6	2.42±0.11
B	8	4.3—4.9	3.2—3.9	24±3	48±2	28±2	13±3	0.4±0.1	0.5±0.1	7.0±0.6	7±1	90±1	2.39±0.13
DUSKY RED LATOSOL eutrophic clayey forest													
A	1	6.2	5.6	30	22	48	33	1.6	6.3	9.4	67	0	2.09
B	1	5.7	6.0	18	18	64	0	0.3	1.9	2.9	65	0	1.83
RED-YELLOW LATOSOL dystrophic clayey forest													
A	1	4.2	3.8	21	12	67	3	1.3	0.4	7.5	5	82	1.78
B	1	4.7	4.0	19	8	73	0	0.3	0.3	3.7	8	66	1.77
YELLOW LATOSOL dystrophic clayey forest													
A	12	3.8—4.5	3.1—3.8	45±4	11±1	44±4	26±3	1.6±0.4	0.6±0.1	9.2±1.7	6±1	82±2	1.95±0.05
B	12	4.4—5.1	3.7—4.3	31±4	9±1	60±4	0±0	0.3±0.0	0.3±0.1	3.9±0.0	7±1	87±8	1.80±0.05
IDEM dystrophic loamy forest													
A	8	3.8—4.5	3.2—3.8	75±5	8±2	17±2	7±2	1.0±0.1	0.5±0.1	6.5±0.8	8±2	75±6	2.24±0.24
B	8	4.0—5.1	3.7—4.3	67±4	8±2	25±2	0±0	0.3±0.0	0.2±0.1	3.0±0.4	7±1	85±3	2.09±0.12
QUARTZ SANDS dystrophic forest													
A	4	3.2—5.3	3.2—4.1	93±2	3±1	4±2	2±1	0.7±0.1	0.3±0.1	4.9±0.4	6±1	77±2	2.06±0.04
C	4	4.6—5.6	4.1—4.7	84±1	6±1	10±1	5±2	0.2±0.1	0.1±0.0	2.7±0.4	6±2	80±6	1.94±0.03
IDEM dystrophic cerrado													
A	5	4.8—5.7	3.7—4.4	93±1	3±1	4±1	2±1	0.3±0.0	0.3±0.1	2.1±0.3	18±16	47±16	2.11±0.00
C	5	5.2—5.5	4.1—4.4	88±1	3±1	9±1	2±1	0.1±0.0	0.2±0.0	1.2±0.1	13±2	62±5	2.05±0.00
RED-YELLOW PODZOLIC clayey forest													
A	23	3.8—5.1	3.3—5.0	51±4	23±3	26±2	16±2	1.2±0.4	0.8±0.1	6.6±0.8	19±3	51±6	2.22±0.08
B	23	4.2—5.5	3.5—4.8	27±3	19±2	54±2	3±2	0.4±0.0	0.6±0.1	5.7±0.6	13±2	70±5	1.86±0.08

TABLE 3.—(Continued).

Horiz.[1]	Nº of Sites[2]	pH H₂O 1N KCl (range)		Sand %	Silt %	Clay Total %	Clay Water Disp. %	Organic Carbon %	Exch. Bases[3] me/100 g	CEC[4] me/100 g	Base Sat. %	Sat. Al %	SiO_2/Al_2O_3 (Ki)[5]
IDEM loamy forest													
A	1	4.1	3.6	88	6	6	4	0.9	0.9	4.6	20	36	2.27
B	1	4.4	3.9	66	10	24	0	0.4	0.2	3.3	6	78	1.92
RED-YELLOW PODZOLIC EQUIVALENT eutrophic clayey forest													
A	1	5.5	4.8	48	26	26	16	0.9	4.3	7.0	61	5	2.45
B	1	5.7	5.2	14	31	55	1	0.3	3.3	5.1	66	0	1.44
REDDISH BRUNIZEM clayey forest													
A	4	5.8—7.2	5.2—6.3	23±1	33±3	44±3	28±5	4.0±0.3	31.2±3.7	35.7±4.0	88±4	0±0	2.98±0.17
B	4	5.5—6.3	3.9—5.3	15±7	30±5	55±6	34±13	0.5±0.1	35.2±11.3	39.0±11.8	90±2	0±0	3.32±0.33
TERRA ROXA ESTRUTURADA (REDDISH BROWN LATERITIC) dystrophic clayey forest													
A	1	4.4	4.0	26	18	56	4	1.6	0.7	8.0	9	67	1.92
B	1	5.2	4.4	13	6	81	0	0.6	0.3	4.7	6	50	1.75
IDEM eutrophic clayey forest													
A	11	5.2—6.5	4.4—5.8	30±2	22±1	48±2	34±4	1.7±0.1	8.4±0.9	13.1±0.9	64±3	1±1	2.01±0.04
B	11	5.3—6.5	4.9—6.0	17±2	15±1	68±3	0±0	0.4±0.0	4.4±0.8	6.5±0.9	60±4	0±0	1.97±0.05
UPLAND AND BOTTOM LAND GROUND-WATER LATERITE dystrophic clayey forest													
A	5	4.1—5.7	3.5—4.1	57±13	15±2	28±13	8±2	1.4±0.6	0.7±0.1	8.8±3.4	10±2	65±8	2.54±0.30
B	5	4.8—5.7	3.5—4.2	33±7	20±3	47±8	17±11	0.3±0.0	1.8±1.0	7.0±1.4	21±8	68±9	2.22±0.16
VERTISOL													
A	1	5.1	3.7	35	20	45	5	1.2	15.3	24.7	62	11	3.18
C	1	5.0	3.4	20	22	58	3	0.3	32.4	40.1	81	8	3.30

1/ Depth of B or C ranging from 80 to 140 cm.
2/ Not necessarily proportional to geographic extension of soil kinds or their varieteis.
3/ Sum of bases - comparable to NH4OAC pH 7.0.
4/ Sum of bases plus extractable acidity by Ca(OAC)2, pH 7.0.
5/ Attack by H2SO4 (d=1.47) - comparable to composition of clay fraction.

Table 4.—Summary of some chemical data indicative of the fertility status of the soil kinds and their varieties identified in Transamazonica - Mean and standard deviations.

Horiz. or Depth[1]	Nº of Sites[2]	pH H_2O (range)	Exchangeable Al^3 me/100 g	Exchangeable $Ca + Mg^3$ me/100 g	Exchangeable K^4 me/100 g	"Available" P^4 ppm
ALLUVIAL SOILS dystrophic loamy riparian forest						
Surf.	8	3.9—5.2	1.6±0.1	0.5±0.1	0.05±0.01	3.8±0.6
Subsurf.	8	4.2—5.0	1.9±0.3	0.2±0.0	0.03±0.00	1.4±0.4
CAMBISOL dystrophic loamy or clayey forest						
Surf.	12	4.1—4.7	5.5±0.8	0.9±0.1	0.20±0.03	3.0±1.3
Subsurf.	11	4.0—4.9	5.2±0.7	0.4±0.0	0.10±0.02	1.7±0.8
DUSKY RED LATOSOL eutrophic clayey forest						
Surf.	5	5.1—6.6	0.0±0.0	6.0±1.0	0.24±0.05	2.0±0.5
Subsurf.	5	5.6—6.5	0.0±0.0	2.9±0.7	0.06±0.02	1.3±0.4
RED-YELLOW LATOSOL dystrophic clayey forest						
Surf.	5	4.0—4.2	1.7±0.1	0.3±0.0	0.07±0.01	0.9±0.1
Subsurf.	5	4.1—5.3	1.1±0.2	0.2±0.0	0.04±0.02	0.8±0.1
YELLOW LATOSOL dystrophic clayey forest						
Surf.	95	3.8—4.9	2.2±0.1	0.6±0.1	0.07±0.00	2.6±0.1
Subsurf.	77	4.1—5.1	2.1±0.2	0.3±0.0	0.04±0.00	1.7±0.1
IDEM dystrophic loamy forest						
Surf.	31	3.8—5.3	1.6±0.2	0.4±0.1	0.06±0.01	2.1±0.2
Subsurf.	28	4.0—5.1	1.5±0.1	0.2±0.0	0.04±0.01	1.7±0.3
QUARTZ SANDS dystrophic forest						
Surf.	13	3.8—5.3	1.1±0.2	0.4±0.1	0.05±0.01	4.7±2.1
Subsurf.	11	4.2—5.6	1.0±0.1	0.2±0.0	0.03±0.01	2.0±1.1
IDEM dystrophic *cerrado*						
Surf.	7	4.2—5.7	0.3±0.1	0.3±0.1	0.03±0.00	0.9±0.1
Subsurf.	7	4.3—5.5	0.3±0.0	0.1±0.0	0.02±0.00	0.6±0.1
RED-YELLOW PODZOLIC clayey forest						
Surf.	49	3.8—5.7	1.9±0.2	0.7±0.1	0.13±0.03	1.6±0.2
Subsurf.	48	4.2—5.5	2.4±0.3	0.4±0.0	0.07±0.01	0.8±0.0
IDEM loamy forest						
Surf.	1	4.1	0.5	0.8	0.04	1
Subsurf.	1	4.4	0.7	0.2	0.02	1
RED-YELLOW PODZOLIC EQUIVALENT eutrophic clayey forest						
Surf.	1	5.5	0.2	3.8	0.23	2
Subsurf.	1	5.7	0.1	2.9	0.18	1

TABLE 4.—(Continued).

Horiz. or Depth[1]	N° of Sites[2]	pH H₂O (range)	Exchangeable			"Available" P[4] ppm
			Al[3] me/100 g	Ca + Mg[3] me/100 g	K[4] me/100 g	
REDDISH BRUNIZEM clayey forest						
Surf.	5	5.8—7.2	0.0±0.0	28.5±4.4	0.70±0.08	1.3±0.4
Subsurf.	4	5.5—6.3	0.0±0.0	43.1±10.6	0.78±0.25	1.0±0.0
TERRA ROXA ESTRUTURADA (REDDISH BROWN LATERITIC) dystrophic clayey forest						
Surf.	1	4.4	1.1	0.5	0.09	1
Subsurf.	1	5.2	0.4	0.4	0.03	1
IDEM eutrophic clayey forest						
Surf.	40	5.1—6.9	0.1±0.0	7.5±0.5	0.27±0.04	1.9±0.2
Subsurf.	38	5.1—6.9	0.1±0.0	4.8±0.5	0.15±0.03	1.3±0.1
UPLAND AND BOTTOM LAND GROUND-WATER LATERITE dystrophic clayey forest						
Surf.	12	3.8—5.7	3.6±0.7	0.6±0.1	0.16±0.03	2.8±0.4
Subsurf.	10	4.2—5.8	4.5±1.0	0.7±0.2	0.07±0.02	2.5±0.9
VERTISOL forest						
Surf.	1	5.1	1.9	15.1	0.11	2
Subsurf.	1	5.0	3.0	32.2	0.04	1

1/ Surface soil 0-20 cm; subsurface soil ranging from 80 to 120 cm.

2/ Not necessarily proportional to geographic extension of soil kinds or their varieties.

3/ 1N KCl extraction.

4/ Double acids (0.05 N HCl and 0.025 N N₂SO₄) extraction.

III SUMMARY

Information is presented on the soils, parent rocks, climate and topography of the Central Plateau and the Transamazonic Highway of Brazil. The soils are tentatively classified at the great group level of the Soil Taxonomy and in accordance to the Brazilian soil classification system. The potential fertility of some of the region and their significance to agriculture is indicated.

IV ACKNOWLEDGEMENT

Thanks are due to Seção de Estatística Experimental e Análise Econômica de IPEACS EMBRAPA for statistic computation. CPP - EMRAPA.

V REFERENCES

ALMEIDA, F. F. M., y LIMA, M. A. 1959. Planalto Centro-Occidental e Pantanal Mato-Grossense. Guia de Excursão N° 1. Cons. Nac. de Geogr. Río de Janeiro.

BARBOSA, C., et al. 1966. Geologia estratigráfica, estructural e economica da área do "Projeto Araguaia". Monografía N° XIX. Div. de Geol. e Miner. DNPM. Min. das Minas e Energia. Rio de Janeiro.

COMISSAO DE SOLOS. 1960. Levantamento de reconhecimento dos solos do Estado de Sao Paulo. Bol. N° 12. SNPA. CNEPA. Min. da Agricultura. Río de Janeiro.

COMISSAO DE SOLOS. 1962. Levantamento de reconhecimento dos solos da regiao sob influencia do Reservatório de Furnas. Bol. N° 13. SNPA. CNEPA. Min. da Agricultura. Río de Janeiro.

COMPANHIA DE PESQUISA DE RECURSOS MINERAIS. 1972. Esboço geológico preliminar. Trecho Itaituba-Estreito In: Bol. Téc. N° 55. IPEAN. Min. da Agricultura. Belém.

DIVISAO DE PESQUISA PEDOLOGICA. 1971. Mapa esquemático dos solos das Regioes Norte, Meio-Norte e Centro-Oeste do Brasil - Texto Explicativo. Bol. Téc. N° 17. DNPEA. Min. da Agricultura. Rio de Janeiro.

DIVISAO DE PESQUISA PEDOLOGICA. 1971. Levantamento de reconhecimento dos solos do sul do Estado de Mato Grosso. Bol. Téc. N° 18. DNPEA. Min. da Agricultural. Rio de Janeiro.

DIVISAO DE PESQUISA PEDOLOGICA. 1973. Estudo expedito de solos no trecho Itaituba-Estreito da rodovia Transamazónica para fins de classificação e correlação. Bol. Téc. N° 31. DNPEA. Min. da Agricultura. Rio de Janeiro.

DIVISAO DE PESQUISA PEDOLOGICA. 1973. Investigação exploratória dos solos que ocorren na rodovia Transamazónica (Trecho Itaituba-Estreito). Bol. Téc. N° 41. DNPEA. Min. da Agricultura. Rio de Janeiro.

DIVISAO DE PESQUISA PEDOLOGICA. 1973. Levantamento de reconhecimento dos solos de uma área prioritária situada na rodovia Transamazónica entre Altamira e Itaituba. Bol. Téc. N° 42. DNPEA. Min. da Agricultura. Rio de Janeiro.

DIVISAO DE PESQUISA PEDOLOGICA. Dados de análises de solos. Arquivos. DNPEA. Min. da Agricultura. Rio de Janeiro.

EQUIPE DE PEDOLOGIA E FERTILIDADE DE SOLO. 1970. Levantamento semidetalhado dos solos de áreas do Ministério da Agricultura no Distrito Federal. Bol. Téc. N° 8. EPE. Min. da Agricultura. Rio de Janeiro.

FALESI, I. C. 1972. Solos da rodovia Transamazónica. Bol. Téc. N° 55. IPEAN, DNPEA. Min. da Agricultura. Belém.

FREITAS, F. G. et al. 1972. Relatorio de viagem efectuada ao Estado de Goiás para clasificação dos solos onde foram instalados experimentos pelo Projeto FAO/ANDA/ABCAR. DPP. DNPEA. Min. da Agricultura. Rio de Janeiro. (Unpublished).

GRUPO EXECUTIVO DE RACIONALIZAÇAO DA CAFEICULTURA. 1972. Reconhecimento detalhado e aptidão agrícola dos solos em área piloto no sul do Estado de Minas Gerais. IBC. Min. da Indústria e Comércio. Rio de Janeiro.

JACOMINE, P. K. T. 1969. Descrição das características morfológicas, físicas, químicas e mineralógicas de alguns perfis de solos sob vegetação de cerrado. Bol. Téc. N° 11. EPFS. Min. da Agricultura. Rio de Janeiro.

MOTHCI, E. P. *et al.* 1973. Levantamento de reconhecimento dos solos do Triangulo Mineiro NC. Relatório ao CNPq. DPP. DNPEA. Min. da Agricultura. Rio de Janeiro. (Type-written report).

SOIL SURVEY STAFF. 1970. Selected chapters from the unedited text of Soil Taxonomy of the National Cooperative Soil Survey. SCS. USDA. Washington, D. C.

THE AMERICAN INTERNATIONAL ASSOCIATION FOR ECONOMIC AND SOCIAL DEVELOPMENT. 1963. Survey of the Agriculture Potential of the Central Plateau of Brazil. Rio de Janeiro.

WRIGHT, A. C. S. and BENNEMA, J. 1965. The soil resources of Latin America. World Soil Resources Reports Nº 18. Soil Map of the World FAO/UNESCO Project. FAO. Rome.

2 Soils of the Lowlands of Peru

CARLOS ZAMORA J.

I INTRODUCTION

Peru, with a surface area of 1,285,215.60 Km² and a total population somewhat over 13.5 million is located between latitude South 0°01'48" and 18°21'03", a typical intertropical location. In addition, the Andes Mountains extending in a South-East and North-West direction throughout the country and a thermic modifier to the West, generated by the Humbolt Current, we have the main factors responsible for the marked contrast and heterogeneity of the country's geography. Environmental characteristics vary greatly within short west to east distances. An arid, cool environment practically free of vegetation is present on the west coast, changing to abrupt relief, cold climates with highland vegetation and perpetual snows, and eastward to humid, tropical climate of dense vegetation, respectively represented by the traditional natural regions of the Coast, Sierra or Andes and Jungle.

Soils, being a product of the environment and of factors such as climate, vegetation, parental or lithological material and geomorphology, are complex and present great variabilities throughout the country.

This paper outlines the morphological characteristics, geographic distribution and natural classification of the most important soils within the lowland areas of Peru. They cover about 60% of the territory, ranging from, the Coastal Desert found as a thin strip along the Pacific Ocean, arid, grayish land practically devoid of vegetation, to the extensive Amazon Plains, with tropical humid climate and dense and exuberant vegetation (Figure 1 shows the distribution of the lowlands along an East-West transect).

Between these two lowland regions, with diametrically opposed characteristics and different climates, vegetation and soil, we find the gigantic Andes Mountains with an elevation of over 5000 meters separating them at average distances of 300 to 500 kms.

The nomenclature used in this report is the FAO/UNESCO soil mapping units (FAO, 1968).

II PERUVIAN DESERT

The Coastal Desert of Peru is a thin strip approximately 2000 kms long and a maximum width of 150 kms. It comprises large extensions of flat land and dry plains, low hills, marine terraces that reach an elevation of over 1000 meters and uninterrupted numerous alluvial valleys, generally of a torrential nature, that run from east to west. Climatic conditions are

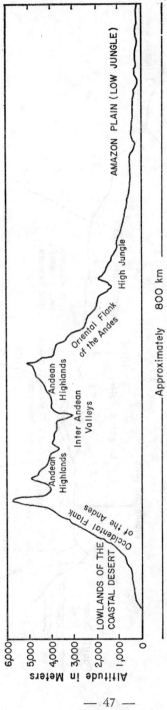

Figure 1. Soils distribution in the lowlands of Peru. Transversal section.

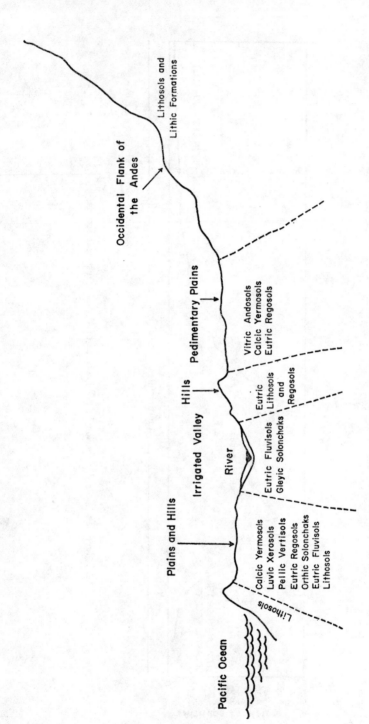

Figure 2. Soils distribution in the lowlands of the Peruvian Coastal Desert.

extremely arid in general with an average annual rainfall of less than 50 mm
an da maximum of 300 mm in the extreme northern region and the
easternmost interior. The mean temperature varies between 12°C and
24°C. Generally, vegetation is scarce, ranging from disperse cactus to
forest with some arboreous species, typical of the vegetation in the northern
part of this region.

In the Coastal Desert we find three distinct geomorphic and physiographic areas: Irrigated alluvial valleys, plateaus or coastal terraces, and
hills and slopes as well as branches from the western flank of the Andes,
overlooking the Ocean. Within each of these geomorphic areas soils of
different morphology, development stages and agricultural potential are
found. The following is a description of the outstanding characteristics
presented by lowland soils in the Peruvian Coastal Desert. The distribution
of these soils is illustrated in Figure 2.

Fluvisols

This group is made up of soils formed on deposits of recent alluvial origin, with adequate drainage and predominantly flat surfaces, with
less than 2% slope. Fluvisols are scattered throughout the irrigated agricultural valleys adjacent to the 52 intermittent or perennial rivers that flow
on to the Coastal Desert from the Sierra. Fluvisols occur beside the
numerous streams of sporadic flow and river beds recently filled by
alluvium converging towards the hydrographic system of the agricultural
valleys.

Morphologically, Fluvisols are typically stratified with little pedogenic
development. They present many depth and texture variations; with deep
clayey soils found in close associations in with shallow sandy soils. Distribution of these soils throughout the valley is usually complex and heterogeneous, showing an intricate pattern based on the variable torrential flow, typical
of most rivers from the area. Generally, thick superficial soils are found
and where gravel-tone accumulations are a predominant physical characteristic . Thick, clayey textured soils are found in the central and lower part of
the alluvial plains.

A cross section of the valleys, beginning with the main rivers, permits
us to establish the following edaphic morphology: Low terraces parallel to
the river, formed by the last fluvial deposits consist of shallow soils, resting
on coarse materials, mainly sand, gravel and stones (skeletal soils). During
the flooding season these soils are eroded and the materials redeposited near
by. Next are the intermediate terraces (formed at 1 to 3 levels) with deep
soils of medium to fine texture. These are the most important agricultural
soils.

Chemically, Fluvisols are eutric, with slightly alkaline to alkaline reaction (pH 7.1 to 8). Many of them are definitely calcareous (Calcareous Fluvisols). Organic matter content is low, fluctuating between less than 0.5%
to a maximum of 2% and consequently so is the nitrogen level. This
represents the most significant characteristic of Fluvisols in the alluvial
coastal desert valleys, since nitrogen use is imperative for adequate, economic
agricultural production. Phosphorus levels vary from medium to low. These
Fluvsiols have high potassium contents, which is the dominant macronutrient

in their chemical composition. Boron is abundant in Fluvisols of the high southern coast located between the Yauca River Valley (Department of Arequipa) and the Caplina River Valley surroundings (Department of Tacna).

From the standpoint of actual or potential agricultural use, Fluvisols of the irrigated areas are the most important edaphic group for intensive agricultural practices in the country, because of adequate water supply, high production capacity and good physical-chemical characteristics. The capacity of irrigated Fluvisols is reflected by the fact that they produce almost 50% of the gross national agricultural product and practically 50% of the country's population is settled on these soils.

According to Soil Taxonomy (1973) the soils are classified in the Entisols Order, Fluvent Suborder and Ustifluvent Great Group in the case of the wettest alluvial valley soils and Torrifluvent for driest coastal flat land soils.

Regosols

These soils comprise the desert flat lands of the coastal plains of Peru. These dry sands, or Eutric Regosols, are made up of essentially sandy and loose soils, of aeolic origin and with excessive drainage.

Topography is varied, ranging from flat to undulated to mountainous. Their geographic distribution is broad, mostly in the Central Coast (between Pisco and Ica) and far North in the flat lands of the Sechura and Mancora Desert (Department of Piura).

Morphologically, they are characterized by homogenous profiles of micaceous sandy nature, without structure, over 150 cm deep and slightly alkaline reaction tending to calcareous. Vegetation found on these soils varies from inexistant or disperse to xerophytic graminae *(Chaetochloa spp)* to some arboric species such as "Sapote" *(Capparis sp)* typical of the Eutric Regosols predominant in the Northern Coast.

Part of the so-called hills or Xerophytic Forests nourished by marine fog condensation, located at 500 to 700 meters above sea level occur on Eutric Regosols of fine sandy texture presenting a deep Al horizon (Lachay, Pasamayo and Ilo Hills) brought about by the seasonal accumulation of organic matter.

Their agricultural potential is varied and closely related to topography and size of sand particles. These are important and decisive factors which influence adaptability of Eutric Regosols for agricultural purposes. Regosols of fine to medium sand texture in a homogenous land setting are most suited for cultivation of desert crops as long as adequate water supplies are available for irrigation.

According to the Soil Taxonomy (1973) they belong to the Entisol Order, Psamment Suborder and Ustipsamment Great Group (Regosols characteristic of the irrigated areas or irrigated alluvial valleys) and Torripsamment typical of the drier coastal plains.

Solonchaks

Solonchaks are saline soils typical of the lowlands of the Coastal Desert developed on recent deposits generally of alluvial origin, but with saline concentrations distributed throughout their profile to a depth of 1.20 m or more. Electrical conductivity surpasses the critical level of 15 mmhos per cm and tends to present salic horizons at a depth of 100 cms. Many of these salic horizons are hardened or cemented by chlorides, gypsum or calcium giving origin to the "Hardpan Solonchaks". The landscape is predominantely flat and slightly depressed, frequently with inadequate drainage which contributes to salt accumulation.

The geographic distribution of Solonchaks is significant, since together with the Eutric Regosols and dry Eutric Fluvisols they cover large extensions within the desert flatlands. Studies carried out by ONERN on the Central and Southern Coastal Plains, show a total area of over 1000000 has of such soils.

The Morphology of typical profiles of Solonchaks depends on whether they are *Orthic Solonchaks* or *Gleyic Solonchaks*. Orthic Solonchaks present marked stratification and predominantly sandy texture with a weakly developed A horizon. These soils vary from well to imperfectly drained. On the other hand, Gleyic Solonchaks have a much deeper and darker profile due to the organic matter accumulation. One of their typical characteristics is a gleyic horizon. These soils are usually found alongside beaches or ancient Fluvisols of irrigated valleys transformed by halomorphic processes. Their topography varies from depressed to flat.

According to the Soil Taxonomy (1973) Orthic Solonchak groups are classified within, the Aridisol Order the Orthid Suborder and Salorthid Great Group; Gleyic Solonchaks are grouped within the Aquept Suborder and the Halaaquept Great Group.

With regard to their agricultural potential, Solonchaks offer serious limitations due to salinity problems. Their utilization is subject to elimination or reduction of salts to low toxicity levels for normal crop production.

Yermosols

Yermosols are typical edaphic groups of the desert coastal plains, with low salt concentrations. They are found in the flat lands of the northern Coast and the desert between the Pisco and Grande Rivers. Within this group, Calcic Yermosols are worth mentioning. They are characterized by high contents of calcium carbonate both in the mass and power form or by calciuc and/or gypsic horizons at different depths. The Calcic Yermosols have a poorly developed A horizon with vescicular structure and sandy-loam texture.

In areas where relatively fine materials of alluvial origin are predominant Luvic Yermosols are found, characterized by a somewhat deeper A horizons which rest upon argillic B horizons structured in polyhedral blocks. On Calcic Yermosols there is practically no vegetation. Luvic Yermosols sustain herbaceous and arboreous vegetation in the Northern Coast.

The agricultural potential and use of Yermosols depends greatly on the topography of the area and the permanent supply of water. Luvic Yermosols have the greater production potential.

According to the Soil Taxonomy (1973) they belong to the Aridisol Order, Orthid Suborder and Calciorthid Great Group (Calcic Yermosols) and Haplargids (Luvic Yermosols).

Xerosols

Xerosols form the edaphic group of greaterf pedologic development within the Coastal Desert and also are of major importance due to
their agricultural potential. They have developed from fine materials of
moderate drainage and under varied topographical conditions, ranging from
flat to undulated to mountainous. Their geographical distribution is
centered around the coastal flatlands, mainly on the northern Coast (Departments of Piura and Tumbes), closely associated with Pellic Vertisols,
and on the Central-Southern Coast towards the interior (Department of
Ica).

Their morphology is characterized by a relatively well developed A
horizon resting upon an argillic B horizon with blocky structure which
characterizes the Luvic Xerosols. The presence of calcic horizons and
soft powdery concretions in the lower portion or underneath the argillic B
is predominant in these soils. Their herbaceous vegetation and arboreous
species used for lumber, are at the present greatly diminished due to
indiscriminatory exploitation practices and excessive grazing.

From the agricultural viewpoint, Luvic Xerosols present great agricultural possibilities. They are considered productive lands once arid climatic conditions are improved through permanent irrigation.

According to the Soil Taxonomy (1973), these soils belong to the
Aridisol Order, Argid Suborder, Haplargids Great Group and Mollic
Haplargid Subgroup.

Vertisols

This group comprises clayey soils of expandible and extremely
plastic nature. They are found in the northern Coast and towards the
interior in plains of undulated to mountainous topography, closely associated with the Luvic Xerosols, extending like a vast belt towards the
Ecuador border to the North. Their vegetative cover varies from herbaceous
to arboreal, with certain indicator species of this edaphogenic group such as
Luffa operculata.

Morphologically, the Vertisols of the Peruvian Coastal desert belong
to the Pellic group. They have chromas less than 1.5 in the first 30 to 50
cms; they have a depth of over 1.2 m, are heavy montmorillonitic clays
which crack during the prolonged dry season and present the typical Gilgai
microrelief. The structure is made up of sizable parallelipids and in many
cases they present the typical shiny surfaces (slickensides) caused by the
natural movement of soil masses which characterizes this type of soil.
Generally they are underlaid by granitoid material and in the lower portion
of the profile small pulverulent calcareous masses are found.

With adequate management they are considered moderately good
soils for agriculture. They are of great value for crops suited to the ecological
environment predominant in the northern part of the Coast, such as cotton,
particularly those Vertisols located on moderate topographical settings.
Once conditioned for agricultural purposes they are noted for their high
productivity and water retention, important factors for soils under permanent irrigation. It is worth pointing out that a great part of the soils of

the San Lorenzo Irrigation Project (Department of Piura) belongs to the Pellic Vertisol Subgroup and have produced high crop yields.

According to the Soil Taxonomy (1973) these soils are included in the Vertisol Order, Ustert or Torrent suborder and Pellustert Great Group.

Andosols

Vitric Andosols are found throughout the Coastal Desert plains in the southern part of Peru, on tablelands located over 1000 meters above sea level typical of Arequipa, Moquegua and Tacna Departments. These soils are associated with Yermosols, Fluvisols, Solonchaks (most of them with hardpans), Regosols and Lithosols which make up the edaphic landscape of the southern Coast.

Vitric Andosols, under aridic conditions, are soils slightly developed and are considered as Regosols derived from volcanic ashes or Andosols as some authors have named them. Vegetation is almost completely absent, limited to dispersed xerophytic formations such as *Opuntia cactacea* and other tubular types. The topography is predominantly mild and monotonous.

Morphologically, they are characterized by a thin, grayish, loose, brittle, porous (vesicular) poorly granulated ochric epipedon and with low organic matter content, less than 1%. Underneath the ochric A horizon, a transitional AC horizon may exist, light brown to light grayish brown in color, very brittle without much structure. Then comes the homogeneus C horizon, light gray, loose, without structure, mainly made up of pyroclastic vitric material which dominates the sand, silt and gravel fraction. Mineralogical studies of clay fractions in these soils show the presence of amorphous clay without any set structural pattern to X-rays, and with a low cation exchange capacity. The reaction of these soils is mainly neutral.

At the present time, the majority of these soils are not in use due to lack of adequate water supply. In areas with available water supply or close to water sources, cryophilic crops such as alfalfa, potatoes, vegetables and olives are grown. These soils together with medium-textured Yermosols and Fluvisols comprise the new expansion areas for agricultuer in the southern Coast of the country.

According to the Soil Taxonomy (1973) they belong to the Inceptisol Order, Andept Suborder and Vitrandept Great Group.

Lithosols and Lithic Formations

Lithosols and Lithic Formations (nonedaphic) are shallow soils or soils on denuded rock exposures respectively, formed on parental material of varied lithology, steep slopes with gradients over 100%. They form the hills that make up a large part of the Acient Coastal Mountain Range as well as the steep branches of the Western Andean Range.

Morphologically, Lithosols present dwarf profiles, with a thin A horizons generally of a gravel-stony nature, which rests directly on consolidated rock or rocky detritus.

Agricultural use of these soils is practically non-existent due to their shallow, rocky nature and abrupt topography which eliminates any possibility of irrigation, consequently they are devoted exclusively to forestry.

According to the Soil Taxonomy (1973) they mainly correspond to the Lithic Subgroups of the Entisols and Inceptisols.

III   AMAZON JUNGLE

The lowlands of the eastern part of the country comprise the vast Amazonic Low Forest (Selva Baja) made up of non-consolidated sediments mainly of the Tertiary or Pleisstocene, in which kaolinitic clays and quartz sands are predominant. This area which comprises the upper part of the Amazon River represents the most extensive, scarcely populated, less explored region in the country, with a total surface of about 55 million hectares, approximately 43% of the total area of Peru. Recent Quaternary (Holocene) deposits are a small proportion of the geological configuration of the area.

The Amazon Plain has mean altitudes of less than 300 meters. Average temperature exceeds 24°C, mostly up to latitude 12°S. Annual rainfall varies between 2000 and 4000 mm for the humid zone and 1500 mm or less for the sub-humid regions with marked dry seasons. The predominant native vegetation consists in most part of evergreen forests. Trees are generally large and form dense groups with the exception of areas with poor drainage where palms (Mauritia flexuosa, mainly) and many herboceous species are abundant. A group of species of tall and thick trees, many of them of important commercial value are found in the area.

The geomorphic configuration of the Low Jungle can be divided into two physiographic units, low terraces subject to flooding of recent alluvial origin, and the second, of an extensive undulated surface with various degrees of dissection due to continuous erosion processes, which make up the deep sediments of the Tertiary and Pleistocene. This geomorphic unit covers about 80% of the Amazonic Plain and is where strongly weathered soils are found.

In the following sections, the morphological characteristics of low land soils in the Amazonic plain are described. Figure 3 shows the distribution of such soils in the various landscapes.

Fluvisols

This group combines soils derived from recent alluvial sediments deposited by the large rivers such as the Amazon, Huallaga, Marañón, Ucayali, Napo, Tigre, Urubamba, Madre de Dios and others. They are distributed along the banks, islands and low terraces that are periodically flooded.

Topography of the area is flat with 0-4% slopes. Native vegetation is predominantly low forests with typical riverine vegetation including isolated palm trees of hydrophitic habitat (Mauritia flexuosa, mainly). Predominant Fluvisols are eutric without major diagnostic horizons, with fine sandy loam and silty clay loam texture and stratified morphology.

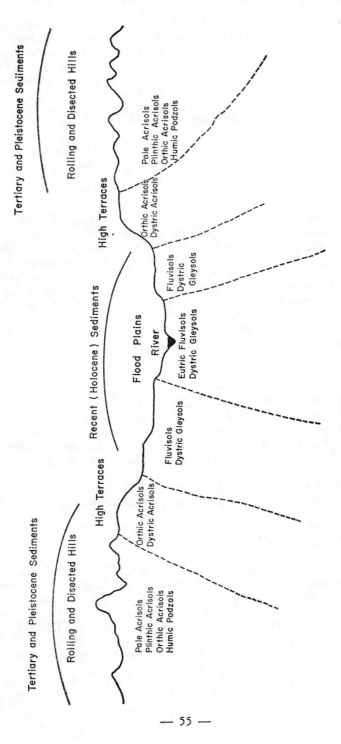

Figure 3. Soils distribution in the lowlands of the Peruvian Amazon Basin.

Tertiary and Pleistocene Sediments

Rolling and Disected Hills

High Terraces

Recent (Holocene) Sediments

Flood Plains

River

Tertiary and Pleistocene Sediments

Rolling and Disected Hills

High Terraces

Pale Acrisols
Plinthic Acrisols
Orthic Acrisols
Humic Podzols

Orthic Acrisols
Dystric Acrisols

Fluvisols
Dystric
Gleysols

Eutric Fluvisols
Dystric Gleysols

Fluvisols
Dystric Gleysols

Orthic Acrisols
Dystric Acrisols

Pale Acrisols
Plinthic Acrisols
Orthic Acrisols
Humic Podzols

Due to definite hydromorphic influence, many of these soils have been transformed into Gleysols which complete the groups of soils within the flood plains. Chemically, Fluvisols are of slightly acid to neutral reaction (pH 6.5 to 7.0) and contain moderate amounts of organic matter in the A horizon. Productivity of these soils is good and they receive annual fertilization from the relatively fine sediments deposited.

Fluvisols are of great agricultural importance in the main urban centers and where subsistance agricultural system based on cassava, corn, plantain and papaya exist.

According to the Soil Taxonomy (1973), they belong to the Entisol Order, Fluvent Suborder and Tropofluvent Great Group.

Gleysols

Gleysols comprise a group of soils formed from moderately fine material on relatively recent alluvial deposits and are closely associated with Eutric Fluvisols. Physiographically, they are found on low terraces subject to flooding of flat or concave topography and with gradients between 0 and 2%. Native vegetation is mostly low forest including extensive areas of hydrophilic palms *(Mauritia flexuosa* and *Jessenia sp.)*. They are locally known as "Aguajales" due to the common name of one of the palm species, the aguaje.

Morphologically, they present a thin ochric horizon with partially decomposed organic matter or an umbric, acid, fairly prominent horizon to a depth of 30 cm. This prominence is followed by a cambic horizon with stratified layers or zones with noticeable mottling. Fluctuating water levels vary between 80 and 120 cms below the surface,

Chemically, they are very acid soils (pH 4.0 to 5.0) which groups them as Dystric Gleysols with base saturation below 50%.

Due to periodical flooding and serious drainage problems, their use for agriculture and cattle raising is limited. The presence of hydrophitic palms (Aguajes) in this soil is of economic significance due to their fruit production.

According to the Soil Taxonomy (1973), these soils belong to the Order Inceptisol, Suborder Aquept, Great Group Tropaquept and Subgroup Typic Tropaquepts.

Paleo Acrisols (Nitosols?)

This group together with the Plinthic Acrisols perhaps comprises the most extensive soils in the Amazonic plains. They rest on lacustrine and marine alluvial material made up of friable kaolinitic clays. They are found in an undulated terrain consisting of old terraces, low hills in various degrees of dissection and slopes ranging from 3 to 50%. Generally they present good drainage, in comparison with Plinthic Acrisols. Climax tropical evergreen forest covers these soils, including numerous species of commercial interest.

Morphologically, Paleo Acrisols have deep, intensively weathered profiles. Their main characteristic is the presence of a deep argillic B horizon with a depth of over 1.50 m with a clay content no less than 20% throughout the profile. Generally the A2 horizon is diffuse or absent, so the A horizon rests on the argillic. This horizon has a subangular blocky structure and clay skins which may be clearly seen both in the inner and outer parts of the natural aggregates. The color of these soils varies from dark brown, to yellow brown, and dark yellowish red.

According to their chemical characteristics they are extremely acid soils (pH under 5.0) with medium to low contents or organic matter. In the argillic B horizon the base saturation is below 35%.

These soils are highly weathered and have marked nutritional deficiencies, which make them the problem soils of the Amazonic Region and the country. They may be adapted for the cultivation of certain crops adapted to these humid regions but adequate technology is needed for economic production. Usually they are suitable for mixed agricultural systems based on permanent crops and livestock production. Nevertheless, it is worth pointing out that their main potential lies in adequate exploitation of their forest resources.

According to the Soil Taxonomy (1973), these soils are classified in the Ultisol Order, Udult Suborder and Paleudult Great Group.

Plinthic Acrisols

As has been previously stated. Plinthic Acrisols together with Paleo Acrisols form the most extensive and representative edaphic group of the Peruvian Amazonic plain. As in the case of Paleo Acrisols, they have developed from ancient alluvial sediments based on friable kaolinitic clays located on undulated terraces, low hills (marked hill side formation) with slopes varying 2% to 50%. Natural drainage of these soils is usually inadequate. The native vegetation consist of large trees with certain species of commercial interest.

Morphologically, they present a strongly weathered and developed profile with extensive mottling, based on iron oxide (pseudo plinthite) over a grayish clay substructure. These soils may be precursors of the true Plinthic Acrisols which present in their profile typical plinthite layers that usually harden irreversibly upon exposure. In most cases, studied in the Amazonic Peneplain, this red and gray mass does not harden upon exposure. On the other hand, it is worth mentioning the fact that typical plinthiform samples have been discovered but without adequate morphological description of the soil where they originally appeared. These soils have subangular blocky structure and clay skins.

From a chemical viewpoint, they are extremely acid (pH below 4.0) with medium to low organic matter content and base saturation below 35% in the argillic B horizon.

For agricultural purposes they must be adequately managed. Any strong transformation from the prevailing forest vegetation to an agricultural or livestock system may lead to irreparable damage to the ecological environment. Because of their inadequate darinage and deficient nutritional conditions they are apt for certain hydrophitic crops such as rice. Use of these soils for pastures may be limited.

According to the Soil Taxonomy System (1973), these soils are classified within the Ultisols Order, Udult Suborder and Plinthudult Great Group or Plinthic Paleudult Subgroup.

Orthic Acrisols

Originally, Orthic Acrisols were considered the main soils of the Amazonic region of Peru. At present systematic soil studies carried out by ONERN and further research regarding soil characterization in the Peruvian humid tropics have pointed out that the geographical distributiion as well as proportion of these soils is more limited than what had been initially imagined. Nevertheless, together with Plinthic Acrisols and Paleo Acrisols they represent the main soils in the Amazonic Peneplain of the country. They are found in the southern part of the amazonic jungle, (Department of Madre de Dios). Physiographically, they extend throughout the hills and mountain sides with steep slopes (over 20%) where argillic sandy materials are predominant. They have open drainage with native climax forest vegetation and certain wood species of commercial interest.

Based on their physiographic characteristics and the predominance of argillic sandy materials, these soils present a shallow argillic B which separated them from the Paleo Acrisols. Their coloring vary from yellowish brown to yellowish red and their texture from sandy clay loam to sandy clay with clay films present but not clearly visible in the natural aggregates found in subangular polyhedral form.

Chemically, they are extremely acid (pH below 4.0) with base saturation levels below 35% in the argillic B horizons. Their agricultural value lies in perennial crops native to the invironment and adequate exploitation of forest resources.

According to the Soil Taxonomy System (1973), they belong to the Ultisol Order, Udult Suborder and Tropudult Great Group.

Podzols

Podzols have been identified within an extensive triangle formed by both banks of the Marañon and Ucayali rivers and the beginning of the Amazon. They are generally found in high ancient terraces with an undulated to flat surface and have developed from highly silicic and strongly leached materials. Their drainage is free, sometimes excessive and their vegetation is of low commercial value for lumber.

Morphological, they present a thin horizon darkened by large ammounts of organic matter which rests on an extensive and deep A2 highly elluviated with silicic or quartz materials, loose structure and white yellowish or whitish color. Many of these soils found near Iquitos, due to extensive and deep A2 horizons form actual giant Podzols or Arenosols (Quartsipsamments). In groups where the A2 elluvial horizon is shallower, a humic (Bh) horizon with secondary organic matter coating can be found. Chemically, they are nutritionally poor and very acid (pH below 4.0).

Due to inadequate edaphic characteristics for the establishment of tropical crops and pastures, these soils must be kept as protection forests or for restricted exploitation of certain wood species of commercial interest.

According to the Soil Taxonomy System (1973), many of these soils belong to the Spodosol Order, Humod Suborder and Tropohumod Great Group. Those which show intense mottling are classified as Tropaquods.

Ferrasols

Traditionally, these soils have been considered the typical edaphic group of the humid tropical and forest regions of Peru. Today, thanks to more precise information gathered by ONERN and to greater knowledge regarding internationally accepted definitions and concepts on morphological soil characteristics of these soils, we can state that up to the moment, no soil profile has been found that fits with the definition of Ferrasols or Oxisols (according to the Soil Taxonomy System) in the lowlands of the Peruvian Amazon.

IV CONCLUSIONS AND SUMMARY

One common property of the lowland soils of Peru is their low *natural fertility*. This aspect is limited to the extensive Amazonic plain where paleo, plinthic and orthic Acrisols, Dystric Podzols and Gleysols are found. These soils are characterized by their low cation exchange capacity and base saturation levels below 35%.

Another serious limitation for the use of soils in the lowlands is their water deficiency. This is mostly found in the Coastal Desert because of its extremely arid climatic condition where present diversified agricultural techniques are possible only through irrigation. Among soils with this type of limitation we find the Yermosols, Xerosols, Regosols, Fluvisols, Solonchaks, Vertisols and Vitric Andosols.

Poor drainage is another limiting factor specially in the eastern forest regions of the lowlands of Peru. Most of the irrigated valleys of the Coastal Desert are also seriously affected by this hydromorphic process which limits to a great extent their productivity.

V REFERENCES

FAO. Soil map of the world. FAO World Soil Resources Report N° 32. Rome, 1968.

ONERN, Archivo Técnico de Suelos; División de Suelos y Fisiografía de ONERN; Lima, Perú. (Unpublished report).

SOIL SURVEY STAFF. Soil Taxonomy. U. S. Dpt. Agric. Soil. Cons. Service. 1973.

ZAMORA, C. Mapa de Suelos del Perú a escala 1; 1'000,000 (Material inédito); ONERN, Lima, Perú, 1968.

ZAMORA, C. Esquema de los Suelos de la Región Selvática del Perú; ONERN, Lima, Perú, 1968.

ZAMORA, C. Los Suelos de Podzol de las Regiones Tropicales del Perú; ONERN, Lima, Perú, 1968.

ZAMORA, C. Los Suelos de los Departamentos de Tumbes y Piura (Informe inédito); ONERN, Lima, Perú, 1973.

ZAMORA, C. Regiones Edáficas del Perú, ONERN, Lima, Perú, 1972.

ZAMORA, C. and ECHENIQUE, J. Estudio de los Suelos de la Zona Yurimaguas; ONERN, Lima, Perú, 1967.

ZAMORA, C. and ECHENIQUE, J. Estudio de Suelos de la Zona de los Ríos Inambari, Madre de Dios; ONERN, Lima, Perú, 1972.

3 Soils of the Eastern Region of Colombia

RAMIRO GUERRERO M.

I INTRODUCTION

The Eastern Region of Colombia represents an important part of the national territory. It comprises the area east of the Eastern Cordillera. The northern sector is commonly known as the Eastern Plains (Llanos Orientales) which belongs to the Orinoc River basin. The southern portion is known as Amazonia, where rivers form part of the upper Amazon River basin (Figure 1).

At present, beef cattle and rice production in the Llanos are of national economic importance, while in Amazonia only forest and native fauna exploitation are of any significance. The future development of a beef industry with modern management processing and marketing techniques, is likely to serve as a permanent source of meat for internal consumption and for export. The possibility of growing certain tropical crops with modern technology, also exists.

The Llanos and Amazonia have as a whole many positive characterisitcs, such as good physical soil properties, gentle topography, absence of floods, portion of the Meta river, low price of land, road connections with major cities, and navigable rivers connected with the Atlantic Ocean, allow trade with Venezuela as well as Peru and Brazil. Although this area is one of the most underdeveloped in the country, lately much interest in its development has been shown both by official entities and private enterprises. The facts that it is a frontier region and the expectations of development are probably the reasons for this interest.

In 1966, FAO compiled much of the available information about the Llanos including a reconnaissance soil survey of 13 million hectares. Leon (1964, 1968) analized samples from the Llanos and found that vermiculite-chlorite, kaolinite, goethite, quartz, and amorphous sesquioxides were the predominant clay minerals. He concluded that nutrient content was extremely low. Recently Guerrero (1971a), Goosen (1971), Malagon (1973), Cortes et al. (1973) and Benavides (1973) conducted characterization and classification studies on both the Llanos and the Amazonia, as will be subsequently discussed.

The purposes of this paper are:

1) To present information obtained by various researchers with respect to physical, chemical, and mineralogical characteristics of soils in the Eastern Region of Colombia.

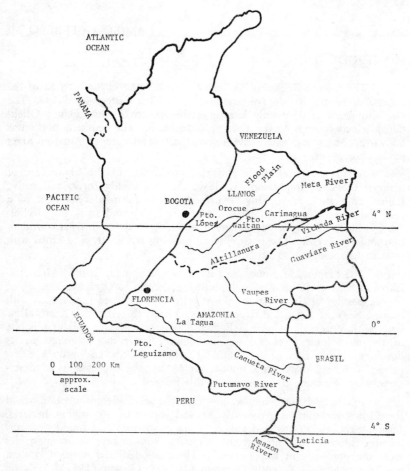

Figure 1. Colombian Orinoco and Amazonic Regions and studied
sites-location.

2) To summarize these findings and to relate them with soil correlation and classification.

3) To summarize the basic information for agricultural research and development programs.

The present paper does not review literature on the subject because this has been done previously (Guerrero 1971a; Gossen 1971; Cortes *et al.*, 1973; Benavides 1973; Malagon 1973), except the implications of certain soil characteristics to their immediate use. The data presented cover a large urea where ICA, CIAT, and the Ministry of Defense are presently involved in agriculture and/or colonization research programs.

II GENERAL DESCRIPTION OF THE AREAS

a) *Llanos Orientales:*

The area can be split in two major regions. flood plains north of the Meta River and the *Altillanura* (high plains) south of that river. It is located between Puerto Lopez and Orocue at 4°51'N, approximately 250 to 300 metres above sea level. To the south, it merges with the Amazon Region, to the west with the Piedmont of the Colombian Eastern Range and to east with Venezuela. Most of the information presented in this section is based on a FAO publication (1965).

The prevailing climate according to the Koeppen-Geier classification system is Av or plateau climate. Average annual rainfall is 1744 mm in Orocue, increasing up to 4000 mm towards the west. A long rainy season from April to November is followed by a short, almost totally dry period from December to March. The mean annual temperature is approximately 28°C, practically uniform throughout the year. Maximum and minimum daily temperatures present greater variation than average monthly temperatures. Average relative humidity is 80% during the rainy season and 50 to 60% during the dry season. Potential evapotranspiration is high at the end of the dry period, when stored water levels decrease to a minimum during February and March.

Parent material consists of mixed alluvial sediments deposited perhaps during Pleistocene. According to FAO (1965), all superficial sediments in the Eastern Plains come from the Eastern Mountain Range and the degree of sedimentation is related to various glaciation phases, tectonic movements and mountain erosion. The Range formations consist mainly of sandstone, conglomerates, clay slates, slates, granodiorites and limestones.

Sediment deposition took place in inverse order to the original stratum position in the source area, that is to say, top sediments were deposited first and at greater depth. The presence of higher cliffs on the southern side of the River, following an almost direct line, serves as evidence of a fault line along the Meta River (Figure 2).

Some climatic changes also occurred, during which, loess and sand were transported by the wind and deposited. At present, during the dry season some materials are still transported from the beaches and islands of the Meta River. Goosen (1970) gives great importance to the aeolic influence in these soils and concludes that "loess is the parent material of Llanos soils".

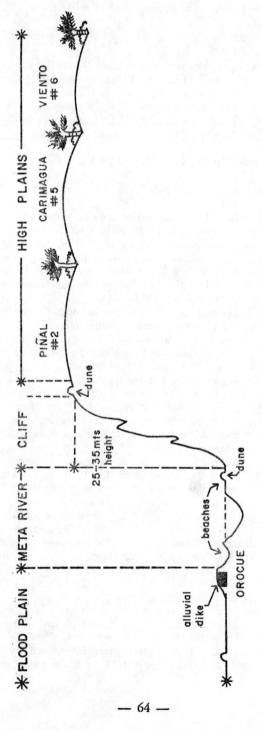

Figure 2. Cross section outline showing relative position of Highplains, Flooding plains and selected soil profiles. (Guerrero 1971a).

Topography is flat, slightly convex and most of the area is well drained, however, drainage catenas exist because the soils close to depressions have a high and fluctuating water table. The fault line along the Meta River serves as limit to the plateau's northern section either as an almost completely vertical fault scarp or as steep cliffs with 12 to 50% slopes, approximately 25 to 30 meters high (Figure 2). This stratum is essentially a reservoir, explaining the existence of flood plains to the north and of non floodable areas south of the Meta River. Nevertheless, according to the FAO study, these plains are considered alluvial sediments. There is not much evidence of this on the surface. There are no ancient channels, natural levees nor depressions. The surface is smooth, as if all irregularities had been covered and leveled. This is probably due to wind action during the dry season. Surface material is granulometrically similar to loess (FAO, 1965).

The dominant vegetation is tropical savannas. About 90% of the region consists of immense plains, free of trees, almost exclusively covered with native, short grasses, of the genera *Trachypogon* and *Axonopus*. The remaining areas are swamp covered with moriche palm forests and gallery forests along drainage courses.

Population density is below 2 persons per km². Cattle and supplies are transported both by land and by river. Land is almost exclucively used for cattle raising, with a carrying capacity of less than 0.1 head per ha. usually under primitive management. Cattle ranches are large and usually extend from 10000 to 20000 hectares. A 10000 ha. ranch is not considered large.

Part of the area is being used for irrigated and upland rice production. To a lesser extent subsistance crops such as plantain, cassava, corn, citrus fruits, mangoes and cashews are found close to the households. Some cassava and corn is grown in a shifting cultivation system. Lately, ICA and CIAT have tried new agricultural techniques with headquarters at the Carimagua Agricultural Experiment Station (Fig. 1).

b) *Amazonia:*

The area is located approximately between 4°N and 4°S and 67 to 77°W longitude. Its limits are the Llanos: to the North, the foothills of the Eastern Range to the west, the Putumayo and Amazon Rivers to the south which separate Colombia from Peru and Brazil, and the Brazilian Amazon Region to the east. Much of the following information has been summarized from Carrera and Arevalo (1972), Cortes et al., (1973) and Benavides (1973).

The Amazonic climate is hot and humid; rain is abundant during the entire year in contrast with the Llanos. There is no dry season. Maximum difference of mean monthly temperature is no greater than 5°C. Annual average rainfall is 2300 mm with local variations such as 3000 mm in Leticia and 3900 mm in Florencia and Puerto Asís.

Geomorphologically, the Amazonia is divided in two areas: The Amazonic Plains and the Vaupes Salient. The Amazonic Plains to the south are formed by low flatlands of sedimentary deposits mainly from the Tertiary that were deposited under lake or marine water. In some locations, these sediments rest on Pebas and Barreira formations which also serve as parent material for many Brazilian soils. The Vaupes Salient is formed by Precambrian rocks from the Guyana Shield, with general slope towards the Llanos. It is characterized by the presence of tertiary sediments some of them believed to be 445 to 1200 million years old. Altitude varies between 500 metres above sea level close to the mountains to 100 metres above sea level on the Brazilian border.

Physiography and topography present a greater degree of undulation and hills in the Piedmont but become flatter towards the east. Large rivers run between banks 10 to 25 m high, sometimes present only on one side, as in Puerto Leguizamo and Leticia. Generally, three main physiographic areas are predominant: a) "Highlands' slightly undulated, with slopes varying from 3 to 12%. This represents the largest area in the region. The highlands are frequently dissected by "short wave" dendritic pattern water currents that leave in between slightly convexed areas descending towards the concave drainage zones, hence producing a catena or toposequence. b) Terraces, more common to the west, with flat or slightly undulated topography when dissected. c) Alluvial plains some active, found along river banks where fluvial processes have produced characteristic levees, flood plains, and swamps.

The vegetation consists of tropical evergreen forest. A great variety of forest species and a small number of palms are characteristic of the highlands. The number of palms increase and other species decreases in the alluvial plains. In general, and in spite of large number of trees, the amount of commercial wood per hectare is low. In certain parts, for example, along the Negro and Inirida Rivers, xeromorphic vegetation is present formed mainly by small trees and shrubs, believed to have originated from degraded soil effects or as products of different climatic conditions.

The area is unpopulated, except for certain few extinguishing tribes. The most common means of communication is the canoe, which allows the use of the large rivers of the area. People work as hunters, fishermen or farmers. Colonization is spontaneous and sometimes directed by INCORA. In general terms, over 90% of the area is made up of virgin forests, the remaining area has been cleared and is now used for subsistence crops and/or pasture and extensive cattle production. Cassava is the most common crop, being the main staple of the local people, other important crops are corn, rice, plantain, sugar cane, pineapple and to a lower extent, cocoa, oil palm, rubber, and some fruit trees. Furthermore, part of the local and migratory populaiton hunts animals for skin exports.

III   MATERIALS AND METHODS

Locations

This paper presents partial information regarding soil profiles studied by previous researchers. The author described and analyzed seven soil profiles representative of a sector in the Llanos Altillanura close to Orocue. Sites were selected according to the position in the landscape (well drained and moderately well drained components of a catena) and distance from the river (Figure 2). Furthermore, a summary is made of the main physical, chemical and mineralogical characteristics of three profiles from the Colombian Amazonia, and nine representative profiles, recently described and classified by Benavides (1973). Some information regarding soil profiles and samples of the plowed layer are also included in the Appendix.

Sampling

Landscape description and sampling was done in test pits according to procedures and terminology described in the Soil Survey Manual (Soil Survey Staff, 1951).

Characterization Methods

The methods used most frequently by different researchers were: Granulometric distribution was performed through: the Calgon-pipette method (Kilmer and Alexander, 1949); or Centrifugal (Kittrick and Hope, 1963). Water dispersible clay was determined in 20 grams of air dried soil, agitated in demineralized water, transfered to a cylinder and measured by volume. Free iron oxides were extracted by the dithionite method (described by Kittrick and Hope, 1963).

Soil pH was determined using a glass electrode in a 1:1 water-soil ratio and in 1:1 1N-KCl. Organic carbon was determined by the methods described by Peech and Walkley (Soil Conservation Service, 1967). Exchangeable hydrogen and exchangeable aluminum were extracted by N KCl and titrated with 0.1 N HCl, using phenolphthalein as indicator according to McLean (1965). Exchangeable cations were extracted with ammonium acetate at pH 7.0; Ca and Mg were determined by atomic absorption, K and Na by flame photometry. Cation Exchange Capacity was obtained by the sum of exchangeable bases plus exchangeable Al. Base saturation percentage was calculated on this basis.

To determine clay and silt mineralogy, iron-free samples were prepared from the following fractions: <0.2 μ, 0.2-2 μ, 2-5 μ, and 5-20 μ. Diffractograms of these particles were obtained according to the procedure described by Jackson (1956), in a General Electric XRD-5 X-Ray Unit with copper-nickel filter for K-Alfa radiation, at a rate of $2°$-2θ per minute. Mineralogy of the sand fraction was determined in oil of different refraction indexes and in Canada Balsam for fine and very fine sand particles. Thin sections were prepared as indicated by Buol and Fadness (1961) and were described according to terminology suggested by Brewer (1964).

Other special methods or modifications of original methods are shown in FAO (1965), Goosen (1971), Cortes (1973), Malagon (1973), and Benavides (1973).

IV   RESULTS AND DISCUSSION

Following is a brief discussion of the outstanding results obtained in selected profile soil studies made by Guerrero (1971a) in the Eastern Plain Region and Benavides (1973) in the Colombia Amazonia. Results of physical, chemical and mienralogical studies obtained by other researchers are also discussed and presented in the Appendix.

Particle Size

Removal of free iron and organic matter increased clay content over 50%. This was interpreted as dispersion of silt-sized aggregates. Before iron and organic matter removal, most of the clay was present as stable aggregates cemented in the silt fraction by organic matter and iron. Clay increases upon dispersion, increased at the expense of silt content.

Table 1 also shows that over 70% of clay particles in selected samples, correspond to the fine clay fraction. This may be attributed to in-situ clay formations,, related with the sedimentation processes of the initial material at various distances to the river banks instead of illuviation.

In all samples treated with Calgon without iron removal, clay content increased with depth and in profiles south of the Meta River while sand content was higher in upper horizons and profiles closer to the river. These data point out that parent materials of soils 1 to 3 could have originated from aeolic deposits brought from beaches north of the Meta River during the dry season when such materials are exposed and there is a prevalence of North-East Trade Winds.

Water Dispersable Clay

Water dispersable clay content in the first three horizons of four Llanos soil profiles was similar to that obtained by the Calgon-pipette Method (Table 1). Below the third horizon, however, water dispersible clay content decreased sharply. This indicates higher degree of clay stability in lower horizons and tends to confirm their oxic nature. (Soil Survey Staff, 1970).

Free Iron Oxides

Free iron oxide contents increased with depth and it seemed to be directly related to clay content obtained after removing iron with dithionite (Table 1). Furthermore, free iron oxide contents increased with distances south of the Meta River. Horizons with 5YR 4/8 and 2.5YR 4/8 colors showed more iron than horizons with 10R 4/8 to the north and closer to the river bank. A larger Fe_2O_3 content was not related with presence of non-hardening pseudoplinthic concretions since these were found in an erratic pattern both in red and orange subsoils. (Guerrero, 1971a).

In Amazon soils (Benavides, 1973) free iron oxide contents varied greatly among profiles, 13% to 0.2%, but presenting higher values in very fine clay soils.

Bennema (1966) compared total iron and aluminum content in three different Brazilian soils. In general, he concluded that the Fe_2O_3 content was low in Red Yellow Latosols (below 10%), medium in Dark Red Latosols (10-18%) and high in Dusky Red Latosols (20-34%). Moura-

Table 1.—Some physical properties of Llanos soils (adapted from Guerrero 1971a.).

Soil No	Depth	Granulometric Distribution						Water Dispers. Clay	Fe₂O₃
		Calgon-pipet with organic matter removal			With organic matter & free iron removal				
		Sand	Silt	Clay	Coarse Clay $(2\text{-}0.2\mu)$	Fine Clay $(<0.2\mu)$	Total Clay		
	cm.	%	%	%	%	%	%	%	%
2	0 — 20	44	39	17	10	21	31	11	3.7
	20 — 34	41	40	19	10	21	31	15	4.1
	125 — 178	33	37	30	13	39	52	4	6.1
5	0 — 12	12	50	38	—	—	—	26	—
	12 — 32	11	48	41	16	57	73	35	9.5
	88 — 148	12	43	45	16	47	63	3	9.3
6	0 — 10	9	45	46	—	—	—	36	—
	10 — 19	8	48	44	17	50	67	38	10.7
	105 — 140	7	34	59	20	62	82	3	11.9

Filho (1968) also reported a 23% average for free iron oxide extracted with sodium dithionite in Dusky Red Latosol classified at Typic Eutrustox, while the Soil Commission (1960) found values varying between 3 and 9% of total iron oxide for a Dark Red Latosol. Bornemisza and Igue (1967) obtained average Fe₂O₃ values of 10.1%, 2.0%, and 3.4% respectively for Red, Yellow Latosols and "Terra Roxa" of the Brazilian Amazonia. Likewise, Pratt et al. (1969 studying iron oxide content of some A horizons from São Paulo soils found the following average Fe₂O₃ values: for Haplorthox, 3-6%; for pure Terra Roxa (Acrorthox) 17.1%. Such data confirm the large variation in iron oxide content in different Latosols and Oxisols.

Soil Reaction

pH values in Llanos and Amazon soils are presented in Tables 2 and 3 and in the Appendix. Obtained values show these soils to be acid and strongly acid as would be expected for tropical soils of this nature. In general, values both in water and KCl tend to increase with depth, which indicates leaching of bases from the upper horizons. pH values did not vary greatly between sites nor did they show any special geographic or physiographical tendencies.

Table 2.—Chemical properties of the Altillanura soils of the Llanos. (Adapted from Guerrero, 1971a).

Soil Nº	Depth	1:1 H₂O	Sum of Bases	Exch. Al	Exch. H	Sum of Cations	CEC (1)	B.S. (2)	OC
	cm.	1:1:			meq/100 g soil			%	
2	0 — 20	4.6	0.7	1.7	0.7	3.1	5.4	23	1.2
	20 — 34	4.9	0.4	1.5	0.6	2.4	4.8	14	0.7
	125 — 178	4.8	0.2	1.0	0.4	1.7	4.4	18	—
5	0 — 12	4.5	0.9	2.9	0.9	4.7	10.7	19	2.2
	12 — 32	4.6	0.3	2.3	0.5	3.1	8.7	11	1.2
	88 — 148	5.1	0.1	0.3	0.3	0.8	5.9	25	0.3
6	0 — 10	4.7	1.0	3.4	0.7	5.1	13.6	20	3.1
	10 — 19	4.6	0.6	2.7	0.6	3.9	11.4	15	2.1
	105 — 140	5.1	0.2	0.1	0.3	0.7	7.0	36	—

(1) By ammonium acetate method.

(2) Based on sum of cations (1).

Organic Carbon

Organic carbon content in selected horizons from Llanos soils at 1 m depth varied between 3.10% and 0.16%, but most values were over 0.6% (approximately 1% organic matter) (Table 2). In both areas, organic matter values were higher in the upper horizons and decreased progressively with depth. Some relatively high values could have been attributed to grass root system or to ants and other macro-organisms, or both, as is seen in the soil description (Appendix 11).

Exchangeable Hydrogen and Aluminum

In Table 2 and 3 and in the Appendix, exchangeable acidity are reported as exchangeable hydrogen and/or exchangeable aluminum. It was found that aluminum is mainly responsible for exchangeable acidity, as Coleman et al. (1959), Jackson (1968), and other soil researchers have concluded.

Aluminum saturation values are greater than 60%. Under these conditions, more plant growth is affected by the aluminum toxicity and phosphorus applied as fertilizer is readily fixed unless lime is applied (Kamprath, 1967; 1972b; 1972c).

Table 3.—Chemical and physical characteristics of three representative soil profiles of the Colombian Amazon Region. (Adapted from Benavides, 1973).

Horizon	Depth	Clay	pH (H₂O)	Exch. Al	Sum of Base	CEC (1)	BS (2)	OC
	cm	%		meq/100 g soil			%	
Profile 5, LETICIA = UDOXIC DYSTROPEPT								
A1	0 — 10	40	4.6	5.2	0.7	6.1	11	1.9
B21	10 — 30	40	4.8	5.1	0.4	5.8	7	0.9
B22	83 — 140	47	4.9	6.4	0.4	5.3	6	0.2
Profile 6, LEGUIZAMO = TYPIC DYSTROPEPT								
A1	0 — 20	24	4.9	4.3	3.1	7.5	41	1.4
B21	20 — 80	49	4.8	7.3	2.0	9.9	20	0.4
IIB23	133 — 173	38	4.9	11.6	1.0	13.7	7	0.1
Profile 8, FLORENCIA = UDOXIC DYSTROPEPT								
A1	0 — 16	37	4.8	3.2	2.1	5.1	36	2.0
B21	16 — 85	52	4.7	6.7	0.7	5.7	10	0.5
B22	85 — 173	49	4.9	6.3	0.7	7.2	8	0.2

(1) Effective cation exchange capacity: Exchangeable bases plus Exchangeable acidity.

(2) Percent base saturation based on effective CEC.

Kamprath (1972 a,b,c) presents data which indicate these soils to be highly weathered predominantly satured with exchangeable aluminum and with low exchangeable base content (Table 4).

Cation Exchange Capacity, Exchangeable Bases and Base Saturation

In general, values obtained for cation exchange capacity in plain soils were fairly low, especially in the case of subsurface soils (Tables 2 and 3). Generally, values are higher in upper horizons where the organic matter content is higher, CEC decreases in intermediate horizons and slightly increases again in lower horizons. In Amazonia, effective CEC ranged from 5 to 20 meq/100g, but for soils with 2:1 clays values up to 50 meq/ grams were found.

Nevertheless, it is important to keep in mind that CEC with ammonium acetate at pH 7.0 includes pH dependent charge. Consequently, CEC differences determined by ammonium acetate and by cation addition methods, must be attributed to clay and organic matter contents, dependent on pH (Coleman *et al.*, 1959).

Table 4.—Soil pH, exchangeable cations and aluminum saturation of 26 soils from the Colombian Llanos (Kamprath, 1972a).

Comparison	pH	Exch Ca and Mg	Exch Al	Al Satn
		meq/100 g		%
Average	—	1.54	3.05	68
Range	4.15 — 5.12	0.05 — 9.09	0.60 — 5.80	29 — 86

In general, the exchangeable base content was extremely low, especially calcium and potassium in the Llanos. Higher values in upper horizons are attributed to biological recycling, as has been reported in other soils.

Base saturation percentages ranged between 1% to 17% but most values were around 5 to 20%. There was no apparent correlation between base saturation and location, but surface horizons and lower horizons tended to present higher values.

Likewise, the interpretation of data obtained in Appendix 1 through 8 indicates strong acidity, high exchangeable aluminum content and Al saturation usually over 60%, while base content is low and frequently extremely low. Organic matter content is surprisingly high, and possibly higher than what might be expected for soils of this nature, perhaps due to reasons noted by Buol (1972) and Malagon (1973). With normal and neutral ammonium acetate methods the cation exchange capacity is relatively high, especially for some surface horizons due to organic matter content, but low effective CEC values are low in regard to high clay content as a consequence of low activity and predominance of kaolinitic clays, Fe and Al oxides.

Appendix 9 shows average values of selected characteristics in Red and Red Yellow Latosols, under cerrado vegetation in Minas Gerais, Goias and the Federal District of Brazil according to data presented by Cline and Buol (1973). Comparative analysis of data obtained show similar values and tendencies in both Colombian and Brazilian soils.

Soil Fertility Determination

In the Appendix, pH, organic matter, exchangeable bases (Ca, Mg and K) and acid extractable phosphorus data are presented for soils of both areas. Acidity, organic matter and base content are similar to those previously discussed.

Likewise, extractable phosphorus content in surface layers was low and extremely low. Results obtained by ICA and CIAT in the Llanos have indicated that phosphorus is the most limiting element for agricultural production (Spain and Ruiz, 1968; Owen, 1971; Alvarado and Rodríguez, 1972). Recently, Fox (1973) has presented certain data showing phosphate absorption in some Llanos Oxisols of Colombia (Table 5).

Table 5.—Adsorbed phosphate and soil silica solubility in various Colombian soils.

Site	Adsorbed P		Si in sature extract
	In 0.02 ppm solution	In 0.2 ppm solution	
	Micrograms per Gram		ppm
PALMIRA, VALLE:			
Series 00-01	0	20	19.3
Series 20-24	0	25	19.4
El Piñal:	50	200	12.6
Pachaquiaro			
Lower Terrace	40	240	11.1
LA LIBERTAD:			
Lower Terrace	50	300	10.2
Upper Terrace	100	400	7.0
La Concordia	150	400	6.8
Carimagua	100	400	13.7
Las Gaviotas	130	430	5.0

The author considers phosphorus absorption in Colombia soils to be lower than in Hawaii, perhaps due to two factors: a) lower clay content, b) silica solubility in saturated extract higher than for Oxisols. Hence, phosphorus absorption in Colombian soils decrease when Si solubility increases.

Clay and Silt Mineralogy

Table 6 partially shows results obtained from clay X-rays diffractograms in A and B horizons from profiles 2,5 and 6 in the Llanos. Figure 3 is a diffractogram of the 0.2-2.0 μ fraction which is representative of other samples (Guerrero, 1971). Table 7 summarizes predominant clay minerals in selected horizons of three profiles of Amazonic soil. (Benavides, 1973).
In Llanos soils, with certain few exceptions (Guerrero, 1971a) kaolinite, intergrade 2:1-2:2 minerals, andr pyrophyllite were common to all samples. Quartz, mica, feldspar, vermiculite, and a type of vermiculite-mica stratification were found only in specific size particles and in different horizons. "True chlorite" seemed to be absent or present only in traces. Mica and feldspar were not found in silt particles of upper horizons from profile 2 (sample 9), but persisted throughout the subsoil horizons (sample 13) as in other samples. This seems to indicate that mineral

weathering has reached more advanced levels in upper sandy loam layers, in well drained soils close to the Meta River. The absence of mica of feldspar in fine clay particles of all horizons suggests that clay has been weathered to a greater extent than silt particles, which agrees with Jackson's clay weathering sequence (1946b). The presence of relatively significant quantities of pyrophyllite in soil profiles indicates a possible development of this material during the pedogenesis stage or a different sedimentation source.

Table 6.—Summary of clay minerals in selected Llanos soils. (Adapted from Guerrero, 1971a).

Soil Nº	Depth	Particle Size (μ)	
		$<$ .2	2-5
2	20 — 34	K3 I2 P1	K1 I1 P1 Q3
	178 — 208	K3 I1 PT	K1 IT P1 M1 Q3 F1
5	12 — 32	K3 I2 PT	K2 I1 P1 M1 Q3 VT
	88 — 148	K3 I2	K1 I1 P1 M1 Q3 F2 S1
6	10 — 19	K3 I2 PT	K1 I1 P1 Q3 S1
	105 — 140	K3 I1	K1 IT P1 M1 Q2 S1

KEY: K — Kaolinite
I — 2:1-2:2 intergrades
P — Pyrophyllite
M — Mica
Q — Quartz
F — Feldspar
V — Vermiculite
S — Vermiculite-Mica stratification

Semi quantitative estimate

3 — Abundant (over 50%)
2 — Medium (25-50%)
1 — Few (10-25%)
T — Traces

Absence of gibbsite could probably be explained by the so called "anti-gibbsitic effect" which is a mechanism through which free Al is used for lattice construction. (Jackson, 1965a). This aluminum placement tends to inhibit free $Al(OH)_3$ formation in soiils provided that silicated clay, 2:1 type, weathering be active.

In soils studied by Benavides (1973) the predominant clay mineral in clay particles of soil profiles was also kaolinite (over 40%). Mica was also determined in all soils with ranges varying from 8 to 45%. Likewise, vermiculite and minor quantities of 2:1-2:2 type clays were found in all soils. In B and C horizons of the Leguizamo 6 profile (Table 7) poorly crystalized montmorillonite was determined. Benavides assumes that most kaolinites and micas have been inherited from sediments that make up parental material and that montmorillonite has occurred through a mica-vermiculite-montmorillonite process.

Table 7.—Clay mineralogy in three profiles representative of the Colombian Amazon Region. (Adapted from Benavides, 1973).

HORIZON	DEPTH cm	MINERALS IN CLAY FRACTION (1)
Profile 5, TACANA = UDOXIC DYSTROPEPT		
A1	0 — 10	K4 V2 V/C2 Mi1 Q1 G1
B21	30 — 50	K4 V2 V/C2 Mi1 Q1 G1 P
B21	70 — 83	K3 V2 V/C2 Mi1 Q2 G1 P1
Profile 6, LEGUIZAMO = TYPIC DYSTROPEPT		
A1	0 — 20	K4 Mi2 M1 V1 V/C1 Q1 P1
B21	20 — 80	K4 M2 V1 V/C1 Q1 P1
B22	80 — 133	K4 M2 Mi2 V1 V/C1 Q1
IIC2	215 — 243	K3 M3 V1 V/C1 Mi1
Profile 8, FLORENCIA = UDOXIC DYSTROPEPT		
A1	0 — 16	K4 Mi2 V1 V/C1 G1
B21	16 — 85	K4 Mi2 V1 V/C1 G1
B22	85 — 173	K4 Mi2 V1 V/C1 G1

(1) KEY: K   = Caolinite
        Mi = Mica
        V   = Vermiculite
        C   = Chlorite
        V/C = 2:1-2:2 intergrades
        M   = Montmorillonite
        Q   = Quartz
        G   = Gibbsite
        P   = Pyrophyllite

Relative Abundance

1 < 10%
2 = 10-25%
3 = 25-50%
4 > 55%

Sand Mineralogy

In general, quartz was the prevailing mineral found in the fine sand (105-250 microns) and in very fine sand fraction (50-105 microns) in both areas. Quartz grains were usually subangular and did not show significant changes in form in the different profiles.

Mica and feldspar content was practically insignificant in the Llanos soils, while in sand fractions of certain Amazon soils volcanic glass, mica and 2:1-type minerals were found.

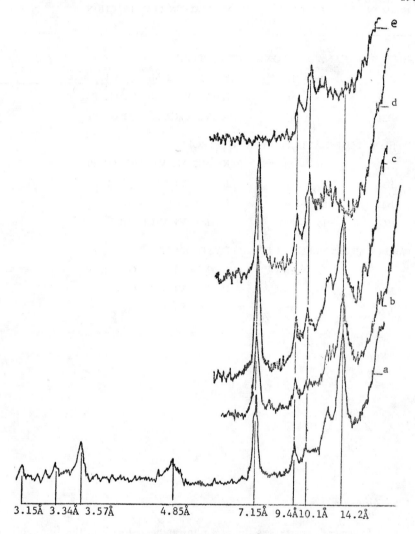

3.15Å 3.34Å 3.57Å   4.85Å   7.15Å 9.4Å10.1Å 14.2Å

Figure 3.   Clay X-Ray Diffractogram .2-2.0 μ of Sample 30
(profile 5, 88-148 cm): a = Mg saturated at 25°C;
b = Mg saturated at 25°C solvated in glycolethylene;
c = K saturated at 25°C; d = saturated at 350°C;
e = K saturated warmed at 550°C. (Guerrero, 1971a).

Thin Sections

Thin section observations in Llanos soils did not show any evidence of clay skin (argillans) surrounding clods, on non-capillary porous walls or on soil channels which agrees with profile descriptions. In some cases, a slight tendency of clay accumulation existed but this was interpreted rather as pressure or compression surfaces (Cady, 1960, Brewer, 1964).

Soil Classification

Data obtained by Guerrero (1971a) for Llanos soil identified oxic horizons, which places these soils within the Oxisol order. Climatic data on the area (FAO, 1965) shows that the subsoil remains dry during 60 consecutive days or longer during most years. Hence, some soil profiles would classify as typic Haplustox, Profile 2 would classify as integrated ultic (Ultic Haplustox) since cationic exchange capacity is over 13.5 meq/100 grams of clay, cation retention over 6 meq/100 grams of clay and considering that clay content increases and reaches the point which indicates argillic horizons.

The relatively high 2:1-2:2 intergrade clay minerals in most samples indicates the ultic nature of these soils. Apparently, larger quantities of weatherable material and/or argillic horizons of greater depth due to solum, could occur. Lack of clay particles in upper horizons could be explained by self-destruction mechanisms during the alternate dry-humid periods predominant in the area. Nevertheless, presence of clay material at greater depth is not common, since no evidence of this appeared in explorations carried out by means of holes opened at deeper levels.

The present classification (Table 8) concurrs with previous taxonomic groupings suggested by Guerrero (1963) and FAO (1965) for soils within the same area. Malagon (1973) also recently classified as Tropeptic Haplorthox two Llanos soil profiles from the Puerto Gaitan, Mancacias River region; the author considered the soil moisture regime to be udic due to increased rainfall to the west. However, Goosen (1971) classified as Dystropepts those soils classified by FAO (1965), Guerrero (1971) and Malagon (1973) as Oxisols.

Goosen considered that a cambic horizon has been formed in what was previously a very deep A horizon in an Ultisol and furthermore, low water soluble clay percentages, high silt percentage and low free iron content are Oxisol characteristics. Based on this, Goosen considers them to be Inceptisols with Oxic subgroups. From available data in order to classify these soils in families they would be placed in the clayey kaolinitic, isohyperthermic family. According to the FAO System of Classification (1970) they would classify as Xanthic or Rhodic Ferrasols.

Colombian Amazon soils were classified by Cortes (1973) mainly as Typic Eutropepts, Aquic Dystropepts, Typic Haplorthox and Typic Gibbsiorthox. He points out that even though cation exchange capacity seems relatively high for typical oxic horizons, other criteria were prevalent in establishing the oxic nature such as: a) little evidence and inadequate climate for argillic horizons, b) almost total absence of weatherable

Table 8.—Classification of representative soils of the eastern region of Colombia (Soil Taxonomy Nomenclature).

AREA AND DESCRIPTION	SOURCE	TAXONOMIC GROUPS*
1. ORINOCO REGION		
a. *High Plains*	FAO (1965)	Oxisols
	Guerrero (1971)	Typic (3) & Ultic Haplustox (2)
		Typic Umbraquox (2)
	Goosen (1971)	Oxic Palehumultic Dystropept (2)
	Malagón (1973)	Tropeptic Haplorthox (3)
b. *Floodable*	FAO (1965)	Oxisols & Aquepts (several)
plains	Goosen (1971)	Ultic Plinthaquept (1)
	Malagón (1973)	Typic Tropaquept (1)
2. AMAZON REGION		
a. Terraces	Cortés (1973)	Tropeptic & Typic Haplorthox (3)
b. Hills		Typic Gibbsiorthox (1)
c. Undulations		Oxic & Aquic Dystropept (2)
d. Terraces		Typic Eutropept (1)
e. Undulations	Benavides (1973)	Udoxic & Typic Dystropepts (7)
		Aquic Paleudults (2)

* The numbers in parenthesis represent the number of profiles studied.

minerals, c) kaolinite predominance in clay fraction, d) absence of water dispersable clay, e) cation exchange capacity close to that of oxic, f) solum depth.

Benavides (1973) classified as Dystropepts 7 of 9 profiles studied, because he considered that even though clay fraction mineralogy is fundamentally dominated by kaolinite, there are extremely high percentages of mica (sometimes up to 45%), of montmorillonite, feldspar, and other weatherable minerals, materials of extremely high cation exchange capacity (up to 50 meq/100 grams of soil) to consider these soils Oxisols. However, the oxic character of such soils are identified since five of them are classed in Udoxic subgroups. The other Dystropepts are typical and the two remaining profiles are classified as Aquic Paleudults. These results are partially in concurrence with results obtained in North Carolina State University (1972) reporting the presence of Ultisols, Alfisols, and even

Mollisols in the Yurimagua and Iquitos area (Peruvian Amazonic Jungle) which would indicate that in many places within the Amazonic Basin, contrary to what has so far been believed, probably Ultisols and not Oxisols are the predominant soils.

V SUMMARY

Available information concerning Colombian Llanos and Amazon soils indicates that these soils are developed on material poor in nutrients and that, due to pedogenetic processes common to tropical regions, have reached a high degree of weathering. Under these circumstances, exchangeable bases have been removed from upper horizons. Quartz, amorphous · iron and aluminum oxides and kaolinitic clay are predominant in the clay fraction. Development of most crops is limited due to low fertility levels. However, it is worth pointing out that chemical and/or mineralogical characteristics of Amazonia soils, differ remarkably from those soils of the Llanos observed by Guerrero (1972) and North Carolina State University (1972).

Consequently, any agricultural development program established in the Colombian Llanos or Amazon regions should be based on soil properties. Therefore, such research should have priority in relation to soil management techniques, mainly soil acidity neutralization, increased fertility, organic matter conservation, land clearing, and erosion control as has also been suggested by Sanchez (1971a,b) for jungle and humid regions in Latin America.

VI REFERENCES

ALVARADO, E. and M. RODRIGUEZ. 1971. Informe Anual de Labores - Estación Experimental Carimagua. CIAT-Programa Nacional Suelos ICA. Carimagua. (Type-written).

BENAVIDES, S. T. 1973. Mineralogical and Chemical Characteristics of Some Soil of the Amazonia of Colombia. Umpublished Ph.D. Thesis, Dept. of Soil Science, N. C. S. U., Raleigh, U.S.A.

BENNEMA, J. 1966. Classification of Brazilian soils. Report to the Government of Brazil, Report N° 2197, FAO, Rome.

BORNEMISZA, E. and K. IGUE. 1967. Free iron and aluminum oxides in tropical soils (in Spanish). Turrialba 17:23-30.

BREWER, R. 1964. Fabric and Mineral Analysis of Soils. Wiley and Sons, New York.

BUOL, S. W. 1972. Soil Genesis, Morphology and Classification. In: A Review of Soils Research in Tropical Latin America. Soil Sc. Dept., N. C. S. U., Raleigh, N. C. pp. 2-51.

BUOL, S. W. and D. M. FADNESS. 1961. New methods of impregnating fragile material for thin sectioning. Soil Sci, Soc. Amer. Proc. 25:253.

CADY, J. C. 1960. Mineral occurrence in relation to soil profile differentiation. Trans. 7th Int. Congr. Soil Sci. 4:418-424. Madison, Wisconsin.

CARRERA, E. and D. AREVALO. 1972. Reconocimiento Semi-detallado de Suelos del Sector Puerto Leguízamo-La Tagua. Instituto Geográfico "Agustín Codazzi", Archcicvcocs Bogotá, D. E. (Type-written).

CLINE, M. G. and S. W. BUOL. 1973. Soil of the Central Plateau of Brazil.. Agronomy-mimeo 73-13. Cornell University, Ithaca, N. Y.

COLEMAN, N. T., S. B. WEED and R. J. McCRACKEN. 1959. Cation exchange capacity and exchangeable cations in Piedmont soils of North Carolina, Soil Sci. Soc. Amer. Proc. 23:146-149.

COMISSAO DE SOLOS. 1960. Levantamento do reconhecimento dos solos do Estado de Sao Paulo. Boletín N° 12, Ministerio de Agricultura, Río de Janeiro, Brazil.

CORTES, A. and J. VARELA. 1972. Informe del Estudio Preliminar de Suelos de la Región La Tagua-Puerto Leguízamo. Centro Inter-Americano de Fotointerpretación, CIAF. Bogotá. (Mimeo).

CORTES, A., J. JIMENEZ and J. REY. 1973. Génesis, Clasificación y Aptitud de Explotación de Algunos Suelos de la Orinoquía y la Amazonía Colombianas. Universidad Jorge Tadeo Lozano-Colciencias. Bogotá.

CHAPMAN, H. D. 1965. Cation exchange capacity. In: Methods of Soils Analysis. Agronomy series N° 9, pp. 891-901. Soil Sci. Soc. Amer., Madison, Wisconsin.

FOOD and AGRICULTURAL ORGANIZATION. 1965. Soil survey of the Llanos Orientales-Colombia. A series of six volumes with maps and appendixes (English and Spanish editions). FAO/S.F.: 11/Col. Rome.

FOOD AND AGRICULTURAL ORGANIZATION. 1970. Key to soils units for the soil map of the world. Land and Water Development Division. W.S./A7 460. Rome.

FOX, R. L. and S. T. BENAVIDES. 1974. Phosphorus of Oxisols. In: III Coloquio Sociedad Colombiana de la Ciencia del Suelo. Bogotá. pp. 137-175.

GOOSEN, D. 1971. Physiography and soils of the Llanos Orientales. Colombia. International Institute for Aerial Survey and Earth Sciences, I. T. C. Amsterdam, The Netherlands.

GUERRERO, R. 1963. Soils of Colombia and their relationship to the new classification system of the United States. Unpublished M. S. Thesis, Department of Soil Science, Cornell University, Ithaca, New York.

GUERRERO, R. 1971a. Soils of the Colombia Llanos Orientales-composition and classification of selected soil profiles. Unpublished Ph. D. Thesis, Department of Soil Science, North Carolina State University. Raleigh, N. C.

GUERRERO, R. 1971b. Informe de Comisión - Interventoría del ICA en el reconocimiento de suelos de la Granja Macagual, Florencia. Programa Nacional de Suelos, ICA, Archivos. Bogotá. (Type-written).

GUERRERO, R. 1972a. Informe de Comisión - Colonización Militar en el Sector Puerto Leguízamo-La Tagua. Programa Nacional de Suelos, ICA, Archivos. Bogotá. (Type-written).

GUERRERO, R. 1972b. Informe de Comisión - Evaluación y Manejo de suelos de los Territorios Amazónicos de Venezuela y Brasil. Grupo de Trabajo FAO/PNUD en Manaos. Bogotá. (Mimeo).

JACKSON, M. L. 1956. Soil Chemical Analysis - Advanced Course. Published by the author. Madison, Wisconsin.

JACKSON, M. L. 1963. Aluminum bonding in soils: A unifying principle in soil science. Soil Sci. Soc. Amer. Proc. 27:1-10.

JACKSON, M. L. 1964a. Soil clay mineralogical analysis. *In:* Soil Clay Mineralogy - A Symposium, C.I. Rich and G. W. Kunze (Ed.), Univ. of N. C. Press, Chapel Hill, N. C. pp. 245-294.

JACKSON, M. L. 1964b. Chemical composition of soils. *In:* Chemistry of the soil, F. E. Bear (Ed.), 2nd Edition, Reinhold Publishing Co., pp. 71-141.

KAMPRATH, E. J. 1967. Soil acidity and response to liming. Tech Bull. Nº 4. International Soil Testing Series, North Carolina Agr. Exp. Sta., Raleigh, N. C.

KAMPRATH, E. J. 1972a. Soil acidity and liming. *In:* Soils of the humid tropics. Committee on tropical soils. National Academy of Sciences. Washington, D. C. pp. 136-149.

KAMPRATH, E. J. 1972b. Soil acidity and liming. *In:* A review of soils research in tropical Latin America. Soil Sc. Dept., N. C. S. U. Raleigh. pp. 167-182.

KAMPRATH, E. J. 1972c. Phosphorus. *In:* A Review of Soils Research in Tropical Latin America. Soil Sc. Dept., N. C. S. U. Raleigh, pp. 205-237.

KILMER, V. and L. T. ALEXANDER. 1949. Methods of making mechanical analyses of soils. Soil Sci. 68:15-24.

KITTRICK, J. A. and E. W. HOPE. 1963. A procedure for the particle size separation of soils for x-ray diffraction analysis. Soil Sci. 96:319-325.

LEON, A. 1964. Estudios químicos y mineralógicos de diez suelos colombianos. Agr. Trop. (Colombia). 20:442-451.

LEON, A. 1968. Chemistry of some tropical acid soils of Colombia, S. A. Unpublished Ph.D. Thesis, Univ. of California, Riverside, California. Univ. Microfilms, Ann Arbor, Michigan, Order Nº 68-9760.

MALAGON-CASTRO, D. 1973. Characterization and Genesis of Selected Soils in the Eastern Plains of Colombia. Unpublished Ph.D. Thesis. Department of Agronomy, University of Nebraska. U.S.A.

McCLEAN, F. O. 1965. Aluminum. *In:* Methods of soil analysis. Agr. Series Nº 9, ASA. Wisconsin. pp. 978-998.

MOURA-FILHO, W. 1968. Characterization of the physical, chemical, and micromorphological changes engendered by the cultivation of a soil in the Triangulo of Minas Gerais, Brazil. Unpublished M. S. Thesis, Department of Soil Science, North Carolina State University, Raleigh, N. C.

NORTH CAROLINA STATE UNVERSRITY. 1973. Research in the Amazonan Jungle-soil characterization studies. *In:* Research on Tropical soils, Annual Report. N.C.S.U., Raleigh.

OWEN, E. 1971. Informe Anual de Labores realizadas en los Llanos Orientales de Colombia. Programa Nacional de Suelos, ICA. Bogotá. (Mimeo).

PRATT, P. F., F. F. PATERSON and C. S. HOLZHEY. 1969. Qualitative mineralogy and chemical properties of a few soils from Sao Paulo. Brasil. Turrialba 19:491-496.

SANCHEZ, P. A. 1971a. Summary of Research Needs. Research on soils of the Latin American Tropics. Annual Report. Soil Sci. Dept., N.C.S.U. Raleigh. pp. 42-43.

SANCHEZ, P. A. 1971b. Management in the humid forested region. Research on soils of the Latin American tropics. Annual Report. Soil Sci. Dept. N.C.S.U. Raleigh. pp. 10-17.

SOIL CONSERVATION SERVICE. 1967. Soil survey laboratory methods and procedures for collecting soil samples. Soil Surv. Inv. Rep., N° 1, U.S.D.A., Washington, D. C.

SOIL SURVEY STAFF. 1951. Soil Survey Manual and Supplement. Handbook N° 18, U.S.D.A., Washington, D. C.

SOIL SURVEY STAFF. 1970. Selected chapters from the unedited text of the soil taxonomy of the National Cooperative Soil Survey. Soil Conservation Service, U.S.D.A., Washington, D. C.

SPAIN, J. M. and A. RUIZ. 1968. Soils an dthe Development Process in the tropics. The Rockefeller Foundation and ICA. Paper presented at the Annual Meeting, ASA, New Orleans.

VIVAS, N. 1970. Informe de comisión a la Comisaría Especial del Guainía. Programa de Pastos y Forrajes, ICA, Villavicencio. (Mimeo).

Appendix 1.—Selected physical and chemical characteristics of two soil series representative of the Highplains in the Llanos Orientales. (Adapted from FAO, 1965).

Horizon	Depth	Clay	pH	Exch. Bases	Exch Al	CEC	Base Satn.	Org. C	Free Fe$_2$O$_3$
	cm	%		meq/100 gr. soil			——	%	——
Oxisol = Horizontal Series									
A1	0 — 8	47	4.4	0.8	3.3	16.8	5	2.7	2.5
A3	8 — 19	51	4.4	0.6	2.9	13.1	5	1.8	2.4
B3	66 — 100	56	5.4	0.4	1.1	7.5	6	0.5	2.8
Oxisol = Shangri La Series									
A1	0 — 15	14	4.6	0.7	0.9	3.3	21	0.7	—
A3	15 — 32	20	4.8	0.5	0.9	3.3	15	0.5	—
B22	65 — 100	27	5.3	0.4	0.4	2.6	15	0.3	—

Appendix 2.—Physical and chemical characteristics selected from two profiles of representative soils of the Highplain and one profile from the Flooding plains of the Eastern Plains in Colombia. (Goosen, 1971).

Soil	Depth	Clay	pH H$_2$O	Sum of Bases	Exch. Al	CEC NH$_4$OAc pH 7.0	B.S.	Org. C
	cm	%		meq/100 gr. soil			%	
a) ALTILLANURA								
Horizonte Series = Oxic Palehumultic Dystropept.								
A11	0 — 8	46	4.3	0.6	5.0	15	4.3	3.3
A12	8 — 19	45	4.5	0.4	4.4	11	3.1	2.0
B23	66 — 100	57	5.7	0.4	1.9	8	4.9	0.8
Lagunazo Series = Oxic Palehumultic Dystropept.								
A11	0 — 15	29	4.6	0.4	3.6	10	4.5	1.7
A12	15 — 40	32	5.0	0.4	2.9	8	4.8	0.8
B22	65 — 95	34	5.3	0.4	2.6	6	7.4	0.5
b) ALUVIAL FLOOD PLAIN								
Corocora Series = Cumulic Humic Ultic Plinthaquept								
A1 g	0 — 10	53	4.7	9.1	3.7	28	33	2.2
B2 g	10 — 42	53	5.1	5.1	5.4	21	24	0.8
IIB22 g cn	68 — 100	34	5.4	7.5	3.2	9	80	0.1

Appendix 3.—Chemical properties of two soil profiles from the Eastern Plains of Colombia. (Adapted from Malagon-Castro, 1973).

Horizon	Depth	Clay (Pipet)	pH H₂O	Ex. Al	Sum of Bases	C.E.C. (1)	B.S. (2)	O.C.	Fe₂O₃ Free
	cm	%			meq/100 g soil		—	%	—
GAITAN Soil (High plain) = Tropetic Haplorthox (3)									
A1	0 — 9	35	4.6	1.3	0.2	10	2	1.6	6.9
A3	9 — 23	34	4.4	—	0.1	9	1	—	—
IIB1	23 — 47	36	4.5	0.9	0.2	7	2	0.5	8.1
OROCUE Soil (Floodplains) Typic Tropaquept (3)									
A1	0 — 21	36	4.7	5.1	0.2	14	2	1.6	1.4
A3	21 — 36	38	4.5	3.5	0.2	9	2	—	—
IIB2	36 — 62	37	4.7	1.4	0.1	5	2	0.5	0.7

(1) By ammonium acetate.

(2) Based on (1)

(3) Clay mineral estimates: Quartz > 40%; Kaolinite > Al-Vermiculite > 20% (or Al-chlorite).

Appendix 4.—Chemical and physical properties of soil samples taken from A horizon (0-20 cms) from regional test plots in the Llanos. (Adapted from the National Soil Program files).

Site	Texture	pH	Exch. Bases	Exch. Al	CEC	B.S.	Org. C
			meq/100 g soil		(1)		%
Potosí	CL	4.9	1.7	2.6	4.3	43	2.8
Las Leonas	CL	4.6	1.7	3.7	5.4	32	2.7
Atlan	CL	4.9	1.7	0.9	2.6	64	1.2
El Piñal	SL	4.9	0.5	1.0	1.5	33	0.7
Caviona	SL	4.9	0.2	1.1	1.3	14	0.7
CARIMAGUA:							
Marañón	CL	4.8	0.9	3.2	4.1	22	2.5
Marañón	CL	4.5	1.3	4.1	5.4	25	2.7
Yopare	SL	4.7	0.8	1.5	2.3	37	1.2
Patio	CL	4.8	1.7	3.0	4.7 (2)	36	2.9
Yopare	L	4.9	0.2	1.7	15.6	1	—
Agronomía	L	4.6	0.8	3.3	13.4	6	2.6

(1) By addition of exchangeable cations.

(2) By Ammonium acetate.

Appendix 5.—Some physical and chemical properties of soil and plow layer samples of typical soils from Granja Macagual (Florencia) ICA, (Guerrero, 1971b).

Sample	Depth	Texture	pH	Exch. Acid	Exch. Bases	CEC (1)	BS (2)	OC
	cm				meq/100 gr. soil		%	
MORELIA, 12-25% (Mesones)								
1A	5 — 30	C	5.0	9.1	1.3	10.4	13	0.5
1B	30 — 50	C	5.1	9.1	1.3	10.4	13	0.6
1C	75 — 90	C	5.1	7.2	1.3	8.5	16	1.0
MORELIA, 25-50% (Mesones)								
5A	0 — 30	CS	4.6	9.0	1.3	10.3	13	0.9
5B	30 — 80	CS	4.8	8.8	0.9	9.7	9	0.6
5C	80 — 150	SL	4.9	10.4	1.3	11.7	11	0.3
PLOW LAYER SAMPLES								
# 122	0 — 20	S	5.2	5.1	1.7	6.8	25	1.1
123	0 — 20	S	4.7	1.6	3.8	5.4	70	2.5
124	0 — 20	C	5.5	0.5	6.8	7.3	93	3.0
125	0 — 20	C	4.7	4.1	1.7	5.8	29	2.2
126	0 — 20	C	4.8	3.4	1.3	4.7	28	3.0
127	0 — 20	C	4.1	3.7	1.3	5.0	26	2.1
128	0 — 20	C	4.9	3.6	2.1	5.7	37	1.5
129	0 — 20	C	4.6	2.7	6.7	9.4	71	2.0
130	0 — 20	CL	4.7	4.1	1.3	5.4	24	2.2
131	0 — 20	SL	4.8	3.4	3.1	6.5	47	2.1

(1) Effective: Ex. Base addition + Ex. Aciditv.

(2) Based on (1).

Appendix 6.—Physical and chemical properties of selected soil profiles from the La Tagua-Pto. Leguizamo region. (Adapted from Cortes and Varela, 1972).

Depth	Clay	pH	Exch. Al	Exch. Bases	CEC (1)	B.S. (2)	OC
	%			meq/100 gr. soil		%	
CAPITAN TONO, PROFILE 2							
00 — 04	38	5.7	5.7	2.1	41	51	4.5
04 — 18	46	4.8	0.2	3.7	22	16	1.2
55 — 100X	68	4.0	—	1.8	40	5	01.
CAPITAN TONO, PROFILE 3							
00 — 04	46	4.8	1.1	16.9	45	38	4.6
04 — 19	59	4.6	15.3	2.0	27	8	1.2
75 — X	62	4.6	—	1.6	28	6	0.2
LA TAGUA, PROFILE 5							
00 — 11	24	4.6	2.5	1.2	13	9	1.8
11 — 15	28	4.8	3.6	0.6	10	6	0.8
15 — 32	34	4.9	4.9	0.5	10	5	0.7
75 — 140	36	4.9	—	0.5	9	5	0.3
LA CORNAMUZA, PROFILE 7							
00 — 08	26	4.8	4.2	1.8	15	12	2.0
08 — 14	28	4.8	5.5	1.3	15	9	1.0
25 — 56	40	5.0	—.	1.4	21	7	0.4

(1) By ammonium acetate.

(2) Based on (1).

Appendix 7.—Some physical and chemical properties of profiles selected from representative soils of the Colombian Amazon Region. (Adapted from Cortes *et al.*, 1973).

Horizon	Depth	Total Clay	pH	Exch. Al	Exch. Bases	CEC (1)	B.S. (2)	OC
	cm	%			meq/100 g soil		%	
ARARACUARA = OXIC DYSTROPEPT								
A11	0 — 27	34	4.8	3.3	0.14	10.7	1.31	1.3
A12	27 — 46	33	4.9	3.5	0.16	10.7	1.45	0.9
B22	88 — 150	35	5.2	2.4	0.10	2.5	4.03	0.2
PUERTO ARARA = AQUIC DYSTROPEPT								
A1	0 — 17	12	4.3	2.5	0.20	5.5	3.62	0.5
B21	17 — 63	21	4.5	3.9	0.17	6.4	2.69	0.2
B22 g	63 — 150X	50	4.4	12.6	0.21	7.8	2.70	0.1
PUERTO LEGUIZAMO = TROPEPTIC HAPLORTHOX								
A1	0 — 13	58	4.5	4.9	4.53	30.5	14.85	3.9
B21	13 — 70	62	4.7	12.9	1.90	22.5	8.44	0.7
B22 g	70 — 150X	69	4.8	19.9	0.43	27.6	1.56	0.3

(1) By ammonium acetate.

(2) Based on (1).

Appendix 8.—Some physical and chemical properties of soil profiles from river banks - from the Guaviare, Inirida and Orinoco Rivers, Guainia and Vichada "Comisarias" (Vivas, 1970).

Depth	Clay	pH	Exch. Al	Exch. Bases	CEC (1)	B.S. (2)	OC
cm	%			meq/100 gr. soil			%
0 — 20	21	5.2	1.5	3.3	4.8	68	0.7
20 — 40	14	5.2	1.0	2.5	3.5	72	0.5
40 — 60	18	5.3	1.1	2.1	3.3	63	2.2
+ 60	29	5.3	1.6	2.9	4.5	65	0.5
0 — 20	47	4.9	3.0	3.2	6.2	52	2.3
20 — 40	48	5.1	3.4	2.5	5.8	42	1.7
40 — 60	58	5.0	4.6	2.0	6.6	31	1.3
0 — 20	21	5.3	0.3	5.0	5.3	94	1.2
20 — 40	20	5.5	0.5	4.7	5.2	90	0.9
40 — 60	18	5.5	0.7	2.7	3.4	79	0.5
+ 60	16	5.4	0.4	3.3	3.7	89	0.5
0 — 20	25	5.2	2.8	2.2	5.0	44	0.8
20 — 40	32	5.1	2.8	2.7	5.5	49	0.6
0 — 20	23	4.9	3.1	1.4	4.5	32	2.1
20 — 40	25	4.8	3.1	0.5	3.6	15	2.0
+ 60	29	4.9	2.7	0.9	3.6	24	1.5
0 — 20	19	5.4	0.7	3.8	4.4	84	0.9
20 — 40	21	5.5	0.7	3.8	4.4	84	0.7

(1) Effective: Adding bases and ex. Al.

(2) Based on (1).

Appendix 9.—Average values of selected characteristics in some Dark Red and Yellowish Red Latosols from the Brazilian Central High-plain. (Adapted from Cline and Buol, 1973).

Soils	Horizon or Depth	Clay	pH H$_2$O	Carbon	CEC	BS
		(%)	Range	(%)	meq/100 g (add.)	(%)
DARK RED LATOSOL						
Clay	Topsoil	60	4.3 — 5.2	2.4	10.2	11
Clay	75 cms.	63	4.6 — 5.8	0.9	5.2	14
Loam	Topsoil	19	4.3	0.9	4.8	11
Loam	75 cms.	24	4.9	0.3	2.5	15
RED YELLOW LATOSOL						
Clay	Topsoil	47	4.2 — 5.1	1.7	8.6	7
Clay	75 cms.	53	4.5 — 6.0	0.7	4.4	9
Loam	Topsoil	21	4.4 — 5.2	0.8	4.0	13
Loam	75 cms.	26	4.5 — 5.6	0.4	2.4	17

Appendix 10.—Analysis of Llanos soils by the North Carolina Methods. (Guerrero, 1971a).

Soil Nº	Depth	pH	Organic Matetr	Ca	Mg	K	P
	cm		%		lb/Acre		
2	0 — 20	4.5	2.0	48	12	29	2.4
	20 — 34	4.7	1.3	64	10	17	2.4
	125 — 178	4.9	0.3	64	12	14	0.0
5	0 — 12	4.6	4.0	80	17	37	2.4
	12 — 32	4.6	2.0	64	14	29	2.4
	88 — 148	5.2	0.6	64	10	20	0.0
6	0 — 10	4.8	6.5	304	60	78	2.4
	10 — 19	4.6	4.0	64	17	37	2.4
	105 — 140	5.3	0.7	64	7	17	0.0

APPENDIX 11.—SOIL PROFILE Nº 5, CARIMAGUA (Guerrero, 1971)

Description: Pit by R. Guerrero and S. W. Buol.

Date: August 4, 1969.

Location: Approximately 2-2.5 km north of the Sta. Rita, Puerto Carreno cross road, open savanna.

Vegetation: Dense, treeless savanna.

Physiography: Open and slightly convex savanna at higher position than site Nº 4.

Parent Material: Mixed acid alluvial sediments.

Slope: 0-1%.

Drainage: Well drained.

Erosion: None.

Depth to Water Table: Deep.

Remarks: No plinthite nodules in 155 cm depth. Poor horizonation. Site is representative of "open" savanna.

0 - 12 cm	Dark brown to brown (7.5YR 4/4); silty clay loam; weak, medium, subangular blocky structure; slightly sticky and slightly plastic; many roots but less than in previous profiles; gradual, smooth boundary.
12 - 32 cm	Dark reddish brown (5YR 3/4); silty clay; massive that breaks into strong, fine subangular blocky structure; sticky and slightly plastic; less roots than above and high termite activity; gradual, wavy boundary.
32 - 58 cm	Yellowish red (5YR 4/6) with few, fine and distinct, light yellowish brown (10YR 6/4) mottlings; silty clay; moderate, medium and fine subangular blocky structure; friable when moist, sticky when wet; few, small roots and pockets of dark organic material transported from above; no reaction to H_2O_2; gradual, wavy boundary.
58 - 88 cm	Yellowish red (5YR 5/8); clay; strong to moderate, fine subangular blocky structure; slightly plastic when wet; few, fine roots; few pockets of organic material; gradual, wavy boundary.
88 - 148 cm	(By auger below 130 cm). Yellowish red (5YR 4/8); clay; sticky.
148 - 155 cm	Redder; clay.

APPENDIX 12.—SOIL PROFILE N? 6, LEGUIZAMO (Benavides, 1973)

Location: Municipio Leguizamo; Km 2 Leguízamo-La Tagua road.
Altitude: About 150 m above sea level.
Relief: Gently undulating.
Slope: 3-7%.
Position of the profile: Upper part of a hillslope with 3%.
Erosion: Not apparent.
Vegetation: Originally tropical rain forest; presently grasses.
Parent material: Post-Pleistocene sediments.
Water table: Very deep.
Drainage: Well drained.
Moisture conditions of the profile: Moist, all profile.
Date sampled: July 4, 1971.

A1 HORIZON; 0-20 cm: Brown (7.5 YR 4/4); clay loam; moderate fine pores; common fine roots; many earthworms; smooth clear boundary. friable, slightly sticky, plastic; many fine, common medium tubular angular blocky that breaks to moderate fine granular structure; hard,

B21 HORIZON; 20-80 cm: Reddish brown with common coarse faint brown 10 YR 5/3 spots; moderate medium prismatic structure that breaks to moderate fine and medium angular blocky and to moderate fine granules; friable, very sticky, very plastic; many fine and very fine tubular pores; few fine roots; few earthworms, diffuse boundary.

B21cn HORIZON; 80-81/82 cm: Hard discontinous layer of sesquioxidic concretions with reniform shape; yellowish red and dushy red; abrupt boundary.

B22 HORIZON; 81/82-133cm: Yellowish red (5 YR 4/6); clay; moderate medium prismatic structure that breaks into moderate fine and medium angular and subangular blocky structure; friable, very sticky, very plastic; may fine tubular pores; some hard platy fragments (pedodes?) of clay; few fine roots; gradual, wavy boundary.

IIB23 HORIZON; 133-173cm: Yellowish red (5 YR 4/8) with common fine and coarse distinct yellowish brown (10 YR 5/6) and very pale brown (10 YR 8/3); moderate fine and medium prismatic structure that breaks to moderate medium and fine angular blocks and granules; friable, sticky, plastic; common medium and fine tubular pores; some of which have continuous films of brown color; common hard fragments of clay, gray inside and violet in surface; smooth, clear boundary.

IIC1 HORIZON; 173-215cm: Reddish brown (2.5 YR 4/4) with common medium distinct light yellowish brown (2.5 Y 6/4) around pore walls; sandy clay loam; massive with tendency to angular blocks; friable, slightly sticky; slightly plastic; common fine and very fine tubular pores; common small fragments of mica; smooth clear boundary.

4 Relationships Between U.S. Soil Taxonomy, the Brazilian Soil Classification System, and FAO/UNESCO Soil Units

FRIEDRICK H. BEINROTH

I INTRODUCTION

In reflection of growing government interest in natural resources, most countries in tropical America are engaged in active soil survey. An intrinsic element and important aspect of these programs is the classification of soils.

Soil surveys are expensive and no government or institution would be inclined to support such activities unless they are of practical value. Yet, while many soil surveys have been extremely useful, some have failed. The inadequacies were mostly the result either of failure to identify the purposes for making the soil survey or failure to maintain strict scientific control over the identification, description and classification of the soils. To be useful, soil surveys must be both practical in purpose and scientific in construction. The classification systems applied in soil survey must, therefore, be capable of meeting these requirements and should in particular facilitate comparisons of soils for both similarities and differences (Smith, 1965). Viewed in the context of this perspective, the classification of soils is not a mere academic exercise, as some would see it. It is a scientific means for a practical end.

Whereas there is, in general, international agreement on botanical, zoological, mineralogical and similar classifications, there exist several kinds of soil classification and many more are possible. This is partly a reflection of the fact that soil classification systems have been developed largely by government institutions for specific purposes and particular pedologic conditions. As a consequence, several systems of soil classification are currently in use in tropical America.

In a recent review of soil survey methods in Latin America, Van Wambeke (1973) reports that national systems of soil classification are employed in Brazil and Panama. In the French territories, soils are correlated with taxa of the classification developed by ORSTOM (Aubert, 1966). The Central American countries have usually compared their soils with the great soil groups established during the original soil survey of Hawaii (Cline, 1955). In the British Antilles soil series are recognized but are neither correlated nor placed in a taxonomic system, and the same holds true for Guatemala where the arrangement of soil series is merely alphabetic.

Costa de Lemos (1971) reports that in several Latin American countries, notably Chile, Colombia, Mexico, Perú, and Venezuela, efforts are under way to classify soils according to the U.S. Soil Taxonomy (Soil Survey Staff, 1970).

By virtue of the recently published soil map of South America (FAO/UNESCO, 1971), the soils of this sub-continent have also been correlated with units of the legend for the FAO/UNESCO Soil Map of the World (FAO, 1970).

In terms of area of application, the U.S. Soil Taxonomy, the Brazilian system and the FAO/UNESCO scheme are the most important soil classifications used in tropical America. It is the objective of this paper to discuss and compare these systems and to evaluate their role in the agricultural development process.

II APPROACHES TO SOIL CLASSIFICATION

In most of the existing systems of soil classification there is the basic assumption that there are individual soils that can be treated as a population. While former concepts would regard the pedosphere not as a universe of individuals but as a kind of continuum varying from place to place in reflection of changing soil-forming conditions, the present view considers soil as a "collection of bodies" (Soil Survey Staff, 1960). Cline (1961) pointed out that "the perspective in which we view our model has changed from one in which the whole is emphasized and its parts are loosely defined and indistinct to one in which the parts are sharply in focus and the whole is an organized collection of parts". This change signifies a major breakthrough in pedologic thinking and provided the scientific basis for taxonomic classification systems.

Although there are as many classifications conceivable as there are objectives for grouping, there are basically only two fundamentally different approaches to soil classification. One can group soils for a great variety of technical purposes and thus establish technical groupings, etch for a limited objective and with a special bias dictated by the objective (Cline, 1949).

In natural or taxonomic classifications, on the other hand, the objective is to show relationships in the greatest number and most important properties without reference to a specific practical purpose. To quote Cline (1949), "the natural classification, therefore, performs the extremely important function of organizing, naming, and defining the classes that are the basic units used (a) to identify the sample individuals that are the objects of research, (b) to organize the data of research for discovering relationships within the population, (c) to formulate generalizations about the population from these relationships, and (d) to apply these generalizations to specific cases that have not been studied directly".

There are two main methods of elaborating natural systems: one may reason from ideas to facts, or from facts to ideas. In the first case the method is analytic and descending and such sysrtems are of necessity essentially genetic (Manil, 1959). The second method is synthetic or ascending and requires a great amount of data about recognizable bodies of soil, especially those identified as soil series. The U.S. Soil Taxonomy essentially is an example of this type, whereas the Brazilian classification may be considered a "system built from above" (Van Wambeke, 1973).

Because soil classification in tropical America is chiefly employed in soil surveys and these are expected to be of practical use, an argument in favor of technical systems of classification could be made. However, Smith (1965) has stated that soil survey, although practical in its purpose, must also have reasonable scientific standards. In particular, a soil survey should not become obsolete with changing agricultural technology and it should further facilitate the interpretation for a variety of uses some of which might not have been anticipated at the time when it was made. It is evident that these requirements can only be met if a taxonomic system is used. Yet, at least one more step beyond the taxonomic classification is needed to order the "natural" groups into "practical" groups (Smith, 1965). There are compelling reasons for flexible criteria below some level of generalization that are not subject to the restrictions of definition inherent in taxonomic classes (Cline, 1963). This can be accomplished by groupings of phases of classes on the basis of characteristics that are important to the purpose of the moment (Smith, 1965).

III STRUCTURE, DIFFERENTIAE AND NOMENCLATURE OF THE THREE SYSTEMS

In contriving a taxonomic system of classification and thus to arrive at an "orderly abstract of knowledge, and concepts derived from knowledge" (Cline, 1963), three main problems are encountered. These are the selection of differentiating criteria, the definition of classes and their grouping in categories, and the nomenclature of taxa. The systems discussed below represent three different endeavors.

a) *U.S. Soil Taxonomy*

This system is an attempt at a comprehensive taxonomic classification of soils. For reasons explained by Kellogg (1963), it has been developed over the past 20 years in the Soil Conservation Service of the USDA under the leadership of G. D. Smith with cooperation of soil scientists of U.S. universities and certain pedologists from other countries. The system went through a series of approximations of which the "7th Approximation" was published in 1960 (Soil Survey Staff, 1960). After substantial revisions it is now in press and will be available in the near future as a book entitled "Soil Taxonomy: A Basic System of Soil Classification for Making and Interpreting Soil Surveys".

In developing the basic rationales of the system its authors were influenced by Bridgeman's "Logic of Modern Physics" (Bridgeman, 1927). They also drew on Western European experience, particularly on the definitions of concepts basic to the French classification (Smith, 1965). More than 70 years of soil survey provided the detailed information without which the development of the system would have been impossible.

Like most taxonomic systems, Soil Taxonomy is a multi-categoric system. Each category is an aggregate of taxa, defined at about the same level of abstraction, with the smallest number of classes in the highest category and the largest number in the lowest category. In order of decreasing rank these categories are: order, suborder, great group, subgroup, family, and series.

Applying concepts of pedogenic processes ,orders, suborders and great groups are differentiated on the basis of the presence or absence of a variety of combinations of diagnostic horizons and soil properties.

Three levels of such sets are employed in the three highest categories, each set of properties marking pedogenic processes that operate within the sets characterizing the higher category or categories. Examples of differentiae used at the order level are diagnostic horizons, such as the oxic and spodic horizons or the mollic epipedon. Soil moisture regime and extreme chemical or mineralogical properties like the presence of large amounts of allophane are examples of criteria for differentiating suborders. Properties that appear to be superimposed on the diagnostic features of the orders and suborders, such as various kinds of pans or the presence of plinthite, are used to differentiate great groups.

Subgroups are subdivisions of great groups representing either the central concept of the category, intergrades to other great groups, or extragrades which have additional aberrant properties.

Families and series are distinguished on the basis of properties selected to create taxa are successively more homogeneous for practical uses of soils. Thus, families attempt to provide classes having relative homogeneity in properties important to the growth of plants, and series are subdivisions of families intended to give the greatest homogeneity of properties within the genetic soil or the rooting zone, consistent with the occurrence of mappable areas at scales of detailed soil surveys.

On the rationale that the same processes operate in most soils, though at widely different rates and intensities, the classification of tropical soils in Soil Taxonomy is consistent with that of other orders. Soils of tropical areas are differentiated by their soil temperature regime, and importance is given to the degree of continuity of biologic activity: Soils of the humid tropics are distinguished at high categoric levels, order, suborders or great groups. With few exceptions, e.g. Torrox and Torrerts, soils of arid and semi-arid tropical regions are differentiated at the family level because seasonal lack of soil moisture is not unique to the tropics (Smith, 1965).

Evidently, the classes of Soil Taxonomy have been formed in consideration of concepts of pedogenic processes. However, as these causes are not fit as diagnostic criteria, some of their more prominent effects were selected as differentiae. Insofar as possible properties that are the result of soil genesis were chosen as differentiae because such properties carry the maximum number of accesory properties and have geographic implications of susceptibility to mapping. As a basic principle, these differentiae are soil properties and there are defined operations to identify them (Smith, 1965). The Soil Survey Manual and the Soil Survey Laboratory Methods (Soil Survey Staff, 1951 and 1967) provide the definitions and procedures essential for these operations.

The nomenclature of Soil Taxonomy marks a complete departure from past practice. It was not conceived to mystify the outsider as some might think, but because the old names were ambiguous, of diverse linguistic provenance, difficult to re-define and generally unsuited for use in systematic taxonomy. Therefore, new names were coined, largely from

Greek and Latin roots, that fit any modern European language without translation. The name of each taxon clearly indicates the place of the taxon in the system and connotes some of its most important properties.

For more detailed analyses of various aspects of the new system reference is made to the papers by Cline (1963), Flach (1963), Heller (1963), Johnson (1963), Orvedal and Austin (1963), Riecken (1963), and Simonson (1963).

b) *Brazilian System of Soil Classification*

When soil survey activities were started in Brazil some 20 years ago, the soil classification system of Baldwin, Kellogg and Thorp (1938) in its revised form (Thorp and Smith, 1949) was employed. However, as the soil surveys proceeded it soon became evident that the then U.S. system did not afford satisfactory groupings for the soils of Brazil. Neither did the taxa of the "7th Approximation" (Soil Survey Staff, 1960) appear to provide suitable classes for Brazilian soils, particularly as the classification of Oxisols was not fully elaborated at that time (Bennema, 1966).

It was, therefore, decided to develop a system of classification specifically for Brazilian soils. J. Bennema of the FAO and M. Camargo of the "Divisao de Pedologia e Fertilidade do Solo" (DPFS) assumed the leadership, and the new system was first published in 1964 (Bennema and Camargo, 1964). Further development of the scheme is in full progress with particular emphasis on the classification of the soils formerly called Red-Yellow Podzolics and Latosols.

The Brazilian system in its present form recognized twelve "soil classes of high level" each of which is subdivided at four successively lower levels. These categories are not formally named and have not yet been developed in equal detail for all high-level classes. New taxa may be added as new knowledge materializes and the Brazilian system thus constitutes an example of a descending classification.

Considerable progress has been made in the classification of the two high level classes that comprise the main tropical soils of Brazil (Costa de Lemos, 1968). These two classes are separated, at the highest level, on the basis of the presence of a latosolic or a textural B horizon which are roughly analogous to the oxic and argillic horizons of Soil Taxonomy. At the next lower level, mainly chemical characteristics, such as cation exchange capacity and base saturation, are employed to establish classes. The criteria used to subdivide the third level include iron content as related to soil color and type of parent rock, Al_2O_3/Fe_2O_3 ratios, and the degree of A horizon development. Classes of the fourth level are differentiated chiefly on the basis of color, profile differentiation, and presence or absence of plinthite. At the lowest level, texture is used to distinguish among classes of soils with latosolic B horizons, whereas type of parent rock is applied in the case of soils with textural B horizons. The use of "phases of vegetation" has been proposed to characterize the ecological conditions which a given mapping unit represents, but these have only been developed for tropical forests. (Bennema, 1966).

The nomenclature of the Brazilian classification is heterogenous. In eight of the twelve high-level soil classes descriptive terms are employed such as "Soil with solonetzic B horizons", "Red, Yellow and White Sand", or "Hydromorphic Soils". The names of great soil groups of the classification of Baldwin, Kellogg and Thorp (1938) were retained for the classes of Lithosols, Podzols and Regosols. The more recent term Grumusol is used to name the remaining high-level class. With the exception of the term Latosol, no names are given to taxa of the lower levels. These classes are briefly described in the fashion of a key and carry numerical designations.

c) *FAO/UNESCO Legend*

In 1961 FAO and UNESCO initiated a joint project for the preparation of the Soil Map of the World at a scale of 1:5,000,000. One of the most important aspects of this project was the correlation of soil units used in various parts of the world with the aim of preparing a universal legend. Field correlation activities and research undertaken to this effect eventually led to the publication of the "Definitions of Soil Units for the Soil Map of the World" (Dudal, 1968). Subsequent to minor revisions, the final key to soil units was distributed in 1970 (FAO, 1970). The legend was first applied in the two sheets of the Soil Map of the World covering South America (FAO/UNESCO, 1971).

The FAO/UNESCO legend is a bicategorical scheme which recognizes 26 higher classes subdivided into 104 soil units. For map units, three textural classes, three slope classes, and nine phases are provided. The soil units have been selected on the basis of their significance as resources for production, present knowledge of pedogenesis, and the feasibility of representing them on small scale maps. As a consequence, the soil units established may not strictly adhere to taxonomic rules and may belong to different levels of generalization (Dudal, 1968). It is further obvious that the FAO/UNESCO legend was not conceived as a taxonomic classification proper. Rather, it basically constitutes an organized compilation of definitions of map units and may be considered a compromise between a taxonomic and technical classification.

Soil units of the FAO/UNESCO legend are differentiated on the basis of quantitative criteria similar to those of U.S. Soil Taxonomy. In particular the definitions of most of the diagnostic horizons have been drawn largely from Soil Taxonomy and are, therefore, identical in both schemes as regards nomenclature and essence, though not detail, of definition. In addition to the diagnostic horizons of Soil Taxonomy, the FAO/UNESCO scheme further recognizes gleyic, plinthic and thionic horizons. At the phase level, classes of texture and slope, and phases to indicate the presence of hard rock, stones, gravel, indurated layers, and salinity and alkalinity may be employed as modifiers of the soil units.

The nomenclature of the units of the higher category of the FAO/UNESCO legend reflects a tendency to retain traditionally established names such as Chernozems, Podzols, Solonchaks, and Rendzinas. Also adopted were names that have become popular in recent years like Vertisols, Rankers, Andosols, and Ferralsols. The need to coin new terms was nevertheless felt in cases where existing names were liable to cause confusion due to different usage in different countries. Some of these new names include Luvisols, Acrisols, Yermosols and Nitosols. Twenty-eight connotive terms such as mollic, takyric, dystric or luvic are used as adjectives to the names of units of the higher category to form the names of the lower category soil units. The etymology of this nomenclature and the justification for its selection are discussed in detail by Dudal (1968).

IV COMPARISON AND CORRELATION

The foregoing discussion indicates that the U.S. Soil Taxonomy, the Classification of Brazilian Soils and the FAO/UNESCO Legend are systems that were contrived on divergent rationales for different purposes. As a consequence the schemes differ in structure, nomenclature and definitions. These inherent differences of the three schemes severely compounds the problem of correlating their taxa.

The number of taxa distinguished at comparable levels of abstraction varies significantly in the three systems. Considering, for example, a class which is defined almost identically in all three schemes, the order Oxisols of Soil Taxonomy has five suborders, 19 great groups and 35 subgroups; the Ferralsols of the FAO/UNESCO legend are split into six soil units; and the Soils with latosolic B Horizons of the Brazilian scheme comprise five classes of Latosols which are subdivided at two lower categories with 6 and 10 classes, respectively. It is thus improbable that taxa of one system can be matched with exact counterparts in another system.

An analysis of the schemes suggests that six of the 26 higher category units of the FAO/UNESCO legend correspond closely to orders of Soil Taxonomy; e.g. Acrisols = Ultisols, Ferrasols = Oxisols and Podzols = Spodosols; but not all Oxisols are Ferrasols, Plinthaquox are Gleysols. The remaining 20 units are approximately equivalent to suborders or great groups; e.g. Rendzinas = Rendolls and Nitosols = palegreat groups of Alfisols and Ultisols. The lower category soil units are roughly equivalent to great groups and, in some cases, to suborders or subgroups; e.g. some Humic Ferrasols = Humox, some Haplic Luvisols = Hapludalfs, and some Dystric Nitosols = Oxic Palehumults. It is, therefore, impossible to correlate soil units of the FAO/UNESCO legend and taxa of Soil Taxonomy at a consistent categoric level.

As regards the Brazilian classification, the high level classes of this system can, in most instances, be related to orders of Soil Taxonomy and high category units of the FAO scheme. Lower category taxa of the Brazilian classification cannot be matched unequivocally with classes below the highest categories of the two other systems.

The main difficulty encountered in correlating taxa of the three schemes is that different criteria are employed in their definitions. Thus, in Soil Taxonomy udic and ustic soil moisture regimes are used as a differentiae at the high categoric level of suborder or great group. Neither the FAO/UNESCO scheme nor the Brazilian classification consider these criteria, although in the latter system phases of vegetation provide some indication of it.

The FAO/UNESCO units and taxa of Soil Taxonomy are often thought to have a high degree of correlation because both schemes use similar or identical differentiae and definitions. However, additional criteria are applied in Soil Taxonomy, some of the same criteira, e.g. the natric horizon ,are used at different levels of generalization and the key to soil unit of the FAO/UNESCO legend is structured differently than that of Soil Taxonomy. Also, definitions are less precise in the FAO system. For example, Acrisols are defined as soils with argillic horizons having a base saturation of less than 50 percent (by NH_4 OAc) in at least some part of the B horizon and Luvisols are other soils with argillic horizons. As Alfisols are only required to have a base saturation of more than 35 percent (by sum of cations) at 125 cm depth, some Alfisols, such as Ultic Tropudalfs, may actually be Acrisols, although customarily Alfisols are correlated with Luvisols.

In the Brazilian classification, color figures prominently as a differentia in addition to criteria like iron content and parent rock which are not used in the two other systems. Cation exchange capacity is an important differentiating criterion in all system but is employed with different numerical values in the Brazilian Classification. Bennema (1966) has pointed out that the latosolic B horizon is, in many aspects, "similar to the oxic horizon of Soil Taxonomy, ... the most important difference being that a latosolic B horizon can never include a textural B horizon, while an oxic horizon may include an argillic horizon". This statement cannot go unchallenged. First, an oxic horizon is, of course, exclusive of an argillic horizon. Second, the vertical increase in clay in latosolic B horizons may be such that it meets the requirement for an argillic horizon if some clay skins are present. Thus, some soils classified as Latosols may be and in fact often are really Ultisols rather than Oxisols.[1]

With respect to the correlation of taxa, it is well to remember that the name of a taxon only conveys specific quantitative information about those properties which are differentiating criteria in its definition. The more specific the definition of a taxon, the more specific statements can be made about its properties. Vice versa, a greater number of criteria have to be known to allow positive placement in specifically defined taxa. The correlation of taxa has to be made on the basis of the information contained in its name plus consideration of the position of the taxon in the key. Three examples follow to substantiate these points.

1. *Haplorthox,* as defined in Soil Taxonomy, are soils with oxic horizons, a CEC of between 1.5 and 16 meq/100g. of clay, and a base saturation of less than 35 percent. In the Brazilian Classification, Haplorthox therefore can be either one kind of taxon defined as "Latosols wiht a CEC of less than 6.5 meq/100 of clay and a base saturation of less than 50 percent" or another kind defined as "Latosols with a CEC of less than 6.5 meq/100 g. of clay".

— In the FAO/UNESCO scheme, Haploxthox may be Rhodic, Xanthic or Orthic Ferralsols. In neither the Brazilian nor the FAO/UNESCO system can Haplorthox be accurately placed on the basis of the

1/ Buol, S. W. personal communication 1973.

information contained in its definition because color, iron content and type of parent rock are not diagnostic criteria.

2. The *Terra Roxa Legítima* of Brazil is classified as a soil with a latosolic B horizon with a CEC of less than 6.5 meq/100 g of clay, a moderately or weakly developed A horizon, more than 18 percent Fe_2O_3, and colors of 2.5 YR or redder. These soils may occur as savanna phase, semievergreen forest phase, and semi-deciduos forest phase (Bennema, 1966). Assuming that the semi-evergreen phase indicates a udic moisture regime, this class of soils corresponds with the Orthox of Soil Taxonomy and may be either Gibbsiorthox, Acrorthox or Haplorthox. If their moisture regime is ustic, these soils are Acrustox or Haplustox. In the FAO scheme, the Terra Roxa Legítima may quality for Acric, Rhodic or Otrhic Ferralsols. Again, more specific placements are not possible because the criteria of the Brazilian classification are not the same as those of Soil Taxonomy and the FAO system.

3. The FAO/UNESCO soil unit of Ochric Andosols comprises soils that, by definition, are derived from volcanic ash, have no mollic or umbric A horizons but have a smeary consistence. These soils belong with the suborder of Andepts of Soil Taxonomy. However, the information contained in the definition of Ochric Andosols does not allow a positive placement at the great group level. While they could be Cryandepts, Durandepts, Hydrandepts, Placandepts or Dystrandepts, they probably correlate with Hydrandepts because of their smeary consistence. The Brazilian classification in its present form does not provide taxa for soils developed from volcanic ash, as these are not important in Bazil.

It is obvious that the three systems are not compatible in many aspects, and correlation of their taxa can, in most cases, not be achieved unequivocally. This writer disagrees with statements to the effect that the three systems "have a high degree of correlation ... and are fairly easily translated" (Buol, 1972). It appears that only the taxa of the highest categories of each scheme can be correlated with some accuracy (see Table 1). This is substantiated by a correlation of FAO/UNESCO soil units with Soil Taxonomy taxa prepared by Dudal and reproduced in Buol (1972). Although generally satisfactory and providing approximate equivalents, the table should not be used where exact correlations are needed. This became evident, for example, in a recent effort to place all of the soil series of the State of Hawaii in the FAO/UNESCO scheme (Beinroth and Ikawa, 1973). While it is not possible to develop precise correlation tables that are valid in all instances, an individual soil can, of course, be classified into any of the three systems if those properties are known which are used as differentiae in the respective schemes.

V CRITICAL CONSIDERATIONS

Soil classification in Tropical America is made primarily as part of soil survey program that are carried out for purposes of agricultural development. This objective imposes certain specific requirements on the soil classification employed. Quoting from Smith (1965), such a classification should have the following attributes:

Table 1.—Approximate Correlation of Taxa of the Highest Category of U.S. Soil Taxonomy, the Brazilian Classification and the FAO/UNESCO Legend.

U.S. Soil Taxonomy (Soil Survey Staff, 1970)	FAO/UNESCO Soil Units (FAO, 1970)	Brazilian Classification (Bennema, 1966)
Alfisols	*Luvisols*, Planosols, Nitosols, Podzoluvisols, Solonetz	Non Hydromorphic Soils with Textural B Horizons, CEC > 24 meq/100 g, base saturation > 35% (Class III) Soils with a Hardpan (Class VI) Hydromorphic Soils (Class XII)
Aridisols	*Yermosols, Xerosols*, Solonetz, Solonchaks	Soils with Solonetzic B Horizons (Class IV) Soils with a Hardpan (Class VI)
Entisols	*Fluvisols, Lithosols, Regosols*, Gleysols, Arenosols	Lithosols (Class VIII) Regosols (Class IX) Red, Yellow and White Sands (Class X) Hydromorphic Soils (Class XII)
Histosols	*Histosols*	Hydromorphic Soils including Organic Soils (Class XII)
Inceptisols	*Cambisols, Gleysols, Andosols*, Solonchaks, Rankers	Non Hydromorpsic Soils with Incipient B Horizons (Class V) Hydromorphic Soils (Class XII)
Mollisols	*Chernozems, Phaeozems, Kastanozems, Greyzems, Rendzinas, Gleysols*, Planosols, Solonchaks, Solonetz	Non Hydromorphic Soils with Textural B Horizons, CEC > 24 meq/100 g, base saturation > 35% (Class III) Hydromorphic Soils (Class XII)
Oxisols	*Ferralsols*, Gleysols	Soils with Latosolic B Horizons (Class I) Hydromorphic Soils (Class XII)
Spodosols	*Podzols*	Podzols (Class XI) Hydromorphic Soils (Class XII)
Ultisols	*Acrisols*, Nitosols	Non Hydromorphic Soils with Textural B Horizons, CEC > 24 meq/100 g, base saturation < 35% (Class II) Hydromorphic Soils (Class XII)
Vertisols	*Vertisols*	Grumosols (Class VII) Hydromorphic Soils (Class XII)

Note: 1) The table should be read from left to right.

2) Italics indicate the predominant FAO/UNESCO correlatives. of the respective orders of Soil Taxonomy.

1. "Definitions of taxa should be operational so that they carrey the same meaning to each user".

2. "Differentiae should be soil properties that may be observed in the field or that may be inferred from properties observable in the field".

2. "The classification should be a multi-categoric system and should have a large number of lower categories. These should be as specific as possible about a great many soil properties to allow transfer of experience. Higher categories are essential for comparisons of soils of large areas".

4. "Taxa must be concepts of real bodies of soil".

5. "The classification must be capable of providing taxa for all soils in a lanscape and not just selected pedons".

6. "The classification should be capable of modification to fit new knowledge".

The three systems discussed meet these requirements to varying degrees. Soil Taxonomy is by far the most elaborate and most quantitative of the three schemes and is particularly precise in the definition of taxa in terms of soil properties subject to measurement by defined methods. Although, therefore, criteria and definitions are operational, considerable effort may be involved in their determination in some cases. For example, oxic horizons with a certain clay distribution become argillic horizons if clay skins occupy more than 1 percent of the volume (Soil Survey Staff, 1970). Considering the tedious and costly process of preparing thin-sections and the number of counts necessary to get confidence at the 1 percent level, this differentia appears to be unoperational from a practical point of view. Yet, a decision at the highest categoric level —Oxisols vs. Ultisols or Alfisols— may have to be based on this criterion.

In general, a considerable amount of quantitative morphological, analytical, and climatological data are needed to allow a positive placement in the lowest category of the system. Many of these criteria, such as soil moisture regime and mineralogy class, are not directly observable or cannot be inferred conclusively in the field. This detail of information is, however, indispensable if taxa are to be established which are sufficiently specific to be useful for transfer of experience. In the precision of definitions lies both the strenght of Soil Taxonomy and its limitations as regards applicability in places where laboratory facilities and financial resources are scarce. (The latter is, of course, not a fault of the system per se).

With respect to item 5 above, it is important to realize that not all soils of the world can be classified satisfactorily in Soil Taxonomy. This reflects the fact that Soil Taxonomy is essentially a national system developed mainly on the basis of detailed information on the roughly 10,000 soil series found in the United States and Puerto Rico. Cline (1963) has pointed out "that the system is incomplete in terms of classes, criteria of classes and precision of definitions ... crudely related to the amount, validity ,and genetic correlations of data available". This is especially true for the class of Oxisols which is based largely on the 28 series of Oxisols occurring in the State of Hawaii and Puerto Rico (Soil Survey Staff, 1972). For these soils the system provides satisfactory groupings, but Oxisols from other regions may not fit well into the scheme. A similar situation exists for those tropical soils derived from volcanic ash. This would constitute a serious defect if Soil Taxonomy were to be a universal system, which it is not. It should be noted that while the "7th Approximation" was called "A Comprehensive System", the system is presently named "Soil Taxonomy of the National Cooperative Soil Survey".

The new U.S. system has been subject to much criticism, more often than not merely a reflection of improper understanding. More substantial criticism, particularly from outside the Soil Conservation Service, was voiced concerning the fact that the system underwent constant changes. Thus, the definition of Mollisols, e.g., was changed to exclude those having isohyperthermic temperature regimes and COLE —values of more than 0.09, necessitating a shift of some Puerto Rican Mollisols to Inceptisols. Although in most cases the changes did not affect high— level criteria and were thus less disruptive, the continuous modifications discouraged pedologists outside the U.S. to use the scheme. With the forthcoming publication of Soil Taxonomy this drawback will be eliminated. It will be used in this form for some time, but periodic revisions are intended to accomodate new knowledge, particularly about soils from outside the United States.

As regards the application of Soil Taxonomy in tropical America, its general use is not advocated because it likely is not the best adapted system for the kinds of ongoing soil survey programs and their purposes. Proper classification in Soil Taxonomy depends heavily on quantitative data which it may not be possible to obtain in soil survey activities carried out under time pressure and with limited funds. Where Soil Taxonomy is used in lieu of a national system, it should be adapted to provide for any of the soils tha tare not properly identified in the scheme. It is, however, recommended that Soil Taxonomy be used as a system of reference for international communication, especially in technical papers. The Brazilian classification is still too far from completion to be thoroughly and objectively evaluated. In its present form, some criteira are not operational, e.g. definitions do not say exactly what a "weakly developed A horizon" is. Also, the use of type of parent rock as a differentiae is not beyond criticism because on old geomorphic surfaces pedogenesis is frequently multicyclic and the parent material may or may not be derived from the underlying bedrock. Further, there is no key provided to ensure mutually exclusive classes. In addition there is a tendency to concentrate on selected pedons considered representative of certain sets of genetic factors for the abstraction of differentiae (Van Wambeke, 1973). The structure of the system, however, permits the addition of new taxa. Although this classification has been designed for use in national soil survey programs, it appears that it is not always completely applied. Thus in the recently published "Soils of the Transamazon Highway" (Falesi, 1972), Yellow, Latosols are distinguished while such a class is not recognized in the published scheme (Costa de Lemos, 1968).

The usefulness of the lowest taxa of the Brazilian classification for purposes of transfer of agrotechnology cannot be assessed properly at this time. Although detailed information is collected for the pedon typifying a soil unit, the units on the maps at scales of 1:500,000 or 1:1,000,000 are not necessary taxonomic units and individual soils included in the map unit may diverge considerably from the typifying pedon. Whereas these maps are very useful for broad regional planning, maps where mapping units more closely correspond to the lowest taxonomic units are needed to test if the lowest taxa carry suffiicent information for recommending management practices at the farm level.

The FAO/UNESCO legend has not been designed as a taxonomic classification sensu stricto and should, therefore, not be judged on the criteria mentioned above. The main merit of the FAO scheme is that it will provide a vehicle for the comparison of well —defined, mutually exclusive, but by necessity rather broad groups of soils on a world— wide scale once all the sheets of the Soil Map of the World have been published.

Altogether 104 units delineated on maps at a scale of 1:5,000,000 however, cannot provide an effective basis for determining soil management requirements or to transfer experience. If the American, the Soviet and all other experiences are a guide, a classification system with a number of categories and more precisely defined lowest taxa are required for this purpose (Smith, 1965).

VI APPLICABILITY TO THE AGRICULTURAL DEVELOPMENT PROCESS

It is an important function of soil classification to provide a framework for a systematic land resources appraisal based on soil surveys. An equally important function of soil classification should be to facilitate the transfer of experience gained with a given kind of soil in one place to a similar kind of soil in another place.

The bulk of the world's research on soil management has been carried out in temperate regions but the transfer of this experience into the tropics has met with varying success. Therefore, the transfer process should be primarily within tropical regions. While this may be a reasonable statement of principle, its application is difficult. First, although an appreciable body of information about soil management in the tropics has been accumulated, experience is still lacking, particularly for "problem soils". Yet, in view of demographic pressures and limited financial recources, many countries neither have the time nor the funds required to build up through experimemntation the body of agrotechnological knowledge that modern agriculture needs. Second, the mechanisms of transferring existing experience within the tropics have not been studied in detail. It appears that principles can be transferred among regions but their applications commonly cannot.

There are indications, however, that soil classification and in particular the U.S. Soil Taxonomy can play a significant role in this transfer process. Because classes of Soil Taxonomy are defined in terms of soil, properties and because soil behavior correlates with soil properties, taxa of the system should reflect behavioral patterns. As soil families are, within a given subgroup, differentiated primarily on the basis of soil properties important to plant growth and indicative of soil-waterroot relationships, taxa of this category should have the greatest prediction value. Soils classified into the same soil families should, therefore, have nearly the same management requirements and similar potentials for crop production . This assumption was recently substantiated in a study of soils of the southern United States (DeMent *et al.*, 1971). The study further showed that only general kinds of soil behavior van be predicted within classes of the broader defined higher categories. This would indicate that taxa of the FAO/UNESCO and Brazilian schemes are less well suited for specific management predictions and recommendations, whereas the family level of Soil Taxonomy should afford a better basis for transfer of technology.

However, the validity of family criteria with regard to management predictions at the farm level has not been widely tested for tropical soils. Therefore, the Universities of Hawaii and Puerto Rico plan to initiate parallel projects focused on research along these lines. It is hoped that these studies will either demonstrate the usefulness of the present criteria and/or indicate new o radditional parameters which better characterize some of the management problems peculiar to tropical soils, such as distribution of electrical charge, Al-toxicity, moisture stress in the growing seasons, etc.

Independently of, but related to, this research an effort should be made to classify the soils of the mayor agricultural experiment stations of tropical America according to the family category of Soil Taxonomy. This would make possible specific comparisons of soils and experimental results at an international level. It would also generate compatible and standardized data on some benchmark soils of tropical America.

Although a clear distinction has to be made between such soil identification analyses and analyses for agricultural purposes, these data would be extremely valuable for use in the soil data storage and retrieval system being developed by FAO (1971).

Soil classification thus constitutes an important element in the agricultural development process because it a) provides the frame-work according to which land resources are inventoried in soil surveys, b) affords a basis for international communication of pedologists and agronomists (if a generally known system is used), and c) should prove useful in the exchange and transfer of knowledge and experience among tropical countries.

VII   CONCLUSIONS

1.   Soil classification is of central importance to the agricultural development process in tropical America because it is used in soil surveys made for systematic appraisals of land resources.

2.   The classification of Brazilian Soils, U.S. Soil Taxonomy and the FAO/UNESCO Legend are the systems most extensively used in tropical America. These three schemes are unlike as regards structural organization, precision of definition and number of taxa, choice of differentiating criteria, and nomenclature.

3.   Unequivocal correlation of taxa of the three schemes cannot be achieved with accuracy in many cases; only approximate equivalents of higher category classes can be established.

4. A multi-categoric system of soil classification with specifically defined lowest category taxa is a prerequisite for meaninfful transfer of agricultural experience.

5. The soil classification systems should be evaluated with respect to their suitability for purposes of agricultural planning and technology transfer. In particular, the validity of family criteria of Soil Taxonomy should be tested for tropical soils with the objective to test the feasibility of employing soil classification in the process of transfer of agro-technology.

6. The U.S. Soil Taxonomy should be used as a system of reference for international communication. It is recommended that the soils of the main agricultural experiment stations of tropical America be classified according to this system to allow comparisons of soils and agronomic experience at an internaitonal level.

VIII ACKNOWLEDGEMENTS

This study was supported by the U.S. Agency for International Development through the Institutional Grants Programm, Section 211 (d) under grant AID/csd 2857.

The author wishes to acknowledge valuable contributions made by Dr. M. G. Cline, Cornell University, and Dr. A. Van Wambeke, University of Ghent, Belgium, both of whom kindly reviewed the manuscript of this paper.

IX REFERENCES

AUBERT, G. 1965. Classification des sols utilisée par la Section de Pédologie de l' ORSTOM. Cah. ORSTOM, Sér, Pédol. 3:269-288.

BALDWIN, M., C. E. KELLOGG, and J. THORP. 1938. Soil classificatiou. *In:* Soils and Men. Yearbook of Agriculture 1938. U. S. Dept. Agr., U. S. Govt. Printing Office, Washington, D. C., pp. 979-1001.

BEINROTH, F. H., and H. IKAWA. 1973. Classification of the soil series of the State of Hawaii in different systems. *In preparation.*

BENNEMA, J. and M. N. CAMARGO. 1964. Esboço parcial de segunda aproximaçao de classificaçao de solos brasileiros. Ministério de Agricultura, DPFS, Río de Janeiro, Brazil.

BENNEMA, J. 1966. Classification of Brazilian soils, report to the Government of Brazil. UNDP Project BRA/TE/LA, Report N° 2197, FAO, Rome, Italy, 83 pp.

BRIDGEMAN, P. W. 1927. The Logic of Modern Phisics. MacMillan, New York.

BUOL, S. W. 1973. Soil genesis, morphology and classification. *In:* Sánchez, P. (ed.) A Review of Soils Research in Tropical Latin America. North Carolina. Agr. Exp. Sta. Tech. Bull. 219:1-38.

CLINE, M. G. 1949. Basic principles of soil classification. *Soil Sci.* 67:81-91.

CLINE, M. G. 1955. Soil Survey of the Territory of Hawaii. Series 1939, N° 25. U. S. Dept. Agr. in coop. with Hawaii Agr. Exp. Sta., U. S. Govt. Printing Office, Washington, D. C., 644 pp. with maps.

CLINE, M. G. 1961. The changing model of soil. *Soil Sci. Soc. Amer. Proc.* 25(6): 442-6.

CLINE, M. G. 1963a. The new soil classification system. Cornell University, Agronomy Mimeo N° 62-6.

CLINE, M. G. 1963b. Logic of the new soil classification system. *Soil Sci.* 96: 17-22.

COSTA DE LEMOS, R. 1968. The main tropical soils of Brazil. *In:* Approaches to Soil Classification. World Soil Res. Rep. N° 32, FAO, Rome, Italy, pp. 95-106.

COSTA DE LEMOS, R. 1971. Progress in soil survey and its application in Latin America. *In:* Systematic Land and Water Resources Appraisal. Latin American Land and Water. Bulletin N° 1, FAO, Santiago, Chile, pp. 102-112.

DeMENT, J. A., K. K. YOUNG and L. J. BARTELLI. 1971. Soil Taxonomy and soil survey interpretations. Amer. Soc. Agron., Agronomy Abstracts, p. 101.

DUDAL, R. 1968. Definitions of Soil Units for the Soil Map of the World. World Soil Res. Rep. N° 33, FAO, Rome, Italy, 72 pp.

FALESI, I. C. 1972. Solos da Rodovia Transamazônica. Instituto de Pesquisa Agropecuaria do Norte, Boletín Técnico N° 55. Belém, Brasil, 196 pp.

FAO, 1970. Key to soil units for the soil map of the world. AGL: SM/70/2, WS/A7460, FAO, Rome Italy, 16 pp.

FAO, Soil Resources, Development and Conservation Service. 1971. Soil data processing as an aid to regional land use planning. *In:* Systematic Land and Water Resources Appraisal. Latin American Land and Water Bulletin N° 1, FAO, Santiago, Chile, pp. 313-317.

FAO/UNESCO. 1971. Soil map of the world, 1:5.000.000. Vol. IV, South America. UNESCO, París, France, 193 pp. with 2 maps.

FLACH, K. W. 1963. Soil investigations and the Seventh Approximation. *Soil Sci. Soc. Amer. Proc.* 27(2):226-228.

HELLER, J. L. 1963. The nomenclature of soils, or what's in a name? *Soil. Sci. Soc. Amer. Proc.* 27(2):212-215.

JOHNSON, W. M. 1963. Relation of the new comprehensive soil classification system to soil mapping. *Soil Sci.* 96: 31-34.

KELLOGG, C. E. 1963. Why a new system of soil classification? *Soil Sci.* 96: 1-5.

MANIL, G. 1959. General considerations on the problem of soil classification. *J. Soil Sci.* 10: 5-13.

ORVEDAL, A. C. 1963. The 7th Approximation: its application in engineering. *Soil Sci. Soc. Amer. Proc.* 27(2):62-67.

ORVEDAL, A. C. and M. E. Austin. 1963. Some geographic aspects of the Seventh Approximation. *Soil Sci. Soc. Amer. Proc.* 27(2):228-231.

RIECKEN, F. F. 1963. Some aspects of soil classification in farming. *Soil Sci.* 96: 49-61.

SIMONSON, R. W. 1963. Soil correlation and the new classification system. *Soil Sci.* 96: 23-30.

SMITH, G. D. 1965. Lectures on soil classification. *Pedologie, spec.* N° 4, 134 pp.

SOIL SURVEY STAFF. 1951. Soil Survey Manual. U. S. Dept. Agr. Handbook Nº 18, U. S. Govt. Printing Office, Washington, D. C., 503 pp.

SOIL SURVEY STAFF. 1960. Soil Classification, A Comprehensive System, 7th Approximation. U. S. Dept. Agr. Soil Cons. Serv., U. S. Govt. Printing Office, Washington, D. C., 265 pp.

SOIL SURVEY STAFF. 1967. Soil survey laboratory methods and procedures for collecting soil samples. U. S. Dept. Agr., Soil Cons. Serv., Soil Survey Inv. Rep. Nº 1, U. S. Govt. Printing Office, Washington, D. C., 50 pp.

SOIL SURVEY STAFF. 1970. Soil Taxonomy of the National Cooperative Soil Survey. Selected chapters from the unedited text. U. S. Dept. Agr., Soil Cons. Serv., Washington, D. C.

SOIL SURVEY STAFF. 1972. Soil Series of the United States, Puerto Rico and the Virgin Islands: Their Taxonomic Classification. U. S. Dept. Agr., Soil Cons. Serv., U. S. Govt. Printing Office, Washington, D. C., 378 pp.

THORP, J. and G. D. SMITH. 1949. Higher categories of soil classification: order, suborder, and great soil groups. Soil Sci. 67: 117-126.

VAN WAMBEKE, A. 1973. Examen de los métodos de levantamiento de suelos en América Latina. Boletín Latinoamericano sobre Fomento de Tierras y Aguas Nº 2. FAO, Santiago, Chile, 49 pp.

5 Land Use Classification in the Lowlands of Bolivia

THOMAS T. COCHRANE

I INTRODUCTION

It is interesting to reflect that at a time when concern is being expressed on the ability of the world to feed its rising population, there are many millions of hectares of arable lands in the lowland tropics, as yet virgin and only partly explored. It is difficult to assess with any accuracy the total area of these lands but, in the South American continent alone, there are probably over 500 million hectares. This appears to be a paradox.

The reasons for the tardy development of these lands are many and varied. In the Amazonian regions of Brazil, Bolivia, Perú and Colombia, important factors include the collapse of the rubber industry in the early part of this century, disease problems especially malaria, communication difficulties and years of political unrest.

Looking to the future, a heritage of large areas of undeveloped tropical lands may well prove to be a blessing. Provided that they can be used to produce marketable agricultural produce economically, the effect of production from these lands in expanding a country's economy could be considerable. Furthermore, there are immediate benefits to be gained by settling undeveloped land in countries with poverty and unemployment, in that new jobs can be created and a new sense of purpose given to individual human beings. These factors are generally well appreciated.

During the last twenty five years, most countries left with legacies of sizeable undeveloped territories have made serious attempts to open them up for settlement. Unfortunately, for many reasons including a lack of an adequate appreciation of land and soil conditions, many of the attempts at colonization have failed.

It is observed that there is inconsistency in the approach commonly used in opening up virgin tropical lands in the South American continent. The normal procedure is to carry out a land use potential study; unfortunately, this is often confined to a local area considered suitable for settlement, and may cover only a small percentage of the available territory. The result is that, as often as not, settlement schemes are implemented, leaving the question of further development to chance.

The advantages of gaining a comprehensive picture of the land use potential of a large undeveloped tract of country are many. Estimates can be made as to the total areas available for the growth of specific crops. The costs of developing one part of the territory compared to another, can be assessed. Road networks can be aligned to best serve future transport of produce to markets and other types of infra-structure, including administrative centres, hospitals, and agricultural stations, can be located on convenient sites.

Regretably, in the past one of the main reasons why land use potential studies of extensive tracts of humid tropical lands have rarely been carired out before attempts at development, has been the high costs involved in terms of time, personnel and money. For example, in 1964, less than 300,000 hectares of the lowlands of Bolivia had been covered by any type of land use classification mapping, although over US$ 3,000,000[1] had been spen in such endeavour. It was obvious that there was a need to develop relatively cheap and speedy methods for this work.

II   A BRIEF DESCRIPTION OF THE BOLIVIAN LOWLANDS

The lowlands of Bolivia cover an area of 70,000,000 hectares, or a little under two thirds of the country's total land surface.

To the west, as shown Figure 1, are the forested low valley regions and foot-hills of the Andes where the climate is tropical an dthe rainfall high. foot-hills of the Andes where the climate is tropical and the rainfall high. Further north and east is the wide expanse of the Bolivian sector of the Amazon basin, spreading from the foot-hills of the Andes to the Mato Grosso of the Brazilian frontier. A vast savanna known as the "Pampas de Mojos" covers the central portion of this region, where rainfall patterns are markedly seasonal. East of the "elbow" of the Andes, where they change from a northwest to southeast to a north to south orientation, is the recent alluvial plain of the Santa Cruz district, the hub of agricultural development in Bolivia.

6North and east of the Santa Cruz district is the "Brazilian Shield". This is gently rolling to broken countryside with lowish rainfall where savannas and forests intermingle. Finally, to the southeast of Santa Cruz lies the region of the "Gran Chaco", covered by xerophytic forests.

In 1964 the writer was given the task, as a member of the British Tropical Agricultural Mission to Bolivia, of mapping and assessing land use potential in lowland Bolivia. The efforts made is a case history in the development of a methodology. Some aspects could well be applied on a broader front, and particularly to those countries containing the territories making up the Amazon Basin.

III   THE LAND SYSTEMS MAP OF CENTRAL TROPICAL BOLIVIA

For the practical purpose of describing land, it is axiomatic that it should be subdivided into units according to common parameters. In the case of the Bolivian lowlands, the question was asked, "which parameters should be used to define land units?".

From a perusal of the literature it was noted that land units were defined in many ways, the majority of which were sub-divisions of soil surveys, of debatable validity. However, one study was of special significance to this particular problem namely, the "General Report on Survey of Katherine-Darwin Region. 1946" by Christian and Stewart (1953). These scientists developed a new approach to the definition of land units which they termed "Land Systems" and defined neatly as "an area or group of

---

1/   E. D. Hansen, USAID soil scientist, personal communication.

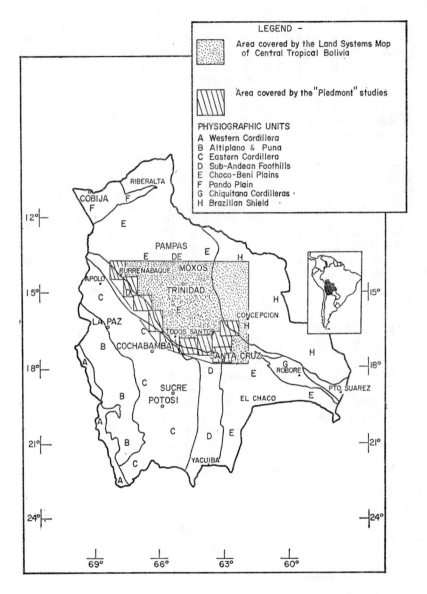

LEGEND –

Area covered by the Land Systems Map of Central Tropical Bolivia

Area covered by the "Piedmont" studies

PHYSIOGRAPHIC UNITS
A Western Cordillera
B Altiplano & Puna
C Eastern Cordillera
D Sub-Andean Foothills
E Choco-Beni Plains
F Pando Plain
G Chiquitana Cordilleras
H Brazilian Shield

Figure 1. Physiographic units of Bolivia.

areas throughout which there is a recurring pattern of topography, soils and vegetation". The concept of Land Systems has been discussed in detail by Christian (1958).

While Land Systems need not necessarily equate with land use potential and their definition may have degrees of validity dependant on the age of the landscape, the basic geology and the type of parent rock, the climatic regime and the vegetation pattern, the method was adopted as it offered a means of classifying land within the resources available in Bolivia. Further, it lent itself to programming in advance and relatively speedy implementation. In fact, subsequent work showed that through the use of overall aerial photographic indices and mosaics, the selection of strips of typical stereoscopic photographs for close study, and judicious ground checking, Land Systems could be readily identified throughout the contrasting physiography of Bolivia.

The delineation of Land Systems is now invariably used by the writer as the first phase of any project in assessing land use potential, irrespective of the amount of final detail required. A lot of basic land information is collected which assists in the programming of future more detailed studies. For example, in carrying out the work on "A Land Systems Map of Central Tropical Bolivia", (Cochrane 1967), see Figure 1 for the area covered), it was noted that there was a high degree of correlation between vegetation and certain soil properties, especially soil drainage. Furthermore, the type of vegetation followed differences in climate, particularly rainfall. In this context, Wright et al., (1959) in their study of "Land in British Honduras" have made comparable observations.

The Land Systems work was subsequently refined and developed, as is noted in section VI of this paper.

IV THE BOLIVIAN PIEDMONT STUDIES

The values of a map classifying land in terms of Land Systems is indisputable. However, although such information is of considerable value in helping to formulate broad plans for a region, it is not sufficient for its detailed development planning. For example, the information needed for the Bolivian Government in order to initiate colonization in the Central Piedmont and Santa Cruz regions was:

a) Accurate maps showing:

   (i)   Soils suitable for crop production.

   (ii) Sufficient topographic detail to illustrate the morphology of the area and thus, the practicability of providing infrastructure such as road communications.

b) Detailed predictions as to which crops might be cultivated on any one tract of land.

c) Information on major soil limitations to crop production.

In order to provide this information, a study was carried out which was recorded in the report "An Initial Assessment of the Land Use Potential of the Central Piedmont and Santa Cruz Regions of Bolivia" (Cochrane 1968).

To facilitate realistic predictions of the suitability of land for crop production, an analysis was first made of major tropical crop and pasture plant requirements according to common environmental parameters of both climate and soil. Details have been recorded by the writer (1969).

In some cases it was difficult to define the type of environment most suited to the culture of a particular crop from information available in the literature. It had to be remembered that crops are often grown in non-optimal environmental circumstances for economic reasons and, that cultivars of many crops are adapted to varying conditions; typical examples are cotton, maize and tobacco.

Nevertheless, it was possible to group major tropical crops according to certain common denominators; soil and climatic factors were separated for the purpose of scrutinizing the information. They are considered separately below.

Soil conditions

Most tropical crops can be grown on a wide range of soils differing in origin and age, provided that:

a) There are no serious topographical limitations to their physical cultivation, especially those that induce erosion and flooding.

b) Soil drainage and aeration are satisfactory or can be made so.

c) There is a sufficient depth of soil to allow plants to grow healthy roots and there are no physical limitations in the soil such as hard pans or high water tables which limit the root system.

d) The fertility of the soil is adequate or, can be made adequate for specific crop requirements; soil pH falls within the range 4.5 to 6.5 and there are no toxic factors.

Certain crops, such as tea, *(Camelia sinensis)*, or wet-land yute, *(Corchorus capsularis)*, demand specific soil requirements; other crops such as avocado pear, *(Persea americana)*, are grown more successfully under certain soil conditions.

In brief, it was seen that any study involving the assessment of land use potential must involve a clear appraisal of the main properties of the various soils that occur in a region.

Climatic conditions

Despite the seemingly exacting climatic conditions required by tropical crops, it was noted that within a given latitude, provided that average temperatures were in the range of about 18°C to 30°C and winds were not too strong or could be overcome by shelter belts, altitude and the nature of the moisture regime were key parameters in defining land suitability for crops.

a) *Altitude.* A separation according to altitude into highland and lowland crops could readily be made, although there was evidence to suggest a correlation between altitude and latitude. e.g. Arabica coffee is cultivated with a reasonable degree of success in some lowland districts. For this reason, in defining highland as opposed to lowland crops it is advisable to state the latitudinal range over which predictions as to the suitability of land for crop production are to be made.

b) *Moisture Regimes.* It was feasible to group crops into classes according to their approximate minimal moisture requirements. For lowland crops a table similar to Table 1 was drawn up grouping crops into 5 classes according to their minimal moisture requirements; the terms used to describe these classes were, Wet, Very Humid, Humid, Semi-humid and Dry. Short term annual crops were largely confined to the Semi-humid class. Obviously, many crops allocated to one class would also grow well in a class with a more humid moisture regime.

Whilst it was relatively easy to group crops into classes according to similarities in moisture requirements from an inspection of rainfall data, especially that indicating the seasonal distribution of rainfall, it was more difficult to define these classes in absolute values. Consequently, it was decided to define the moisture regime classes only for a specific region, rather than attempt to define classes for lowland tropical conditions generally.

In the Piedmont studies moisture regimes were defined in terms of the length of the dry season. A dry month was defined as one in which the potential evapotranspiration exceeded the precipitation. Evapotranspiration was calculated using the Thornthwaite's method (1957). Unfortunately, Thornthwaite's evapotranspiration calculations do not necessarily correlate with actual measurements made in Tropical South America, as illustrated by Hargreaves, (1972a). Moreover, this early work did not take into account rainfall reliability, a very important factor in agriculture. Consequently, it has since been superseded by the methodology in the writer's recent work titled "The Agricultural Land Use Potential of Bolivia. A Land Systems Map" (1973), which is discussed in Section VI.

A Further Note on Climate. Apart from altitude and moisture regime separations, the literature indicated some interesting climatic preferences and tolerances; fo rexample, citrus, *(Citrus* spp.), prefers high sunshine hours; pigeon pea, *(Cajanus cajan),* is photopeirodic and papaya, *(Carica papaya),* will tolerate mild temperatures. It was essential therefore to detail and carefully analyse climatic information in the study of land use potential.

The Soil Studies

The soils of the Piedmont were mapped to show enough topographical detail to illustrate the accessibility of the region, to delineate important soil differences, particularly drainage and land-form, and where practicable, to identify soil units. A soil unit was defined as "an area of

Table 1.—Moisture regime classes for tropical lowland crops and pastures. Approximate "minimal" moisture regimes that will permit healthy plant growth. Bolivian Lowlands. Less than 1000 m elevation.

| Name | Moisture Regimes | | | SUGGESTED CROPS, GRASSES AND LEGUMES |
| | Dry Months | Moist Months | | |
	Consecutive months with MAI* less than 0.33	Consecutive months with MAI greater than 0.66	Consecutive months with MAI greater than 0.66 plus months with MAI between 0.66 and 0.33	
Wet	0 to 3	8 to 12	9 to 12	*Crops:* Derris, lonchocarpus, rubber. *Plus:* Crops of the "very humid", "humid" and "semi humid" moisture regimes (see below).
Very Humid	4	3 to 7	8	*Crops:* Bananas, cacao, cinnamon, clove, coconut, liberica coffee, robusta coffee, ginger, jute, nutmeg, oil palm, pepper, tanie, yam. *Grasses:* Capín gordura, Capín planta (para), guinea, pangola, setaria. *Legumes:* Centro, green leafed desmodium, silver leafed desmodium, tropical kudzu, lotononis. *Plus:* Crops of the "humid" and "semi humid" moisture regimes. (See below).
Humid	5	3 to 7	7	*Crops:* Avocado pear, cashew, citrus, mango, papaya, pigeon pea, pineapple, soursop, sugar-cane. *Grasses:* Elephant ("merkeron"), yaragua (Hyparrhenia rufa), rhodes. *Legumes:* Atro, glycine (Soyperennne), stylo. *Plus:* Crops of the "semi humid" moisture regime. (See below).
Semi Humid	7	2 to 5	5	*Crops:* Cassava, castor bean, cotton, cousin-mahoe, finger millet, groundnut, kenaf, maize, rice, simsim, sisal, sorghum, soya bean, sweet potato. *Grasses:* Bermuda, buffel, gramma negra (Paspalum notatum), dwarf guinea. *Legumes:* Townsville.
Dry	less than 7	0 to 4	less than 5	*Note:* Irrigation needed for satisfactory crop growth, but some possibility for culture of drought resistant plant species.

* MAI = Moisture Availability Index.

comparable soil suitable for the culture of specified crops". A collateral programme of soil analyses and pot trials supported the study. Every effort was made to identify major soil conditions affecting plant growth.

Accurate topographical maps were available for about 10% of the regions. Uncontrolled aerial photographs at a scale of approximately 1 to 40,000 were available and mapping was carried out directly onto these photographs, referencing the checking and plotting of soil boundaries in the field to easily recognisable topographical features. Care was taken in the compilation of the final maps to preserve major topographical features, because of the paucity of ground control and base maps.

The procedure called for a preliminary interpretation of the aerial photographs based on the information already gained in carrying out the Land System studies. It was necessary to plan field work in such a way that adequate transects of the typical features of land-form, topography and vegetation could be made in order to check the veracity of the preliminary photo-interpretation and, if necessary, gain sufficient information for a repeat of modified photo-interpretation.

Vegetation

The preliminary studies for the Land System mapping showed that vegetation, as seen on the aerial photographs and in the field, was often related to soil conditions and could be used in helping to delineate soil boundaries.

Where the virgin vegetation showed on the photographs in any one climatic zone, this could be used almost invariably as an indicator of soil drainage; by studying changes in canopy height and density of the vegetation, along with an estimation of the palm population, it was relatively easy to separate drainage classes. It was necessary however, to check the validity of the interpretation through field work before final separations were made.

Differences in vegetation were observed from one climatic zone to another, although these were much more gradual than those associated with soil drainage. In many causes, differences in soil drainage masked vegetation changes due to climate.

It was found that the description of forest communities used by Eyre (1963) i.e. Tropical Rain Forest, Evergreen Seasonal Forest, Semi-Evergreen Seasonal Forest, Deciduous Seasonal Forest, Savanna, etc., had useful application in the Bolivian lowlands. Morever, within any one major class of forest, it was useful to identify sub-seres, principally on the basis of average canopy height and palm population, as these differences were usually induced by variations in the soil drainage patterns.

It was interesting to observe that minor vegetational changes, which generally could not be detected by photo-interpretation, often proved useful in helping to identify soil conditions in the field. Refering to the Palacios river region, it was found that, where soil drainage was poor, the underbrush was almost exclusively patujucillo, *(Alisma cordifolia)*; under conditions of somewhat impeded drainage woody shrubs such as "chocolatillo" *(Erytroxylon brasilensis)*, were common; where soil drainage was good, ferns predominated in the shrub layer.

Geomorphology and Topography

Aerial photographs proved particularly useful in providing information on the geomorphology of a region. Old eroded terrace surfaces, recently upthrusted plain surfaces and colluvial soils could readily be distinguished; these have characteristics which affect land use potential.

Geology and Soil Parent Material

A knowledge of the basic geology of an area can be of the greatest assistance to soil mapping. For example, it was found that there were marked differences between soils developed in alluvium derived from the Piedmont foothills of Tertiary sandstone origin and those developed in alluvium deposited by the large river systems that penetrate well back into the Andean mountains and receive their silt loads from the erosion of a wide range of parent material. Large river systems (e.g. the Chapare river of central Bolivia), often deposit considerable fans of mineral rich, silty alluvium which contrasts markedly with the poor, sandy alluvium high in quartz particles, derived from the many minor rivers draining the immediate Sub-Andean arenaceous pediments.

In the past, the rich alluvial soils formed by the major rivers were considered typical of the whole of the Piedmont area and this led to a faulty appraisal of the region as highly suitable for settlement. Now, however, it is clear that good settlement sites are confined to a few relatively small areas of well drained soils derived from the major river systems.

Soil Examination and Classification

In collecting soil information in the field, standardized techniques were adopted to enable data comparison with other parts of the world.

Soil profile pits were dug to at least a metre in depth on representative sites and the soil examined, described and sampled. Additionally, numerous small inspection pits were dug to lesser depths, as this was found to be a faster and surer way of detecting soil changes than by using an auger; the need for digging pits was lessened by observing the natural disturbances of the soil due to activities of ants and animals, and by noting changes in vegetation. Soil descriptions followed the criteria specified in the Soil Survey Manual, USDA (1951).

For the convenience of carrying out field work and the subsequent computer analysis of data, soil information was registered on cards in a coded form. The cards were very convenient under tropical bush conditions where insects, heat and rain make normal methods of recording difficult. It might be added that the FAO system for describing soils (1968), lends itself readily to coding, and the writer has subsequently (1969), coded this scheme onto cards.

Analysing Soil Data by Electronic Computer

Examples of the use which can be made of electronic computers in the statistical analyses of soil profile data has been recorded by the writer (1969). The work was initiated in 1965 with the help of Dr. L. D. Swindale of the University of Hawaii. Effectively, providing field work is carried out carefully, significant correlations can often be found between given sets of soil properties.

There are many possibilities for the use of the computer in analysing soil survey data, the results of which can be applied with advantage in the planning of future agronomic investigations. For this reason, profile description data should be assessed in as quantitative a manner as possible in the field. The amount of data which can be analysed, and the complexity of the analyses, will depend on the computer size but, as advances in the field of computers in rapid, there would appear to be a very interesting future for this type of work. Provided that the initial soil survey programme is well conceived, future soil survey work should include the compilation of data for the more accurate appraisal of soil properties, by the computer.

Concerning the number of profile pits that can be regarded as minimal for the definition of any one soil unit with the objective of detailed computer analysis, 15 to 25 might be suggested. Establishing this range implies that soil survey work can be carried out systematically, quickly and yield more information than was possible in the past. More detailed chemical and physical analyses can be justified and unnecessary profile pit sampling avoided.

Soil Laboratory Analyses

The type of laboratory analyses carried out for the Bolivian work was predetermined, and the methodology followed very closely to that of a latter FAO publication, Soil Bulletin Nº 10, (1970). Routine soil analyses included pH values, electrical conductivity, free carbonates, "exchangeable" calcium, magnesium, potassium, and sodium, total exchangeable bases, cation exchange capacity, phosphorus, (both the Truog and Olsen procedures) and organic matter content. The interpretation of the analytical data relied heavily on experience in the interpretation of comparable analyses carried out elsewhere in the tropics, although a parallel programme of pot tests was carried out, to provide a better local guide for data interpretation.

Soil Classification

Most of the soils in the Piedmont were geologically relatively young. Parent material therefore, would be expected to have a considerable effect on soil properties. In reviewing soil survey work where parent material has strongly influenced the delineation of soil boundaries and soil properties, the work of Taylor and Sutherland (1936) on the soils of the northern part of New Zealand was of particular interest. These workers illustrated the value of arranging soils according to "soil suites" as an aid to land use predictions. The "soil suite" can be described as a type of soil development sequence, and has been discussed fully by Taylor and Pohlen (1962).

Essentially, it transpires that if soils are arranged into suites, likely properties of members of the suites about which very little is known can be predicted with some degree of confidence.

A modification of Taylor and Sutherland's technique was used in the initial classification of soils in the Bolivian Piedmont studies, and it was found very useful in helping to organise data. Individual soil sequences were not shown, but diagrams were drawn up which identified soils according to the:

a) Relative age of the parent material of the soil.
b) Position of the soils in the landscape, the topography and the land-form.
c) Drainage. This often was proven to be a reflection of the position of the soil in the landscape.

The soil suite approach has a restricted application. For example, in the appraisal of the soils of the Brazilian Shield area, Map 1, the separation of soil units on the basis of land-form would prove more useful. It is true to say that the type of terrain will determine the techniques which should be adopted to facilitate the collation of soil information in the most effective way.

The object of classifying soils is to enable comparison to be made of soil wherever they may occur. In the case of the Bolivian Piedmont studies, having described soils and classified then into suites, the task of grouping soils according to other systems was very much simplified. Soils were in fact classified in terms approximating those suggested for the preparation of the third draft of the "Soil Map of South America" (FAO, 1967) and, also, an attempt was made to classify soils in terms of the USDA "Comprehensive Soil Classification" (1966).

Pot Trials

Pot trials were carried out, (Cochrane 1968, 1969) parallel to the other studies to help with the interpretation of soil analytical data; at the same time they provided a preliminary picture of soil fertility, although reservations must be made in transfering findings in pot trials to field conditions. The programme was supported by leaf analyses.

Large pots, each containing a cubic foot of topsoil, using Dwarf Cavendish banana plants as "indicator" plants, were used. The trials were laid out in small sheltered fields. Dwarf Cavendish banana plants were chosen as indicator plants as they are found growing in many parts of lowland Bolivia. Experience showed that the trials were considerably easier to handle than the small glasshouse pot trials, although obviously, they require large amounts of soil. Factorial designs, such as 2^4 using phosphorus, potash, sulphur and magnesium, were used for the major trials. Additionally, minor observation trials were carried out with 4 to 6 pots, that relied heavily on leaf analytical studies and the observation of visual deficiency symptons. Visual deficiency symptoms showed in several of the pot trials.

Visual Deficiency Symptoms

The observation of visual deficiency symptoms of cultivated plants, providing due care is used, can often give a lead as to major soil deficiencies. The Dwarf Cavendish bananas, seen growing in many regions of lowland Bolivia, were particularly useful in this respect.

The Cost of Carrying out the Piedmont Studies

The cost of carrying out the assessment of land use potential of the Bolivian Piedmont has been recorded by the writer (1969). The Piedmont project covered some 5,000,000 hectares of terrain and, as an extra, the Land Systems Map of Central Tropical Bolivia was made which covered 19,000,000 hectares. The combined costs of these projects, excluding the pedologist's salary, amounted to US$ 26,950 over a 3 year, 3 month period. It can be claimed therefore that the assessment of land use potential can be carired out very cheaply.

V DETAILED SOIL SURVEY AND AGRONOMIC WORK

Having firmly identified the Santa Cruz district as the most promising region for rapid agricultural development, work was intensified in that area. This included a more detailed mapping of soil resources (Paz *et al.*, 1970) and the laying down of regional fertilizer trials.

The soil mapping paid particular attention to the identification of textural differences and water-table heights, in view of the findings of previous work which indicated their obvious influence on crops grown in the district.

The fertilizer trials, which used sugar-cane as a test plant, were supported by soil and especially leaf analyses. Results from these trials are presently being published; in several instances, minor element limitations were identified through the use of leaf analytical data combined with statistical analyses. The technique involved the systematic sampling of the Top Visible Dewlap leaf of the sugar-cane of individual plots during the most vigorous growth phase. Complete chemical analyses were carried of the leaf nutirent levels and, where differences were noted between plots, these were subjected to the same statistical analyses as "yield" data For example, in the case of an experiment which gave a large response to sulphate of ammonia applications (83 tonnes to 148 tonnes), with the application of 500 kg of sulphate of ammonium per hectare, not only leaf nitrogen but also leaf manganese levels showed statistically very significant increases.

It is worthy to mention that with recent advances in quantitative analytical techniques, especially the development of atomic absorption spectometry, even small laboratories can provide a high volume, and in depth, analytical service to support agronomic and soil investigations.

VI THE LAND SYSTEMS MAP OF BOLIVIA

Apart from the agronomic work, Land Systems mapping was continued throughout lowland Bolivia. The work "The Land Use Potential of Bolivia, A Land Systems Map" as published by the writer in 1973. This work provides an overall guide to agricultural possibilities in Bolivia, and technically is a substantial modification on the earlier approach in mapping Land Systems.

A Land Systems was defined as a "unit of land with one or more repetitive patterns of topography, vegetation, soils and climate". To facilitate presentation and comparison of sysrtems, and following from a suggestion,[1] Land Systems were classified into Land Regions. Land Regions contain Land Systems with similar topography and under-lying rock. In turn, Land Regions were classified into Land Provinces, each of which contains Land Regions with the same gross geological structure.

The Land Systems map was produced by studying the existing aerial photographic cover, in the field checking, and by analysing past soil and geological reports. Furthermore, soil technicians of the Bolivian Ministry of Agriculture and the Agrarian Reform Institute, kindly contributed to the study by supplying descriptions of soil profiles, particularly in the Bolivian Highlands.

The original map was made at a scale of 1 to 1,000,000 and 208 Land Systems were established. Notes for individual Land Systems were recorded under the following headings: Location, Area, Physiography, Altitude, Geology, Hydrology, Climate, Soils, Vegetation and Agricultural and Animal Production Potential. Some specific notes related to moisture regimes, soils and vegetation follow.

Moisture Regimes

As indicated in section IV under the heading "Climatic conditions, b) Moisture Regimes", the study incorporated technological advances for the evaluation of water balance, as a result of work by Christiansen and Hargreaves (1969). Hargreaves collaborated with the study by computing water balance figures from data collected from the 47 meteorological stations throughout Bolivia.

The method used was identical to that recorded by Hargreaves (1972a, 1972b), and has two major advantages; rainfall reliability is taken into account and Potential Evapotranspiration (ETP) calculations correlate with recorded data in tropical South America.

Hargreaves defines the Moisture Availability Index, which is the dependable precipitation at the 75% probability level (PD75), or the rainfall that in 3 years out of 4, will be equal or greater than the calculated figure, divided by the potential evapotranspiration i.e.

$$MAI = \frac{PD75}{ETP}$$

A MAI of greater than one implies that the soil has excessive moisture and vice-versa. Nevertheless, field experience has shown that there is little difference between crops growing in a MAI circunmstance of 0.66 to 1.00, and consequently 0.66 was taken as an approximate moisture sufficiency level. With decreasing MAI plants suffer more and more moisture stress. At a MAI of approx. 0.33, they will usually suffer badly from drought.

---

[1] M. G. Bauden, Overseas Development Administration, U.K., personnal communication.

Crop Coefficients

A Table of Crop Coefficients prepared by Hargreaves which could be used to convert Potential Evapotranspiration to irrigation requirements. The Coefficients are ratios of crop water use to potential use. They vary with different plants because different plants vary in their ability to with-stand drough, in their form and leaf characteristics, rooting depths, plant densities, heights and the time of year when growth is made. The Crops Coefficients were included to help agronomists determine moisture regimes and irrigation requirements, for any specific circumstance, more precisely. Nevertheless, many plant species that are short, dense, uniformly vegetated and actively growing have approximately equal evapotranspiration ratios providing soil water is not limiting.

These and allied concepts, were borne in mind in defining the Moisture Regime Classes of the Major Tropical Crops in the Bolivian lowlands, Table 1. The regimes were defined in terms of both the number the number of consecutive dry months (with a MAI of less than 0.33) and the number and intensity of consecutive moist months (with MAI of consecutive dry months (with a MAI of less than 0.33) and the number and intensity of consecutive moist months (with MAI greater than 0.33 but less than 0.66 and greater than 0.66 respectively).

A Sketch map, Figure 2, was included in the study that provides an approximate idea as to moisture regime classes in terms of tropical crops for lowland Bolivia. This map also shows the number of months in the year when the Moisture Availability Index is less than 0.33 in the Highlands of Bolivia.

It might be argued that Moisture Regime Classes are not defined very accurately. This is so. However, the value of the method is in providing basic data upon which, by careful evaluation of all factors concerned (e.g. type and cultivar of crop, stage of growth, type of soil, etc.) it is possible to make a sounder prediction of the suitability of the Moisture Regime of any soil circumstance for any particular crop. Furthermore, the method provides data for calculating irrigation need.

Soils

The soils were described in terms of those properties that affect plant growth, as indicated in section IV for the Piedmont Studies.

Soils often varied considerably within any one Land System, and an attempt was made to describe key soils found on the varying phases of the land-form. Approximately 2,500 soil profile descriptions were examined in compiling the soil data. Selected typical profiles with analytical data were appended.

Vegetation

This was discussed in terms of natural, introduced and cultivated vegetation. The broad natural vegetation classes, as in the case of the Bolivian Piedmont Studies, approximated those outlined by Eyre (1963).

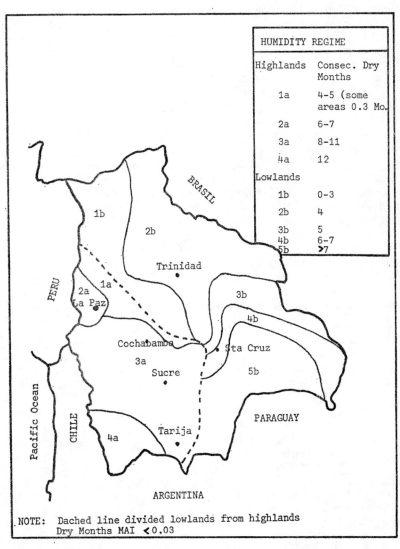

FIGURE 2 Moisture regime map of BOLIVIA

Apart from the notes on the individual Land Systems, the report provides an overall orientation on the physiography geology and climate of Bolivia. Additionally, some specific observations related to the Bolivian lowlands were made because of the lack of knowledge concerning this recently mapped terrain. For example, it was explained that there is a considerable potential fo rthe development of the cotton, oil seed, sugarcane, cereal, cacao, coffee, and cattle industries. The need to conserve forestry resources was emphasized. Colonization prospects were considered in terms of priorities. Finally, suggestions were made for the location of a new road network to open up the region.

VII SUMMARY AND OBSERVATIONS

This disertation was written to give some brief insights into the spectrum of scientific disciplines used, and the development of methodology in the assessment of land use potential, with special emphasis on the Bolivian experience. Technology is never stationary, and no claim is made to having developed a "new system" for such work; rather, it is emphasized that techniques should be employed according to the dictates of any specific situation.

It is contended that the assessment of land use potential on a broad basis is fundamental to the development process in Tropical America. Further, it has been shown that by using advances in methodology and modern techniques, this can be carried out accurately, speedily and cheaply, and at virtually any level of intensity warranted by particular circumstance.

VIII REFERENCES

CHRISTIAN, C. S. and STEWART, G. A. 1953. General Report on Survey of Katherine - Darwin Región, 1946. Land Research Series N° 1, C.S.I.R.O., Melbourne, Australia.

CHRISTIAN, C. S. 1958. The Concept of Land Units and Land Systems. Proc. Ninth Pacific Sci. Cong., 20: 74-81.

CHRISTIANSEN, J. E. and HARGREAVES, G. H. (1969). Irrigation Requirements from Evaporation. International Commssion on Irrigation and Drainage, Seventh Congress, pp. 23-570, 23-596.

COCHRANE, T. T. 1967. A Land Systems Map of Central Tropical Bolivia. Ministerio de Agricultura, Misión Británica en Agricultura Tropical, La Paz, Bolivia.

COCHRANE, T. T. 1968. An Initial Asessment of the Land Use Potential of the Central Piedmont and the Santa Cruz Regions of Tropical Bolivia. Ministerio de Agricultura, Misión Británica en Agricultura Tropical, La Paz, Bolivia.

COCHRANE, T. T. 1969. A method for the Initial Assessment of Land Use Potenial in the Underdeveloped Regions of the Humid Tropics. PhD. Thesis. University of the West Indies, Imperial College of Tropical Agriculture, St. Augustine, Trinidad, W. I.

COCHRANE, T. T. 1973. The Agricultural Land Use Potential of Bolivia. A Land System Map. Land Resources Division, Overseas Development Administration, Foreign and Commonwealth Office, Great Britain, for Ministerio de Agricultura, La Paz, Bolivia.

DEWIS, J. and FREITAS, F. 1970. Método físico y químico de análisis de suelos y aguas. FAO, Boletín Sobre Suelos Nº 10. Roma, Italia, 250 pp.

EYRE, S. R. 1963. Vegetation and Soils. A World Picture. Aldina Pub. Co., Chicago. 196-263.

FAO. 1963. First Meeting on Soil Survey, Correlation and Interpretation for Latin America. W. S. R. O., Rome. 2: 15-22.

FAO. 1968. Guidelines for Soil Profile Description. Soil Survey and Fertility Branch, Land and Water Resources Division, Rome.

HARGREAVES, G. H. 1972. The Estimation of Potential and Crop Evapotranspiration. AID Contract AID/csd-2167. Utah State University, Logan, Utah, USA.

HARGREAVES, G. H. and ASCE, F. 1972. The evaluation of Water Deficiencies. Dep. of Agr. and Irrigation Engineering, College of Engineering, Utah State University, Logan, U.S.A.

PAZ, P., QUIROGA, S., BLANCO, F. and OROS, R. 1970. Informe Sobre los Mapas de suelos Semidetallados del Distrito de Santa Cruz. Ministerio de Agricultura, C.N.E.C.A., Misión Británica en Agricultura Tropical, Santa Cruz, Bolivia.

TAYLOR, N. H. and SUTHERLAND, C. F. 1936. Field Work in North Auckland. N. Z. Dept. Sci. and Ind. Research, Annual Report, 47-49.

TAYLOR, N. H. and POHLEN, I. J. 1962. Soil Survey Method. N. Z. Dept. Sci. and Ind. Research, Soil Bureau Bull. 25: 151-154.

THORNTHWAITE, C. W. and MATHER, J. R. 1957. Instructions and Tables for Computing Potential Evapotranspiration and the Water Balance. Crexel Inst. of Tech. Lab. of Climatology. Pub. in Climatology, X, 3: 185-311.

U.S.D.A. 1951. (Rissue 1962). Soil Survey Manual. U.S.D.A. Agric. Handbook 18 and Supplement to Agricultural Handbook Nº 18, USDA. Washington, D. C.

U.S.D.A. 1966. Key to Orders, Suborders and Great Groups of the Comprehensive Soil Classification. Mimeo Report. Soil Conservation Service, USDA, Washington, D. C.

WRIGHT, A. C. S., ROMEY, D. H., ARBUDILE, R. and VIAL, V. E. 1959. Land in British Honduras. Report of the British Honduras Land Use Survey Team. H.M.S.O., London.

6 Soil Fertility Capability Classification

STANLEY W. BUOL, PEDRO A. SANCHEZ,
ROBERT B. CATE, Jr., and MICHAEL A. GRANGER

I INTRODUCTION

Within the field of soil science there is a clear difference between the subdisciplines of soil survey and soil fertility. Frequently these groups compete against each other for the dominant role in providing information about the agricultural potential of a country. The soil survey faction desires to produce maps which will inventory existing conditions, while the fertility group evaluates the potential of the soil for crop production through soil tests and field experiments. Both of these functions attain some degree of significance in shaping the agricultural plans of an area.

The roles of these two groups have tended to mutually exclude each other and have resulted in different approaches in providing information. The major difference appears to be one of emphasis. Most soil taxonomic systems stress subsoil features as major diagnostic criteria in the hierarchical grouping of soils and use the characteristics of the topsoil only at the lower categories. The fertility group in general confines its sampling to the plowed layer or the upper 20 centimeters of the soil. Thus the two groups really see two different soils while examining the same pedon.

Until very recently, soil surveyors were strongly biased by theories of soil genesis; they found the topsoil too easily modified by man to reflect the genesis processes adequately. In present soil surveys, an eroded soil would be classified like its uneroded counterpart at all but the lowest level (or phase). This approach was followed because the subsoil had not changed, even though the soil's productive potential had changed drastically. The present concept of the "control section" in the U.S. Soil Taxonomy system carried this bias down to the family level. Families thus classified have uniform properties only in the subsoil. In North Carolina, for example, 70% of the crop yield variability due to soil can be attributed to topsoil properties (Sopher and McCracken, 1973).

The two groups are further alienated because of the divergent nature of their immediate, but not long-range, objectives. Soil surveyors attempt to provide information that will serve the needs of all potential land users over several decades, while the soil-fertility specialist attempts to evaluate the fertility needs of a given crop for one or at most a few years; he will then reevaluate the soil. Thus the survey system attempts to be the storehouse of those physical and chemical soil properties with quasistable stature; the fertility group deals with the less stable components.

The amount of information needed by soil fertility specialists is only a fraction of the data gathered by soil survey groups. It appears desirable to design a soil classification system which is only concerned with criteria relevant to soil fertility problems. Such a system would be considered a technical system as compared to a natural system (Cline, 1949).

The purpose of this paper is to present the concept of a fertility-capability soil classification system and to provide examples of how it could be utilized to bridge the gap between the sub-disciplines - soil survey and soil fertility.

II CONCEPT

As a technical soil classification system, a fertility-capability system should be considered in the same class as the land capability grouping, the engineering classification, the wild life suitability, woodland suitability, and septic tank suitability soil classification systems. These groupings are found in any of the modern soil survey reports of the National Cooperative Soil Survey of the United States. In no way does it replace or conflict with the various natural sysrtems of soil taxonomy in use in vairous parts of the world. It is designed to group the soils of the world according to criteria that appear to have direct influence on the interactions of applied fertilizers and closely related fertility management practices (Buol, 1972).

There is a general tendency to overinterpret the usefulness of any technical grouping beyond its intended use. For that reason it should be pointed out that this system does no more than provide a framework within which all soils of the world are grouped according to a few of their characteristics that have been selected to reflect their relevance to soil fertility management.

It is important to keep a technical system of classification simple. It has to be specific and concise enough to be easily understood. To this end ,only those factors recognized to play a direct role in the interaction of fertilizer and soil materials are included. Such factors as rockiness or slope, which are important to equipment operations or irirgations are not considered.

There is often the tendency to use a technical system as the basis for soil mapping. This has generally proven to be false economy because, as the land use changes, questions are asked about other soil parameters not included in the criteria of the technical system; and duplication of field work is often required. This technical system can be used to interpret soil survey maps provided certain basic soil profile data are available. Thus, the criteria in this system are so defined that soils can be grouped from their existing taxonomic placement in the new Soil Taxonomy (Soil Survey Staff, 1970) and from most other soil classification systems.

Since it is anticipated that the primary use will be by soil fertility specialists in extrapolating their results from one field to another, an attempt has been made to provide guidelines that can be determined either in the field or with a minimum of laboratory work. Since it is obvious that many of the criteria are mutually exclusive, it should be pointed out that it is impractical to expect that all of the criteria will need to be tested at each site.

III FORMAT

Type and Substrata Type

The system consists of three levels (Table 1). The *Type* is the highest category; it is determined by the average texture of the plowed layer or upper 20 cm, whichever is shallower. USDA textures have been employed (Soil Survey Staff, 1951), and a field estimate of texture by feel is probably adequate in the absence of laboratory data.

The Substrata Type is the texture of the subsoil that occurs within 50 cm of the surface. It is used if the subsoil texture differs from that of the surface (Type) within the defined limits. If no textural change of this magnitude is present, no *Substrata Type* designation is employed. For example, a sandy soil where the clayey or argillic horizon begins at 60 cm below the surface would be designated as *S*, whereas a similar soil with the argillic horizon beginning 40 cm below the surface would be designated as SC (sandy over clayey). On the other hand, if a sandy soil with a texture of sand in the surface has a sandy loam subsoil, it will be designated SL (sandy over loamy); if the subsoil is a loamy sand only S (sandy) is employed.

Condition Modifiers

Unless otherwise defined the condition modifiers, in general, refer to chemical or physical properties of the plowed layer or top 20 cm, whichever is shallower. The modifiers indicate specific fertility limitations with different possible interpretations. Although the definition of these modifiers is written in rather specific terms in Table 1, it is not necessary to obtain the characterization with that degree of precision in order to make the system functional.

Condition modifiers are used as lower case letters for coding the soils. The following discussion attempts to explain the rationale for each modifier and serves as a guide to air placement of soils when insufficient data exists. The lower case letters used have been selected hopefully to provide easy association with the condition described.

g: This modifier refers to a gley condition in the soil as an indication of the presence of a water-saturation within 60 cm of the surface during some part of the year. It should be indicative of soils that could benefit from drainage practices, or soils usually good for rice production. It fits the Aquic soil moisture regime definition in the U.S. Soil Taxonomy, but is not mutually exclusive of the "d" modifier (below) when strong rainy and dry seasons occur.

d: This modifier refers to an annual dry season of at least 60 consecutive days. It is defined to roughly correspond to Ustic, Xeric, Torric, and Aridic moisture regimes of the U.S. Soil Taxonomy. Its significance in fertility management is not fully recognized, but there are indications of several consequences regarding nitrogen response and planting date relationships at the onset of the rains following the dry period (Hardy, 1946).

Table 1.—Fertility-capability classification.[1]

TYPE:

    Texture is average of plowed layer or 20 cm depth, (8") whatever is shallower.
S = Sandy topsoils: loamy sands and sands (USDA).
L = Loamy topsoils: < 35% clay but not loamy sand or sand.
C = Clayey topsoils: > 35% clay.
O = Organic soils: > 30% O.M. to a depth of 50 cm or more.

SUBSTRATA TYPE:

    Used if textural change or hard root restricting layer is encountered within 50 cm (20").
S = Sandy subsoil: texture as in type.
L = Loamy subsoil: texture as in type.
C = Clayey subsoil: texture as in type.
R = Rock or other hard root restricting layer.

CONDITION MODIFIERS:

    In plowed layer or 20 cm (8"), whichever is shallower unless otherwise specified (*).

*g = (Gley):

    Mottles $\leq$ 2 chroma within 60 cm of surface and below all A horizons or saturated with H_2O for > 60 days in most years.

*d = (Dry):

    Ustis or xeric environment; dry > 60 consecutive days per year within 20-60 cm depth.

e = (Low CEC):

    < 4 meq/100 soil by Σ bases + unbuffered Al.
< 7 meq/100 soil by Σ cations at pH 7.
< 10 meq/100 soil by Σ cations + Al + H at pH 8.2.

*a = (Al toxic):

    > 60% Al saturation of CEC by (Σ bases and unbuffered Al) within 50 cm.
> 67% Al saturation of CEC by (Σ sations at pH 7) within 50 cm.
> 86% Al saturation of CEC by (Σ cations at pH 8.2) within 50 cm.
or pH < 5.0 in 1:1 H_2O except in organic soils.

*h = (Acid):
10-60% Al saturation of CEC by (Σ bases and unbuffered Al) within 50 cm. or pH in 1:1 H_2O between 5.0 and 6.0.

i = (Fe-P fixation):

    % free Fe_2O_3/% clay > 0.2 or hues redder than 5 YR and granular structure.

x = (X-ray amorphous):

    pH > 10 in 1N NaF or positive to field NaF test or other indirect evidences of allophane dominance in clay fraction.

[1] Proposed Feb., 1974.

TABLE 1.—(Continued).

*v = (Vertisol):

Very sticky plastic clay > 35% clay and > 50% of 2:1 expanding clays; COLE > 0.09. Severe topsoil shrinking and swelling.

*k = (K deficient):

< 10% weatherable minerals in silt and sand fraction within 50 cm or exch. K < 0.20 meq/100 g or K < 2% of Σ of bases, if Σ of bases < 10 meq/100 g.

*b = (Basic Reaction):

Free $CaCO_3$ within 50 cm (fizzing with HCl) or pH > 7.3.

*s = (Salinity):

4 mmhos/cm of saturated extract at 25°C within 1 meter.

*n = (Natric):

> 15% Na saturation of CEC within 50 cm.

*c = (Cat clay):

pH in 1:1 H_2O is < 3.5 after drying, Jarosite mottles with hues 2.5Y or yellower and chromas 6 or more within 60 cm.

e: This modifier refers to soils with very low cation exchange capacities in the plowed layer. Three levels are indicated as diagnostic, depending upon the techniques used for determination. Significant fertility problems related to cation leaching could be inferred by this condition as well as its relationship to liming recommendations.

a: This modifier refers to high concentrations of aluminum which may be toxic to most agronomic crops. It also implies a high degree of phosphorus fixation by aluminum compounds (Kamprath, 1970; Woodruff and Kamprath, 1965), and utilization of different soil test interpretation functions (ISFEIP, 1968).

h: This modifier refers to a moderate level of acidity that would retard the growth of some aluminum sensitive plants (Evans and Kamprath, 1970). Since both "a" and "h" conditions are often altered by liming or by the residual acidity of various fertilizer sources, the soil should be examined to a depth of 50 cm. Employment of these modifiers will reflect the severity of future lime requirements.

i: This modifier is intended for those soils where phosphorus fixation by iron compounds is of major importance. The iron/clay ratio criterion for this modifier given in Table 1 is frequently difficult to obtain and thus a color-structure criteria has been given for field use. It is thought that this modifier will be closely aligned with the Oxisol order.

x: This modifier attempts to delimit soils with allophane dominated mineralogy. We are primarily interested in the high phosphorus-fixing capacity and low rate of nitrogen mineralization of such soils. Preliminary indications are that the simple NaF tests (Fieldes and Perrot, 1966) may correlate with the phosphorus fixation potential of such soils.

v: This modifier indicates clayey soils dominated by 2:1 expanding clays. The fertility implications are for high permanent-charge CEC and difficulties in water management and soil tillage. It is thought that this modifier will be closely aligned with the Vertisol order and some vertic subgroups.

k: Many soils have small quantities of potassium bearing minerals, and profitable responses to potassium fertilizers are expected. This modifier attempts to delimit those soils where it is almost certain that potassium will be needed in an agronomic fertility program. Criteria set forth in Table 1 concerning mineralogy have been adapted from taxonomic limits (Soil Survey Staff, 1970) and the limits for soil-test potassium have been adapted from several reports (Boyer, 1970).

b: This modifier delimits calcareous soils or, more specifically, free carbonate within 50 cm and phosphorus fixation by calcium compounds.

s: This modifier separates those soils with sufficient salinity to present problems for most crops. It is based on general criteria developed by the U.S. Salinity Laboratory (U.S. Salinity Laboratory Staff, 1954).

n: Sodium is considered because of its effect on clay dispersion and on moisture availability. This modifier is designed to delineate soils with a sodium problem. The limits for both s and n modifiers are those set by the U.S. Soil Salinity Laboratory (U.S. Salinity Laboratory Staff, 1954).

c: This modifier indicates the presence of acid sulfate soils and the associated management problems (Moorman, 1963).

To aid in grouping soils from existing soil surveys, a standard format has been adapted. Table 2 shows a filled-in example of this format. Such a work sheet will allow the systematic placement of profile information in field plots where no survey information exists because it provides a format for the researcher to record his soil observations. It is anticipated that, when certain conditions are suspected but not determined in the field, samples can be taken and classified upon laboratory characterization of these samples.

IV RESULTS OF TRIAL GROUPINGS

The first evaluation consisted of determining how soil profiles would be grouped according to this system. This was tested at three levels: world-wide, national and local.

World-Wide Groupings

Published profile descriptions and analytical data of 244 soil profiles representing a broad geographical and morphological range were grouped according to this system. This sample consisted of the 69 profiles described in the Seventh Approximation (Soil Survey Staff, 1960), most of which

Table 2.—Fertility-cabability soil classification sample coding sheet.

DATA SOURCE: Soil Map of Africa - D'Hoore 1964.

LOCATION: Africa   DATE: 4-10-73.   INITIALS: P.A.S.

Profile No	Profile identification	Type and Substrata types	Modifiers	Check List												
				1 g	2 d	3 e	4 a	5 h	6 i	7 x	8 v	9 k	10 b	11 s	12 n	13 o
2b	Subdesert soil, N. W. Kenya	SR	dbn		X								X		X	
4	Juvenile soil on volcanic ash, Tanzania	S	dx		X					X						
7b	Rendzina, Madagascar	C	dvb		X						X		X			
12b	Podzol, undiff., Madagascar	SR	eak			X	X					X				
13	Soils lessives, S. Africa	L	ga	X			X									
16	Eutrophic brown soil, Congo	S	dx		X					X						
17	Eutrophic brown soil on ferromagnesium rock, Ivory Coast	L														
20	Ferruginous trop. soil, Senegal	SC	dek		X	X						X				
21	Ferruginous trop. soil, Angola	LC	d		X											
23	Humic ferrisol, Zaire	C	da		X	X	X									
26	Ferralitic, yellow br., Congo	S	eak			X	X					X				

are from the United States; the 33 profiles described in the South America volume of the World Soils Map (FAO-UNESCO, 1971), and the 36 profiles appearing in the explanatory monograph of the Soil Map of Africa (D'Hoore, 1964). Also included are 46 profiles from the Philippines, 40 from the Amazon Basin, and 18 profiles from the Southeastern United States with which the authors have personal experience. Although in some cases it was necessary to substitute judgment for missing data, it was possible to group all soils according to the system.

Eleven of the possible 13 type-substrata type combinations were identified in this sample. Types L (loamy), C (clayey) and LC (loamy topsoil over clayey subsoil) and S (sandy) accounted for 92 percent of the population (Table 3). A total of 117 type-substrata type-modifier combinations were identified. The frequency distribution of the most common modifiers are shown in Tabla 4. These 10 modifiers accounted for 51 percent of the population.

Many possible combinations were not found due to the mutual exclusiveness of the criteria. Five of the modifiers (v, n, s, x, i) never occurred alone, reflecting the fact that several of these fertility-related parameters occur together in many soils (Table 5). No profile characteristic produced the modifier "c" (cat clay) in this particular sample.

Country Grouping

The second evaluation was done at a country level, to determine the range in properties found within national boundaries. All of the 678 profiles described in the soil survey reports of Brazil were classified according to this system.

Table 3.—Frequency distribution of fertility-capability groupings in the world-wide survey.

Type and Substrata Types	Frequency of Occurrence		Condition Modifier Combinations
	N⁰	%	N⁰
L	82	34	31
C	72	30	31
LC	47	19	24
S	22	9	14
SL	4	1	4
CL	3	1	3
Others (3)	14	6	10
Total	244	100	117

Table 4.—Most common modifier combinations found in the world wide survey.

Modifier	Interpretation	Frequency
		Nº
a	Aluminum toxicity	28
gak	Aquic, Al toxicity, K deficient	17
ga	Aquic, Aluminum toxicity	14
eah	Low CEC, Al toxicity, K deficient	13
—	No limitations	12
g	Aquic	11
d	Dry season	8
gh	Aquic, acid	8
db	Dry season, calcareous	8
dvb	Dry season, vertic calcareous	6

Table 5.—Occurrence of condition modifiers alone or in combination with others in the Brazil samples.

Modifier	Alone	In combination with others	Total
	Nº of profiles		
a	28	78	106
g	11	74	85
d	8	64	72
k	3	70	73
e	1	39	40
b	1	36	37
h	4	20	24
v	0	17	17
n	0	13	13
s	0	11	11
x	0	10	10
i	0	6	6
c	0	0	0

Table 6.—Frequency distribution of fertility-capability groupings found in 678 soils of Brazil.

Type and Substrata Types	Frequency of Occurrence		Condition Modifier Combinations
	Nº	%	Nº
L	223	33	17
C	195	29	19
LC	112	16	14
S	93	14	12
SL	39	6	9
CL	7	1	4
Others (3)	7	1	7
Total	678	100	84

Table 7.—Most common type-modifies combinations found in the Brazilian sample.

Combinations Condition Modifier	Type-Substrata Types						Total
	L	C	LC	S	SL	Other	
	Nº of Soils						
d	44	39	39	4	2	6	134
di	33	32	17	4	1	0	87
dea	40	21	7	19	4	1	92
deh	27	5	8	33	11	1	85
dai	2	22	1	0	1	1	27
da	11	21	8	1	0	1	42
dh	20	16	11	1	1	1	50
db	8	12	8	1	0	2	31
dhi	10	8	8	0	0	1	31
dehi	6	0	0	9	0	0	15
deai	9	4	1	10	3	0	25
Total	214	180	108	82	23	14	619

Nine out of the possible 13 type-substrata type combinations were found in this group (Table 6). In striking agreement with the world-wide sample the L, C, CL and S classes accounted for 92 percent of the population. A total of 84 type-substrata type-modifier combinations were found. Considering only the combinations that comprise at least 1% of the population (9 profiles) this reduces the total to 23 combinations (Table 7). These combinations accounted for 75% of the Brazilian soil profile samples.

The fact that such a large number of profiles can be grouped into 23 fertility-related combinations suggest that this system may simplify interpretations of fertility-related problems. The Brazilian survey did not include several modifiers which were simply not found in the profiles such as "v", "x" and "c". These local modifications undoubtedly account for the simplification in these groups.

The interpretation of this survey raises interesting points. A large majority of the soils (78%) were either clayey, loamy or loamy over clayey without root-restricting layers. About 20% of the profiles had only "d" or "k" limitations. More than 35% of the profiles showed low cation exchange capacities (e) on the surface in spite of their relatively fine texture. This observation reflects the relatively high stage of weathering of many Brazilian soils. It is interesting to note that the "e" modifier almost always occurred in combination with others (only 10 times alone). The survey also showed that these soils are predominantly acid. About 27% are aluminum toxic (a) and 28% have the "h" modifier. Only 5 percent were calcareous. The "i" modifier (denoting high phosphorus fixation by iron compounds) appeared in 27 percent of the samples.

The world-wide and Brazilian survey indicated that soils belonging to the same taxonomic group (i.e. Paleudults, Latosol Roxo, etc.) exhibit a wide range in fertility- capability. Consequently, the natural taxonomy cannot be directly translated into this technical system. The specific fertility-capability parameters have to be evaluated independently of this taxonomy on each individual soil. By definition, however, some direct extrapolation can be made. Most Oxisols will have the "i" modifier; all Vertisols will have the "v"; most Andepts the "x", and all aquic subgroups the "g" modifier.

Local Grouping

The third evaluation consisted of determining the number of groupings found in a management area. The soil survey of Wake County, North Carolina (Cawthorn, 1970) was used for this purpose. This county soil survey report has 145 mapping units (soil phases) from 40 soil series. When the soils were arranged by fertility capability groups, only six type substrata type combinations and five modifiers were used. The 145 mapping units in this county can thus be reduced to 15 units for fertility interpretation (Table 8).

V RELEVANCE TO FERTILIZER RESPONSE

The first test of the usefulness of the system in terms of fertility response data was conducted on a series of 73 potato fertilization experi-

Table 8.—Fertility-capability grouping of Wake County, North Carolina soils.

Condition Modifier Combinations	Type-Substrata Types							Total
	LC	C	SC	L	SL	LR	S	
				Nº of Soils				
h	34	17	—	6	—	2	—	59
a	48	—	—	—	—	—	—	48
eh	—	—	12	—	—	—	—	12
ea	—	—	—	—	7	—	—	7
av	4	2	—	—	—	—	—	6
ga	2	—	—	3	—	—	1	6
gh	2	—	—	2	—	—	—	4
ges	—	—	—	—	—	—	1	1
Total	90	19	12	11	7	2	2	143

ments conducted throughout the Sierra of Peru by McCollum and Valverde (1968). The 73 experimental sites were grouped into five fertility-capability units (Table 9). The average yield response to phosphorus of the five groups is shown in Fig. 1. The response curves of the Lhd and Lad soils were completely different from the other three. The response pattern of the Lbd, Lbxd and Cbd soils were essentially linear and not significantly different. Consequently for this case the response pattern of 73 experiemnts can be grouped into three categories, Lhd, Lad and Lbd soils. Fig. 1 also shows the dramatic difference in maximum and optimum level for the other soils is probably beyond the range of rates studied.

After these soils were grouped by fertility capability classes and by soil test results, the gross returns to fertilizer applications were evaluated and compared with the gross returns to fertilizers when all the soils were given a single blanket recommendation. With a blanket recommendation the returns to fertilizer was US$ 770/ha. When fertilizer recommendations were based on soil test results (phosphorus, pH and exchangeable soil potassium), the average returns were increased to about US$ 860/ha (Ryan and Perrin, 1973). Estimation of optimum fertilizer rates from average group response curves generated by grouping the soils into fertility capability classes, showed that the gross returns to fertilizers at these rates would be on the order of US$ 920/ha. However when fertilizer rates were based both on soil test results and on fertility capability classes, the erturns to fertilizer applications further increased in about U.S.$ 965.[1]

[1] R. K. Perrin, Associate Professor of Economics, N. C. S. U., Personal Com. munication.

Table 9.—Classification of soils in 1967-71 Peru potato trials.

Number of sites	Fertility-capacity classification
23	Lad (Loamy, aluminum toxicity)
27	Lhd (Loamy, acid)
11	Lbd (Loamy, CaCO₃)
6	Lbxd (Loamy, CaCO₃, amorphous)
6	Cbd (Clayey, CaCO₃)

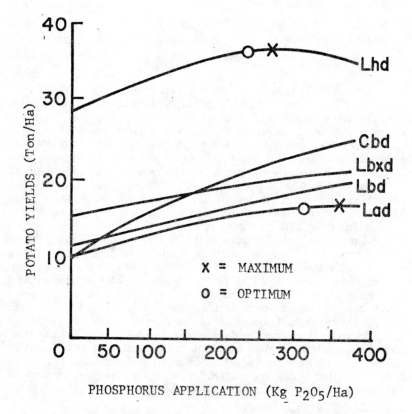

Figure 1. Differential phosphorus response of different fertility capability groupings in the Peru potato experiments.

This first agronomic evaluation shows promise for using this new technical system. Its complementary nature with soil test recommendations suggest that the use of both tools has a positive interaction. The relative contribution of fertility-capability groupings and soil tests is expected to vary with the degree of management intensity. In relatively extensive systems such as this example from Peru, fertility-capability groupings may play a more sensitive role than soil testing. However, as fields develop a fertilization history, soil testing is expected to be a more sensitive parameter. Further testing is needed to fully evaluate its usefulness in other areas.

VI CONCLUSIONS

The proposed technical soil classification system groups soils according to criteria of significance to scientists in fertility, and soil testing. It provides a mechanism whereby either existing soils data from soil survey reports or on-site examination of an area, can be used to group soils into reasonably homogeneous classes for the purpose of extrapolating fertility data. In no way does it replace soil testing which is necessary to monitor annual changes in soil-fertility levels due to management practices. It does, however, provide the "soil-tester" with somewhat uniform groups within which he can feel comfortable in extrapolating soil test information. The homogenizing effect brought about by the use of criteria significant to soil-fertility evaluation tends to further reduce the number of mapping units or soil series in a large management area to a relatively few working classes.

Other potential uses appear probable. For example, analyses of economic returns from fertilizer use can now be examined by groups of soil expected to respond similarly to fertilizer. It may also lead to identification of groups of soils with similar micronutrient requirements.

In total, it provides a system of soil grouping that relates directly to one use of soil, that of managing soil fertility, and thereby should provide a basis for the areal extrapolation of fertility management techniques. If incorporated in soil survey reports it should offer a mechanism for the soil survey to be of greater value in soil fertility management.

VII SUMMARY

A technical soil classification system for grouping soils with similar fertility limitations is presented. Soils are grouped at the highest categorical level according to topsoil and substrata textures. Thirteen modifiers are defined to delimit specific fertility-related parameters. Trial groupings of soil profiles in a world-wide sample showed the number of possible units to be 127. When applied to one specific country, Brazil, most of the 678 soil profiles studied were grouped into 24 fertility-capability categories. A county soil map with 145 mapping units was reduced to 15 fertility-capability groups. When this system was used to group soils from field fertility experiments from the Sierra of Peru, the 73 sites used were grouped into five fertility classes. Each of them produced a different phosphorus response surve. When fertilizer rate recommendations were made by fertility-capability groupings, the net return to fertilizers increased significantly. When both soil tests and fertility-capability groupings were used to determine fertilizer rates ,the net return increased further. The application of this system should bridge the gap between soil fertility and soil classification.

VIII ACKNOWLEDGEMENTS

The authors are grateful to the Centro de Pesquisas Pedológicas, EMBRAPA, Brazil and the Ministerio de Agricultura of Peru for permission to interpret unpublished data.

This work was supported in part by Contract AID/csd 2806 with the U.S. Agency for International Development. Published as Paper N° 4324 of the Journal Series of the North Carolina Agricultural Experiment Station, North Carolina State University.

IX REFERENCES

BOYER, J. 1970. Soil potassium. *In:* Soils of the Humid Tropics. National Academy of Sciences, Washington, D. C. pp. 102-135.

BUOL, S. W. 1972. Fertility Capability Soil Classification System. Agronomic-Economic Research on Tropical Soils - Annual Report for 1971 and 1972. Soil Science Dept., North Carolina State Univ., Contrac AID/csd 2806.

CAWTHORN, J. W. 1970. Soil Survey of Wake County, North Carolina. U. S. Dept. of Agric., Soil Conservation Service.

CLINE, M. G. 1949. Basic principles of soil classification. Soil Sci. 67:81-91.

D'HOORE, J. L. 1964. Soil map of Africa - scale 1:5,000,000 - explanatory monograph. Commission for Technical Cooperation in Africa. Publ. 93. Lagos, Nigeria.

EVANS, C. E. and E. J. KAMPRATH. 1970. Lime response as related to percent Al saturation, solution Al and organic matter content. Soil Sci. Soc. Amer. Proc. 34:393-396.

FAO-UNESCO. 1971. Soil map of the world 1:5,000,000 Volume IV. South America. UNESCO, París.

FIELDES, M. and Q. PERROT. 1966. The nature of allophane in soils. 3. Rapid field and laboratory test for allophane. New Zeland J. of Sci. 93:623-629.

HARDY, F. 1946. Seasonal fluctuations of soil moisture and nitrate in a humid tropical climate. Trop. Agric. (Trin), 23:40-49.

INTERNATIONAL FERTILITY EVALUATION AND IMPROVEMENT PROGRAM. 1968. The Fertilizer Requirements of Countries in Latin America. Annual Report. Contract AID/csd-287, North Carolina State University.

KAMPRATH, E. J. 1970. Exchangeable aluminum as a criterion for liming leached mineral soils. Soil Sci. Soc. Amer. Proc. 34:252-254.

McCOLLUM, R. E. and C. VALVERDE. 1968. The Fertilization of Potatoes in Perú. Nort Carolina Agric. Exp. Sta. Tech. Bull. 185.

MOORMAN, F. R. 1963. Acid sulfate coils (cat-clays) of the tropics. Soil Sci. 95:271-275.

RYAN, G. and R. K. PERRIN. 1973. The Estimation and Use of a Generalized Response Function for Potatoes in the Sierra of Perú. North Carolina Agric. Exp. Sta. Tech. Bull. 214.

SOIL SURVEY STAFF. 1951. Soil Survey Manual. U. S. Dept. of Agr. Handbook 18.

SOIL SURVREY STAFF. 1960. Soil classification, a comprehensive system 7th approximation. U. S. Dept. of Agric., U. S. Govt. Printing Office, Washington, D. C.

SOIL SURVEY STAFF. 1970. Selected chapters from the unedited text of the Soil Taxonomy of the National Cooperative Soil Survey. U.S.D.A., U. S. Govt. Printing Office, Washington, D. C.

SOPHER, C. D. and R. J. McCRACKEN. 1973. Relationships between soil properties, management practices, and corn yields on South Atlantic Coastal Plain soils. Agron. J. 65:595-600.

U. S. SALINITY LABORATORY STAFF. 1954. Diagnosis and improvement of saline and alkali soils. U. S. Dept. of Agr. Handbook 60. U. S. Govt. Printing Office, Washington, D. C.

WOODRUFF, J. R. and E, J. KAMPRATH. 1965. Phosphorus adsorption maxima as measured by the Langmuir isotherms and its relationship to phosphorus availability. Soil Sci. Soc. Amer. Proc. 29:148-150.

SECTION II

SOIL - PLANT - WATER RELATIONS

7 Soil-water Relations in Oxisols of Puerto Rico and Brazil

JAMES M. WOLF

I INTRODUCCION

In vast areas of the humid tropics soils are strongly leached and very acidic. Soil acidity is commonly associated with aluminum toxicity. These factors create a hostile soil environment which chemically limits the depth of rooting of aluminum sensitive crops. For example, rooting of corn and sorghum is effectively limited to a shallow zone of soil which has been reclaimed by soil amendments. This severely limits the amount of soil-water and nutrients which a crop can utilize.

In the case of water, rooting limitations increase the likelihood of yield decreases when rainfall distribution is anything short of ideal. Many areas of the tropics, Puerto Rico and Central Brazil included, may be characterized by rainfall distributions adequate in total amount but irregular in distribution. For example, during December and January in Central Brazil, it is not uncommon to experience two weeks or more of rainless days often coupled with high solar radiation and high potential evapotranspiration. This is known locally as a "veranico". To assess the potential for successful cropping, information regarding climatic conditions must be combined with data on depth of rooting and superimposed upon those soil physical properties which affect the water supplying characteristics of the soil.

The purpose of this paper is to report on water supplying characteristics of certain Oxisols in Puerto Rico and Brazil and to illustrate how this type of information may be of value in assessing the potential for development in tropical areas.

II METHODOLOGY

The basic objective of the work in Puerto Rico and an ancillary objective of the Brazil work was to determine how much water is stored in the soil and available for crops. For six locations, the relationship between soil-water content and tension, and available water holding capacities of selected soils were determined. In addition, bulk densities, capillary conductivities, lateral water movement and infiltration were evaluated, the results of which will be reported at a later date.

In Puerto Rico tensiometers were installed in 3 m x 3 m plots. The areas were flooded with water and then covered with plastic to present evaporation. Water movement during infiltration and drainage was monitored using the tensiometers. This instrumentation permitted calculation of capillary conductivities and gave information on soil-water tension vs. time relations. Gravimetric determinations of soil-water contents were made at selected tensions for correlation with water contents as determined indirectly using the tensiometers.

A preliminary evaluation of appropriate methodology was conducted during the course of the studies in Puerto Rico. Moisture characterizations were obtained through standard laboratory techniques using both disturbed and undisturbed samples. In the tension range 0-¾ bar, undisturbed soil cores were taken and run in the laboratory using Tempe Cells and pressure plate apparatus. In the same range, the characteristics were determined for disturbed samples. Between 1 and 15 bars, disturbed and undisturbed samples were run on the pressure plate appartus.

There techniques were compared and the following methodology was adopted: That undisturbed soil cores should be used to determine water retention in the wet range (0-¾ bar), and that disturbed samples should be used to measure water retention in the dry range (1-15 bars). An overestimation of soil-water content will be made either by using disturbed samples on the pressure plate in the wet range, or by running undisturbed core samples on the pressure plate apparatus in the dry range. For example, at ⅓ bar, disturbed samples gave up to 19% more water when compared with ⅓ bar determinations on undisturbed core samples. On the other hand, undisturbed core samples at high tensions never completely dewatered due to low capillary conductivities and spatial considerations of the samples.

The importance of low tension determinations was underscored by the Puerto Rico work, in which the bulk of the water was released at less than ¾ bar. Also, disturbance of "undisturbed" cores can affect accuracy. Therefore, in Brazil, we went to a system of *in situ* measurements. Tensiometers and gypsum blocks were installed in growing crops and tension or resistance readings were correlated with soil-water contents determined gravimetrically. In addition, in the tension range 1-15 bars, disturbed samples were run on the pressure plate apparatus. Both in Brazil and in Puerto Rico percent soil water by weight was converted to percent by volume using bulk density factors determined in the field.

While the methods for evaluation of data from this study are limited, they suggest that for both accuracy and time considerations, *in situ* determination of water release characteristics at tensions less than ¾ bar is preferred. Therefore I would recommend techniques similar to those we have used in Brazil where relationships of soil-water content versus tension were determined *in situ* rather than in the laboratory. For Oxisols it is important to determine soil-water properties under the conditions of field structure which the plant experiences rather than under artificial laboratory conditions. This is especially crucial for Oxisols where, as we shall see, the bulk of the available water is held at low tensions, and where, soil structure and not texture is the overriding consideration in determining soil-water release.

III RESULTS AND DISCUSSION

Before reporting on how much water is available in the soils studied, it is first necessary to define the range of water availability. For a lower limit of water availability, good correlation has been established between permanent wilting point and 15 bar percentage. Thus the latter may be taken to mark the lower limit of water availability. This is not to say that water is equally available to plants at these high soil-water tensions. For an upper limit of water availability we have used a water content associated with a soil-water tension of 1/10 bar. This is the approximate tension to which these soils will drain after being saturated and allowed to drain freely in the absence of evapotranspiration (ET).

Fo rthe best estimate of an upper limit to water availability, one should determine soil-water contents gravimetrically in the field after 2-3 days of free drainage, but no evaporation. In lieu of field determinations, the data presented in Figure 1 indicate that the 1/10 bar percentage would be the most appropriate for fixing an upper limit to water availability on Oxisols, regardless of texture.

Presented in Figure 1 are curves which show the effect of water loss by percolation upon soil-water tensions for two soils, a loamy sand and a clay. These data are for the 30-centimeter depth and are from plots

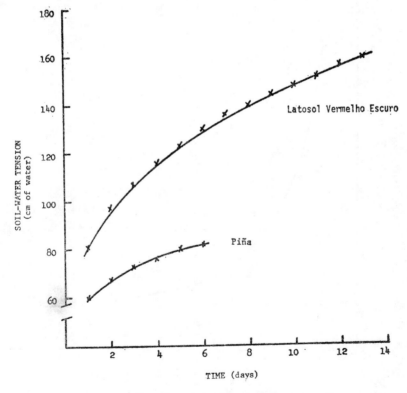

Figure 1. The effect of water loss by percolation upon soil-water tension with time. (Measurements made in the field at a depth of 30 centimeters in a plot covered to prevent evaporation).

covered to prevent evaporation. Soil-water tensions after 2-3 days of free drainage but no evaporation are in the range 1/15 to 1/10 bar. It took more than 80 days for soil-water tensions to reach $1/3$ bar. During this time, tensions continued to change reflecting slow drainage.

Figure 2 is a graph of the deep percolation with time occuring from a 60-centimeter profile on the Latosol Vermelho Escuro (LVE-Brazil). Percolation at 2 days is as large as probable crop evapotranspiration (ET). Even after two weeks, percolation from the covered soil may be as large as 20% of crop ET, reflecting continued drainage of significant amounts of water. If changes in soil-water contents are to be the basis for determining crop water use, it will then be necessary to establish relationships between deep percolation and soil-water content and to subtract this internal drainage component from other soil-water changes which occur in the profile.

The fact that substantial percolation occurs in these soils under unsaturated conditions may have other important management implications.

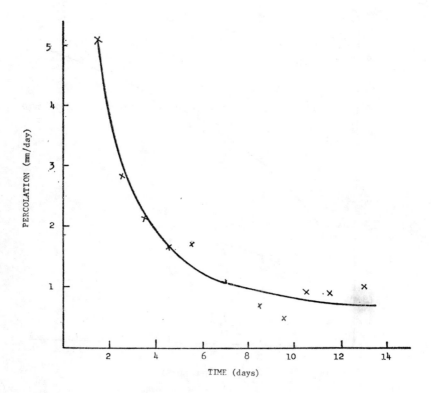

Figure 2. The relationship of the percolation rate with time from a 60-centimeter profile of the LVE. (Determinations made in a covered plot under field conditions).

Miller *et al.*, (1965) and others, have shown that ion movement is tremendously more efficient under unsaturated flow conditions. Since unsaturated flow is substantial in these Oxisols we may expect large amounts of ionic transport and redistribution with time. For example, this can mean continued leaching and loss of fertilizer material many days after a rainfall or irrigation. Equally important, it suggests that liming mateirals may continue to redistribute with time. In these soils, deep lime movement may be a possibility without deep placement of the material. This possibility merits further study.

Presented in Figure 3 are soil-water release curves relating volumetric water and tension for three Oxisols. These have been developed for various depths in each soil but for simplicity only the 30-centimeter depth is presented here. In general, curves for other depths in one profile are similar in Oxisols where horizonation is not pronounced. The similarity in shape of the curves is readily noted, in spite of the fact that two soils, Catalina and LVE are clays, and Piña a loamy sand. One may say that clayey Oxisols simulate a sand in their water release characteristics, although the actual amount in storage between a clay and a sand may differ considerably. In view of the fact that clayey Oxisols, like sands, have very high intake rates, one can also draw the analogy between water movement in the clay system and in a sand. However, the analogy is not complete because it is feasible to effect major changes in water release characteristics in clayey Oxisols by radical changes in soil structure which would be impossible by manipulating a sand.

The abrupt change in water release characteristics between a soil at tensions less than 1 bar and the same soil at tensions greater than 1 bar suggests that there may be two types of water conducting avenues responsible for water movement. These avenues may be termed capillary pores, (micropores between soil particles) and non-capillary pores (macropores between soil aggregates). It might then be hypothesized that the major amount of soil-water movement in the wet range occurs between the surfaces of structurally stable aggregates (or in non-capillary pores), whereas in the dry range, water movement is in the capillary pores and is therefore much more tortuous. These results suggest that structural stability, type of structure and type of clay are more useful parameters than texture for characterizing water relations in these soils.

Use of soil-water release curves allows calculation of water storage. Presented in Table 1 and Figure 4 are measurements of the amount of water stored in the soils studied. The amount of water (in millimeters) stored in the top 30 centimeters of the soil profile was determined to be 36, 50, and 60 mm for Piña, LVE and Catalina respectively. This amount of water is very limited when one realizes that evapotranspiration can be 6 millimeters per day or more. One can compare soil-water storage on Oxisols with similar figures determined for temperate soils. For example, it is not uncommon in California clay loams to have 100 mm of water storage in a 30 cm profile.

Figure 4 compares the water holding capacity for 30- and 60-centimeter rooting depths on 3 Oxisols. For the sandy Piña soil, 75% of the available water is released at tensions between approximately 1/10 and 1 bar. On the LVE, 65% of the available water is released at less than

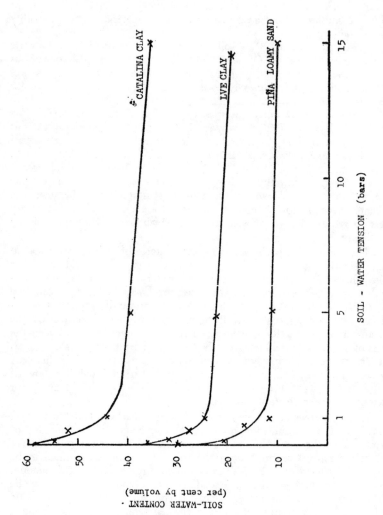

Figure 3. Soil-water release characteristics for three oxisols at the 30 centimeter depth.

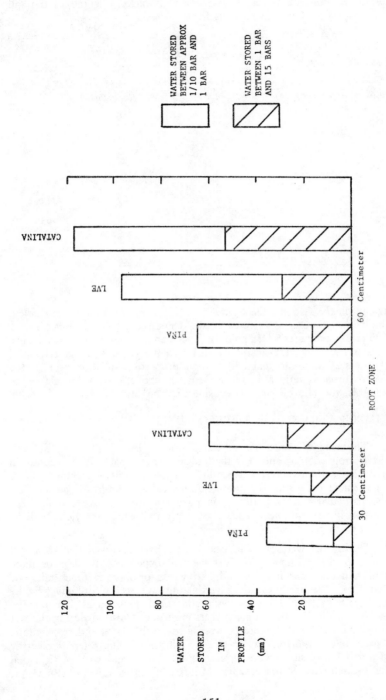

Figure 4. A comparison of water storage capacities within two tension ranges for three oxisols.

Table 1.—Amount of available water (in millimeters) stored in the soil profile at various tensions for three soils.

Soil Moisture Tension	Available H₂O (mm)		
	Piña	LVE	Catalina
bars	30-Centimeter Profile		
Approx. 1/10	36	50	60
Approx. 1/10	8	17	27
Approx. 1	0	0	0
	60-Centimeter Profile		
Approx. 1	65	97	117
Approx. 15	17	29	53
Approx. 15	0	0	0

1 bar and on the Catalina the figure is 55%. Thus for all Oxisols studied, the bulk of the water is released between approximately 1/10 bar and 1 bar. Figure 5 compares water holding capacities for four Puerto Rican soils, two Oxisols and two Ultisols. In contrast to the Oxisols, water release in the Ultisols is more gradual and a high proportion of the water in the tropical Ultisols is only available at tensions above 1 bar. In relation to the Oxisols, the Ultisols may be considered droughty.

IV   IMPLICATIONS FOR DEVELOPMENT

The narrow range of soil-water storage in Oxisols coupled with restricted crop rooting and less than ideal rainfall patterns can result in yields which will vary greatly depending on the rainfall distribution. Since management of these soils for production agriculture requires large fertilizer inputs, particularly phosphorus, it is risky for the farmer to sink large amounts in inputs without adequate assurance that each year yields will be sufficient to recover these investments.

During the wet season in Brasilia, we have observed that corn will wilt after 6 days without rain. Yet we will experience 10 days or more without rain one year in two, and two weeks or more without rain one year in five. We are presently investigating wet season drought severity as measured by probability analysis and field experimentation on the Latosol Vermelho Escuro. In some years even one irrigation during the wet season may make the difference between a reasonable yield and crop failure. The joint research effort in Brasilia by North Carolina State University and Cornell University, (with funding by USAID), and with participation by the research wing of the Brazilian Ministry of Agriculture (EMBRAPA),

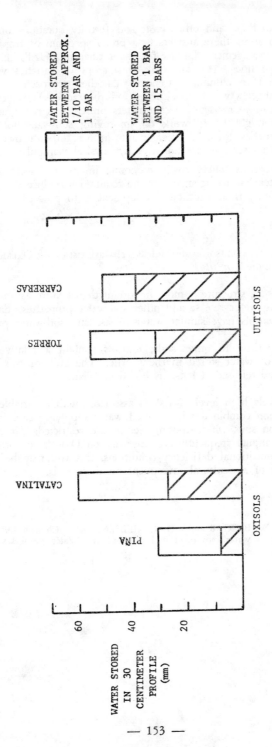

Figure 5. A comparison of water storage capacities within two tension ranges on Puerto Rican oxisols and ultisols.

seeks answers to these and other basic soil fertility questions on Oxisols and attempts to apply these answers to a broad spectrum of tropical soils.

Present management options for the farmer in Brazil's cerrado can take one of two lines. He can work with crops or varieties which are relatively tolerant to aluminum toxicity. Another approach is to work with soil amendments which reclaim the soil root zone. However, liming soil to a depth of more than 30 centimeters presently is not practical. A third approach might be to work on improving soil-water-holding and release characteristics through green manuring or through incorporation of organic residues such as rice hulls, or by physical manipulation.

On these soils where costly economic inputs are necessary, more research and intensive management will be required to reduce the prospects of yield uncertainty if agricultural development is to proceed.

V SUMMARY

1) The low tension soil-water release characteristics of Oxisols should be determined *in situ*.

2) For Oxisols, structure is more important than texture as an index to predicting water release and other soil-water properties. Sandy and clayey Oxisols have similar water release and soil-water properties.

3) In comparison to other soils, Oxisols contain a relatively small amount of water stored in the profile. The bulk of this water is stored and released at tensions less than 1 bar.

4) A relatively high level of risk is associated with a variable rainfall distribution combined with limited water supplying capacity, particularly on soils where rooting depths are restricted. Since a high level of inputs frequently are necessary on Oxisols to correct toxic and/or nutritional deficiency conditions, this risk may be a severe inhibitor of agricultural investment on these soils.

VI REFERENCE

MILLER, R. J., J. W. BIGGAR and y D. R. NIELSEN. 1965. Chloride Displacement in relation to water movement and distribution. Water Resourses Research 1: 63-73.

8 Soil-water Relations in Soils Derived From Volcanic Ash of Central America

WARREN M. FORSYTHE

I INTRODUCTION

Soils derived from volcanic ash cover a substantial area of Central America. They are to be found associated with the chain of volcanoes that begins with the Barú volcano in Panamá and ends in Southern México. Because of west-bound winds, most of the ash has been deposited on the Pacific slopes. Soils derived from ash are to be found mainly in the highlands and Pacific slopes of Chiriquí Province in Panamá, the Central Plateau of Costa Rica, the area between Granada, León and Chinandega in Nicaragua, and in the highland valleys and Pascific slopes of El Salvador, Guatemala and Honduras. There are no volcanic cones in Honduras (Martini 1969). Soils derived from volcanic rock, alluvial deposits with varying mixtures of sedimentary and other rock material, are to be bound associated some areas of Africa or Brazil, and this has been attributed to rejuvenation with soils derived from volcanic ash.

The purpose of this paper is to give a perspective of the information and research done in Central America on soil-water relations of these soils. Climate, soil water retention, infiltration, drainage, and erosion, shall be considered. These subjects will be treated for the range of soils from fresh ash to ones in an advanced state of development and weathering, considering the above-mentioned countries.

II DISCUSSION

Range of Soil Genesis

The ideas of Fields (1955), Dudal and Soepraptohardjo (1960), Besoaín (1969), Martini (1969), and Flach (1969), in relation to the development of soils derived from volcanic ash, may be summarized in Figure 1, and will be used to consider the soil-water relations of these soils. It appears that most of the Latosols in Central America derived from volcanic ash are Ultisols and are not as old (Oxisols) as those found in some areas of Africa or Brazil, and this has been attributed to rejuvenation

Climate and Water Balance

In general, average annual temperatures range from about 25-30°C at sea level to about 22°C at 600 m altitude on the Atlantic side and at

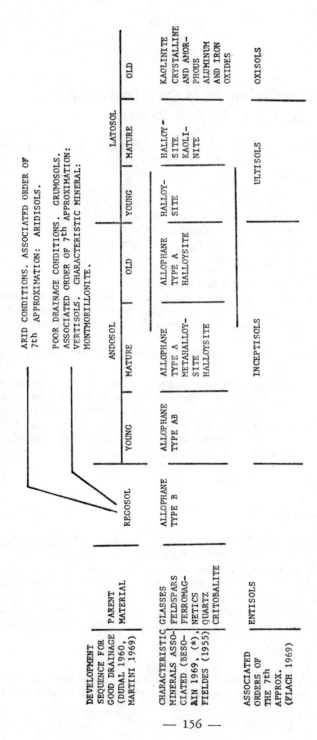

Figure 1.   Development sequence of soils derived from volcanic ash, with associated characteristic mineralogy and soil orders according to the seventh approximation.

(*)   Personal communication.

800 m on the Pacific side. At 2000 m altitude average annual temperatures in Costa Fica are around 10°C (Coen 1958, Vives 1971). Rainfall on the Pacific slopes range from 1000-2500 mm annually, occurring during 6 to 9 months of the year, usually between May and December. Due to predominant winds from the East, the Atlantic slopes have more rainfall, which ranges from 2500 mm to 5000 mm annually, generally with no pronounced dry season (Martini 1969, República de Nicaragua 1970, Oficina de Planificación 1966).

Table 1 gives rainfall, temperature and pan evaporation data for three areas of Central América. In Costa Rica, Turrialba represents the beginning of the Atlantic climate, having just one month of a slight moisture deficit (rainfall-pan evaporation) of 45 mm and eleven months of moisture excess ranging from 9 to 269 mm with a monthly average of 137 mm, while Alajuela represents the beginning of the Pacific climate having five months of deficit ranging from 108 to 207 mm with a monthly average of 163 mm, and seven months of excess ranging from 65 to 206 mm with a monthly average of 139 mm. Chinandega, in Nicaragua, repre· sents the Pacific coastal climate with five months of deficit ranging from 117 to 170 mm with a monthly average of 142 mm, and seven months of excess ranging from 10 to 490 mm with a monthly average of 175 mm. It is interesting to note that although the Pacific areas have a long period of strong water deficit, the months of excess are in general more intense than those of the Turrialba area. However, Turrialba represents the starting point of the Atlantic climate with an average annual rainfall of approximately 2600 mm.

We should expect intense monthly rainfall excesses in the Atlantic zone where the average annual rainfall varies from 2500-5000 mm. For example, three years of rainfall data in the Santa Clara farm in Guápiles, Costa Rica (Jaramillo and Jorge 1969), which is to be found on the Atlantic plains (100 m altitude, 10°13'N and 83°44'W), indicate an average annual rainfall of 4619 mm, with twelve months of excess ranging from 68 to 428 mm with a monthly average of 277 mm. In this case the Blaney-Criddle formula was used to estimate potential evapotranspiration. The rainfall excesses are more intense than those of Turrialba, Alajuela or Chinandega. The excess rainfall in the Atlantic zone suggests the need for drainage and water control. The Pacific zone experiences intense excesses and intense deficits of water, suggesting the need for drainage and water control on the one hand coupled with water conservation and irrigation on the other. There are several small irrigation projects in the Pacific area.

Since very few weather stations in Central America have type A pans which are considered one of the most reliable indices of potential evapotranspiration (Legarda and Forsythe 1972) it is important to find formulas to evaluate this quantity, that are accurate and that can use the information available from the modest weather stations in the area. Legarda and Forsythe (1972) found that the formulas of García-López (multiplied by a factor of 1.23), Papadakis (multiplied by a factor of 1.22) and Van Bavel (multiplied by a factor of 1.78) had the best characteristics of correlation and agreement for the Central American and Caribbean area ranging from Costa Rica to Jamaica. It is important to point out that

Table 1.—Monthly mean temperature in °C, rainfall and pan evaporation (USWB Type A) in mm for some areas of Central America (CATIE, 1973; Universidad de Costa Rica, Estación Experimental 1970; Oficina de Planificación, Nicaragua, 1966).

Location	Parameter	MONTH											
		J	F	M	A	M	J	J	A	S	O	N	D
Turrialba, C. R.	Rainfall 1944-70	176	148	79	135	225	285	270	234	250	249	283	348
602 m altitude, 9°53'N and 83°28'W	Temperature 1958-70	21.0	21.1	21.9	22.3	23.1	23.2	22.8	22.8	23.0	22.8	22.1	21.4
	Evaporation 1968-73	97	103	123	126	120	106	96	103	112	115	85	79
UCR, Exp. Sta. Alajuela, C. R.	Rainfall 1961-69	4	15	4	63	8	314	223	231	323	315	170	28
840 m altitude, 10°01'N and 84°16'W	Temperature 1961-69	23.0	23.4	24.2	24.2	23.3	22.5	22.8	22.5	22.3	22.0	22.2	22.5
	Evaporation 1969-70	179	217	211	187	160	114	107	114	117	116	105	136
Chinandega, Nic.	Rainfall 1958-65	0	5	0	50	145	397	257	205	380	610	130	10
90 m altitude, 12°39'N and 87°03'W	Temperature 1958-65	23.9	24.2	26.4	27.0	26.8	26.2	26.6	26.4	26.0	25.7	25.2	24.1
	Evaporation 1958-65	152	117	170	167	135	125	145	135	125	120	112	138

Thornthwaite's widely used formula was considered unsuitable for use in this area, having poor agreement and correlation. Poor performance of Thornthwaite's formula was also found in another tropical area, Pasaje, Ecuador (17 m altitude, 3°20'S and 79°50'W) by Hasan and Jones (1972). It is interesting to note that the three most successful formulas found by Legarda and Forsythe (1972) use relative humidity or try to evaluate it in their computation. Considering the data of García and López (1970), Legarda and Forsythe (1972) and Hasan and Jones (1972), it is the writer's impression that for a given location found in the tropical belt between 15°N and 15°S, variations in relative humidity play a dominant role in changes in evaporation and thus evapotranspiration.

The Central American area experiences high rainfall intensities as can be appreciated in Tables 2 and 3. This means that rains can have high erosive power and a formidable flood-producing capacity. During December 1970 at Turrialba, Costa Rica, a rainfall intensity of 120 mm/hour was experienced for 10 minutes (CATIE, Turrialba, 1973). In El Salvador during August of 1936 a 10 minute rain with an intensity of 1800 mm/ hour occurred (Bourne *et al.*, 1946). Needless to say, this country suffers from severe erosion problems.

Soil Water Retention

In Nicaragua, soils of recent ash and other Entisols are to be found near volcanoes such as Cosigüina and Momotombo. These soils have a gravelly, loamy-sand texture and their water holding capacity is extremely low (República de Nicaragua 1970). This is due to the presence of a small quantity of allophane.

The Inceptisols, which include the sub-order Andepts, range from the young Andepts with a predominance of allophane in the clay complex and low bulk densities (0.3-0.7 g/ml), to the old Andepts which tend to have a predominance of halloysite mixed with allophane in the clay complex and bulk densities ranging from 0.7 to 0.9 g/ml. The young Andepts are found in areas of continuously high rainfall (3000-4000 mm) and have a high volumetric available water holding capacity ($1/3$-15 bars) of 20 to 30% for samples conserved at field moisture before analysis (Forsythe *et al.* 1969, Forsythe and Vázquez 1973, Luzuriaga 1970). Examples of this soil are the Birrisito and Cervantes series found between Turrialba and Cartago together with soils found between Cartago and the Irazú volcano, and around the area of San José de la Montaña and Vara Blanca in Costa Rica. These soils generally are Dystrandepts. Their gravimetric water retention for samples conserved at field moisture range from 90-144% at $1/3$ bar to 50-85% at 15 bars suction. Their low bulk densities explain the resulting volumetric available water holding capacity of 20-30%.

The old Inceptisols with a predominance of halloysite in the clay complex are found in areas that experience a dry season. Colmet-Daage *et al.*, 1968 and Forsythe *et al.*, 1969 identified such soils in the León-Chinandega coastal zone of Nicaragua. The Alajuela-Heredia area (Forsythe and Vásquez 1973) of Costa Rica has similar soils. Available volumetric water retention ranges from 18-25% for samples conserved at field moisture.

Table 2.—Rainfall intensities for the upper watershed of the Reventado river, Costa Rica. Pacayas Station. Annual rainfall 1456 mm, altitude 1735 m, 9°55'N and 83°48'W (ICE, 1965).

	RETURN INTERVAL OF 5 YEARS				
Time (minutes)	5	10	15	30	60
Intensity (mm/h)	158	122	101	77	50
	RETURN INTERVAL OF 10 YEARS				
Time (minutes)	5	10	15	30	60
Intensity (mm/h)	185	143	120	85	57
	RETURN INTERVAL OF 50 YEARS				
Time (minutes)	5	10	15	30	60
Intensity (mm/h)	275	215	180	125	88

Table 3.—Rainfall intensities of El Pito Chocolá, Suchitepéquez, Guatemala. Annual rainfall 3991 mm, altitude 830 m, 14°37'N and 91° 25'W. (Data of E. García Martíuez, 1965, reported by Neira, 1970).

	RETURN INTERVAL OF 5 YEARS				
Time (minutes)	5	10	15	30	60
Intensity (mm/h)	117	112	106	94	75
	RETURN INTERVAL OF 10 YEARS				
Time (minutes)	5	10	15	30	60
Intensity (mm/h)	122	117	111	98	82

When soil samples of Andepts for moisture retention studies are previously air-dried, a loss in moisture retention has been observed (Colmet-Daage and Cucalón 1965; Forsythe et al., 1969; Forsythe and Vásquez 1973). A young Andept of Costa Rica (Birrisito series) with allophane being the predominant clay mineral was studied by Forsythe and Vásquez (1973) and was found to lose about 45% of its volumetric available water holding capacity, when the samples were previously air-dried. A more mature Andept with metahalloysite as the principal clay mineral (Alajuela series) was found to lose approximately 30% of its volumetric available water holding capacity. Colmet-Daage et al., (1968) found about a 20% loss of the available water holding capacity on airdryirng a similar soil close to the Masaya volcano in Nicaragua. However, soils in the León-Chinandega area showed no loss in water retention.

In the study of Forsythe and Vásquez (1973) a logarithmic function was found to provide a good fit for the plotting of soil moisture versus suction data. The losses of total porosity per unit mass on drying, which is also equal to the reduction in the bulk specific volume, can be used as a mechanism to explain the loss of gravimetric water retention. Besides the magnitude, there is an interesting difference between the water loss of the *Alajuela* series and that that of the Birrisito series. Air-drying caused no significant loss in the 15 bar value for the Alajuela soil, whereas the Birrisito soil, which has allophane as the predominant clay material, lost approximately 36% of its 15 bar value. As a result of all these effects, Forsythe (1972, 1974) has proposed a standard procedure for determining soil water retention of soils derived from volcanic ash, using undisturbed samples 1 cm deep which have been conserved at field moisture. This procedure uses the standard pressure plate apparatus.

There are older Inceptisols which have been considered as Latosols because of their red color. Such soils as the Paraíso and Colorado series (Gavande 1968, Macías 1969, Knox and Maldonado 1969) of Costa Rica, are examples. Knox and Maldonado (1969) consider these soils as borderline cases between Humitropepts and Tropohumults. These soils have a volumetric available moisture retention of only 11-13% in spite of a very high clay content (Colorado 74-87% and Paraíso 77-92%). Soils such as Dolega clay of Panamá (Tirado 1970) and the red soils found 23 km west of Managua and in Nandaime (Colmet-Daage et al., 1968; Forsythe et al., 1969) are probably similar to the above-mentioned soils. Red clay soils are also to be found in El Salvador (Bourne et al., 1946; Rico 1964). The young and mature Andepts previously discussed have a high total porosity which ranges between 63-76%, whereas the older Andepts and incipient Ultisols have total porosities between 59-71%. As a result, these soils at field capacity (⅓ bar moisture) have abundant air space.

Many soils derived from volcanic ash of Nicaragua have a hardpan (talpetate) whose depth can vary from 30 to 90 cm (República de Nicaragua 1970). The shallow hardpans can restrict root development and thus the water storage capacity of the soil profile. Similar soils are found in El Salvador (Bourne et al., 1946; Rico 1964) and Guatemala (Simmons et al., 1959).

Soils of recent ash and other Entisols found near volcanoes such as Cosigüina and Momotombo in Nicaragua are reported to have rapid infiltration (República de Nicaragua 1970). However, fresh ash fallen from volcanoes that erupt hot ash tend to form crusts near the volcano, presumably due to heat cementation. The 1963 eruption of the Irazú volcano of Costa Rica produced such crusts which have restricted infiltration. The resulting watershed produces a high percentage of run-off, and this is considered one of the contributing factors to a disastrous rock and mud avalanche which occurred in Cartago in December of that year (ICE 1965).

The Inceptisols of all ages except those with shallow hardpans show high infiltration rates. The Alajuela and Colorado series of Costa Rica, mentioned earlier, have initial infiltration rates (by flooding) of between 18-42 cm/hour and after a two hour time lapse, of between 10-12 cm/hour. It is interesting to note that the Colorado series with 74-87% clay had an initial infiltration rate of 42 cm/hour and a 2 hour rate of 12 cm/hour.

Inceptisols derived from volcanic ash and mixed with other parent material demonstrate the ash influence. The Buenos Aires and San Jorge series in the Rivas area of Nicaragua have initial infiltration rates of 45-70 cm/hour and 2 hour rates of 7-21 cm/hour (Valencia 1961). Valley soils derived from volcanic alluvium show a range of infiltration rates according to age and topographic position. Mazariegos (1965, 1966) in his study of the Valley of Asunción Mita, Jutiapa, in Guatemala, has found soils with 2 hour infiltration rates ranging from 9.9 cm/hour to 0.4 cm/hour. Vertisols are formed from volcanic ash alluvium in mountain valleys and coastal lowlands. In Nicaragua (República de Nicaragua 1970) these soils are described as having imperfect drainage. The soils with lower infiltration rates found by Mazariegos in Guatemala are clay-textured and appear to be Vertisols.

The high infiltration rate and deep profile of the volcanic Inceptisols easily gives them a classification of hydrological group A (minimum infiltration rate 0.76-1.14 cm/hour, according to Musgrave and Holtan 1964). This hydrological classification of the U.S. Soil Conservation Service rates the soil as having high water absorption capacities for U.S. rainfall intensities, and thus giving rise to relatively little run-off. However, it appears that the very high rainfall and rainfall intensities experienced in some Central American areas would justify a study of a classification for this area.

When irrigation is considered another infiltration classification is used. The U.S. Bureau of Reclamation (1953) considers a soil to be first class for flood irrigation if its 2-hour infiltration rate varies from 2.0-6.4 cm/hour. Soils with slower or faster intake rates have lower ratings. This is due to the difficulty of obtaining a satisfactory rate of advance of water on the soil surface with manageable water flows and the consequent poor distribution of water along the furrows due to excessive intake at the beginning of the run. Thus, the high infiltration rates of the Inceptisols makes flood irrigation difficult and inefficient. These soils are suitable for sprinker irrigation or flood irrigation with very short furrows. The author has observed that some farmers in the area are using 25 m long furrows on these types of soils. However, the problem of inefficiency of application should be studied. The difficulties of irrigating this type of soil in Nicaragua were pointed out by Valencia (1961).

Drainage

The need for drainage during periods of excess water both on the Atlantic and Pacific zones can be appreciated from the weather data. Both surface and internal drainage are important. Because of the quantity and intensity of the rainfall, standing water is to be found on relatively flat soils (less than 3% slope) with 2-hours infiltration rates of 2-4 cm/hour (or less) under Turrialba conditions. This occurs principally during the months that have more than 150 mm of excess rain in relation to pan evaporation. Water accumulates and stands in the depressions of unsmoothed land, and crop growth is affected. Field observations indicated that beans *(Phaseolus vulgaris* L.) were severely affected by standing water. This damage was always associated with root diseases. However, Forsythe and Pinchinat (1971) under controlled greenhouse conditions with fumigated soil, showed that one flooding of 12 hours duration per week is enough to lower bean yields of by 90%. This was considered a direct effect of flooding, because no pathogenic diseases were recognized. An effective measure used to combat this problem has been cultivation on cambered beds of 6 to 12 meters in width. With this system the soil depressions can be smoothed out and quick surface drainage under the rainy tropical conditions of Turrialba is provided.

Field observations in Turrialba have indicated that sweet potatoes, cassava, corn, sugar cane, and African stargrass, are also affected by standing water.

Internal drainage is necessary in soils derived from volcanic ash during periods of excess water when a shallow water table is produced by the topographic conditions of mountain valleys or coastal lowlands. Under Turrialba weather conditions for a soil of the U.S. Conservation Service hydrological class C (2-hour infiltration rate of 0.38-0.13 cm/hour) a drainage coefficient of 8.7 mm/day has been estimated. For more infiltrable soils this figure for the same area will be greater. In the Atlantic and Pacific zones where monthly rainfall excesses are greater than that of Turrialba, the drainage coefficients should be larger. The Inceptisols derived from volcanic ash are generally described as of high permeability. The Baudrit series of Alajuela, Costa Rica (Chirinos 1957) studied by Wydler (1969) has a subsoil hydraulic conductivity of 3 m/day, which may be considered high. The Old Vega series in Guápiles, Costa Rica (Jiménez 1972) was studied by Jaramillo and Jorge (1969) and its subsoil was found to have a hydraulic conductivity of 3.2 m/day.

Inceptisols with hardpans have impeded drainage and permeability and Vertisols are described as having impeded drainage and low permeability (República de Nicaragua 1970).

The high rainfall intensities observed in the Central American area indicate the strong erosive power that these rains have. Erosion has generally been noticed in the Pacific area of Central America and is outstanding in El Salvador (Bourne 1946) and the Pacific zone of Nicaragua (República de Nicaragua 1970). Erosion is also observed in the Central Plateau and Pacific zone of Costa Rica (Torres 1950). Deforestation, cultivation on steep slopes and the lack of conservation practices contribute to this problem. Soils derived from volcanic ash with shallow hardpans have been observed to suffer severely from erosion in Nicaragua due to their reduced infiltration (República de Nicaragua 1970). A quantitative study of the individual factors which contribute to the problem would help in a rational planning and evaluation of present conservation practices. Some of these factors are the erosive power of the rainfall and the erodability of the soils. In Panama extensive erosion has been observed on steep and rolling terrain. Sheet erosion has been noted on overgrazed land, and terrain burned-over as a result of slash and burn agriculture. It is also noticed where poor farm practices have left the land exposed (República de Panamá 1970).

III   CONCLUSION

As the Central American population pressure increases, there is an increasing necessity to use more efficiently the exploitable soil-water resources of the area and to conserve valuable watershed and forest reserves, which are threatened by population penetration. In the areas where there is water deficit, soil water conservation and irrigation contribute to increased productivity of the land and in areas where there is an excess of water, drainage and water control has a similar effect on the land. There is a great opportunity to apply this technology more widely in the area. All the Central American countries have small irrigation projects and the number is increasing. There is a need to apply drainage technology more widely. A more extensive quantitative evaluation of the climatic, soil and water resources for the purposes of agriculture and conservation is needed in order to facilitate tehir efficient use.

IV   SUMMARY

The Atlantic zone of Central America has intense water excesses (rainfall-pan evaporation) which require surface and internal drainage. The Pacific zone has 6 to 9 months of intense water excesses and the rest of the year experiences intense deficits, requiring irrigation in addition to drainage. Relative humidity appears to be the dominating factor in the evaporation of the area, and high rainfall intensities promote erosion and flooding. Young and mature Andepts have a high available water holding capacity but its evaluation is lowered if samples are previously air-dried. Old Andepts, many of which have been called Latosols because of their red color, have medium capacities. Inceptisols of volcanic ash without hardpans have high infiltration rates and hydraulic conductivity. Water erosion is a problem in the Pacific zone. Stress is made on the need to apply irrigation and drainage technology in Central America, and to carry out a more extensive quantitative evaluation of the climatic, soil and water resources for the purposes of agriculture and conservation.

V REFERENCES

BESOAIN, E. 1969. Clay mineralogy of volcanic ash soils. *In:* Panel on Volcanic Ash Soils in Latin America. Turrialba, Costa Rica, IICA-FAO. B. 1.1-16.

BOURNE, W. C. *et al.* 1946. Preliminary survey of conservation possibilities in El Salvador. Servicio Cooperativo Interamericano de Salud Pública de El Salvador, 167 p.

BUREAU of RECLAMATION (U. S.). 1953. Land classification handbook. U. S. Dept. Interior, Bureau Reclam. Publ. V., Part 2, 53 pp.

CATIE. Boletín meteorológico 1944-73. Turrialba, Costa Rica.

CHIRINOS, H. 1952. Levantamiento agrológico de la Estación Experimental Agrícola de la Universidad de Costa Rica. Tesis. Univ. de Costa Rica, 107 p.

COEN, E. 1958. Algunos aspectos sobre el clima de Costa Rica. Universidad de Costa Rica, 11 p.

COLMET-DAAGE, F. and CUCALON, F. 1965. Caractères hydriques de certains sols des régions bananières d'Equateur. Fruits 20:19-23.

COLMET-DAAGE, F. *et al.* 1968. Caractéristiques de quelques sols dérivés de cendres volcaniques de la Côte Pacifique de Nicaragua. ORSTOM, (Mimeographed).

DUDAL, R. and SOEPRAPTOHARDJO, M. 1960. Some considerations on the genetic relationship between Latosols and Andosols in Java (Indonesia). 7th Intern. Cong. Soil Sci., Madison, Wisc., USA. IV:229-236.

FIELDES, M. 1955. Clay mineralogy of New Zeland soils. Part 2. Allophane and related mineral colloids. New Zealand J. of Sci. and Tech. 37:336-350.

FLACH, K. 1969. The use of the 7th Approximation for the classification of soils from volcanic ash. *In:* Panel on Volcanic Ash Soil in Latin America. Turrialba, Costa Rica, IICA-FAO. A.7.1-18.

FORSYTHE, W. M. 1972. Proposed technique to avoid the effect of air-drying on the water retention of soils derived from volcanic ash. *In:* II Panel on Volcanic Ash Soils of America, June 18-24, 1972, Pasto, Colombia. IICA-Universidad de Nariño. (In press).

FORSYTHE, W. M. 1975. Manual de Laboratorio de Física de Suelos. IICA, Turrialba, Costa Rica. 212 p.

FORSYTHE, W. M., GAVANDE, S. A. and GONZALEZ, M. 1969. Physical properties of soils derived from volcanic ash with consideration of some soils of Latin America. *In:* Panel on Volcanic Ash Soils in Latin America. Turrialba, Costa Rica, IICA-FAO. B. 3.1-6.

FORSYTHE, W. M. and PINCHINAT, A. M. 1971. Tolerancia de la variedad de frijol "27-R" a la inundación. Turrialba 21:228-231.

FORSYTHE, W. M. and VASQUEZ, O. 1973. Effectc of air-drying on the water retention curves of disturbed samples of three soils of Costa Rica derived from volcanic ash. Turrialba, 23:200-207.

GARCIA MARTINEZ, E. 1965. Curva de intensidad de lluvias para Guatemala. Tesis de grado para optar el título de Ingeniero Civil. Guatemala.

GARCIA, J. and LOPEZ, J. 1970. Fórmula para el cálculo de la evapotranspiración potencial adaptada al trópico (15° N - 15° S). Agronomía Tropical (Venezuela) 20(5):335-345.

GAVANDE, S. A. 1968. Water retention characteristics of some Costa Rican soils. Turrialba 18:34-38.

HASAN, M. R. and JONES, P. S. 1972. Measured and predicted evaporation at Pasaje, Ecuador. Proc. ASCE. IR3. 98:511-516.

INSTITUTO COSTARRICENSE DE ELECTRICIDAD (ICE). 1965. Informe sobre el problema del río Reventado. San José, Costa Rica, ICE, octubre 1965. 312 p.

JARAMILLO, R. and JORGE M. 1969. Establecimiento de una metodología para estudios futuros de drenaje de plantaciones de banano. Informe de progreso N° 1. Octubre 1969. Sociedad Agrícola Industrial San Cristóbal, S. A., San José, Costa Rica. 19 p.

JIMENEZ, T. 1972. Génesis, clasificación y capacidad de uso de algunos suelos de la región Atlántica de Costa Rica. Tesis, Univ. de Costa Rica, 180 p.

KNOX, E. G. and MALDONADO, F. 1969. Soils from volcanic ash. Excursion from Turrialba to Volcán Irazú. In: Panel on Volcanic Ash Soils in Latin America. Turrialba, Costa Rica, IICA-FAO. A.8.1-12.

LEGARDA, L. and FORSYTHE, W. M. 1972. Estudio comparativo entre la evaporación calculada por varias fórmulas y la evaporación de tanques, medida en tres lugares tropicales. Turrialba 22:282-292.

LUZURIAGA, C. 1970. Propiedades morfológicas, físicas y químicas y clasificación de seis andosoles de Costa Rica. Tesis Mag. Sc. Turrialba, Costa Rica, IICA, 159 p.

MACIAS, M. 1969. Propiedades morfológicas, físicas, químicas y clasificación de ocho "Latosoles" de Costa Rica. Tesis Mag. Sc. Turrialba, Costa Rica, IICA, 193 p.

MARTINI, J. A. 1969. Geographic distribution and properties af ash-derived soils in Central America. In: Panel on Volcanic Ash Soils in Latin America, Turrialba, Costa Rica, IICA-FAO. A.5.1-17.

MAZARIEGOS, A. 1965. Estudio detallado de suelos y reconocimiento agrológico general para irrigación del Valle de Asunción Mita, Jutiapa, Ministerio de Agricultura, Guatemala, 246 p.

MAZARIEGOS, A. 1966. Estudio de las constantes físicas de los suelos del Valle de Asunción Mita, Jutiapa. Tesis. Univ. de San Carlos de Guatemala, 76 p.

MUSGRAVE, G. W. and HOLTAN, H. N. 1964. Infiltration. In: Handbook of Applied Hydrology, Section 12. Ven Te Chow (editor). New York, McGraw-Hill.

NIERA, H. 1970. Las crecidas en los ríos Achiguate y Guacalate en setiembre de 1969. Naciones Unidas, Programa para el Desarrollo, Organización Meteorológica Mundial. Gobiernos de Costa Rica, El Salvador, Guatemala, Honduras, Nicaragua y Panamá. Naciones Unidas, San José, Costa Rica, Publ. N° 59. 63 p.

OFICINA DE PLANIFICACION (NICARAGUA). 1966. Natural resources-catastral inventory Nicaraguan pilot project. USAID. Inter-American Geodetic Survey. Fort Clayton, Canal Zone.

REPUBLICA DE NICARAGUA. 1970. Reconnaisssance study for the agricultural development of the Pacific zone. Tahal Consulting Eng. Ltd., Tel Aviv. Banco Nacional de Nicaragua.

REPUBLICA DE PANAMA. 1970. Final report on the "Catastro rural de tierras y aguas de Panamá". Vol. I. Rep. de Panamá, Servicio de Investigación, Ministerio de Agricultura y Ganadería. 504 p.

RICO, M. 1964. Report on soils of volcanic ash origin in El Salvador. *In:* Meeting on the Classification and Correlation of Soils from Volcanic Ash. Tokyo, FAO. pp. 23-29.

SIMMONS, C. S., TARANO, J. and PINTO, J. 1969. Clasificación de reconocimiento de los suelos de la República de Guatemala. Instituto Agropecuario Nacional. Edit. Ministerio de Educación Pública, Guatemala. 1.000 p.

TIRADO, G. A. 1970. Propiedades morfológicas, físicas y químicas y clasificación de ocho "Latosoles de Panamá. Tesis Mag. Sc. Turrialba, Costa Rica, IICA, 58 p.

TORRES, A. 1950. Algunos tópicos sobre erosión y conservación de suelos para Costa Rica. Suelo Tico IV:55-61.

UNIVERSIDAD DE COSTA RICA, ESTACION EXPERIMENTAL. Boletín meteorológico 1961-1970. Alajuela, Costa Rica.

VALENCIA, R. 1961. Estudio de suelos del proyecto de irrigación de Rivas. FAO. Ministerio de Agricultura y Ganadería, Managua, Nicaragua, 125 p.

VIVES, L. 1971. Tabulación para uso agrícola de los datos climáticos de Costa Rica. Universidad de Costa Rica. 222 p.

WYDLER, R. 1969. Asistencia técnica en riego al Gobierno de Costa Rica. Resumen de los trabajos realizados en el período noviembre 1967-agosto 1969. FAO. 61 p.

9 Soil-water Relations in Upland Rice

S. K. DeDATTA, F. G. FAYE and R. N. MALLICK

I INTRODUCTION

Since upland rice is grown without irrigation, the intensity and duration of moisture stress often explain the low yields obtained at the farm level (Jana and De Datta, 1971; De Datta and Beachell, 1972).

The moisture stress effects on rice or any other plant result from the function of water within the plant. Low moisture supply and high water loss decrease the plant's water content and cause water stress. Therefore, moisture stress occurs frequently in upland rice because of uneven or inadequate rainfall and rapid drainage due to coarse soil texture or to rolling topography.

As early as 1935, Ueda in Japan reported that both grain yield and dry matter production of rice were highest in the submerged plots and they decreased with decrease in soil moisture content.

Senewiratne and Mikkelsen (1961) and Gunawardena (1966) in evaluating the growth habits of upland and lowland rice, noted that plants subjected to low-moisture treatment showed chlorosis, reduced leaf area, slow leaf development, and delayed internode elongation. Kato (1968) reported that rice plants cultivated on upland fields required much more water than plants on lowland fields to produce equal weights of dry matter. He related the inefficiency of rice plants grown under nonflooded conditions in producing dry matter to the internal water deficit which hinders the assimilation and translocation of solutes.

In the past, physiological processes and conditions of rice plants were mostly correlated with soil moisture content. Chakladar (1946) observed that no rice plants grown under 33 percent saturation formed seeds, though some flowered, while plants grown under 75 and 50 percent saturation formed seeds.

There is a great deal of controversy on how much water the rice plant needs to produce normal yield. Briggs and Shantz (1914) in the United States remarked that rice needs about the same amount of water as do other cereals. Chandra Mohan in India (1965) stated, however, that the water requirement of rice is larger than that of any other crop of a similar field duration and that it varies with soil texture, climate, cultural practices, and duration of the variety grown. According to Halm (1967), rice performs better in submerged and in saturated soils than in soil at field capacity.

Even in humid upland rice areas, dry periods often occur during the growing season of the crop, at least in the upper portion of the soil surface. For example, during a stress period (45 to 60 days after emergence), Krupp *et al.,* (1972) observed that the upland variety Palawan continued to produce roots while tiller production and leaf area development were retarded. The above-ground portions of IR5 plants, on the other hand, continued to develop although rooting was retarded.

Rice yields at field capacity under upland (aerobic) conditions could be low due to iron deficiency on neutral and alkaline soils and manganese and aluminum toxicity on acid soil (Ponnamperuma and Castro, 1972). Part of the yield decrease reported by Ponnamperuma and Castro (1972), however could be due to moisture stress because to keep the soil aerobic, soil moisture tension may rise to 15 centibars (cb) or more which is enough to reduce the grain yield of rice by 1 t/ha (De Datta *et al.,* 1973a). The question is how much yield reduction at low soil moisture tension (around 15 cb) is due to moisture stress in the plant and how much is due to deficiency of nutrients such as nitrogen and iron at that tension?

With lowland rice, we reported earlier (De Datta *et al.,* 1973b) a distinct interaction between soil moisture tension and nitrogen status of plant and soil. At most soil moisture tensions, the grain yields were higher with higher nitrogen levels, and they were much higher with improved varieties (IR20, IR22, and IR24) than with traditional varieties (Peta, Sigadis, and Intan).

Since moisture is more limiting in upland than in lowland rice ,the nitrogen status of soil and plant in upland rice (or in upland crops) is closely associated with the moisture regime in the soil. When moisture supply is low, nitrogen supply is also low, since nitrogen is present close to plant roots and enters the plant's conductive systems chiefly through the water uptake system (Fried and Shapiro, 1961; Barber, 1962; Barber *et al.,* 1963; Bartholomew, 1971). It a low soil moisture level, the soluble nitrogen close to the root zone is not absorbed by the plants grown under upland conditions But soil moisture conditions around the root zone and root activity greatly influence nitrogen uptake by plants under upland conditions (Bartholomew, 1971). Occasional rainfall during dry weather causes the upland crop to look greener and more vigorous, a response generally attributed to an increase in the supply of moisture and soil nitrogen. A much higher percentage of tracer nitrogen was recovered by corn when the rainfall was high during the experimental period. On the other hand, when the soil moisture content decreases, the ratio of nitrogen uptake to water uptake may also decrease (Bartholomew, 1971).

Tisdale and Nelson (1966) stated that uptake of cations and anions increases as soil moisture tension is decreased from the permanent wilting percentage to field capacity. Water held at moisture tension above the wilting point can contain nitrate but would not transport it to the roots; thus, in some soil systems a large amount of nitrogen becomes unavailable to the plants. Soil water is therefore the most important single factor for nitrogen absorption.

Recently, Jana and De Datta (1971) reported that the optimum soil moisture condition for high grain yield and nitrogen response appeared to be between the maximum water holding capacity and the field capacity.

Field and greenhouse experiments were conducted to study the direct effects of moisture stress and moisture-stress-induced soil problems in growth characteristiss, nutrition, and grain yield of upland rice. In other words, moisture stress effects would be categorized as effects in the absence and effects in the presence of soil and nutritional problems.

II MOISTURE STRESS EFFECTS IN THE ABSENCE OF NUTRITIONAL PROBLEMS

A field experiment was conducted under simulated upland condition at the IRRI farm during the 1973 dry season to study the moisture stress effects on upland rice. Figure 1 shows the moisture retention curve for the Maahas clay soil. Table 1 shows other important physical and chemical properties of the soil.

Table 1.—Physical and chemical characteristics of Maahas clay soil in upland rice, experimental area at the IRRI farm.

PHYSICAL	
Sand (%)	27.67
Silt (%)	35.16
Clay (%)	37.17
Texture class	Clay loam
CHEMICAL	
pH (1:1 soil water)	5.8
CEC (me/100 g)	37
Total N (%)	0.15
Organic matter (%)	2.63
Available P (ppm)	0.72

Three moisture treatments were imposed on 48 varieties and experimental lines 14 days after germination. The moisture treatments were (1) continual saturation throughout crop growth, maintained by adding 5.5 mm of water daily, (2) early stress, soil moisture tension of 75 cm maintained during the first 60 days after seedling establishment, after which soil was kept saturated for the rest of the period; the plots were irrigated with 8.25 mm of water whenever the soil moisture tension reached 75 cb, (3) late stress, continual saturation maintained during vegetative stage, and soil moisture tension of 75 cb maintained during the panicle initiation stage and harvest; plots received 8.25 mm of water in response to soil moisture tension of 75 cb.

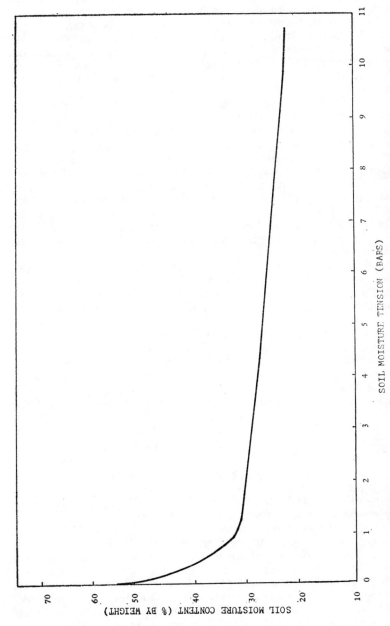

Figure 1. Desorption curve of Maahas clay soil from upland rice, experimental area at IRRI farm (Block upper MN).

Plant characters

Varieties and lines differed greatly in the reduction of plant characters such as height, tiller number, and dry matter production due to early and late stress treatments. Among the upland varieties tested, two from Africa, E-425 and Moroberekan, showed no significant reduction in plant characters due to stress treatments at either the vegetative or reproductive stage (Table 2). The reduction in vegetative growth was significant in the upland varieties M1-48 and OS6 and the experimental line IR1487-372-4. The reduction in growth during the vegetative period has been attributed to auxin imbalance in plants (Senewiratne and Mikkelsen, 1961; Gunawardena, 1966). Among the experimental lines which did not show significant reduction in plant characters, IR1646-623-2 was the best for drought tolerance at both vegetative and reproductive stages (Table 2). Other lines selected as promising for drought tolerance were IR1661-1-170, IR1531-86-2, IR1544-238-2, IR1561-149-3, and IR1721-11-6. IR5 showed no significant reduction in plant height and tiller number due to early stress, but at harvest its dry matter production was significantly reduced (Table 2). IR5 showed significant reduction in plant height and dry matter production due to stress during the reproductive stage confirming our earlier finding that IR5 is highly sensitive to moisture stress during the reproductive stage.

Plants subjected to moisture stress at the reproductive and ripening stages, showed various symptoms of moisture stress. Older leaves died prematurely and the younger leaves and flag leaf wilted. Although the two upland varieties, E-425 and Moroberekan, were good for drought tolerance, being very tall and low tillering, they are not suitable for high yield (De Datta and Beachell, 1972). On the other hand, the improved lines, such as IR1646-623-2, which looked promising for drought tolerance are shorter than what we want for upland rice culture. Among the drought-tolerant promising lines, only IR1531-86-2 had the plant height under upland culture (about 100 cm) which we believe is desirable for the low moisture and fertility conditions that prevail in most farmers fields during dry periods.

Grain yield

Under saturation, the highest grain yield (635 g/m²) was obtained with IR1529-677-2 which had earlier been reported to be a promising line for upland rice (De Datta *et al.*, 1974). The Philippine upland variety Dinalaga produced the lowest grain yield (198 g/m²).

With the early stress treatment, IR5 produced the highest grain yield (456 g/m²), confirming our earlier results. It is one of the best varieties for drought upland conditions (De Datta, 1970) if stress is relieved before panicle initiation (De Datta *et al.*, 1973b). Dinalaga once again produced the lowest yield (156 g/m²). Among the 46 varieties or lines tested, the African upland variety OS6 ranked 25th (325 g/m²) which was, however, the highest among the upland varieties. All the top-yielding lines were from the IRRI general breeding program. IR442-2-58 once again ranked as one of the best under upland conditions (576 g/m²).

Table 2.—Plant height, tiller number and dry weight at harvest of some selected rice varieties and lines under continual saturation and percent reduction of the same growth characters due to soil moisture stress (75 cb) during the vegetative or reproductive stage. IRRI, 1973 dry season.

Varieties/lines	Plant height			Tillers			Dry weight		
	Continual saturation (cm)	Reduction (%)		Continual saturation (no/1-m row)	Reduction (%)		Continual saturation (g/1-m row)	Reduction (%)	
		Early stress	Late stress		Early stress	Late stress		Early stress	Late stress
MI-48	105	18**	2	77	21	4	156	33**	11
Dinalaga	124	6	15**	90	26	7	205	34**	16
E-425	108	4	2	95	14	1	155	16	—5
OS6	110	22**	15*	119	17	1	242	50**	38**
Moroberekan	109	4	4	75	32	3	145	28	10
C-22	123	4	18**	131	2	—2	236	38**	17
IR5	113	5	13**	224	3	17	486	36**	48**
IR661-1-170	66	0	0	197	10	13	162	21	11
IR938-35-2	69	6	1	232	11	2	99	24*	9
IR1487-372-4	77	17*	14	208	2	10	177	24	11
IR1529-430-3	76	5	9	215	22*	—3	180	2	0
IR1529-677-2	77	1	10*	215	6	14	211	14	16
IR1529-680-3	82	20	17	209	44**	1	203	45**	—1
IR1531-86-2	100	—3	7	156	17	—4	196	31	9
IR1544-238-2	64	0	2	218	17	9	136	32	16
IR1561-149-5	67	10	3	247	10	4	140	21	3
IR1646-623-2	71	1	0	180	14	—12	146	21	—18
IR1721-11-6	76	—1	5	238	12	5	165	20	7

*, ** Significant at 5% and 1%, respectively.

For the late stress treatment (Fig. 2), both IR5 (201 g/m^2) and IR442-2-58 (123 g/m^2) gave poor yields similar to those of upland rice varieties OS6 (196 g/m^2) and M1-48 (147 g/m^2).

The average grain yields and the physiological growth stage at which moisture stress was imposed were negatively related (Fig. 3). The later the stress treatment, the greater was the reduction in grain yield, indicating the vulnerability of rice during the reproductive and ripening stages. More varieties were susceptible to high soil moisture tension at the reproductive and ripening stages than during the vegetative period. Data averaged for all varieties and lines showed that late stress resulted in poorer performance than did early stress (Fig. 3).

To establish the effect of stress at various growth stages of rice, the concept of crop susceptibility factor was used. It provided a quantitative means of determining the susceptibility of the crop to a given stress level. Crop susceptibility factors were calculated with the formula proposed by Hiler and Clark (1970).

$$CS_{VM} = \frac{X - M}{X}$$

where CS is the crop susceptibility factor as a function of variety (v) and growth stage (m), X is the yield where no stress was imposed throughout crop growth, M is the yield when stress was imposed at a particular growth stage. Crop susceptibility values increased at later stages of growth (Fig. 3). In other words, as crop susceptibility values increased at later stage of growth, the grain yield decreased linearly (Fig. 3).

The varieties and lines were classified into four groups according to crop susceptibility: (1) varieties and lines susceptible to both vegetative and reproductive stres, (2) lines tolerant to vegetative stress but susceptible to reproductive stress, (3) lines tolerant to both vegetative and reproductive stress, and (4) lines resistant (because of combined tolerance and avoidance of moisture stress) to both vegetative and reproductive stress.

In this experiment, IR1646-623-2 which yielded significantly less than the top yielders IR1721-11-6 and IR1542-43-2 in all treatments was found most tolerant to moisture stress at all growth stages. Therefore, drought tolerance should not be equated entirely with grain yield, since many soil and nutritional problems affect the overall performance of the rice variety under sub-optimal moisture levels. The crop susceptibility factor appears highly promising in evaluating a vairety's capability to recover from drought.

III   MOISTURE STRESS EFFECTS IN THE PRESENCE OF NUTRITIONAL PROBLEMS

Soil problems

A greenhouse experiment was conducted to study the varietal response to various levels of relatively constant soil moisture tension imposed continually throughout the growing period. Maahas clay soil was collected, air dried, and ground to pass through a 2-mm sieve. Plastic pots

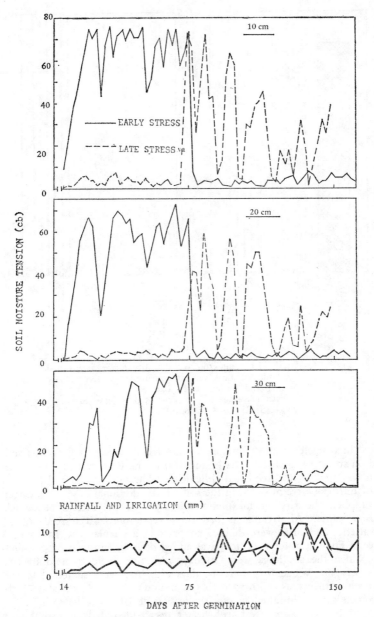

Figure 2. SOIL MOISTURE TENSION IN CENTIBAR (cb) AT 10, 20, AND 30 cm SOIL DEPTHS MEASURED DURING VEGETATIVE (EARLY STRESS) AND REPRODUCTIVE (LATE STRESS) STAGES OF RICE GROWTH. IRRI, 1973 DRY SEASON.

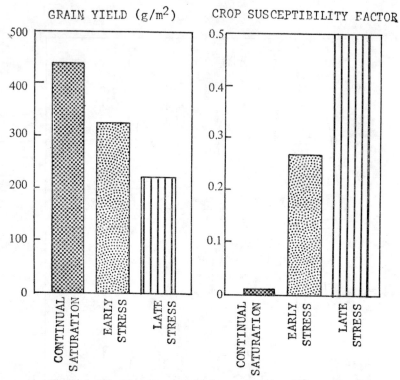

Figure 3. Grain yield and crop susceptibility factor as affected by soil moisture tension during vegetative (Early Stress) and reproductive (Late Stress) stages of rice growth (Average of 48 varieties or lines). Stress = 75 cb. IRRI, 1973 dry season.

(30 cm in diameter and 30 cm long) were filled with 850 g of this soil. Based on surface area, 150 kg/ha N and 180 kg/ha P_2O_5 were applied. Nitrogen was applied in three equal split doses. The phosphorus and the first dose of nitrogen were mixed with the soil. Two additional doses of nitrogen were applied the first at maximum tillering and the second at panicle initiation stages. All treatments had three replications. Ten seeds of 75 rice varieties and lines were dibbled in pairs in a circular pattern about 3 cm deep. Enough water (400 ml) was added daily to ensure good germination. When the seedlings were 10 days old, they were thinned to five plants per pot. When they were 14 days old, they were subjected to soil moisture treatments, as follows: 0 cb (saturation), 17 cb, 33 cb, and 75 cb. Tensiometers were installed in one replication at 10 cm soil depth.

In the saturation treatment, water was added daily to maintain a thin film of water. For the 17- and 33-cb treatments, 400 ml of water was applied whenever the soil moisture tension in a given pot reached those tensions. For the 75-cb tension treatment, the tensiometer was disconnected for 48 hours when the soil moisture tension reached 75 cb, then water was added and the tensiometers were reconnected.

Iron deficiency symptoms occurred on plants in the saturated as well as in the stressed treatments. The degree and expression of symptoms differed between treatments and varieties. The symptoms varied even among lins from the same cross. On the basis of grain yields and susceptibility to iron deficiency, 75 varieties or lines tested were classified into five groups:

1) Eleven were tolerant to soil moisture stress and moderately resistant to iron deficiency; they showed some iron deficiency symptoms although iron content in plants was above the critical level. IR442-2-58 belonged to this group.

2) Six were tolerant to moisture stress and moderately susceptible to iron deficiency; they showed iron deficiency symptoms but the iron concentrations in plants were just above the critical level. IR5 and IR1416-131-5 belonged to this group.

3) Ten were tolerant to moisture stress and susceptible to iron deficiency; they showed iron deficiency symptoms and iron concentrations in plants were below the critical level. IR1541-76-3 was in this group.

4) Thirty-two were susceptible to moisture stress but resistant to iron deficiency; they showed no iron deficiency symptoms and the iron concentrations in plants were above the critical level. The Philippine upland variety M1-48 and the African upland variety OS6 were in the group.

5) Sixteen were susceptible to moisture stress and susceptible to iron deficiency; they showed iron deficiency symptoms and iron concentrations in plants were below critical. IR1514A-E666 belonged to this group.

Table 3 shows data for grain yield and iron, manganese, and phosphorus concentrations in rice straw at harvest, as affected by various levels of soil moisture tension. According Yoshida et al., (1971), rice plants suffer from iron deficiency when the concentration of iron in the straw is below 70 ppm. The upland varieties, such as M1-48 and OS6, accumulated the largest amount of iron at saturation (0 cb) (Table 3). Similar results were obtained by Ponnamperuma and Castro (1972).

In IR1416-131-5, iron concentration was lower and iron deficiency symptoms were greater at higher moisture level. Iron concentration in straw was increased with increased soil moisture tension. As a result of higher iron availability, the grain yield increased with iucreased soil moisture tension.

A few lines, such as IR442-2-58, had iron concentration in the straw above the critical level and produced fairly well at all stress levels.

The extremely low concentraitons of iron in the straw at saturation in IR1541-76-3 (group 3) and in IR1514A-E666 (group 5) were reflected in their grain yields (Table 3).

We believe that manganese concentration in plant tissue aggravated iron deficiency in plants. Although they may not cause manganese toxicity in rice, high manganese concentrations reduce the iron uptake by rice plants.

Table 3.—Plant analysis of some selected varieties and lines of the various groups as affected by different levels of soil moisture tension. IRRI, 1972.

Variety/line	Grain yield (g/pot)			Fe (ppm)			Mn (ppm)			P (%)		
	0 cb	17 cb	33 cb	0 cb	17 cb	33 cb	0 cb	17 cb	33 cb	0 cb	17 cb	33 cb
GROUP 1												
IR442-2-58	23	19	19	112	99	90	795	775	722	0,17	0,14	0,13
GROUP 2												
IR5	15	18	24	76	108	141	575	470	215	0,19	0,18	0,14
IR1416-131-5	5	7	17	71	80	120	725	235	290	0,14	0,14	0,13
GROUP 3												
IR1541-76-3	10	18	16	52	147	75	585	620	225	0,29	0,22	0,18
GROUP 4												
IR1541-76-3												
OS6	17	9	9	165	161	157	320	565	730	0,11	0,16	0,19
M1-48	20	7	6	182	165	115	445	440	600	0,12	0,14	0,17
GROUP 5												
IR1514A-E666	11	13	6	22	221	36	1260	845	650	0,10	0,10	0,12

Thus, the reduction in grain yield resulting from increased soil moisture tension may be caused by soil moisture stress alone or by soil problems, such as iron deficiency, induced by moisture stress or by a combination of both. Moisture stress and soil problems should therefore be considered together in evaluating the suitability of rices for upland culture.

Results further indicate that iron deficiency occurs in upland rice, even on acid soils of pH 5.8. This contention is further substantiated by our field experiments in farmers' fields in Batangas, Philippines, where a large number of rice varieties and experimental lines showed iron deficiency symptoms in upland rice grown on acid soils (pH 5.1 to 5.8). Earlier, Ponnamperuma and Castro (1972) reported iron deficiency to be a problem on neutral and alkaline soils. Our results show that iron deficiency in upland rice occurs widely on acid soils and is closely associated with the moisture status of soil.

Nutritional problems

The relationships between soil moisture level and nitrogen nutrition in upland rice were studied in two field experiments on Maahas clay at the IRRI farm (Table 1) with the early maturing semidwarf IR747B2-6-3 as test variety.

In the experiment conducted during the 1971 wet season, a split-block design was used with water regime on the main plots and N level on the subplots. Plots were separated by 25-cm wide metal bands placed in the soil to a depth of 20 cm. Each treatment had two replications. Nitrogen as ammonium sulfate was applied 16 days after germination at 0, 75, and 150 kg/ha. Tensiometers were installed to measure soil moisture tension at 15- and 30-cm soil depths. Supplemental irrigation was applied in low (3 cm), medium (4 cm), and high (5 cm) amounts.

The experiment was repeated during the 1972 dry season under simulated upland conditions with the same objectives. The rates and N source used were the same as those used in the wet season experiment except that they were applied in two split doeses. Fifty and 100 kg/ha N were applied a week after germination of rice, and the remaining 25 kg/ha N was topdressed at panicle initiation. Soil moisture tensions were recorded at 10-, 20-, and 30-cm soil depths.

Detailed agronomic data were collected in both experiments. Exchangeable NH_4^+ and NO_3^- were determined (Jackson, 1958) from soil samples collected from 0- to 15-cm depth. Total nitrogen in plant samples was determined by the procedure described by Yoshida *et al.*, (1971).

In the wet-season experiment, the highest grain yield, 4.6 t/ha, was obtained at 150 kg/ha N, with 170 mm of supplemental irrigation (Fig. 4). Although grain yields increased significantly with the application of nitrogen and water, the interaction was not significant. The increase in grain yield was primarily due to added nitrogen and to a lesser extent to a higher amount of supplemental water (Fig. 6). Panicle length, percentage of unfilled grains, and 100-grain weight did not vary significantly with varied nitrogen and moisture regime.

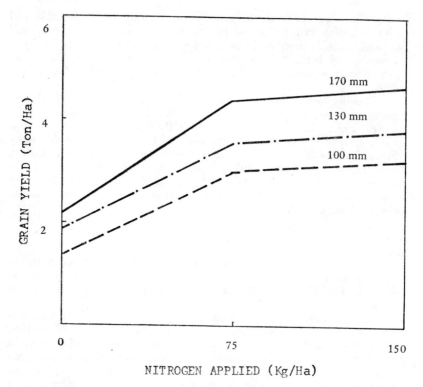

Figure 4. Grain yield of IR747B₂-6-3 rice at three nitrogen levels as affected by three levels of supplemental irrigation IRRI, 1971 wet season.

The soil moisture tension was close to 33 cb for most of the growing season; only for 25 days did moisture tension at 15 cm soil depth rise beyond 33 cb (Fig. 5).

Nitrogen efficiency, as measured in kilogram of rice per millimeter of water, was highest at the highest nitrogen and moisture regime.

In the 1972 dry season experiment, the increase in grain yield was highly significant at all soil moisture regimes and nitrogen levels (Fig. 6). At higher soil moisture levels —at saturation 0 cb and at 33 cb tension— significantly higher grain yields were obtained with 125 kg/ha N. This confirms the earlier finding (Jana and De Datta, 1971) that the response to N increases with increase in moisture regime of the soil.

The grain yield of 3.3 t/ha was obtained with 125 kg/ha N at 17 cb soil moisture tension, which was similar to 3.5 t/ha grain yield obtained at 0 cb, but with 75 kg/ha N. In other words, at lower moisture supply, a higher amount of nitrogen produced similar yield as to that obtained at higher moisture supply but with less nitrogen fertilizer.

The grain yield at saturation (at 0 cb) increased by 31 percent without nitrogen fertilizer, by 30 percent with 75 kg/ha N, and by 52 percent with 125 kg/ha N over that at 33 cb. However, the yield increase over that at 17 cb was 13 percent without fertilizer N, 22 percent with 75 kg/ha N, and 24 percent with 125 kg/ha N.

Although results were similar to those of experiments conducted in Japan (Matsuo, 1957) and in the U.S. (Senewiratne and Mikkelsen, 1961) no quantitative data were available on the level of moisture supply. In the 1971 dry season experiment, the soil moisture tension closely followed the moisture treatments (17 and 33 cb).

Soil and plant nitrogen were greater with increased nitrogen level. With greater moisture supply, nitrogen content in the plants increased, suggesting lower nitrogen supply at higher soil moisture tension causes greater response to fertilizer.

These results demonstrate that increased supply of fertilizer nitrogen can save part of the yield that would be lost from increased moisture stress, since reduced nitrogen supply in soil is one of the changes caused by increased soil moisture tension. Conversely, if moisture supply is adequate, the rate of nitrogen fertilizer could be reduced without significantly reducing grain yield.

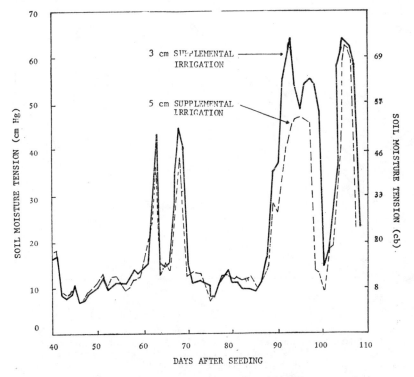

Figure 5. Soil moisture tension in centibar (cb) at 15 cm soil depth during the various stages of rice (IR747B₂-6-3) growth. IRRI, 1971 wet season.

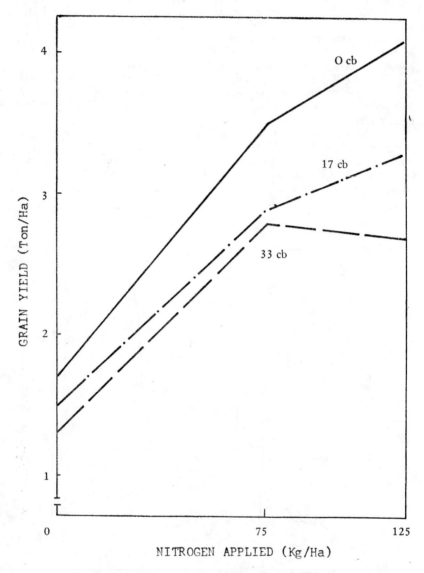

Figure 6. Grain yield of IR747-6-3B₂-6-3 rice at three nitrogen levels as affected by three levels of soil moisture tension (0,17 and 33 centibars). IRRI, 1972 dry season.

IV SUMMARY

Field and greenhouse experiments were conducted to separate the direct effects of moisture stress from effects of soil and nutritional problems induced by moisture stress in upland rice.

In the first experiment, the rice varieties or lines were classified into four groups according to their resistance or susceptibility to moisture stress at the vegetative and reproductive stages of crop growth. IR1646-623-2, which yielded significantly lower than the top-yielding lines IR1721-11-6 and IR1542-43-2 at all moisture tensions, was most tolerant to moisture stress at all growth stages. Furthermore, the drought tolerant variety may or may not have high yield potential. Drought tolerance should therefore not be equated entirely with grain yield alone since many factors affect the yielding ability of a rice variety under sub-optimal moisture level.

In the second experiment, conducted in the greenhouse, 75 rice varieties or lines were subjected to three soil moisture tensions imposed continually throughout the growing period. The rices were classified into five groups according to their resistance or susceptibility to moisture stress and iron deficiency. Only eleven varieties or lines out of 75 were found tolerant to moisture stress and moderately resistant to iron deficiency. IR442-2-58 was in this group.

Additional experiments were conducted in the fields to study the relationship between soil moisture regime and nitrogen nutrition in upland rice. In one experiment, the grain yield of 3.3 t/ha was obtained with 125 kg/ha N at 17 centibar soil moisture tension, which was similar to 3.5 t/ha grain yield at 0 cb tension (saturation) but with 75 kg/ha N. Results demonstrate that increased supply of fertilizer nitrogen can reduce the yield losses due to moderate moisture stress. Conversely, in the presence of adequate moisture supply, the rate of nitrogen fertilizer could be reduced without significantly reducing grain yield.

Finally, our results clearly demonstrate that the reduction in grain yield due to increased soil moisture tension may be due to the direct effects of moisture stress, to moisture-stress-induced soil problems, such as iron deficiency, or to a combination of both. Therefore, moisture stress and soil problems should be considered together in evaluating the suitability of rices for upland culture.

V REFERENCES

BARBER, S. A. 1962. A diffusion and mass flow concept of soil nutrient availability. Soil Sci. 93:39-49.

BARBER, S. A., J. M. WALKER and E. M. VASEY. 1963. Mechanisms for the movement of plant nutrient from the soil and fertilizer to the plant root. Agr. and Food Chem. 11:204-207.

BARTHOLOMEW, F. P. 1971. The limitation of natural process in supplying nitrogen for modern crop production. Proc. Int. Symp. Soil Fert. Eval. 1:619-630.

BRIGGS, L. J. and H. L. SHANTZ. 1914. Relative water requirement of plants. J. Agr. Res. 3:1-63.

CHAKLADAR, M. N. 1946. Influence of soil moisture on yield of paddy. Indian J. Agr. Sci. 16:152-157.

CHANDRA MOHAN, J. 1965. Water requirement of rice crop in Madras. Madras Agr. J. 52(5):230-238.

De DATTA, S. K. 1970. Fertilizers and soil amendments for tropical rice. pp. 106-146. In Rice Production Manual (revised edition, 1970), University of the Philippines College of Agriculture.

De DATTA, S. K. and H. M. BEACHELL. 1972. Varietal response to some factors affecting production of upland rice. In: Rice Breeding, International Rice Research Institute. Los Baños, Philippines. pp. 685-700.

De DATTA, S. K., W. P. ABILAY and G. N. KALWAR. 1973a. Water stress effects in upland rice. In: Water management in Philippine irrigation systems: research and operations. International Rice Research Institute, Los Baños, Philippines. pp. 19-36.

De DATTA, S. K., H. K. KRUPP, E. I. ALVAREZ and S. C. MEDGAL. 1973b. Water management practices in flooded tropical rice. In: Water management in Philippine irrigation systems: research and operations. International Rice Research Institute, Los Baños, Philippines. pp. 1-18.

De DATTA, S. Y., E. L. ARAGON and J. A. MALABUYOC. 1974. Varietal differences in cultural practices for upland rice. Seminar on Variety Improvement and Cooperative Variety Trial, West Africa Rice Development Association Monrovia, January 16-20, 1972. Seminar Proceedings I:35-73.

FRIED, M. and R. E. SHAPIRO. 1961. Soil plant relationship in ion uptake. Ann. Rev. Plant Physiol. 12:91-112.

GUNAWARDENA, R. 1966. PhD. Thesis. University of California, Davis.

HALM, A. T. 1967. Effect of water regime on growth and chemical composition of two rice varieties. Trop. Agr. (Trinidad) 44(1):33-37.

HILER, S. A. and R. N. CLARK. 1970. Stress day index to characterize effects of water stress on crop yields. Paper N° 70-228. In: Papers, Annual Meeting of the American Society of Agricultural Engineers at Minneapolis, Minn., July, 1970, on a program arranged by the Soil and Water Division. pp. 757-761.

JACKSON, M. L. 1958. Soil chemical analysis. Prentice-Hall, Inc., Englewood Cliffs. 498 p.

JANA, R. K. and S. K. De DATTA. 1971. Effects of solar energy and soil moisture tension on the nitrogen response of upland rice. Proc. Internl. Symp. Soil Fert. Eval., New Delhi. pp. 487-497.

KATO, I. 1968. Water management in rice culture in upland fields. Int. Rice Comm. Working Party on Rice, Soils, Water and Fertilizer Practices 8(26):1-21.

KRUPP, H. K., W. P. ABILAY and E. I. ALVAREZ. 1972. Some water stress effects on rice. In: Rice Breeding,, International Rice Research Institute, Los Baños, Philippines. pp. 663-673.

MATSUO, T. 1957. Rice culture in Japan. Yokendo Press Ltd., Tokyo (2nd ed.). 128 p.

PONNAMPERUMA, F. N. and R. U. CASTRO. 1972. Varietal differences in resistance to adverse soil conditions. In: Rice Breeding, International Rice Research Institute, Los Años, Philippines. pp. 677-684.

SENEWIRATNE, S. T. and D. S. MIKKELSEN. 1961. Physiological factors limiting growth and yield of Oriza sativa under unflooded conditions. Plant Soil 14:127-146.

TISDALE, S. L. and W. L. NELSON. 1966. Soil fertility and fertilizers. The MacMillan Co. 694 p.

UEDA, S. 1925. Comparative studies of growth of rice plants as affected by different water contents of soil. II Growth after transplanting to maturity. Proc. Crop Sci. Soc. Japan 7(1):19-38.

YOSHIDA, S., D. A. FORNO and J. M. COCK. 1971. Laboratory manual for physiological studies of rice. International Rice Research Institute, Los Baños, Philippines. 61 p.

10 On-farm Water Management

A. ALVIN BISHOP

I INTRODUCTION

I think it is a good idea for those concerned with agricultural development to exchange ideas occasionally in examination of the various components of agricultural production. I like to think of the agricultural production system as being composed of six major subsystems: water, soils, climate, crops, inputs (fertilizer, chemicals, etc.) and management. You will note that I have placed water at the top of the list which reflects my bias and my rating of the most important production input. I have made better on-farm water management my crusade for the past 30 years or so and especially in the last 2 years when I have been working for AID as their water management specialist. So my bias is quite firmly entrenched. As you all know, without water nothing happens. Soil scientists may argue that without soil nothing happens and this is also true. However, I will continue to rate water as number one and the most important single factor in agricultural production. The purpose of my paper is to highlight the on-farm water management facet of agricultural production and encourage soils scientists to pay greater attention to the complex and powerful water-soils relationships.

I suppose that because 90% of the agricultural crop land of the world is non-irrigated there is a tendency for farmers, perhaps even soil scientists to consider that water is an unmanageable production input to be taken at natures' discretion. What I am saying is that most people do not realize that water is a manageable resource. To some extent this attitude of unmanageability prevails even where irrigation water is available. At a recent symposium concerned with "On-Farm Water Management-Research and Implementation" some of the reasons why farmers do not realize that water is a manageable resource were discussed. One of the chief reasons mentioned for irrigated lands is that many of the options for management decisions have been eliminated by the time the water is delivered to the farm. The institutions responsible for water delivery are not always completely in tune with the farmers desires or the crop requirements. There is also a tendency for the engineers managing the canal systems to feel that their responsability is dicharged if the water is delivered to the farms on an equitable basis. Thus the timing and the amount of water delivery may have very little relationship to the actual crop water needs. There are a large number of problems related to on-farm water management both on irrigated lands and on the rain fed lands. Perhaps at this point, a definition and a concept of on-farm water management is in order.

II WATER MANAGEMENT DEFINED

In a recent paper before the First World Congress on Water Resources, water management was defined by the writer as follows: "water management is the space-time-quantity-quality alternation of the water resource in and between various water uses to meet societal goals". Within this definition the specific concerns for on-farm water management are implied. Some time ago I developed a concept for on-farm management. This concept has been discussed with several groups, however, for the purpose of summarizing a philosophy concerning on-farm water management I would like to present it again here. The concept follows:

"Modern 'On-Farm Water Management' is a complex combination of art and science requiring the application of our best knowledge of water, soils, climate and crops and their interactions, together with inputs of nutrients, pesticides, capital, power (energy) and management for agricultural production. It extends from the production of water as precipitation (either in the watershed or at the farm) to the disposal of the remnants after use. It gives emphasis to timely and sufficient delivery of water to the farm including the conjunctive use of surface water and groundwater and the re-use of irrigation return flow or the sequential use of waters reclaimed from industrial, municipal or other uses. It includes the preparation of the farm land to enhance its efficiency to receive and store water. It employs the necessary water removal systems (drainage works) to control the water table, provide leaching requirements and dispose of unwanted water whether coming from excessive precipitation, excess irrigation or otherwise. It involves the design and construction of devices and structures for the efficient application of water to the land such as field ditches, pipelines, furrows, borders and sprinkler systems. It involves the design and construction of complicated engineering works such as dams, reservoirs, canals and appurtenances for control and modification of the space-time availability of natural water supplies so delivery and application to the farmland can be made on a timely basis. In modern society the need for proper concern for the environment, erosion, pollution, water quality and factors affecting the quality of life are also recognized. Apparent also is the knowledge of and need for institutions, organizations, legislation, laws and regulations providing for an orderly and acceptable development and use of the water resource to meet societal goals".

This concept was developed primarily for irrigated lands to convey the idea that when water is confined to a particular irrigation system it should be completely manageable. The on-farm water management options in a rain fed agriculture, however, are a little bit different and involved different practices than those specifically developed for irrigated lands.

The conditions for on-farm water management generally fall into three major categories. These are: management of natural precipitation, water application (irrigation), water removal (drainage). The basic purpose of water management under these three conditions is to optimize crop production by employing as a production input is a major agricultural concern. I will briefly discuss some of the concepts and practices related to these conditions.

III MANAGEMENT OF PRECIPITATION

Since the major part of the crop land of the world today is non-irirgated the management of the water resources on this land has the greatest potential. However, it is on these lands where water management is almost totally disregarded and water management, such as it is, is probably more inadvertent than planned. This may be overstating the neglect for water management. I'm sure the importance of water is realized by most everyone. However, there seems to be very little being done about it. The general feeling sems to be that the water is taken for granted, comes with the capricious whims of nature and there is little that can be done about it. At this point in time the possibility of turning precipitation on and off like you would a water tap is somewhat remote. Nevertheless it is possible to develop the hydrologic probabilities of precipitation and droughts for a given area or region. The probability of storms of given intensity and total amount as well as the length and severity of droughts can be categorized. With this information the selection of the agricultural crops and related cultural practices can be tailored to utilize the available water more efficiently. I call this water management —the adoption of tillage and cultural practices to harvest the moisture that nature provides, the management of the soil so that infiltration and moisture storage is given a high priority — the timing of planting to obtain maximum benefits from the natural precipitation occurance during the growth cycle of the crop, the selection of those crops and varieties that are best adapted to withstand the drought stresses that are indicated for in the area. You might argue that traditional farming has achieved these agricultural goals and I would agree that within the technology available to the traditional farmer he has selected and maintained those crops and varieties that best suit what he has and the risks he is willing to take. However, there is additional technology which requires adaptations to the developing countries in order to better harvest and utilize the water resource.

Water management for rain fed agriculture might be depicted as an open ended hydrologic system as shown in Figure 1.

As shown in Figure 1 not all of the precipitation from a given storm reaches the soil surface. Some of it evaporates from the vegetative cover.

The water that reaches the soil surface may infiltrate, runoff, evaporate or be stored in surface depressions to later infiltrate or evaporate. Water infiltrated may be stored in the soil to be transpired by crops or percolate beyond the root zone to feed the groundwater resource. From the hydrologic system model it is evident that the useful portion of the precipitation so far as the crop is concerned is that which is transpired. If the transpiration requirements are always satisfied the major concern is with runoff, to control it and prevent erosion. If the transpiration requirements are not satisfied, then in the water management emphasis should be toward increasing moisture available for transpiration by preventing runoff and increasing soil moisture storage by working on these segments of the system which reduce the water available for crops.

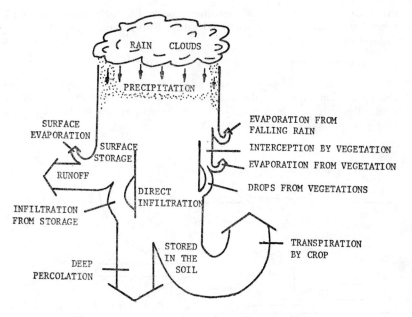

Figure 1.—Hydrologic System for Rain-Fed Agriculture.

It is not uncommon to observe surface runoff from agricultural lands during storms of even moderately low intensity. Runoff of precipitation is perhaps the greatest water management problem on rain fed lands because the water resource is lost from that particular crop land where runoff occurs. Perhaps even more damaging, however, is the erosion that surface runoff causes to the land. Water management practices to prevent runoff need to be emphasized. These practices include bench terraces, retention terraces, drainage terraces, contour furrows, contour farming, strip croppings contour listing and crop residue mulching. Special tillage work such as chiseling, ripping, deep plowing and other similar practices have been found to be effective in increasing the infiltration rate and improving the moisture storage for crop production. The strategy of managing natural precipitation is to alter the physical system so as to minimize runoff, minimize evaporation and eliminate water consumption by unwanted vegetation in order to utilize all of the moisture where it falls for crop production. It is generally considered that water application (irrigation) is not an option on rain fed lands. However, supplemental irrigation should not be overlooked when it can be provided. For even in areas of high rain fall damaging drought and stress conditions in the plants resulting in reduced yields frequently occur. During those periods a single irrigation may sustantially increase yields sufficient to economically justify irrigation. In fact many portable irrigation systems have been installed in areas considered to be to humid for just this purpose. With supplemental irrigation farmers can plant varieties and population for maximum yield, manage and fertilize accordingly. Deficiencies in natural precipitation can be made up by irrigation thus minimizing periodic crop failures or near failures.

IV WATER APPLICATION - IRRIGATION

Where irrigation water is available it is possible to optimize all of the production inputs in the agricultural production system, provided, of course the water can be managed. The hydrologic system for water application (irrigation) is illustrated in Figure 2.

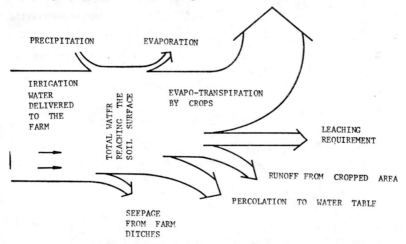

Figure 2. Hydrologic system for irrigated land.

The major part of water supply for this system is provided either from surface or groundwater supplies that have been developed and are subject to management controls. A small, but sometimes an important amount, is provided by precipitation. In some cases an important part of the useable supply may come from uncontrolled groundwater sources such as lateral movement of groundwater from sources outside the farm boundary or by upward movement from a water table. The water management strategy is to have the major portion of the supply disposed of by transpiration through the agricultural plants keeping the remaining disposal streams as small as possible consistant with the specific water quality and farm requirements. As shown, in Figure 2 for most systems, not all of the water delivered to the farm is applied to the land. Some of it seeps from the farm distribution system or evaporates from it. For open ditch systems used intermittently the water required to fill the system may not be recovered and evaporates between fillings.

The major farm losses are represented by runoff from the cropped area and percolation of water to the water table. These losses can be minimized by proper system design, choice of the right irrigation parameters and good management. For example, pump-back irrigation or exactly level land can practically eliminate runoff and the percolation losses can be greatly reduced by the selection of the proper "size of stream — length of run relationship". The leaching requirement has only recently been recognized as a necessity and in many cases it is overlooked and considered as a loss being combined with percolation to the water table.

In the on-farm water management concept presented earlier it was stated that the water management is complex. This complexity is due partly to the fact that irrigation usually involves a community or societal effort. The resource must be shared. The facilities must be shared. A joint effort is usually required to construct the needed irrigation works and the institutions that became involved often provide the farmer with foregone decisions or options difficult or impossible to implement. There are two basic water concerns, those having to do with the physical system by which the space-time quantity and quality alternation of the water resource is achieved and the institutional system through which the societal controls are exerted in order to meet societal goals. A brief discussion of the physical and institutional components of irrigation water management follows.

V PHYSICAL COMPONENTS

Water Supply

Knowledge of the resource is an integral part of management. A hydrologic data base containing information on the timing, amount and dependability of the supply from precipitation, rivers, lakes, reservoirs and ground water is indispensible in any management plan. Unless the extent and nature of the resource is known there is little opportunity for management. This fundamental need for good hydrologic data is a continuing requirement in water management. The international efforts in this regard are represented by the 'International Hydrologic Decade and World Meterological Organization''.

Methods of Water Application

The physical application of water to the land presents a number of alternative methods. The choice of the method of irrigation is not just the simple choice of one method vs. another. A number of factors must be taken into consideration in the selection. For example, the nature of the water supply, its timing, amount and quality soil characteristics, labor, available energy and the availability of technical assistance to design the more sophisticated systems all influence the choice of the method of application. The type of crop is also important as is the personal preferences of the farmer. In most cases any of the methods could be used at a particular site but for specific site conditions, one method will have advantages over the other. For example, if labor is limited and automation is desired, sprinkler or trickle irrigation may be preferred. If energy and capital are limited surface methods will probably be best. The point is, most of the methods of water application could be made to work but there are site specific conditions that would operate to favor one method for that particular site.

At the present time, most of the irrigated land of the world is irrigated by surface methods. It is more labor intensive than the more recent developments of sprinkler and drip irrigation and over the years through the process of trial and error the farmer has developed a workable system for the particular land he is cultivating. Surface irrigation, as with all methods of water application, can be greatly improved with the inputs of recent advances in science. A farmer can level his land using trial and error processes over a period of years observing what happens to the water, delineating the high spots and depressions and finally achieve the precision grading desired. He will not be able to obtain the benefits of uniform water application, uniform stands, better utilization of fertilizer, less weeds and increased yields resulting from precision land grading until the job is finished. With trial and error the job seldom gets done. With modern land leveling and irrigation technology the farmers are able to have the field surveyed and stakes set as a guide for the earth moving and do the land grading in one complete operation, often without losing a crop. He can also incorporate a modern land leveling design with the proper length of run — size of stream relationships. This requires an input of technology beyond the capability of most farmers. The engineering for land leveling along with the proper design of the onfarm irrigation system for the particular soil, crop and method of application employed could all be combined to give the farmer a modern and efficient irrigation system. It is doubtful that even after years of the trial and error process that the best system would evolve without an input of technology. The services required to provide this technological input have only been available to the farmers in the developed countries during the past 25 to 30 years and are not yet available in many of the developing countries. The hydraulics and other requirements for sprinkler irrigation and trickler irrigation, are of even more recent origin and equipment and theory are still being developed.

Water Requirements of Crops

The water requirements of crops has been the subject of considerable research during this century and especially over the past two or three decades. At the present time, there are nearly 20 equations proposed by various researchers around the world that are recognized as having considerable accuracy for estimating crop water requirements. These equations use either solar radiation or temperature with other climatic factors along with crop coefficients to compute the evapotranspiration. Although the climatological and other data necessary for estimating consumptive use are available to the scientists, these data are not available to the farmer. The farmer usually makes the decision of when to irrigate and how much water to apply based on his experience and his powers of observation of water stress ,wilting) in the crop. More often than not the irrigation scheduling has been established with some arbitrary time rotation plan ("turn" every 10 days, two weeks, etc.) often having no relationship to the consumptive use or the crop requirements. In isolated cases a modern irrigation scheduling service utilizing computers is now available to farmers but this is not yet in widespread use, even in developed countries. Extending scientific water scheduling service to all irrigated areas has great potential.

Water Delivery Methods

Other physical considerations in the onfarm water management mix include the water supply and the degree of control that can be exercised by the farmer over it quantity and timing. If the farm is located within a large irrigation system, the method of water delivery will influence the method of water application as well as other on-farm decisions. For example, for sprinkler irrigation or trickle irrigation *continuous flow* is usually essential, whereas surface methods require demand delivery or *rotation* for most farms. For ease in operation of the delivery system serving the farm the irrigation organizations (water companies, canal companies, irrigation districts, etc.) usually prefer rotation or continuous flow or combinations of these methods as the demand method usually imposes other requirements on the system such as storage, larger canal capacity, measurement, etc.

Water Delivery System

Other physical components, usually beyond the farmer's influence, are the major works, the dams, reservoirs, canals and control structures. These also require a community effort with specialized jobs and equipment. Too often the operation of these facilities for the utilization of water at the farm level is given a lower priority than the hydraulics of the operation of other non-agricultural issues related to the system. Fortunately, the situation in this regard is changing, but there is a long way to go before the full potential of water utilization on the farm is realized.

Institutional Problems

The institutional aspects of on-farm water management deal with the organizations o restablishments which exert control in one way or another over the parameters of water management on the farm. Within this category, the social, economic, and political systems are included. Included also is the legal framework related to water laws enacted by national, state, or local bodies which delineate the water rights of the user or set forth the manner in which the management institutions (water companies, water districts or water users associations) can be organized. The water user's organizations themselves and other infrastructure supports are a part of the institutional framework. The local customs, mores, as well as religious affilations and beliefs may also impinge upon the manner in which water may be used or managed.

VI DRAINAGE

The removal and disposal of unwanted water is a necessary facet of onfarm water management. It is a component of both rain fed and irrigated agriculture. The unwanted water may come from precipitation, irrigation, snowmelt, overlandw flow from adjacent lands, floodwaters or waters applied for microclimate control or leaching. Whatever the source of the water its safe and timely removal is important in maintaining high agricultural productivity. On rain fed lands during storms of high intensity or any intensity for that matter where the infiltration rate of the of the soil is exceeded, surface water may accumulate that must be drained away. Prevention of erosion and safe disposal of the surface runoff is required. It is noted that the hydrologic systems shown for both irrigated and rain fed agriculture possess a surface runoff fraction. These systems also show fractions contributing to sub-surface water (disposal streams including deep percolation, seepage, leaching). These sub-surface fractions may cause high water table (water logging) which inhibits crop growth. Whether the water removal system is designed for surface waters, sub-surface waters or a combination of both, it is a vital facet of water management.

The provisions for water removal systems have most of the physical and institutional considerations outlined for water application systems. It is true also that provision for drainage has not usually been included in the plan for mater application systems. Although the severity of the sub-surface problems are difficult to predict and the solutions are obscure until the need for drainage develops, advanced planning for outlet drains and other needed facilities is now standard practice. It is readily apparent that management and disposal of drainage waters is not easily solved on an individual farm basis and the mutual efforts of all concerned farmers of an area or watershed is required.

VII SUMMARY

The overall problem of "on-farm-water-management" is discussed. Farming systems completely dependent on irrigation and others dependent on precipitation and complementary irrigation are considered. The large potential utility of complementary irrigation is pointed out. The need for adequate drainage systems is also pointed out.

SECTION III

SOURCES AND USES OF NITROGEN

11 Potential Significance of Nitrogen Fixation in Rhizosphere Associations of Tropical Grasses

JOHANNA DÖBEREINER and JOHN M. DAY

I INTRODUCTION

Soil management and fertilization in tropical agriculture is usually directed towards relatively low investments applied to large areas because land is available, labor relatively cheap and returns commonly small. While high fertilizer prices and inevitable leaching losses inhibit the use of high rates of mineral nitrogen fertilizers, it seems wise to develop new agricultural systems to avoid, from the beginning, pollution problems. In more advanced agricultural systems based entirely on mineral nitrogen, pollution is reaching alarming dimensions.

This can be achieved by rotations using legume crops and pastures, a practice generally recognized as indispensable for high level lowcost protein production, be it through grain crops or indirectly through animal production. A variety of legume species are now available for tropical regions. There is, however, increasing interest in the possibility of growing nitrogen-fixing grasses, especially the tropical grasses with their much more efficient C-4 dicarboxylic acid photosynthetic pathway. Several research lines have been suggested to increase productivity. The incorporation of NIF+, genes into microorganisms which are dominant in the rhizosphere (Dixon and Postgate, 1972), or into the plant cell itself (Cocking, 1973) are examples. A more concrete and immediate possibility seems to arise from recent findings which demonstrate substantial nitrogen fixation on roots of tropical grasses associated with free living N_2 - fixing bacteria (Rinaudo, 1970; Rinaudo et al., 1971; Balandreau et al., 1973; Döbereiner et al., 1972 and Day, 1973).

In this present paper, these findings are reviewed and the potential of this new nitrogen source is discussed.

II MATERIAL AND METHODS

A general description of the methodology used in these studies seems essential for better understanding and interpretation of the data to be presented. It has been known for more than a decade that tropical grasses enhance multiplication of free-living N_2 - fixing bacteria in their rhizosphere (Döbereiner, 1961, 1966, 1968, 1970), but the breakthrough for estimates on the actual activity of these organisms came with the introduction of the acetylene reduction method (Dilworth, 1966; Schullborn and Burris, 1966). This method is based on the characteristic of nitrogenase to reduce C_2H_2 to C_2H_4 instead of reducing N_2 to NH_3 when C_2H_2 is supplied to an actively N_2 - fixing system. Ethylene can be measured easily and very precisely by gas chromatography utilizing a flame ionization detector and one of several different kinds of Poropak column supports. With this method it is possible to measure nitrogen fixation 1000 times more precisely than that by the more expensive use of $^{15}N_2$ coupled with mass spectroscopy. The major limitation of the acetylene reduction test is that the activity of the enzyme at the time of the assay has been measured and not the amount of nitrogen fixed.

The acetylene reduction test, apart from enzyme preparation, was first used for legume nodules (Koch and Evans, 1966) and lake and soil samples (Stewart et al., 1967; Hardy et al., 1968). Some modification was necessary for its application to rhizosphere associations. Roots removed from soil reduce acetylene, after a lag of 8 to 12 hours. This has not yet been satisfactorily explained (Rinaudo et al., 1971; Döbereiner et al., 1972; Yoshida, 1971). All attempts to eliminate this lag, for example, by removing the root system under N_2, by addition of phosphate buffer or CO_2 in various concentrations as well as different acetylene and oxygen concentrations were unsuccessful, although intact soil plant systems reduce acetylene without lag and are independent of the pO_2 of the gas phase above the soil (Fig. 1). Roots removed from the soil are inactivated in air, showing maximal N_2-ase activity at pO_2 0.04 atm. (Fig. 2). For all these reasons, field samples which cannot be assayed *in situ* have been prepared in the following way: Whole plants are removed from the field, shaken free from soil (rhizosphere soil) and immediately washed in water to avoid drying and excessive oxygen access. About one gram portions of roots are distributed into 50 to 100 ml vials which are closed with serum caps, evacuated and the gas phase replaced by a $N_2:O_2$ mixture with pO_2 0.04 atm. These vials are preincubated without acetylene overnight, then 1% (O_2) and 10% C_2H_2 is injected and reduction rates determined after two to five hours.

When soil cores with intact soil plant systems are required, they may be taken in inverted Leonard jars (glass bottles with the bottom cut off) which are placed into larger jars containing some water (5 cm from bottom). These jars also should be left for at least 24 hours to equilibrate, then the bottle neck is closed with a "subba" seal and 10% acetylene injected. Measurements of C_2H_4 production after one hours are usually satisfactory and after the gas sample has been removed for assay, the bottle neck is opened again and the cores can be used repeatedly after intervals of at least 5 hours. Intact systems of small seeded plants can also be obtained by growing the seedlings in test tubes and fitting "subba" seals to the tubes for the assay.

In situ studies are performed by introducing into the soil 30 cm wide steel cylinder fitted with transparent plastic domes (Balandreau and Dommergues, 1972). Instead of injecting acetylene, small amounts of CaC_2 and water can be used. Limitations to this method are difficulties of acetylene and ethylene diffusion, especially in heavy moist soils (Balandreau et al., 1973; Day[1/]).

1/　Day, I. M.　1973.　Personnal communications.

CHANGE OF GAS PHASE

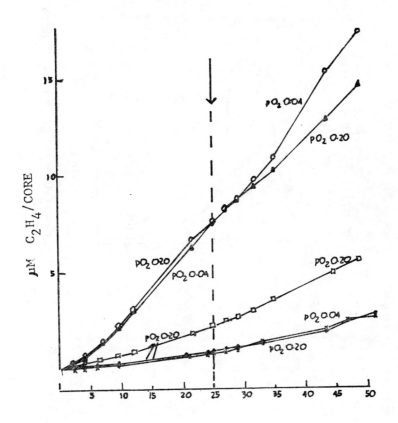

INCUBATION TIME (hr.)

Figure 1. Effect of oxygen tension on nitrogenase activity of *P. notatum* plants, intact in soil cores, incubated in dessicators. (Dobereiner *et al.* 1972).

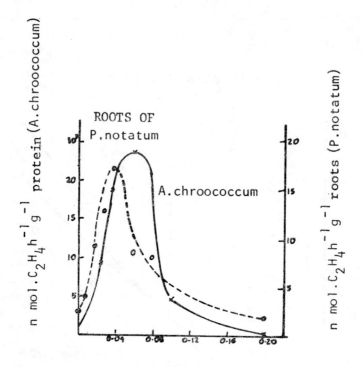

Figure 2.   Effects of oxygen concentration on the nitrogenase activity of *Paspallum notatum* roots and in *A. chroococum* cultures. (Dobereiner *et al.*, 1972: Drozd and Postgate 1972).

III RESULTS

Field data are now available from several tropical countries (Table 1) for the major forage grasses and for rice. As expected, large variations occur between sites but the higher values indicate the potential of such systems. These data also show that most of the nitrogenase activity is situated on the roots with very little found in the soil. Washing the roots actually increases nitrogenase activity (Döbereiner, 1973).

To integrate the nitrogenase activity it is necessary to know more about daily and seasonal variations. Figure 3 shows typical results of the day-night cycle of intact soil- plant systems, very similar to that observed with sorghum seedlings grown in test tubes (Döbereiner and Dart, 1973). Balandreau and Villemin (1973) observed such two peak curves during *in situ* measurements on *Andropogon* and *Hyparrhenia* in Ivory Coast

Table 1.—N₂-fixation potential in rhizosphere associations of field grown tropical grasses. (Minimal and maximal values recorded).

Plant species	Country	N-ase activity (n-moles C_2H_4/g/h) Roots	Soil	Estimate from maximal values (g N/ha/day) Roots[a]	Soil[b]	Reference
Andropogon gayanus (C-4)	Nigeria	15—270	—	302	—	Day & Dart unpublished
Andropogon spp. (C-4)	Ivory Coast	50—380	—	425	—	Balandreau et al. 1973
Brachiaria mutica (C-4)	Brazil	150—750	0	817	0	Dobereiner & Day 1973
B. rugulosa (C-4)	Brazil	5—150	—	166	—	Dobereiner & Day 1973
B. brachylopa (?)	Ivory Coast	100—140	—	157	—	Balandreau et al. 1973
Bulbostylis aphylanthoides	Ivory Coast	74	—	83	—	Balandreau et al. 1973
Cynodon dactilon (C-4)	Brazil	17—269	0—0.068	300	30	Dobereiner & Day 1973
Cynodon dactilon (C-4)	Nigeria	10—50	—	56	—	Day & Dart unpublished
Cyperus sp. (?)	Brazil	10—30	—	33	—	Dobereiner unpublished
Cyperus sp. (?)	Nigeria	2	—	2	—	Day & Dart unpublished
Cyperus obtusiflorus (?	Ivory Coast	30—620	—	694	—	Balandreau et al. 1973
Digitaria decumbens (C-4)	Brazil	21—404	0—0.349	452	156	Dobereiner & Day 1973
Hyparrhenia rufa (C-4)	Brazil	20—30	0—0.148	33	66	Dobereiner & Day 1973
Hyparrhenia rufa (C-4)	Nigeria	30—140	—	156	—	Day & Dart unpublished
Hyparrhenia dissoluta (?)	Nigeria	10—15	—	17	—	Day & Dart unpublished
Hyparrhenia dissoluta (?)	Ivory Coast	—	—	—	—	Balandreau et al. 1973
Melinis minutiflora (C-4)	Brazil	13—41	0—0.187	45	84	Dobereiner & Day 1973
Panicum maximum (C-4)	Brazil	20—299	0—0.148	335	66	Dobereiner & Day 1973
Panicum maximum (C-4)	Nigeria	75	—	84	—	Day & Dart unpublished
Panicum maximum (C-4)	Ivory Coast	(intact system in situ)			8	Balandreau et al. 1973
Paspalum notatum (C-4)	Brazil	2—283	0—0.330	634	148	Dobereiner & Dart 1973
Paspalum comersonii (?)	Nigeria	25—30	—	33	—	Day & Dart unpublished
Pennisetum purpureum (C-4)	Brazil	5—954	0—0.086	1068	38	Dobereiner & Day 1973
Pennisetum purpureum (C-4)	Nigeria	60	—	67	—	Day & Dart unpublished
Zea maíz (C-4)	USA	14—16	—	—	—	Day & Dart unpublished
Zea maíz (C-4)	not stated	10—3000	—	—	—	Balandreau & Dommergues 1972
Oryza sativa (C-3)	Phillipines	8—80	0—2.200	90	550	Yoshida 1971
Oryza sativa (C-3)	Ivory Coast	(intact system in situ)		766	—	Balandreau et al. 1973
Rye grass (C-3)	France	50	—	—	—	Balandreau et al. 1973

a — Based on 5000 kg/roots/ha.
b — Based on 2 x 10⁶ g soil/ha.

savannas. Rice and rye grass which are C-3 plants, apparently do not show the night peak (Balandreau et al, 1973). The nitrogenase activity of intact soil plant systems can be compared with that of the same roots removed from the soil and preincubated overnight the same way as the field samples (Fig. 3). This probably indicates that field data obtained as those in Table 1, underestimate whole day activity.

Seasonal variations for two forage grasses can be observed in Fig. 4. High nitrogenase activity in Elephant grass seems restricted to active growing plants while very little activity was found during the cooler season when the growth of this tropical species is limited, although temperatures would seem adequate for microbial activity (15 to 25°C). Soil humidity during this season decreases but analysis of the data showed that it was not the only reason for the decline in activity. When a large number of samples were taken during the summer, humidity was highly significantly related to nitrogenase activity in Rothamsted soil (Fig. 5).

Once the potential of nitrogen fixation in grass association has been demonstrated, the identification of conditions which permit high fixation rates seem of major importance. Agricultural practices which would be expected to interfere are numerous, but nitrogen, phosphorus and Mo should be given first rank. It can be seen that the application of 20 kg N/ha every two weeks did not affect nitrogenase activity of Elephant grass or Pangola, even after seven applications (Fig. 4). Balandreau et al., (1973) observed increased nitrogenase activity up to 40 ppm of added NH_4 — N in rice systems (Fig. 6), but the activity of field grown maize was reduced to one third by the application of 45 kg N/ha (Balandreau and Dommergues, 1972). In soil plant cores with Paspalum notatum, nitrogenase activity ceased two hours after application of 10 ppm NH^+_4 — N and four hours after supply of the same amount of NO^-_3 — N, but after one week these effects were negligible (Fig. 7). No data are available on the effect of phosphorus and minor elements, but the highest activities recorded in Table 1 were all obtained with high phosphorus fertilizations.

One of the most promising research areas seems to be plant breeding directly to increase nitrogenase activity on roots. Table 2 shows significant differences between ecotypes of Paspallum notatum and P. purpureum cultivars,. Native forms of P. notatum (batatais grass) are the most efficient N_2 - fixers, compared to the improved diploid Pensacola types which were probably bred for response to high mineral nitrogen fertilizer levels.

The main question about the fate of fixed nitrogen might be answered partially by the data presented in Table 3. These grasses growing in vermiculite with nitrogen free nutrient solution behaved practically as legumes. At no time did they show signs of nitrogen deficiency and after two months most of the fixed nitrogen was found in the plant. While this study suggests the transport of fixed nitrogen from the bacterium to the plant, more precise studies will have to be performed with $^{15}N_2$ to confirm the bacterium-to-plant transfer of nitrogen.

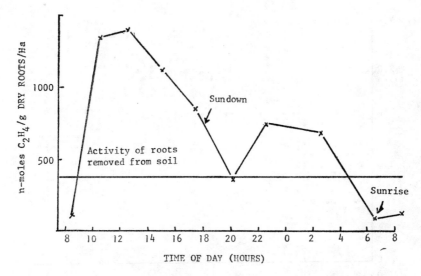

Figure 3. Daily cycle of nitrogenase activity in intact plant-soil cores with *Paspalum notatum* in comparison with activity of exised roots, (Dobereiner & Day, 1973).

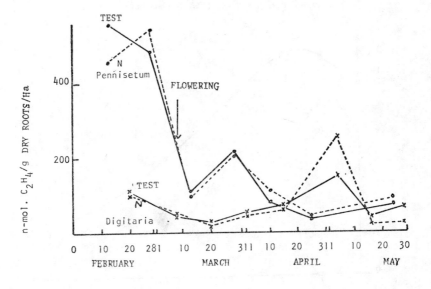

Figure 4. Seasonal variation of N$_2$-ase activity on roots of *Pennisetum purpureum* and *Digitaria decumbens* grown in the field with and without N fertilizer (20 Kg N/Ha as NH$_4$NO$_3$ every two weeks).

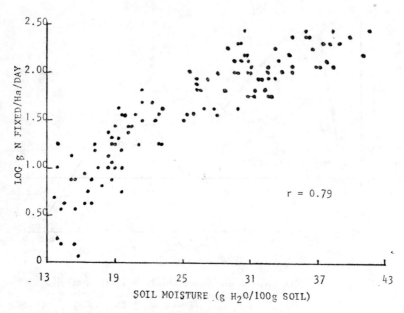

Figure 5.   Effect of soil moisture on nitrogenase activity in a Rothamsted field soil during summer (Day & Dart unpublished).

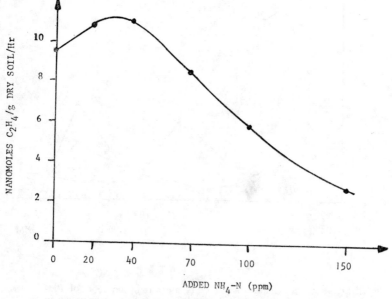

Figure 6.   Effect of NH₄-N additions on nitrogenase activity in the rice Rhizosphere. Rice seedlings in test tubes incubated at 28°C and 30.000 lux (14 H/Day). (Balandreau *et al.* 1973).

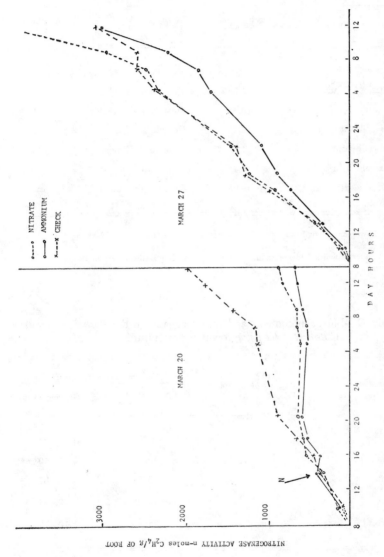

Figure 7. Nitrogenase activity at different hours in presence or absence of N added as NO_3 or NH_4.

Table 2.—Differences between cultivars and ecotypes of *P. notatum* and *P. purpureum* in relation to nitrogenase activity on their roots.*

Paspalum notatum		Pennisetum purpureum	
Cultivar or ecotype	n-moles C_2H_4/ g roots/h	Cultivar	n-moles C_2H_4/ g roots/h
"Batatais" Km 47	39.8	Taiwan A-143*	33.6
"Batatais" Matão	21.0	Taiwan A-144**	60.2
Pensacola Florida	10.3	Puva Napier N° 1	15.8
Pensacola Argentine	12.2	Gigante de Pinda**	93.3
Typhen hybrid	11.4	Elefante de Pinda	33.2
Pensacola hybrid	6.7		
Diff. significant at	p=0.05	Diff. significant at	p=0.01

* Nitrogenase activity determined on extracted roots obtained in field experiments.

** Cultivars which had not started flowering yet while all others were in flower.

Table 3.—Nitrogen contents and nitrogen gains in the *Paspalum notatum - Azotobacter paspali* grown in pot cultures.

	At transplant	Two months after transplanting	
		Dead plants*	Growing plants**
		mg N/pot	
Vermiculite	13.05	40.80	64.40***
Plants	5.47	3.28	63.87
Total	18.52	44.08	128.47
N_2 fixed	—	25.54	109.75

* Mean of 6 pots with dead plants.

** Mean of 33 pots with actively growing plants.

*** Included many fine roots which were impossible to separate from the vermiculite.

IV DISCUSSION

Regardless of the potential for N_2 - fixation in tropical grass association ,the enigma arises why N_2 - fixation appears to be more important in this plant-microbe association compared to others previously investigated. Earlier it was pointed out that the rhizosphere of tropical grasses is a site where most probably substantial nitrogen fixation by free living N_2 - fixing bacteria should be found (Döbereiner, 1968). In addition, constantly high temperatures, higher light energy input and the stimulating effects of a number of tropical grasses on *Azotobacter* or *Beijerinckia* have been observed as factors influencing growth of tropical grasses. Later is was shown that the grasses (except rice) which enhance the development of nitrogen-fixing bacteria in the rhizosphere all posses the C-4 dicarboxylic acid photosynthetic pathway (Hatch and Slack, 1970; Oliveira *et al.*, 1972). This property enables the plant to convert higher light intensities more efficiently with net assimilation rates twice as high as C-3 plants; although, the relative growth rates are similar (Fig. 8). Nitrogen fixation on grass roots is closely related to plant photosynthesis (Fig. 3). Lowest activities are observed in the early morning, and two to three hours after sunrise there is a steep increase of activity which reaches its maximum at midday and decerases towards sundown. The second peak at midnight was attributed by Balandreau and Willemin (1973) to hydrolization of the starch accumulated in the chloroplasts of C-4 plants during the day. By comparing nitrogenase activity of intact systems with that of roots removed from the soil, it seems that the latter represents a residual activity maintained by root reserves while the additional activity during the day and possibly that at night are directly dependent on plant photosynthates.

The amount of energy necessary for the fixation of nitrogen, even in C-4 grasses could hardly be supplied in root exudates, if one accepts the usual ratio of 1 g glucose for 10 mg N fixed. However, several factors can be suggested which have been shown to increase efficiency of nitrogen-fixers and which might differentiate the rhizosphere environments from laboratory environment of monocultures. These factors include low oxygen tensions which can triple fixation (Parker, 1954), low concentrations of carbon compounds which are used more efficiently, especially when all traces of excreted fixed nitrogen are removed, and the observation that nitrogen fixation by root organisms might not be growth linked (Döbereiner, 1974). Generally, measurements of root biomass tend to underestimate total roots. However, if nitrogenase activity is integrated over a 24 hour cycle and root biomass is assumed to have a mean value of 5000 kg roots/ha (Thronghton, 1957) and a conversion factor of 3:1 for C_2H_2:N_2 is used, then values of 1.5 kg N fixed/ha/day are possible in grass ecosystems.

While these high values were reached only during the most active growing season and under specifically favorable conditions, they show the potential of such associations for nitrogen accretion. The challenge of identifying the conditions under which such high nitrogen fixation occurs and of directing agricultural research towards this goal will hopefully attract many research workers in the near future.

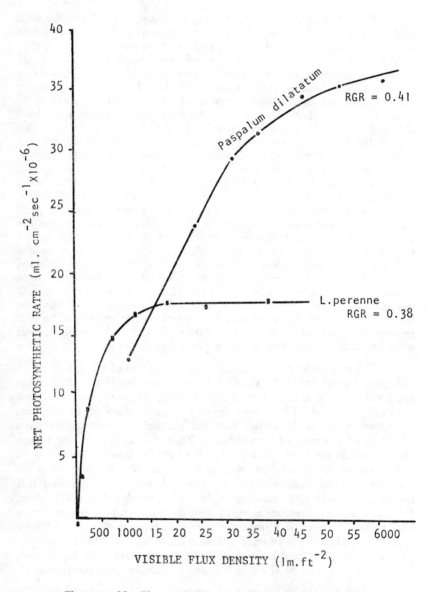

Figure 8. Net Photosynthesis and visible radiative flux density for *Paspalum dilatatum* and *Lolium perenne*. (Cooper, 1966).

V SUMMARY

Recent findings on nitrogen fixation associated with crops or pastures of tropical grasses, as evaluated by the acetylene reduction method are reviewed. Nitrogen fixation potentials of several important forage grasses seem of considerable economic importance with values of up to 1 kg N_2 fixed ha/day estimated. Research lines to define the conditions which lead to such high fixation rates are indicated.

VI REFERENCES

BALANDREAU, J. and DOMMERQUES, Y. 1972. Assaying nitrogenase (C_2H_2) activity in the field. Proc. Intern. Symp. IBP, Upsaala, Sweden.

BALANDREAU, J. and VILLEMIN, G. 1973. Fixation biologique de l'azote moleculaire en savanne de Lamto (Basse Cote d'Ivoire). Resultat preliminaires. Revue Ecol. Biol. Sol., 10:25-33.

BALANDREAU, J., RINAUDO, G., FARES HAMAD, I. and DOMMERQUES, Y. 1973. N_2 fixation in paddy soils. IBP Synthesis Meeting, Edinburgh.

COCKING, E. C. 1973. New approaches to the modification of higher plants to enable them to show nitrogen-fixing activity. Nitrogen Fixation in the Biosphere, IBP Synthesis Meeting, Edinburgh.

COOPER, J. P. 1966. Ann. Rep. Welsh Plant Breeding Sta. p. 22-27.

DILLWORTH, M. J. 1966. Biochim. Biophys. Acta 127:285-294.

DIXON, R. A. and POSTGATE, J. R. 1972. Nature 237:102-103.

DÖBEREINER, J. 1961. Nitrogen fixing bacteria in the rhizosphere of sugarcane. Plant & Soil 14:211-217.

DÖBEREINER, J. 1966. *Azotobacter paspali* n.sp. uma bacteria fixadora de nitrogenio na rizosfera de *Paspalum*. Pesq. Agropec. Bras. 1:357-365.

DÖBEREINER, J. 1968. Non-symbiotic nitrogen fixation in tropical soils. Pesq. Agrop. Bras. 3:1-6.

DÖBEREINER, J. 1970. Further research on *Azotobacter paspali* and its variety specific occurrence in the rhizosphere of *Paspalum notatum* Flugge. Zentralbl. Bakteriol. Parasitknde. Abt. II, 124:224-230.

DÖBEREINER, J. 1974. N_2—fixing bavteria in the rhizosphere. Chapter 4. *In:* A. Quispel (ed.) Biological Nitrogen Fixation. North Holland Publ. Co. Amsterdam.

DÖBEREINER, J. and DAY, J. M. 1973. Nitrogen fixation in the rhizosphere of tropical grasses. Nitrogen Fixation in the Biosphere, IBP Synthesis Meeting, Edinburgh.

DÖBEREINER, J., DAY, J. M. and DART, P. L. 1972. Nitrogenase activity and oxygen sensitivity of the *Paspalum rotataum-Azotobacter paspali* association. J. Gen. Microbiol. 71:103-116.

HARDY, R. W. F., HOLSTEN, R. D., JACKSON, E. K. and BURNS, R. C. 1968. The acetylene-ethylene assay for N_2 fixation: Laboratory and field evaluation. Plant Physiol. 43:1185-1207.

HATCH, M. D. and SLACK, C. R. 1970. Photosynthetic CO_2 fixation pathways. Ann. Rev. Plant Physiol. 21:141-162.

KOCH, B. and EVANS, H. J. 1966. Reduction of acethylene to ethylene by soybean root nodules. Plant Physiol. 41:1748-1750.

OLIVEIRA, B. A. D., FARIA, F. R. S., SOUTO, S. M., CARNEIRO, A. M., DÖBEREINER, J. and ARONOVICH, S. 1973. Identificacao de gramíneas tropicales com via fotosintética "C-4", pela anatomía foliar. Pesq. Agrop. opec. Bras. (in press).

PARKER, A. C. 1954. Effect of oxygen on the fixation of nitrogen by *Azotobacter*. Nature 173:780.

RINAUDO, G. 1970. Fixation Biologique de l'azote dans trois types de sols de rizieres de Cote d'Ivoire. These de Doteur Ing. Faculté des Sciences, Montpellier.

RINAUDO, G., BALANDREAU, J. and DOMMERQUES, Y. 1971. Algal and bacterial non-symbiotic nitrogen fixation in paddy soils. *In:* Nitrogen Fixation in Natural and Agricultural Habitats. Plant & Soil Special. Vol. p. 471-479.

SCHÖLLBORN, R. and BURRIS, R. H. 1966. Fed. Proc. 25:610.

STEWART, W. D. P., FITZGERALD, G. P. and BURRIS, R. H. 1967. *In situ* studies on N: fixation using the acetylene reduction technique. Proc. Nat. Acad. Sci. Am. 58:2071-2078.

THROUGHTON, A. 1957. The underground organs of herbage grasses. Bull. 44, Commonw. Bur. Past. Field. Crops, p. 1-163.

YOSHIDA, T. 1971. Research Results Rep., Soil Microbiology, International Rice Research Institute, Los Baños, Philippines.

12 Soil - Plant - Rhizobium Interaction in Tropical Agriculture

PETER H. GRAHAM and DAVID H. HUBBELL

I INTRODUCTION

Cultivated plants vary in their requirements for combined nitrogen ranging from 380 to 750 kg ha^{-1} yr^{-1} (Date, 1973). Even unimproved savanna may require up to 160 kg ha^{-1} yr^{-1} (Dahlmann et al., 1969). Two processes, nitrogenous fertilization and biological nitrogen fixation, are significant in balancing these requirements. Production of fertilizer nitrogen continues to increase and now approaches 25 MM tons yr^{-1} (Hardy et al., 1971). Unfortunately most of this fertilizer is used in developed countries, especially under systems of intensive agriculture. Thus in the USA and the Netherlands nitrogen fertilizers are applied at a rate equivalent to more than 17 kg/person/year, while in India the proportion is only 0.7 kilos/person/year. (Mishustin and Shilnikova, 1969). This imbalance is unlikely to change in the near future. Even where N - fertilizers ar eavailable their coast, the difficulties of transportation, or the level of application necessary, can render then economically unacceptable. This is common with certain system of beef production (Nuthall and Whitemann, 1972).

Global estimates for biological nitrogen fixation vary between 100 and 500 MM tons yr^{-1} (Donald, 1960; Vincent, 1972; Date, 1973). Free living soil organisms such as *Clostridium* and *Azotobacter* contribute relatively little to this figure (Delwiche and Wijler, 1956, Parker, 1957), though there is now steadily accumulating evidence of significant fixation in some rhizosphere associations (Döbereiner et al., 1973; Dommergues et al., 1973; Yoshida and Ancajas, 1973).

The legume - *Rhizobium* symbiosis is probably the major source of fixed nitrogen. Though estimates vary from less than 100 kg ha^{-1} yr^{-1} to more than 600 kg ha^{-1} yr^{-1} (Table 1), Date (1973) suggests an average fixation between 100 and 200 kg ha^{-1} yr^{-1}. This would be equivalent to applying more than 500 kg (NH$_4$)$_2$ SO$_4$ ha^{-1} yr^{-1}.

Under tropical conditions the manipulation of host, *Rhizobium*, and soil factors needs careful management. Consequently, this review will concentrate on four aspects:

1) Host-*Rhizobium* Interaction.
2) Soil pH.
3) Soil Temperature.
4) Soil Nutrition.

Table 1.—Levels of nitrogen fixation by some representative legume - *Rhizobium* Associations.

LEGUME	N$_2$ Fixed Kg/ha	REFERFENCE
Glycine max.	33-40 /growth cycle	Hardy *et al.*, 1971
Glycine max.	40-120/growth cycle	Sundara Rao, 1971
Glycine max.	40-80 /annum	Erdman, 1959
Trifolium subterraneum	100-200/annum	Erdman, 1959
Stylosanthes guyanensis	-100/annum	Hansell & Norris, 1962
Desmodium intortum	-303/annum	Whitney, 1967
Medicago sativa	150-160/annum	Mishustin & Shilnikova, 1969
Medicago sativa	90-220/annum	Bell & Nutman, 1970

Table 2.—Effectiveness sub-group among the cowpea miscellany.

1. *NON SPECIFIC:*	ARACHIS, CAJANUS, CROTALARIA, CA-LOPOGONIUM, DOLICHOS, P. ATROPUR-PUREUS, P. AUREUS, P. LATHYROIDES, PUERARIA, TERAMNUS, VIGNA.
2. *HIGHLY SPECIFIC:*	GLYCINE MAX, LOTONONIS, LEUCAENA
3. *INTERMEDIATE:*	DESMODIUM, CENTROSEMA, STYLOSAN-THES, LUPINUS

Though most tropical legumes form nodules when inoculated with rhizobia from the so-called "cowpea miscellany" group, differences in effectiveness are common.

Three broad effectiveness groups can be delineated as shown in Table 2. Each of these presents different problems to the soil microbiologist. Species such as *Vigna, Calopogonium, Arachis* and *Pueraria* nodulate freely, usually establishing effective symbioses. (Allen and Allen, 1939; Bowen, 1956; Norris, 1972); even with the native soil microflora (Norris 1972). As a result inoculation will often fail to improve yields (Norris, 1972; Lopes *et al.*, 1970; Date, 1973), as the native Rhizobia compete with and limit the number of nodules produced by the inoculant. It is dangerous to assume that such species will not respond to inoculation. Cowpea group rhizobia, occur widely in the soils of the Llanos Orientales, but because of the extreme acidity few are able to form nodules. Thus inoculation or liming of the soil is essential for adequate nodulation (Fig. 1).

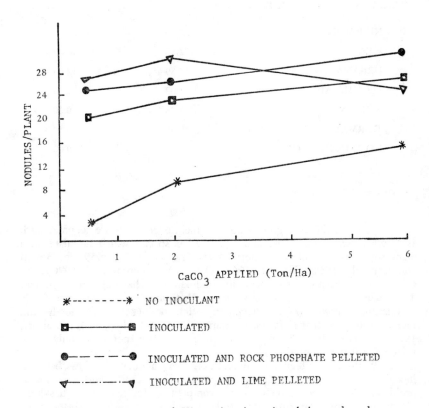

Figure 1. Response of *Vigna sinensis* to inoculation and seed pelleting in Carimagua soil (from Morales *et al.* 1973).

The second group of legumes, have specific *Rhizobium* requirements, ie. Soya (Hamatova, 1965) or *Lotononis* (Norris, 1958). For these species, legume inoculant quality is of particular importance. At present only three or possibly four countries in Latin and Central America produce inoculants of reasonable quality. The remaining areas either do not use inoculants to any extent, or else import them from countries such as USA or Australia. Long ocean voyages and prolonged storage in customs can often be a cause of lowered viability and inoculation response (Table 3). Varietal and photoperiod differences can also influence the efficacy of imported cultures. To overcome such problems each country or economic region needs to develop expertise in inoculant testing and use.

Table 3.—Nodule number per plants in soybean inoculated with various brands of inoculants.

INOCULATED BRAND	ECUADOR, 1970*	
	BOLICHE	PORTOVIEJO
NITRAGIN	31.00	23.35
E. Z.	22.80	26.00
URBANA	12.50	12.80
LEGUME AID	1.00	5.20
NOCTIN	1.20	0.20
DORMAL	0.50	0.50
NO INOCULATION	3.00	0.00

* Data provided by INIAP.

Between the two groups already mentioned lie those legumes such as *Centrosema, Desmodium,* and *Stylosanthes* species which nodulate with many soil rhizobia, but often ineffectively (Bowen, 1956, 1959 a,b; Bowen and Kennedy, 1961; Diatloff, 1968; Date, 1969; Souto *et al,* 1970). In this group, species differences in nodulation behaviour are common. Thus while *Desmodium intortum* and *Desmodium barbatum* are freely nodulating, *Desmodium uncinatum* is often nodulated only slowly and ineffectively by native *Rhizobium* strains (Allen and Allen, 1939; Diatloff, 1968). *Desmodium heterophyllum* will nodulate normally only with rhizobia isolated from this species.

With these legumes competition for nodulation sites between inoculant strain and rhizobia already present in the soil could a be major problem. The phenomenon of strain competition for nodulation has been extensively studied in Australia (Ireland and Vincent, 1968; Date, pers. comm.) a typical result being shown in Fig. 2

— 214 —

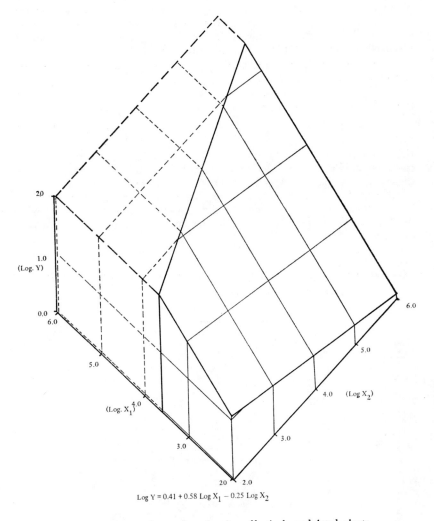

$$\text{Log Y} = 0.41 + 0.58 \text{ Log X}_1 - 0.25 \text{ Log X}_2$$

Figure 2. Regression surface showing effectively nodulated plants (y) as a function of *Rhizobia* in the seed (x_1) and in the soil (x_2).

The approach to soil competition problems encountered by CIAT research group will have 3 branches:

i) To look for the strains of greatest efficiency and competitive ability for each important legume species. CIAT hopes to develop germoplasm capability for tropical strains of *Rhizobium,* and to act as a major preservation and distribution centre for them, (Graham, 1973). As many commercially important legume cultivars are of South American origin (Henzell, 1967) CIAT's location is ideal for this purpose.

ii) To determine rhizobial populations in a range of tropical soils and to assess whether they are equally effective with the commonly grown legume varieties. Effectiveness differences with particular hosts could justify the planting of certain legumes in preference to others.

iii) To study host-*Rhizobium* interaction and how it could be used to limit competition from native rhizobia in soil. Table 4 shows time of first nodule formation in 4 *Stylosanthes* cultivars. Strain 56 nodulated all cultivars rapidly and if used as an inoculant, could perhaps outcompete the native population. A cultivar, slow to nodulate with soil strains, but which would nodulate rapidly with particular inoculant strains is desirable. That such varieties exist is evident in the studies of Souto *et al* (1970) with the *Stylosanthes* variety 1022, and in the known specificity of *D. heterophyllum* and *Stylosanthes hamata.*

Table 4.—Time to first nodule formation in 4 varies of *Stylosanthes* as influenced by inoculant strain.*

	VARIETY				
Strain	La Libertad	David 217	Subserícea	Hamata	Strain means
79	18.3	18.4	14.2	13.6	16.1
278	22.2	23.5	12.2	14.8	18.2
28	19.6	18.3	14.7	17.3	17.4
315	21.0	17.5	18.2	13.2	17.4
56	14.5	13.5	12.9	16.0	14.22
297	15.0	17.6	15.0	16.3	16.2
VARIETY MEANS	18.4	18.1	14.73	15.2	—

* Mean of 15 replications

F (strains) = 19.78***;

F (varieties) = 42.80***

This paper will consider only those aspects important to nodulation and *Rhizobium* survival in soil.

Like plants, rhizobia differ in their resistance to pH *Medic* rhizobia are being most susceptible, and "cowpea" group rhizobia relatively resistant (Loneragan, 1972). It is generally assumed that strains behave similarly in media and in soil, though colloidal and organic material in soil may have some protective action, and aluminium and manganese a limiting influence. In soil of pH 5.5 or less medic, clover and bean rhizobia do not persist, as is evident in Fig. 3. (Danso, pers. comm.). The critical pH for slow-growing root - nodule bacteria in soil is between pH 4.3 and 4.9 (Norris, 1959; Morales *et al.*, 1973).

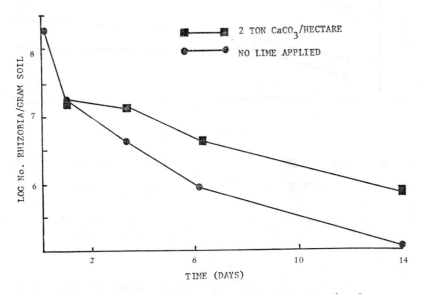

Figure 3. Influence of soil conditions on survival of *R. phaseoli* strain 57 in Carimagua soil (from Danso, Pers. Comm.).

In temperate legumes where nodulation follows root - hair penetration (Fahraeus, 1957) one of the steps in nodule formation is acid sensitive (Munns, 1968, 1970). Thus lucerne plants maintained at pH 4.5 do not nodulate, but those pretreated at pH 5.5 for 2-3 days prior to exposure to a pH of 4.5 nodulate well. Apparently the pretreatment period allowed for multiplication of rhizobia in the rhizosphere and the subsequent initiation of infection.

Strain selection can help to overcome nodulation problems due to acidity (Lie, 1970; Norris, 1972a). With *Leucaena leucocephala*, strains

CB 89 is much more resistant to acidity than is NGR 8 (Norris, 1973; Morales *et al.;* 1973), (Fig. 4). Plant varieties may also differ in the extent to which they promote *Rhizobium* multiplication in the rhizosphere, and hence nodulation at low pH (Fig. 5).

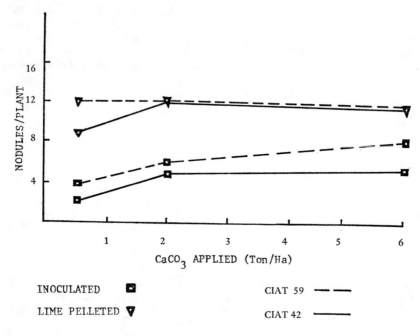

Figure 4. Response of *Leucaena leucocephala* to inoculation with two different *Rhizobium* strains in Carimagua conditions.

Pelleting of leguminous seed with substances such as $CaCO_3$ or rock phosphate has long been used as means of protecting rhizobia from acid soil conditions (Loneragan *et al.*, 1955; Hastings and Drake, 1960; Brockwell, 1963). The advantages of the techniques are summarised by Brockwell (1963) while Date (1970) and Norris (1971a,b; 1972) and Graham *et al.*, (1974) provide technical details of stickers and pelleting substances to be used.

Some controversy exists as to when to employ a limestone pellet, and when rock phosphate. Limestone appears preferable for plants such as clovers, medics or beans, whose rhizobia are likely to be most acid sensitive (Loneragan *et al.*, 1955; Date, 1965, 1970). A typical response to lime pelleting is shown in Fig. 5, with *Phaseolus vulgaris* as the host plant. (Morales, *et al.*, 1973). Norris (1967) reviews other plants benefiting from lime pelleting.

Norris (1967) also distinguishes between lime pelleting as a means of overcoming soil acidity and for the preinoculation of leguminous seed. While acknowledging that lime pelleting can be beneficial under circumstances of acid soils with toxicity problems (Döbereiner and Aranovich, 1965) Norris suggests that the acid resistant tropical rhizobia will not normally benefit from this treatment. At pH 5.2-5.9, the range in which Norris worked, this assumption is probably valid. At lower pH values, as found in the Llanos, tropical species can respond to lime pelleting (Morales et al., 1973). However, this could be a nutritional rather than an acid sensitive response.

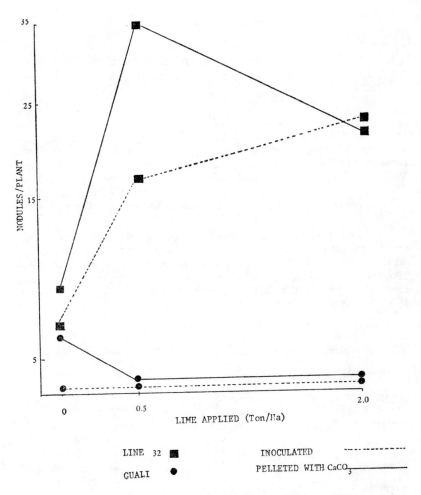

Figure 5. Influence of lime amendment, variety and inoculation on nodule number/plant in Carimagua soil.

Norris (1967, 1971a,b, 1972b) also criticises the use of lime in the preinoculation of tropical legumes seeds suggesting that slow —growing root— nodule bacteria survive poorly when in direct contact with lime. In contrast (Date and Cornish, 1968), working with *Phaseolus atropurpureus* could show no significant difference in *Rhizobium* survival when seedswere rock —phosphate or lime pelleted. As rock phosphate is certainly an adequate pelleting material for slow —growing root— nodule bacteria it is probably safer to use this substance even under conditions of Al or Mn excess, and to await further studies comparing the substances and clarifying the reasons for the differences in response obtained so far.

IV TEMPERATURE EFFECTS

Three aspects of temperature are important to the legume - *Rhizobium* symbiosis.

    i)   Maximum temperature for survival of rhizobia in peat or in soil.

    ii)   Temperature effects limiting nodulation.

    iii)   Temperature requirements for fixation.

In culture rhizobia grow best from 28-32°C (Allen and Allen, 1950) with *Rhizobium meliloti* least affected by rising temperature, as shown in Table 5 (Bowen and Kennedy, 1959). In soil survival varies with conditions, being markedly influenced by soil type (Marshall and Roberts, 1963; Marshall, 1964), duration of elevated temperature (Brockwell and Phillips, 1965; Wilkins, 1967) and *Rhizobium* strains (Chatel and Parker, 1973). *Rhizobium* survival in peat is also affected by strain, peat source and temperature (Graham *et al.*, 1974).

Norris (1970) highlights this aspect of tropical microbiology pointing out that in many areas soil temperature at 2.5 - 5.0 cm depth can range from 40 to 45°C for up to 6 hours a day (Bowen and Kennedy, 1959; Phillipots, 1967; Graham unbublished). In several instances temperature has been reported to be limiting factor in *Rhizobium* survival in soil (Marshall, 1964; Phillipots, 1967; Diatloff, 1970).

Table 5.—Maximum temperature for growth in 3 species of *Rhizobium*.

SPECIES	STRAINS			
	Tested	Lowest	Highest	Mean
R. *MELILOTI*	8	36.5	42.2	41.0
R. *TRIFOLII*	9	31.0	31.4	33.2
R. *SP.*	68	30.0	42.0	35.4

There have been few detailed studied related to the effects of temperature on nodulation and fixation of tropical legumes. Tropical pasture legumes nodulate poorly at 18°C with most having optimum nodulation at 30°C (Table 6). Dart and Mercer (1965) obtained optimum nodulation of *Vigna sinensis* at 27°C, while with *P. vulgaris,* the optimum temperature varies between 28 and 32°C depending upon variety and strain (Graham, unpublished). Under high soil temperature regimes increased rates of inoculum can be of value to enhance nodulation.

Table 6.—Mean nodule number 15 days after inoculation with strain CB 756 and grown at 4 root temperatures with a 14 hr light period and 30/25°C shoot temperature regime.*

Species	ROOT TEMPERATURE (°C)			
	18	24	30	36
GLYCINE WITHTII	0	2.1	8.1	0
DESMODIUM UNCINATUM	0	0.6	9.1	0.3
DESMODIUM INTORTUM	1.4	8.9	10.2	1.5
STYLOSANTHES HUMILIS	0	9.2	13.7	5.5
PHASEOLUS ATROPURPUREUS	0	14.2	17.6	13.5

* After Gibson (1971).

N_2 fixation appears less sensitive to temperature than nodulation. Dart and Day (1971) demonstrated considerable fixation at 35°C in both soybean and cowpea. Hardy et al., (1968) studied fixation in soybeans as affected by temperature, showing diurnal variation, but there are no comparable results relevant to tropical conditions or pasture species.

V NUTRITIONAL FACTORS AFFECTING THE SYMBIOSIS

Hallsworth (1972) cited four factors essential for successful studies of nutritional requirements for nodulation and nitrogen fixation in legumes. These were:

i)   Nutrients applied must be in an available form and at levels adequate for both plant and nodular systems.

ii)   Plants must be able to obtain, either from the native population or by inoculation, effective *Rhizobium* strains.

iii)   Seed should be selected to avoid carry over of trace metals from one planting to the next.

iv)   Trace elements and inoculants must be supplied by a suitable and standardised method.

Failure to consider one or more of these criteria has weakened many of the legume nutrition studies undertaken in tropical America.

Phosphorous is emerging as the element most limiting growth of legumes in tropical and subtropical environments (Loneragan, 1972). The difficulties of supplying phosphorous to the plant illustrate the first point made above. Phosphate deficiency is widespread in tropical soils, but additionally many soils are capable of fixing large quantities of applied P fertilizer. A typical result is shown in Figure 6 where applications of up to 900 kg/ha rock phosphate failed to increase phosphate levels in the plant above 0.18% P, a predetermined deficiency level. In the same soil, yields increased with superphosphate application up to 900 kg ha^{-1}. Influence on nodule dry weight per plant is also shown in Figure 6. As superphosphate in Colombia currently costs columbian pesos 2,700-3,000 per ton, its use with all but band application to grain legumes appears prohibitive. For this reason we have begun studies on vesicular-arbuscular fungus, and their possible use in improving phosphate availability to the plant. The possible

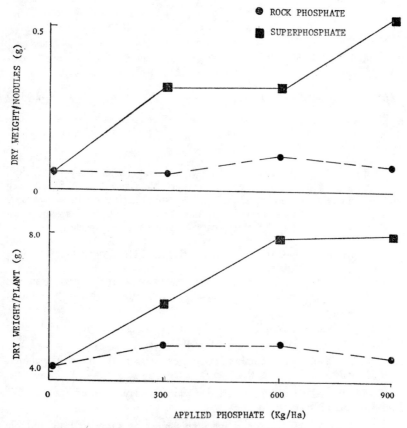

Figure 6.   Influence of form and level of Phosphate on bean development in Popayan soil.

need for a dual inoculation of leguminous seed, with vesicular-arbuscular fungi of the *Endogene* type and with *Rhizobium* would complicate an already confused picture.

Calcium, serves various functions in legumes. While these include pH changes and aluminium and manganese neutralization, only Ca - nodulation interactions will be considered here.

In temperate legumes, pH values below pH 4.0 (subterranean clover) or 4.8 (Lucerne) completely inhibit nodulation. Above pH 5.6 plants nodulate well except when calcium levels are limiting (Lowther, 1970; Munns, 1970). Between these pH limits increasing calcium, increasing pH and increasing inoculation rate replace one another in their effects on nodulation. As Loneragan (1972) states, the nodulation of temperate legumes in moderately acid soils is clearly delicately balanced, and is easily changed by H^+ ion, calcium and or to a lesser extent magnesium. No equivalent studies have been undertaken with tropical legumes, but since the mechanism by which rhizobia gain entry to the roots of such plants appears different (Hubbell and Napoli, 1971) such studies would certainly be warranted.

Since molybdenum is an essential component of the nitrogenase enzyme (Hardy *et al.*, 1971; Burris, 1972), and is least available under acid soil conditions (Hallsworth, 1972), it also is likely to be a limiting factor in many tropical situations. Fertilizer mixes, containing Molybdenum as used in many other countries are not common in the tropics. Various authors have tried to apply molybdenum mixed with the inoculant (Giddens, 1964; Burton and Curly, 1966) or on the pelleted seed (Date and Hillier, 1968; Gartrell, 1969). In these instances nodulation has often been depressed. Molybdic oxide can be incorporated on phosphate pelleted *Siratro* seed, at rates up to 100 g/ha without deterioration in *Rhizobium* viability. Sodium and ammonium molybdate give less satisfactory results. (Graham and Morales, unpublished). Seed applied Mo is much more effective than fertilizer dressing. (Reisenauer, 1963).

VI SUMMARY

Tropical legume microbiology is at the crossroads. Results of recent rhizobium legume studies tend to argue against intensifying efforts in this field. However it is our contention that legumes will have to play an important part in limiting critical protein shortages in the tropics (Dawson, 1970). It is possible that two approaches will have to be adopted, one tailored to the large land holder, the other to the campesino. For the latter, poorly educated and with holdings too small to justify the purchase of inoculant, preinoculated pelleted seed may for the first time be of real value. The large land owner will probably mantain and improve on existing practices. However, an effective legume-rhizobia symbiosis will still require careful management, which will go beyond the manipulation of the host, the infecting agent and the moderation of adverse soil conditions. Strain and variety selections need to be matched to the production site. In addition more care needs to be taken in both the production and testing of inoculants. Other management processes which will require improvement, include such simple steps as inoculation and in planting and fertilizing seeds.

VII REFERENCES

ALLEN, E. K. and ALLEN, O. N. 1950. Biochemical and symbiotic properties of the *Rhizobia*. Bact. Rev. *14*, 273-330.

ALLEN, O. N. and ALLEN, E. K. 1939. Root nodule bacteria of some tropical leguminous plants II. Cross inoculation tests within the cowpea group. Soil Sci. *47*, 63-76.

BELL, F. and NUTMAN, P. S. 1971. Experiments on nitrogen fixation by nodulated lucerne. Plant and Soil Spec. Volume pp. 231-264.

BOWEN, G. D. 1956. Nodulation of legumes indigenous to Queensland. Queensland J. Agric. Sci. *13*, 47-60.

BOWEN, G. D. 1959a. Field studies on nodulation and growth of *Centrosema pubescens*. Queensland J. Agric. Sci. *16*, 253-281.

BOWEN, G. D. 1959b. Specificity of nitrogen fixation in the *Rhizobium* symbiosis of *Centrosema pubescens*. Queensland J. Agric. Sci. *16*, 267-281.

BOWEN, G. D. and KENNEDY, M. M. 1959. Effect of high soil temperature on *Rhizobium spp*. Queensland J. Agric. Sci. *16*, 177-197.

BOWEN, G. D. and KENNEDY, M. M. 1961. Heritable variation in nodulation of *Centrosema pubescens*. Queensland J. Agric. Sci. *18*, 161-170.

BROCKWELL, J. 1963. Seed pelleting as an aid to legume seed inoculation. World Crops. *15*, 334-338.

BROCKWELL, J. and PHILLIPS, L. J. 1965. Survival at high temperature of *Rhizobium meliloti* in peat inoculant on lucerne seed. Aust. J. Agric. Sci. *27*, 332-333.

BURRIS, R. J. 1972. Progress in the biochemistry of nitrogen fixation. Proc. Roy. Soc. London B *172*, 339-354.

BURTON, J. C. and CURLEC, R. L. 1966. Compability of *Rhizobium japonicum* and sodium molybdate when combined in a peat carrier medium. Agron. J. *58*, 327-330.

CHATEL, D. A. and PARKER, C. A. 1973. Survival of field grown *Rhizobia* over the dry summer period in Western Australia. Soil Biol. and Biochem. *5*, 415-424.

DAHLMAN, R. C., OLSON, J. C. and DOKTADER, K. 1969. The nitrogen economy of grassland and dune soil. *In* "Biology and Ecology of Nitrogen" Nat. Acad. Sci. Wash. pp. 54-82.

DART, P. H. and DAY, J. M. 1971. Effects of incubation temperature and oxygen tension on nitrogenase activity of legume root-nodules. Plant and Soil Spec. Volume. pp. 167-184.

DATE, R. A. 1965. Legume inoculation and legume inoculant production. FAO Tech. Bull. 2012 Rome 1965.

DATE, R. A. 1969. A decade of legume inoculant quality control in Australia. J. Aust. Inst. Agric. Sci. *35*, 27-37.

DATE, R. R. 1970. Microbiological problems in the inoculation and nodulation of legumes, Plant and Soil 32, 703-735.

DATE, R. A. 1973. Nitrogen, a major limitation in the productivity of natural communities, crops and pasture in the pacific area. Soil Biol. and Biochem. *5*, 5-18.

DATE, R. A. and CORNISH, R. S. 1968. A comparation of lime and rock phosphate for pelleting temperate and tropical legume seed. J. Aust. Inst. Agric. Sci. *34*, 173-174.

DATE, R. A. and HILLIER, G. R. 1968. Molybdenum application in the lime of lime pelleted subterranean clover seed. J. Aust. Inst. Agric. Sci. *34*, 171-172.

DAWSON, R. C. 1970. Potential for increasing protein production by inoculation of legumes. Plant and Soil *32*, 665-673.

DELWICHE, C. C. and WIJLER, J. 1956. Non symbiotic nitrogen fixation in soil. Plant and Soil 7, 113-129.

DIATLOFF, A. 1968. Nodulation and nitrogen fixation in some *Desmodium* species. QID. J. Agric. Sci. 25, 165-167.

DÖBEREINER, J. and ARONOVICH, S. 1965. Efecto da calagem e da temperatura do solo na fixacao do nitrogeno de *Centrosema pubescens*. Benth. em solo con toxidez de manganez. Proc. IX Intern. Grassl. Cong. Sao Paulo 2, 1121.

DÖBEREINER, J., DAY, J. M. and DART, P. J. 1973. Rhizosphere associations between grasses and nitrogen fixing bacteria. Effects of O_2 on nitrogenase activity in the rhizosphere of *Paspalum notatum*. Soil Biol. and Biochem. 5, 157-160.

DOMMERGUES, Y. *et al.* 1973. Non symbiotic nitrogen fixation in the rhizosphere of rice, maize and different tropical grasses. Soil Biol. and Biochem. 5, 83-89.

DONALD, C. M. 1960. The impact of cheap nitrogen. J. Aust. Inst. Agric. Sci. 26, 319-338.

ERDMAN, L. W. 1959. Legume inoculation. USDA Farmers Bulletin 2003.

GARTHELL, J. W. 1969. The effect of sodium molybdate mixed in the lime pellet on nodulation, nitrogen content and growth of subterraneous clover. Aust. J. Exp. Agric. Anim. Husb. 9, 432-436.

GIBSON, A. 1971. Factors in the physiological and biological environment affecting nodulation and nitrogen fixation by legumes. Plant and Soil Spec. Volume. pp. 139-152.

GIDDENS, J. 1964. Effect of adding molybdenum compounds to soybean inoculants. Agron. J. 56, 362-363.

GRAHAM, P. H. 1973. Role of CIAT and of other International research centres in the post I.B.P. period. Nitrogen fixation in the biosphere, I.B.P. Synthesis Meeting, Edinburgh.

HALLSWORTH, E. G. 1972. Factors affecting the response of grain legumes to the application of fertilizers. IAEA Tech. Rept. 149 p. 1-16.

HAMATOVA, E. 1965. Selection of strains of *Rhizobium japonicum* capable of reliable nodulation in Czechoslovak Soya Varieties Rost. Vyroba 38, 193-209.

HARDY, R. W. F.; BURNS, R. C. and PARSHALL, G. W. 1971. The biochemistry of Nitrogen fixation. Advances in Chemistry 100, 219-247.

HARDY, R. W. F. *et al.* 1968. The acetylene-ethylene assay for N_2 fixation, Laboratory and Field evaluation. Plant. Physiol. 43, 1185-1207.

HARDY, R. W. F. *et al.* 1971. Biological nitrogen fixation: a key to world protein. Plant and Soil Spec. Volume. pp. 561-590.

HASTINGS, A. and DRAKE, A. D. 1960. Inoculation and pelleting of clover seed. N.Z.J. Agric. 101, 326-335.

HENZELL, E. F. 1967. Tropical pasture legumes in Northern Queensland. Proc. Soil Crops. Sci. Soc. Fla. *27*, 322-328.

HENZELL, E. F. and NORRIS, D. O. 1962. Processes by which nitrogen is added to the soil/plant system. Comm. Agric. Bur. Bull. *46*, 1-18.

HUBBELL, D. F. and NAPOLI, C. 1972. Current studies on nodule infection. VI Reunión Latinoamericana de *Rhizobium*, Montevideo.

IRELAND, J. A. and VINCENT, J. M. 1968. A quantitative study of competition for nodule formation. Proc. IX Intern. Soil Sci. Cong. Adelaide *2*, 85-93.

LIE, T. A. 1971. Symbiotic nitrogen fixation under stress conditions. Plant and Soil Spec. Volume. pp. 117-127.

LONERAGAN, J. F. 1972. The soil chemical enviroment in relation to symbiotic nitrogen fixation. IAEA Tech. Rept. 149 p. 17-54.

LONERAGAN, J. F. *et al.* 1955. Lime pelleted clover seeds for nodulation on acid soils. J. Aust. Inst. Agric. Sci. *21*, 264-265.

LOPEZ, E. S.; LOVADINI, L. A. S. and MIYASAKA, S. 1970. Efeito comparativo de diversos materiais para revestimento, em pelletizacao, na nodulacion e fixacao do nitrogenio em soya perene *(Glycine javanica* L.). V. Reuniao Latinoamericana de *Rhizobium*. Río de Janeiro 303-307.

LOWTHER, W. L. 1970. Calcium in the nodulation and growth of legume. Ph. D. Thesis Unic. of West. Australia.

MARSHALL, K. C. 1964. Survival of root - nodule bacteria in dry soils exposed to high temperatures. Aust. J. Agric. Res. *15*, 273-281.

MARSHALL, W. L. and ROBERTS, F. J. 1963. Influence of fine particle materials on survival of *Rhizobium trifolii* in sandy soil. Nature *198*, 410-411.

MISHUSTIN, E. N. and SHILNIKOVA, V. K. 1969. The biological fixation of atmospheric nitrogen by free living bacteria. *In*. "Soil Biology" UNESCO Publication 1969 p. 65-162.

MORALES, V. M.; GRAHAM, P. H. and CAVALLO, R. 1973. Influencia del método de inoculación y el encalamiento del suelo de Carimagua (Llanos Orientales, Colombia) en la nodulación de leguminosas. Turrialba *23*, 52-55.

MOSSE, B. 1973. Advances in the study of vesicular arbuscular micorrhiza. Ann. Rev. Phytopath. *11*, 171-196.

MUNNS, D. N. 1968. Nodulation of *Medicago sativa* in solution culture I. Acid sensitive steps. Plant and Soil *28*, 129-146.

MUNNS, D. N. 1970. Nodulation of *Medicago sativa* in solution culture V. Calcium and pH requirements during infection. Plant and Soil *32*, 90-102.

NORRIS, D. O. 1958. A red strain of *Rhizobium* from *Lotononis bainesii* Baker Aust. J. Agric. Res. *9*, 629-632.

NORRIS, D. O. 1959. Legume bacteriology in the tropics. J. Aust. Inst. Agric. Sci. *25*, 202-207.

NORRIS, D. O. 1967. The intelligent use of inoculation and lime pelleting for tropical legumes. Trop. Grassl. *1*, 107-121.

NORRIS, D. O. 1970. Nodulation of pasture legumes in "Australian Grasslands". R. M. Moore editor, ANU Press Canberra. pp. 339-348.

NORRIS, D. O. 1971a. Seed pelleting to improve nodulation of tropical legumes. The variable response to lime and rock phosphate of eight legumes in the field. Aust. J. Exp. Agric. Anim. Husb. *11*, 282-289.

NORRIS, D. O. 1971b. A field evaluation of inoculant survival under lime and rock phosphate pellet on *Dolichos lablab*. Aust. J. Exp. Agric. Anim. Husb. *11*, 677-683.

NORRIS, D. O. 1972a. The effect of various mineral dust on nodulation of *Desmodium uncinatum*. Aust. J. Exp. Agric. Anim. Husb. *12*, 152-158.

NORRIS, D. O. 1972b. Leguminous plants in tropical pastures. Trop. Grassl. *5*, 159-170.

NORRIS, D. O. 1973. Seed pelleting to improve nodulation of tropical and subtropical legumes. The constrating response to lime pelleting of two *Rhizobium* strains *Leucaena* on *Lucerne leucocephala*. Aust. J. Exp. Agric. Anim. Husb. *13*, 98-101.

NUTHALL, P. L. and WHITEMAN, P. C. 1972. A review and economic evaluation of beef production from legume based and nitrogen fertilized pasture. J. Aust. Inst. Agric. Sci. *38*, 100-108.

PHILLIPOTTS, R. 1967. The effect of soil temperature on nodulation of cowpea *(Vigna sinensis)*. Aust. J. Exp. Agric. Anim. Husb. 7, 372-376.

REISENAUER, H. M. 1963. Relative efficiency of seed and soil applied molybdenum fertilizer. Agron. J. 55, 459-460.

SOUTO, S. M.; COSER, A. C. and DÖBEREINER, J. 1970. Especifidade de uma variedade nativa de "alfalfa de nordeste" *(Stylosanthes gracilis)* H.B.K. na symbioses com *Rhizobium sp*. V Reuniao Latinoamericana de *Rhizobium*. Río de Janeiro, 78-91.

SUNDARA-RAO, W. V. B. 1971. Field experiments on nitrogen fixation by nodulated legumes. Plant and Soil Spec. Volume. pp. 287-291.

VINCENT, J. M. 1972. Nitrogen from microbes. Farrar Memoral Oration 1972, J. Aust. Inst. Agric. Sci. *38*, 236-249.

WHITNEY, A. S.; KANEHIRO, Y. and SHERMAN, G. C. 1967. Nitrogen relationships of three tropical forage legumes in pure stands and in grass mixtures. Agron. J. *59*, 47-50.

WILKINS, J. 1967. The effect of high temperatures on certain root-nodule bacteria. Aust. J. Agric. Res. *18*, 299-304.

YOSHIDA, T. and ANCAJAS, R. R. 1973. The fixation of atmospheric nitrogen in the rice rhizosphere. Soil Biol. and Biochem. *5*, 153-156.

13 Nitrogen Fertilization and Management of Grain Legumes in Central America

RUFO BAZAN

I INTRODUCTION

The term grain legume is a very broad one and involves various species, which constitute the basis of the daily diet of a great percentage of rural and urban population in various countries due to its high protein content. The common bean *(Phaseolus vulgaris L.)* is the most common species in Central America, with numerous varieties of different characteristics in regard to color, size, shape and   nutrient value.

Consequently, the term grain legume in Central America is almost synonymous with the common bean. Thus, this paper emphasizes this species, regardless of different considerations that could be made on varieties. In such a broad area like the one we are considering, the bean is cultivated in various ecological regions, from dry tropical and dry sub-tropical, to low mountain humid tropical conditions where the crop is produced. In many cases, temperature and precipitation conditions are far from ideal, these being: temperatures between 18° to 24°C (Critical maximum 48.8°C and minimum 3°C), precipitation from 300 to 400 mm during crop growth (10). Soils in the Central American area are very variable in their chemical, physical, and microbiological properties since their development involves highly different conditions, especially in regard to climate.

Soils in the Pacific Coast are characterized by hot-dry climate and are subjected to more recent additions of natural volcanic materials. Soils in the Atlantic coast are affected by a hot-humic climate, having less influence from recent volcanic materials, and a high annual rainfall ($>$3000 mm).

II RESEARCH ON GRAIN LEGUMES IN CENTRAL AMERICA

The organization of research on grain legumes in Central America probably deserves consideration. It is being conducted in cooperation and with exchange of information and materials between the countries of the area under the guidance of the Central American Project for the Improvement and Producstion of Bean and Other Grain Legumes (PCMPF), which is a branch of the Central American Cooperative Project for the Improvement of Food Crops (PCCMCA) organized under the auspicies of the Rockefeller Foundation in 1954. Later, in 1965 and up to the present, the Regional Direction for the Northern Zone of the Interamerican Institute of Agricultural Sciences (IICA) has been in charge of the coordination and technical support of the PCMPF.

Research on grain legumes has had from its beginning the goal of searching for alternatives to the problems limiting their production and of reducing the protein deficiencies in the nutrition of the Central American population, as the bean constitutes a basic part of the diet for a great part of the rural and urban population.

III IMPORTANCE OF BEANS IN CENTRAL AMERICA

For the Central American population in general, the bean constitutes, after corn *(Zea mays)*, the most important food. It is a principal part of the diet for low income groups, and is, for them, the main source of protein that in any other case would be very difficult to obtain. The bean provides approximately 33% of the protein consumed.

Statistical information supplied by the Secretaría de Integración Económica Centroamericana (18) for the 1965-69 period (Table 1, Fig. 1) indicated that bean production for the region has an increasing tendency, growing from 158,400 tons in 1965 to a total of 183,400 tons in 1969. In terms of area cultivated, it can be seen in Table 2, Fig. 1, that the area had an increase from 310,800 hectares in 1965 to 328,900 hectares in 1969 or the equivalent of a 1.4% annual increase.

In can be concluded from this information that the yields (Table 3, Fig. 1) were quite uniform; 510 kg/ha in 1965 and 588 kg/ha in 1969. In general it can be seen that El Salvador appears to be the country that shows an evident development in terms of total production and yield per hectare while the cultivated area remained more or less uniform. The case of Costa Rica calls attention because of its low yields.

The net availability of bean (Table 4) is approximately 11 kg/capita/year, which compared with the minimum requirement, (20.4 kg/capita/year) recommended by INCAP gives a deficit of about 9.4 kg/capita/year. These figures show that except in the case of Nicaragua, whose availability is next to that recommended, all the other countries seem

Table 1.—Bean production in Central America 1965-69 (thousands of tons).

Country	1965	1966	1967	1968	1969	Mean
Costa Rica	12.9	7.1	4.2	6.0	9.3	7.9
Nicaragua	39.0	42.0	44.0	44.0	47.7	35.3
El Salvador	16.5	15.5	17.5	21.3	26.2	19.4
Honduras	40.0	41.4	42.9	44.5	47.7	43.3
Guatemala	50.0	44.0	46.0	65.0	55.5	52.2
Total	158.4	150.0	154.6	181.4	184.4	165.8

Table 2.—Area planted to beans 1965-69 (thousands of hectares).

Country	1965	1966	1967	1968	1969	Mean
Costa Rica	35.3	19.3	11.6	16.2	15.2	21.5
Nicaragua	52.0	56.0	68.0	57.6	59.2	58.6
El Salvador	23.5	26.4	28.4	31.7	32.8	28.6
Honduras	57.0	64.7	65.9	67.1	72.9	65.5
Guatemala	143.0	126.0	144.0	152.0	138.8	140.8
Total	310.8	292.4	307.9	324.6	328.9	312.9

Table 3.—Bean yields 1965-69 (kg/ha).

Country	1965	1966	1967	1968	1969	Mean
Costa Rica	366	366	366	365	365	365.6
Nicaragua	750	750	758	766	753	755.4
El Salvador	702	587	616	671	798	674.8
Honduras	702	640	650	663	663	662.6
Guatemala	350	349	319	421	418	373.4
Total	510	510	500	554	558	526.4

Table 4.—Bean availability for human consumption 1965-69 (kg person/ year).

Country	1965	1966	1967	1968	1969	Mean
Costa Rica	9.0	6.9	14.1	11.5	9.4	10.2
Nicaragua	19.1	19.5	21.0	19.0	18.9	19.5
El Salvador	10.5	8.3	8.4	10.3	7.3	9.0
Honduras	6.8	9.5	9.0	6.5	10.3	8.4
Guatemala	10.0	8.1	7.7	11.5	9.3	9.3
Total	10.7	9.8	9.8	12.8	11.1	10.8

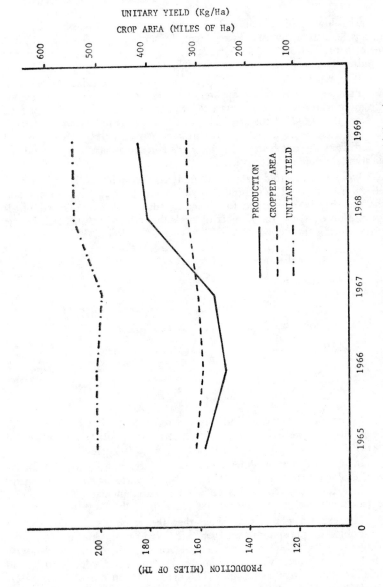

Figure 1. Production, cropped area and bean yields 1965-69 in Central America.

to be meeting a critical situation as the availability levels per capita just cover from 35% to 55% of desirable consumption.

IV NITROGEN AND ITS EFFECTS ON BEAN PRODUCTION.

The low yields obtained in the area, plus an increasing need for food, has lead to an increase in research. In some countries (Table 1) the increase in production, i.e., El Salvador, is due to an increase of cultivated area rather than to an increase of the yield per area.

It is evident that under adequate management, fertilizer use permits larger increases per area, but apparently in the Central American regions fertilization is not commonly practice. Specialists from PCCMCA affirm that "more than 90% of the area cultivated to beans is not being fertilized". We do not exaggerate if we add that in a great part of the 10% fertilized area, fertilizers are not being adequately used in terms of rates, methods of application, or soil characteristics.

From the reported data of PCCMCA, research on the relation of fertilizers to bean yield in Central America is very limited. Experimentation in the area has been oriented to: breeding, diseases and pests and fertilizer use. Consequently, the number of trials on fertilizers distributed by the countries during the period of 1966-71 is relatively low (13).

Costa Rica	12
Nicaragua	16
El Salvador	31
Honduras	27
Guatemala	26
Total	112

In general, the existing information refers to trials with NPK, with nitrogen levels between 0 and 200 kg/N/ha, phosphorus between 0 and 400 kg P_2O_5/ha and potassium between 0 and 200 kg K_2O/ha.

In turn, the results show a great variability, possibly due to differences in ecological conditions (climate and soils), varieties and management. Except in a few cases, the yields obtained in experimental plots are above those yields obtained at a "commercial" level by 100 to 200%.

The experimental results show that the responses to nitrogen are very variable, to phosphorus are generally significant, and to potassium are very scarce. Consequently, in Central America there is a tendency to use fertilizer mixtures with medium to low nitrogen content, high in phosphorus, and without potassium. The most common are 12-34-0, 19-27-0, 19-19-0, 18-46-0, 20-20-0 and others at rates which allow the application of up to 100 kg N/ha, and 300 kg/P_2O_5/ha. The data from Table 5 clearle shows this tendency.

Table 5.—Fertilizer recommendations for beans by country (kg/ha).

Country	Author	Year	N	P_2O_5	K_2O	$N:P_2O_5:K_2O$
Costa Rica	Echeverría	1960	100	140	0	1:1.4:0
	Chacón	1961	100	150	0	1:1.5:0
	Iglesias	1964	50-100	140	0	1:1.4:0
	Anonymous	1965	45	45	45	1:1:0
	Lizárraga	1966	45	90	45	1:2:1
	Anonymous	1969	12	33	0	1:2.75:0
	Anonymous	1969	19	27	0	1:1.4:0
	Anonymous	1969	19	19	0	1:1:0
Nicaragua	Rodríguez M. &					
	Rodríguez L.	1967	45	90	0	1:2:0
	Rodríguez M.	1968	22.5	45-90	0	1:2.4:0
	Anonymous	1969	12	24	12	1:2:1
	Anonymous	1969	18	46	0	1:2.5:0
El Salvador	Anonymous	1956	40	0	0	1:0:0
	Anonymous	1958	33	0	0	1:0:0
	Lizárraga	1966	45	90	45	1:2:1
	Anonymous	1969	20	20	0	1:1:1
	Salazar	1970	40	40	0	1:1:0
Honduras	Lizárraga	1966	45	90	45	1:2:1
Guatemala	Lizárraga	1966	45	90	45	1:2:1
	Masaya	1968	40	40	0	1:1:0

The additional information referring to climate and soil in the experimental areas is very general and does not allow valid conclusions on the possible causes influencing the variable response to nitrogen. However, such responses could be expected if one takes into account that the bean needs high amounts of introgen, compared to that of phosphorus or potassium. Fassbender (5) states that needs are adjusted to the following relation: 1:0.22:0.70 N, P_2O_5, and K_2O respectively.

Other studies on crop conditions in hydroponic solutions confirmed the high absorption of nitrogen by the bean plant, compared to other nutrients (6, 9).

One of the reasons that could explain the low responses to the application of nitrogen fertilizer under field conditions in Central America, would be to assume that since the beans is a legume, it has the capacity to fix atmospheric nitrogen. However, experiments conducted in Costa Rica (4, 7, 14) demonstrate that the inocculation of bean seeds with *Rhizobium* (Nitragine D) is ineffective. Furthermore, the addition of nitrogen fertilizer and innoculation tend to diminish, in many cases, the number of nodules in the root of the plant. Salinas (16) working with soybeans *(Glycine max)* under greenhouse conditions showed that the innoculation with Nitragine (4 g/kg of seeds) and the application of nitrogen on fertilizer (62 kg N/ha) together is necessary to obtain optimum yields. However, he made no observations on the effects on the nodulation.

Observations made by Bazán show that:

1. Under the soil and climate at Turrialba, the bean plant (var. 27-R and Turrialba-4) shows an irregular capacity of nodulation, in the numbef as well as in the size of the nodules. No specific studies have been made on nodulation and fixation of N of grain legumes.

2. Since the bean is an early maturity species (2-3,5 months) it is possible that even though the plant shows a capacity for nodulation, this would not be fast enough to satisfy crop demand. Furthermore, if we take into account that the crop demand is larger in the first 30 to 40 days of the life of the plant.

3. Beans respond positively to increasing applications of N fertilizer.

The results obtained (Figs. 2, 3, and 4) show tendencies that in the period of 1971-72, the highest applied level (130 kg/ha of N) has not reached maximum yields, even though the increase from 0 to 130 kg N/ha is 8%. The results obtained in 1972-73 show evidence of this possibility, because the increase in yield with the application 650 kg/ha of N was 29% compared with the control. However, application beyond 400 kg N/ha could be detrimental to the crop.

It is possible to speculate tha tthe occurance of a long dry spell during most of the vegetative cycle of the crop during 1972-73 could have caused the yield to be relatively low by decreasing the efficiency of the applied fertilizer.

In Central America the response of beans to N applications seem to increase in the presence of phosphorus, while additions of potassium fertilizer tend to decrease it (12).

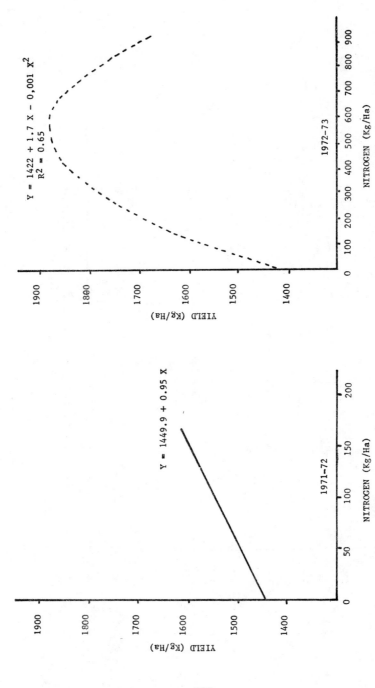

Figure 3. Effect of nitrogen levels on bean yield. 1972-73.

Figure 2. Effect of nitrogen levels on bean yield, in 1971-1972.

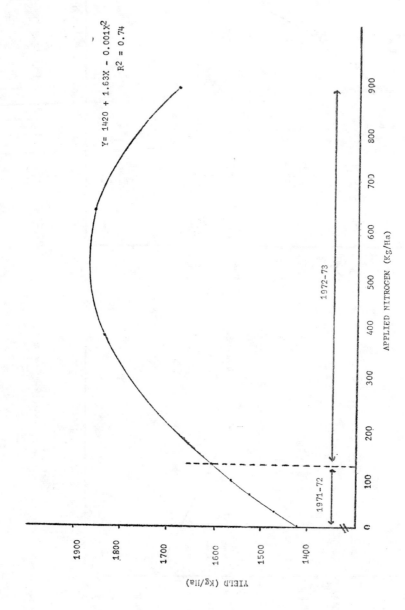

Figure 4. Nitrogen effect on bean yield (1971-1973).

$Y = 1420 + 1.63X - 0.001X^2$

$R^2 = 0.74$

Soil characteristics, for example, high or medium-high in total N (0,3-0,2%), low to extremely low in available phosphorus (<10 ppm) and high to very high in exchangeable K ($>0,35$ meq/100 g soil) could be responsible for the detected responses to the fertilizer applications in soils for beans. However, Martini (8) states that "The more N and P is applied to soils and the higher the plant density, the better are the probabilities of obtaining responses to K".

In this respect, the results obtained at CATIE show that the belief that beans do not respond to K applications cannot be negeralized because that depends on experimental conditions.

Bazán (2) found that at low levels of N and P (62 kg N and 83 kg P_2O_5/ha) there was a linear yield increase at increasing levels of potassium (34 to 276 kg K_2O/ha) in the order of 5.5 kg of dry grain for each kilo of potassium added (Fig. 5-a) while the decrease in yields was 0.9 and 1.6 kg of dry grain for each kilo of N and of P added.

Increasing levels of nitrogen, however, tend to produce increases in the yield in the presence of increasing phosphorus levels and decreasing levels of potassium (Figure 5a,b,c,d and e).

In such diametrically opposed results, the cost/benefit ratios will be the deciding factor of which fertilizer to apply. Under the present circumstances of the high cost of nitrogen and phosphorus fertilizers, the combination of low nitrogen, low phosphorus, and high potassium will be preferable to high nitrogen, high phosphorus and low potassium.

Also, contrasting situations, and even contradicting situations, like the ones presented here, confirm the belief that the responses to nitrogen in grain legumes in Central America are irregular and inconsistent.

V NITROGEN AND THE MANAGEMENT OF LEGUMES

The knowledge of the growth habits of a plant determine the best guide for the fertilization in the management of crops. Masaya (9), and Furlan (6) working in nutrient solution found that the period from 30 to 45 days after seeding is the one of greater absorption, especially K, P, N, and Ca (Fig. 6). That age corresponds to the time of flowering through the initiation of the grain formation. The absorption of N in the first 12 days of age was approximately 5% of the one detected in the period 34-40 days.

These results suggest that the application of nitrogen fertilizers in field conditions and at the time of planting, could result in a low efficiency caused by the non-immediate utilization by the plant, and, consequently, predispose losses by volatization and leaching.

In Central America, the usual practice is to apply the fertilizer at planting time. Without much doubt, that is one of the basic reasons for the irregularity observed in fertilizer responses by beans.

In field experiences, at CATIE, Bazán (3) showed that the split application of the nitrogen fertilizer, 50% at the planting and 50% at 15 to 20 days after planting, increased the bean yield by 10% compared to all applied at planting (Fig. 7). The author does not know of other similar experiences in Central America.

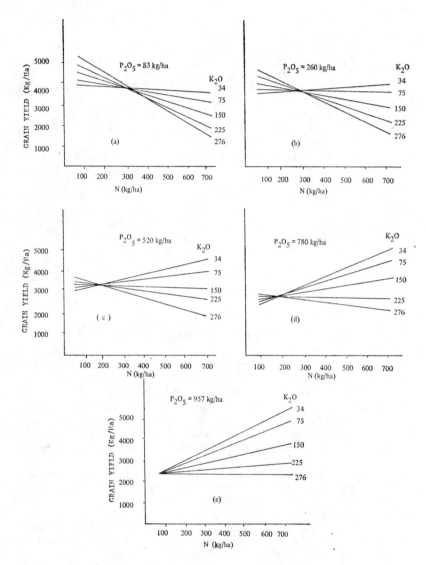

Figure 5. Effect of N, P and K levels on bean yield.

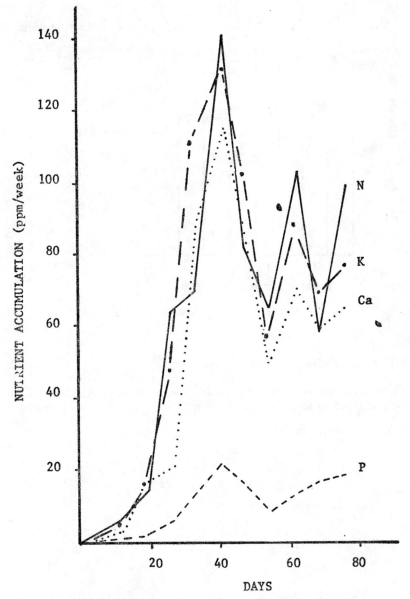

Figure 6. Absorption of N, P, K, Ca, nutrients (Masaya, 1971).

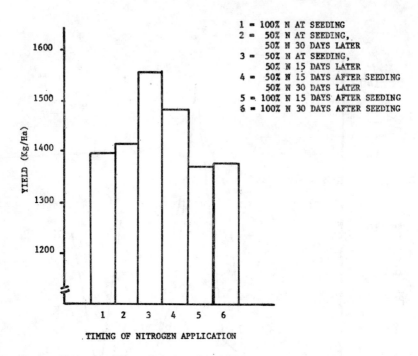

Figure 7.   Effect of timing of N application on bean production.

VI CROPPING SYSTEMS

From the management point of view, beans in Central America can be considered in too categories, involving different degrees of technology:

1. Monocultures

    a. Rudimentary technology
    b. Intermediate technology
    c. Advanced technology

2. Intercrops

    a. Intermediate technology
    b. Advanced technology

Monocultures

This system involves various degrees of technology: the "tapado" (covered) beans is the technique used by the small farmer and is characterized by a slight alteration of the medium. Seeds are broadcast directly on the woodland without other cultural practices!

The application of minimal cultivation practices, like the planting by "espeque" (planting stick) without a previous soil preparation, represents an intermediate technique. .Practices such as seed bed preparation, use of fertilizers, constitutes the more advanced technique.

Intercropping

In this type of system, the degree of tecnology also defines the character of the crop. Among the crops with which bean is normally associated, we have maize, sorghum, tobacco, and coffee.

The achievements obtained in technological advances of bean cultivation leads towards the monoculture with advanced technology. However, in practice, the bean producer in Central America shows the characteristics of the small farmer, using rudimental to intermediate technology on his. crops. He has difficulty to obtain financing and, in general, has a low standard of living. The impact of research advances on this type of farmer has been low to nil.

In this sense, the Central American farmer dedicated to bean cultivation is a typical one. Reports from PCCMCA (15) show that in the majority of Central American countries, bean cultivation is concentrated on small or medium size farms, most of which use traditional croppings methods. In Guatemala (15) the average size of farms involved in bean production is 1.7 hectares.

Furthermore, statistical data shows that bean, usually planted with maize, and other crops, uses approximately 61.9% of the cultivated area in Guatemala. In El Salvador in 1971, 15,000 of the 39,000 hectares planted with bean, were intercropped with maize or another crop (19). For Central America, census data show that more than 50% of the population is found in the rural sector and the great majority of the farmers own small production units of 5 hectares or less (Table 6). It has been mentioned that maize and bean are the most important crops in Central America. A study (17) on the capacity to generate labor by the different crops, based on the number of production units and their size, shows that evidently, maize and bean are two of the manual labor generators (Table 7). These data indicate that bean and maize can be considered the most commonly planted in small farms either as monoculture or intercropped.

These facts leads us to think that a great part of our research efforts on nitrogen use and in the management of legumes is related to production techniques which have little impact on the type of producer who is the main contributor of bean production of these countries.

According to Paez (11) the trend at present, is the traditional approach of physical-biological research, and that recommendations derived from the individual trials are translated into small technological packages wich constitute the optimum in the judgement of each researcher. Then the arithmetical sum of the small packages obtained under the most diverse circumstances and conditions is made, and the result is a bulky technological package, which is projected to the market with the consequent adverse reaction of the consumer. This reaction is due to the ineffectiveness of the recommended package and to its excessive cost, which is not in accord with the general profit level of the production unit. In terms of biological sciences, the arithemetical addition of small packages is not equal to a big technological package that can be launched to the consumer like the prescription to solve his problem. Many times the big package includes unnecessary components and excludes a fundamental ingredient or a critical factor. It is evident that in the case of grain legumes, research should consider this crop as an integral part of the production system.

Table 6.—Production units in Central America.

Country	Farm Size Ha		Area	Number of farms	Estimated 1972 Total Surface ha	Total Number of farms
Guatemala	Small	0—5	14.60	80.33		
	Medium	5—20	14.96	14.61		
	Large	>20	70.44	5.06		
	Total				3.893.178	463.251
El Salvador	Small	0—5	15.64	85.19		
	Medium	5—20	13.67	9.92		
	Large	>20	70.69	4.89		
	Total				1.878.014	251.854
Honduras	Small	0—5	9.79	59.98		
	Medium	5—20	18.40	27.32		
	Large	>20	71.81	13.70		
	Total				2.735.333	197.968
Nicaragua	Small	0—5	3.12	42.06		
	Medium	5—20	5.86	25.88		
	Large	>20	91.02	32.06		
	Total				4.315.463	113.443
Costa Rica	Small	0—5	2.18	45.75		
	Medium	5—20	7.38	24.92		
	Large	>20	90.44	29.33		
	Total				3.020.068	108.549
Central America Total					15.842.057	1.135.065

Table 7.—Relative Importance of the main crops as sources of work in rural areas of Central America.

Crop	Guate-mala	El Sal-vador	Hondu-ras	Nica-ragua	Costa Rica	Average	Rank
Corn	1.0	1.5	1.0	1.0	1.5	1.5	1
Coffee	2.0	2.5	2.5	4.0	2.0	3.0	2
Bean	2.5	3.5	2.5	4.0	4.0	3.6	3
Bananas	8.5	4.5	4.5	3.0	6.5	4.8	4
Rice	8.0	5.5	7.0	7.0	4.0	5.5	5
Sorghum	6.5	7.0	4.5	5.0	—	5.7	6
Sugarcane	6.5	6.5	6.0	8.0	6.5	6.7	7
Fruit Trees	5.0	9.0	11.5	7.0	6.0	7.4	8
Tubers	7.0	—	8.0	9.0	8.5	7.5	9
Cotton	4.0	7.0	9.5	6.0	13.0	7.9	10
Cacao	4.5	15.0	11.5	—	—	10.3	11
Wheat	13.5	14.5	—	11.5	7.0	11.1	12
Vegetables	11.5	—	10.0	12.5	12.0	11.2	13
Tobacco	12.0	12.0	9.0	14.5	11.0	11.5	14
Henequen	13.0	9.0	—	13.5	—	11.8	15
Oil Palm	—	—	—	—	12.0	12.0	16
Sesame	14.0	12.0	13.5	10.0	15.0	12.7	17
Other Crops	—	10.0	—	15.5	—	12.7	18
Sisal	—	—	—	—	13.0	13.0	19
Peanut	14.0	14.0	14.5	16.0	14.0	14.5	20

— Without information.

In Central America CATIE has taken the initiative to begin research on this subject. Such experiments will lead to new concepts on integral and interdisciplinary research, which eliminates the traditional crop or discipline oriented research. It has the advantage of maintaining criteria uniformity on treatment effects, uniform management, homogenity on reports, which will finally be assessed according to agronomical, economical and social criteria.

VI SUMMARY

The effect of fertilization with N, P, and K of beans in Central America is discussed. Emphasis is given to the scarcity and diversity of information existing and to the need of rewriting the research in the field, to satisfy the needs of small farmers responsible for the majority of the production. The importance of growing beans as part of a mixed cropping system is indicated and CATIE's work on this line presented.

VII REFERENCES

1. BAZAN, R. 1973. Efecto de niveles crecientes de nitrógeno en el rendi miento de frijol. Turrialba, Costa Rica, Centro Agronómico Tropical de Investigación y Enseñanza. (En preparación).

2. BAZAN, R. 1973. Las relaciones N, P y K en el rendimiento de frijol. Turrialba, Costa Rica, Centro Agronómico Tropical de Investigación y Enseñanza. (En preparación).

3. BAZAN, R. 1973. Efecto de épocas de aplicación de fertilizante nitroge-nado en el rendimiento de frijol. Turrialba , Costa Rica, Centro Agro-nómico Tropical de Investigación y Enseñanza. (En preparación).

4. CHACON, M. E. 1961. Ensayo sobre fertilización nitrogenada e inocu-lación de frijoles. Tesis de grado. Universidad de Costa Rica.

5. FASSBENDER, H. W. 1967. La fertilización del frijol (Phaseolus sp.). Turrialza 17(1):46-52.

6. FURLAN Jr., J. 1974. Comunicación personal. Centro Agronómico Tro-pical de Investigación y Enseñanza, Turrialba, Costa Rica.

7. IGLESIAS P., G. E. 1962. Ensayo sobre fertilización nitrogenada e inocu-lación. In: Reunión Latinoamericana de Fitotecnia, 5ª, Buenos Aires, INTA, v. 2.

8. MARTINI, J. A. 1968. Guía para la investigación en el abonamiento del frijol para el PCCMCA. Turrialba, Costa Rica, IICA-CTEI. Publ. Misc. 53.

9. MASAYA S., P. 1971. Estudio de la absorción de nutrimentos y creci-miento de raíces en la planta de frijol (P. vulgaris L. var Turrialba-4). Tesis Mag. Sc. Turrialba, Costa Rica, IICA-CTEI.

10. MONTOYA M., J. M. 1969. Zonas ecológicas para frijol en América Central, una metodología. In: Reunión sobre Programación de Investigación y Extensión en Frijol y Otras Leguminosas de Grano para América Central. Turrialba, Costa Rica. pp. 26-34.

11. PAEZ, G. 1973. Modelo de experimento en cadena para la investigación físico-biológica. In Seminario Regional sobre Aspectos Socio Eco-nómicos de la Investigación Agrícola, abril 10-13, 1973, Maracay, Venezuela. Maracay, IICA.

12. PESSOA, C. O. and HERNANDEZ, B. F. 1968. Fertilización y producción de frijol en Parrita, Costa Rica. In Programa Cooperativo Centroa-mericano para el Mejoramiento de Cultivos Alimenticios, Frijol. XV Reunión, San Salvador, El Salvador, 1969.

13. PINCHINAT, A. 1968. Ensayos extensivos de fertilizantes en Centroamérica, 1966-1968 en frijol. Turrialba, Costa Rica, IICA-CTEI, Publ. Misc. 58.

14. QUIRCE, C. 1960. Ensayo de fertilización NPKCa e inoculación de frijoles. Tesis de grado. Universidad de Costa Rica.

15. Reunión Técnica sobre Programación de Investigación y Extensión en Frijol y otras Leguminosas de Grano para América Central. 1969. Turrialba, Costa Rica, v. 1.

16. SALINAS C., J. G. 1973. Efectos de la inoculación y la fertilización nitrogenada sobre la producción de soya *(Glycine max* (L) Merril). Tesis Mag. Sci. Turrialba, Costa Rica, IICA.

17. Seminario sobre Sistemas de Producción Agrícola. 1973. Propuesta. Turrialba, Costa Rica, Centro Agronómico Tropical de Investigación y Enseñanza.

18. SIECA. 1971. Algunos aspectos de la situación del frijol en Centroamérica, 1965-1969. *In* Programa Cooperativo Centroamericano para el Mejoramiento de Cultivos Alimenticios, PCCMCA, XVII Reunión Anual, Panamá, pp. 1-7.

14 Effects of Solar Radiation on the Varietal Response of Rice to Nitrogen on the Coast of Perú

PEDRO A. SANCHEZ, GUILLERMO E. RAMIREZ and
CARLOS PEREZ Y.

I INTRODUCTION

Northern Peru is one of the highest yielding rice growing areas in the world. The average grain yields of about 100,000 has. were in the order of 4 tons/ha when the tall, traditional, late maturing varieties were in widespread use. When short-statured varieties were introduce five years ago, the average yields of farms using the new varieties and cultural practices increased to about 6 tons/ha (3). In experimental plots, replicated grain yields have reached 12.5 ton/ha at 14% moisture without border effects (9). This area is blessel with a tropical desert climate with mean annual temperatures of 22 to 27°C, relatively low night temperatures, high solar radiation, negligible rainfall and low relative humidity. This climate is considered almost ideal for rice growth (4). Intermittently flooded lowland rice is grown in relatively fertile calcareous alluvial soils, which are only deficient in nitrogen when used for rice (1).

Previous investigations have shown that the response of rice to nitrogen is quite different in this region from humid tropical areas. The tall, traditional, lodging-susceptible varieties respond positively up to 160 to 240 Kg N/ha, before decreasing yields due to lodging. The shortstatured varieties respond positively up to 300 or 400 Kg/ha and do not lodge (10). Growth duration was found to be often more important than plant type in determining nitrogen response curves. Varieties of intermediate maturity (160-180 days from seeding to harvest) yielded more and respond to higher nitrogen rates than varieties of shorter or longer growth duration, regardless of plant type (8, 10). This observation is quite different from the experience in humid tropical areas where plant type rather than growth duration is the dominant plant factor affecting nitrogen response (2).

These differences have been attributed to the much higher solar radiation levels and the lower night temperatures found in the coast of Perú, as compared with humid tropical areas such as the jungle of Perú or the Southeast Asian rice belt. The average daily solar radiation during the growing seasin is in the order of 488 langleys, which is about 46% more than the average for the rainy season and 19% more than the dry season average in Los Baños, Philippines (2, 10). The purpose of this investigation is to test the hypothesis that the high solar radiation levels at Lambayeque, Perú are responsible for the higher yields and different varietal response observed.

II PROCEDURE

Field experiments were conducted at the Vista Florida Station of the Centro Regional de Investigaciones Agrarias del Norte located in the center of the Lambayeque Valley (6° 42'S, 79° 47'W, 24 m above sea level) during the 1971-72 and 1972-73 growing seasons. The calcareous alluvial soil is classified an Aridic Haplustoll, fine loamy, mixed, isohyperthermic with an aerobic pH of 8.0, 2.4% organic matter and 31 meq/100 g of cation exchange capacity. The experiment consisted of a split plot design with two solar radiation levels as the main plots, five nitrogen rates as subplots and four varieties as sub-subplots. The 2 x 5 m plots were arranged in a randomized complete block design with three replications. The solar radiation differential (100 vs 57% possible) was accomplished by installing a shade of plastic mesh screen (Fabric Nº 5182102, Chicopee Manufacturing Co., Cornelia, Georgia) calibrated to provide a 43% shade without interfering with air circulation. The nitrogen rates were 0, 100, 200, 300, and 400 kg N/ha as urea. Half the rate was applied close to the rice rows 30 days after transplanting and the other half at panicle initiation. Four varieties were selected to provide the desired combination of plant type and growth duration. Chiclayo is a tall-statured, early maturing variety. Chancay is a recently released short-statured variety from the selection IR 930-31-10 with the same growth duration as Chiclayo. CEL 895 is a tall-statured local variety of intermediate growth duration. The short-statured IR 8 variety is also of intermediate growth duration.

Pregerminated rice seed were sown in ordinary seedbeds on October 25, 1971 and November 2, 1972. Rice seedlings were transplanted at 25 x 25 cm spacing at 46 and 40 days after seeding, respectively. The experiments were kept constantly flooded shortly after transplanting to about two weeks before the harvest of the intermediate maturity varieties. Height, and tiller number were measured at 30 days transplanting, at panicle initiation, 50% flowering and at harvest. Yields were measured in a 5 m² central area devoid of border effects and corrected to 14% moisture. Yield components, grain:straw ratios, dry matter and nitrogen content of the grain and straw were measured at harvest.

III RESULTS AND DISCUSSION

Grain Yields

The grain yield response to nitrogen applications for the two experiments appear in Figs. 1 and 2. At full solar radiation, the four varieties produced different response patterns. The semidwarf varieties IR 8 and Chancay, produced the classic curvilinear response curve with optimum rates in the order of 200 to 300 Kg N/ha. The later maturing variety, IR 8 consistently outyielded the earlier maturing Chancay by more than 1 ton/ha. IR 8 produced the highest grain yield of 11.6 ton/ha at the rate of 300 kg N/ha in the second experiment.

The two tall-statured varieties showed a sharp positive yield response to the first 100 kg N/ha increment and a negative response afterwards, associated with lodging. Like the other plant type, the later maturing variety, CEL 895, produced a larger positive yield response of about 1.5

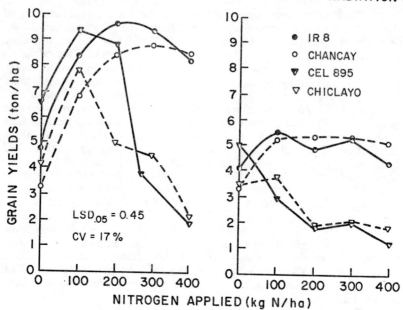

Figure 1. Effects of solar radiation on the varietal response to nitrogen applications. 1971-72 season.

ton/ha higher than the earlier maturing Chiclayo. It is interesting to note that yields of about 9 ton/ha were obtained with the tall-statured CEL 895 variety. In the first year CEL's highest yields were not significantly different from IR 8's and definitely superior to Chancay's optimum yields.

When solar radiation was sharply cut down by shading, these relationships completely changed. The differences due to growth duration within a plant type essentially disappeared. The short-statured varieties responded positively to the first nitrogen increment and remained constant with plateau yields in the order of 5 to 6 ton/ha. The tall-statured varieties responded negatively to nitrogen, attaining their highest yields when no nitrogen was applied. The response curves with shading closely resemble the well known varietal response in humid torpical environments during the rainy season (2).

These results show that a low level of solar radiation accomplished by shading (about 280 langleys/day) limits the yield potential of rice in this environment to about 6.5 tons/ha, while with full solar radiation (about 490 langleys/day) the yield potential increased to about 10 to 11.5 ton/ha. The overall effect of decreasing solar radiation to 57% of the original by shading was to decrease the average yields of the experiment by 59% (3.8 vs 6.0 ton/ha) in the first experiment and by 58% (4.3 vs 7.4 ton/ha) in the second experiment (Tables 1 and 2). These figures suggest that the high overall average yields obtained in Lambayeque are directly related to solar radiation levels.

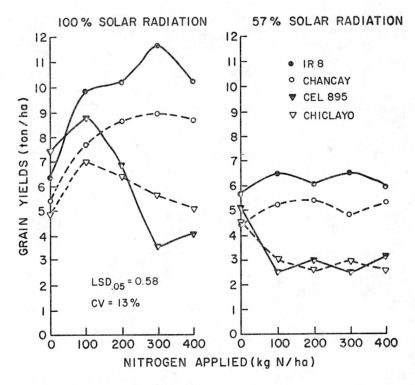

Figure 2. Effects of solar radiation on the varietal response to nitrogen applications. 1972-73 season.

Plant Characteristics

The following parameters were also measured in order to ascertain what the varietal response differences are due to; plant height, tillering, grain:straw ratio, and dry matter production. The main effects of varieties and solar radiation appear in Tables 1 and 2. The ratio of grain to straw at harvest is a useful parameter for estimating the efficiency of plants to concentrate their energy in producing grain (8). Fig. 3 shows the grain: straw ratios of the different treatments for the 1971-72 experiment. The 1972-73 results were essentially the same. Fig. 3 illustrates very vlearly the differences in plant type. IR 8 and Chancay's grain:straw ratios averaged 1.40 while the tall-statured CEL and Chiclayo averaged about half, 0.69 in the two experiments. In all instances, grain:straw ratios decreased with increasing nitrogen rates but the effect was more marked in the tall statured varieties. Decreasing solar radiation, decreased grain-straw ratios significantly but by a small amount (Tables 1 and 2). This was somewhat surprising as other investigations suggests that solar radiation improves the plant's ability to produce more grain with the same straw base.

Table 1.—Main effects of solar radiation on grain yields and plant growth parameters. 1971-72 season. Mean of N rates.

Variety	Solar Radiation	Grain yields	Grain:straw ratio	Total dry matter	Plant height at harvest
	% of max.	ton/ha		ton/ha	cm
IR 8	100	7.48	1.64	12.74	86
	57	4.82	1.35	8.65	82
Chancay	100	7.17	1.57	11.73	81
	57	4.87	1.47	8.23	79
CEL 895	100	6.31	0.98	12.86	145
	57	2.64	0.75	6.18	135
Chiclayo	100	4.77	0.71	11.67	151
	57	2.55	0.69	6.45	144
Mean	100	6.43	1.22	12.25	116
	57	3.78	1.06	7.38	110
LSD.$_{05}$		0.63	0.15	1.40	3

Table 2.—Main effects of solar radiation on garin yields and plant growth parameters. 1972-73 season. Mean of N rates.

Variety	Solar Radiation	Grain yields	Grain:straw ratio	Total dry matter	Plant height at harvest
	% of max.	ton/ha		ton/ha	cm
IR 8	100	9.67	1.40	16.57	90
	57	6.16	1.19	11.51	87
Chancay	100	7.91	1.35	13.87	87
	57	5.05	1.30	8.96	84
CEL 895	100	5.97	0.59	16.42	153
	57	3.30	0.49	10.08	150
Chiclayo	100	5.72	0.75	14.09	151
	57	3.13	0.58	8.41	151
Mean	100	7.37	1.04	15.32	118
	57	4.29	0.90	9.76	117
LSD.$_{05}$		0.58	0.08	1.31	1

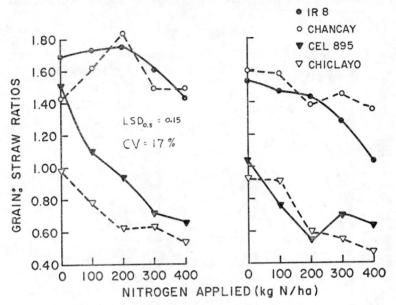

Figure 3. Effects of solar radiation, varieties, and nitrogen rates on grain: straw ratios. 1971-72 season.

The effects of these variables on total dry matter production at harvest is shown in Fig. 4. At full solar radiation, the two tall-statured varieties produced significantly higher dry matter (up to 18 tons/ha) at N levels of 100 and 200 kg N/ha, than the short-statured varieties. At higher N rates, the tall varieties suffered very sharp decreases presumably due to lodging. The short-statured varieties responded in a curvilinear fashion with maximum production at 300 to 400 Kg N/ha. This indicates the absence of lodging in these varieties.

At 57% solar radiation, dry matter production was sharply depressed with no varieties reaching 10 ton/ha. The tall-statured varieties had a negative nitrogen response due to lodging, while the short-statured varieties reached a plateau at 100 kg N/ha and remained constant. The overall effects of decreasing solar radiation to 57% of the original was to decrease dry matter production by 60% in 1971-72 and 64% in 1972-73 (Tables 1 and 2).

No differences in plant height at panicle initiation, flowering or at harvest due to solar radiation were observed in these two experiments. All varieties increased in height with nitrogen applications but the tall statured varieties reached a maximum of about 160 cm while the short-statured varieties went up to 90 cm. The nitrogen rate means, appearing in Tables 1 and 2 show the absence of differences due to solar radiation. This is unexpected since it was generally assumed that as solar radiation decreases, plant height increases. Indeed, CEL and Chiclayo, when grown in the

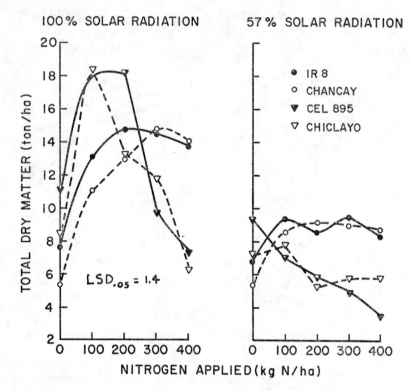

Figure 4. Total dry matter production as affected by solar radiation varieties and nitrogen fertilization. 1971-72 season.

jungle of Perú with low solar radiation and high temperatures reach heights of over 200 cm, lodge before flowering and produce essentially no yields (7). When examining a date of-planting study from the Philippines (2), no differences in plant heights were observed between the dates with highest and lowest solar radiation.

Nitrogen relations

The nitrogen contents of the grain and straw at harvest increased in an approximately linear fashion with rates of application. The varietal means for nitrogen content in the grain ranged from 1.3 to 1.6%, without a consistent trend due to plant type or growth duration (Table 3). Decreasing solar radiation had a marked and significant increase in the N content of the grain as shown in Table 3. The total nitrogen uptake at harvest (grain plus straws) is illustrated in Fig. 5. Under full solar radiation ,the two tall-statured varieties accumulated up to 180 kg N/ha at their optimum yield rates. Their nitrogen uptake sharply decreased at higher rates, presumably due to lodging. The two short-statured varieties accumulated nitrogen

Table 3.—Main effects of solar radiation on nitrogen content, uptake and recovery from fertilizer 1971-72 season.

Variety	Solar Radiation	N content in grain	Total N uptake	Apparent fertilizer N recovery
	%	% N	kg N/ha	%
IR 8	100	1.28	154	43
	57	1.55	130	35
Chancay	100	1.29	146	46
	57	1.50	121	36
CEL 895	100	1.27	130	40
	57	1.32	67	—7
Chiclayo	100	1.43	135	44
	57	1.69	89	17
Mean	100	1.32	141	43
	57	1.51	101	20
LSD.$_{05}$		0.09	19	14

linearly with maximum of 210 kg N/ha rate. This figure illustrates the inability of the tall-statured plant types to make use of higher N rates.

At 57% solar radiation, nitrogen uptake was sharply decreased but the short-statured varieties produced a positive response with maximum levels in the order of 150 kg N/ha. The tall-statured varieties were more affected by decreasing solar radiation than the short-statured ones.

The overall effect of decreasing solar radiation to 57% of the possible was to decrease nitrogen uptake to approximately 40%, in spite of increasing substantially the N content of the grain. Under low solar radiation, the plants apparently could not take advantage of the higher nitrogen contents.

Calculations of the apparent recovery of added nitrogen, based on uptake differences are shown in Table 3. The recovery of added N decreased with increasing N rates as previously observed, but this decrease was more marked in the tall-statured varieties. The mean recovery by the four varieties at full solar radiation was not sinificantly different among themselves. The average recovery 43% is much higher than previously reported for this area (10) due to the fact that this experiment was constantly flooded, thus eliminating large denitrification and leaching losses due to alternate flooding and drying. At the lower solar radiation level, the recovery by the short statured varieties dropped to about 35%, while that tall-statured varieties became essentially negative. The overall effects

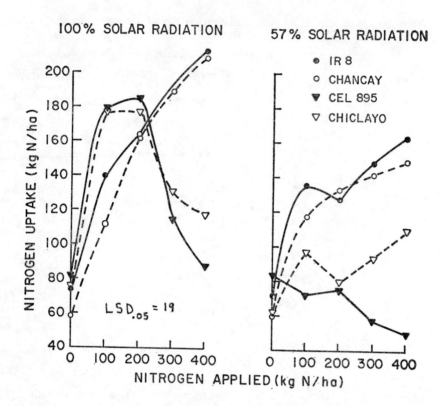

Figure 5.   Nitrogens uptake at harvest as affected by solar radiation, varieties, and nitrogen fertilization.

of reducing solar radiation was to cut the recovery of added nitrogen by more than half.

Yield components

In order to attempt to explain the specific reasons why yields decreased due to lower solar radiation, they yield components were examined (Table 4). The number of panicles per m² decreased with lower solar radiation but only tho 88% of the full solar radiation levels. Tiller production at panicle initiation, 50% flowering and at harvest showed no significant differences. The number of filled grains per panicle decreased significantly in all varieties but Chancay with lower solar radiation. The weight of 100 filled grains decreased significantly with lower solar radiation only in the Chancay variety, while the others showed no significant trends. The overall differences in grain sterility shed no particular light. Consequently, decreases in yields due to lower solar radiation were associated with decreases in the number of grains per panicle and the 100 grain weight, but not in a clear enough fashion to guarantee a firm conclusion.

Table 4.—Main effects of solar radiation on grain yield components at harvest 1971-72 season. Mean of N rates.

Variety	Solar Radiation	Panicles per m2	Filled grains per panicle	Weight 100 grains	Sterile spiklets
	%	No.	No.	g	%
IR 8	100	309	86	2.80	15
	57	250	65	2.80	23
Chancay	100	479	69	2.30	19
	57	424	65	2.07	23
CEL 895	100	297	83	2.93	16
	57	264	70	2.78	13
Chiclayo	100	301	90	2.65	13
	57	275	74	2.54	14
Aucrage	100	346	82	2.67	16
	57	304	69	2.55	18
LSD.05		70	12	0.14	6

IV CONCLUSIONS

These experiments have demonstrated that the high grain yield levels obtained in the northern coast of Perú are intimately related with the high solar radiation level of the area. It also explains the high nitrogen rates needed due to the large quantities of nitrogen taken up by rice plants in this environment. The plant parameters associated with yield increases due to solar radiation seem to be primarily increases in total dry matrter production and smaller increases in grain:straw ratios, filled grains per panicle and in one instance the 100 grain weight. This experiment also shows that the interaction between plant type and growth duration exists only at high solar radiation levels and disappears when solar radiation is decreased.

This type of work has several implications to agricultural development. It shows the dramatically beneficial influence of solar radiation in increasing rice yields and the efficiency of fertilizer nitrogen utilization. It seems safe to assume that similar relationships may take place in other crops. Although man cannot increase solar radiation *per se*, he can manage this parameter by selecting planting dates that coincide with periods of higher solar radiation. Montaño *et al.* (6) have shown that this produces higher economic returns in the Philippines.

There is a tremendous range in solar radiation levels in Tropical Latin America. This can be gleaned at a large scale from Landsberg's data (5), but at a more specific level from local meteorological stations equiped with a phyrheliometer. There is also a marked seasonality in solar radiation, usually ascociated in inverse proportion with rainfall. In many areas, supplemental irrigation might be necessary to take advantage of higher solar radiation but in others relatively minor adjustments in planting date may provide the same effect. Tropical agronomists should pay more attention to measuring and evaluating this crucial parameter to crop production.

V SUMMARY

Two shading experiments were conducted in two consecutive years in the Lambayeque valley of northern Perú in order to determine whether the higher yields and nitrogen response rates needed were caused by the high solar radiation of this tropical desert climate. The experiment also attempted to determine whether the effects of growth duration on nitrogen response were associated with high solar radiation levels. The results indicated that when solar radiation was reduced to 57% of the possible, the overall rice yields decreased to 58 and 59% in each experiment. High solar radiation markedly increased optimum yields (as high as 11.8 ton/ha) which required higher nitrogen rates. The interaction between plant type and growth duration in nitrogen response was only observed at full solar radiation. When solar radiation was reduced the introgen response curves were essentially similar to those obtained in low solar radiation, humid tropical conditions. Increasing solar radiation doubled dry matter production and the recovery of added fertilizer nitrogen. It also prevented lodging of tall-statured varieties at rates of 100 Kg/ha. Plant height, tillering, panicle production and grain sterility were not affected by solar radiation. Grain:straw ratios, the number of filled grains per panicle and in one variety, the 100 grain weight, significantly decreased with decerasing solar radiation.

VI REFERENCES

1. CARMEN, M. L. 1968. Yield of rice as affected by fertilizer rates, soils and meteorological factors. Ph.D. Thesis, Iowa State University, Ames. (Diss. Abstr. 68:14777).

2. DeDATTA, S. K. and P. M. ZARATE. 1970. Environmental conditions affecting the growth characteristics, nitrogen response and grain yield of tropical rice. Biometeorology 4(1):71-89.

3. HERNANDEZ, J., K. KAWANO, H. HUERTA, A. GAVIDIA and D. CUMPA. 1972. Avances obtenidos en la investigación arrocera, Programa Nacional de Arroz. Arroz (Perú) 6(32):25-36.

4. KAWANO, K. and S. VELAZQUEZ. 1972. Tipo de planta de arroz bajo condiciones climáticas casi ideales. Fitotecnia Latinoamericana 8(2): 66-73.

5. LANDSBERG, H. E. 1961. Solar radiation at the earth's surface. Solar Energy 5:95-98.

6. MONTAÑO, C. B., R. BARKER and S. K. DeDATTA. 1973. The effect of solar energy on rice yield response to nitrogen. Agronomy Abstracts 1973:193.

7. NUREÑA, M. A., J. VELEZ and K. KAWANO. 1970. Características varietales relacionadas con altos rendimientos de arroz en condiciones primitivas de secano. Progr. Nac. Arroz (Perú) Inf. Téc. 43.

8. SANCHEZ, P. A. 1972. Fertilización y manejo del nitrógeno en el cultivo de arroz tropical. Suelos Ecuatoriales 4(1):197-240. *(In:* English North Carolina Agr. Exp. Sta. Tech. Bull. 213).

9. SANCHEZ, P. A. and N. LARREAL, L. 1972. Influence of seedling age at transplanting on rice performance. Agron. Jour. 64:828-833.

10. SANCHEZ, P. A., G. E. RAMIREZ and M. V. de CALDERON. 1973. Rice responses to nitrogen under high solar radiation and intermittent flooding in Perú. Agron. Journ. 65:523-529.

SECTION IV

MANAGEMENT OF ACID SOILS

15 Lime Response of Corn and Beans in Typical Ultisols and Oxisols of Puerto Rico

FERNANDO ABRUÑA, ROBERT W. PEARSON and
RAUL PEREZ-ESCOLAR

I INTRODUCTION

Acid-soil infertility is a major cause of low crop yields throughout the humid tropics, where world's greatest potential for meeting its future food requirements lie. Specific factors responsible for low yields on acid soils include Al and Mn toxicity and deficiencies or imbalances among the basic cations. Sometimes other unidentified factors or interactions between factor appears to be operating.

Nitrogen is often the most critically limiting nutrient for crop production in the humid tropics, and heavy applications are required for maximum yields of many non leguminous crops (McCollum and Valverde, 1968; Vicente-Chandler et al. 1967, Berger, 1972). In fact applications of over 100 kg/ha of N are generally indicated for grain crops and potatoes, while applications of around 600 kg are required for intensive grass forage production. In Puerto Rico, extensive areas of the steep, mountainous interior are not suited to production of clean cultivated crops but can, with proper management, produce high yields of milk and beef on heavily fertilized grass pastures (Caro-Costas et al., 1972 a; 1972 b). Since the cheapest and most easily available N sources are residually acid, the naturally high soil acidity in much of the humid areas of the Island is intensified by the required fertilizer applications. For example, Pearson et al., (1961) showed that soil pH could be reduced by more than a pH unit in well buffered soils in only 2 years by application of 900 kg/ha of N annually as ammonium sulfate to grass pasture. Under these conditions even crops not usually considered to be acid sensitive soon require liming for satisfactory yields. Thus, Abruña et al., (1964) reported a sharp response to lime by 3 heavily fertilized tropical grasses. In terms of Napier grass yields, surface application of the limestone was as effective as incorporation in the 0-6" zone and one application was as efefctive as the same quantity split into 2 at 2-year intervals. In this study Napier grass yield on a strongly acid Oxisol was doubled by liming and those of Guinea, Napier and Pangola growing on an Ultisol were increased around 30%. Progressive and rapid development of yield response to liming was clearly shown over the first 4 years of this study.

In other experiments in Puerto Rico yields of sugar cane on an Ultisol after 7 years of heavy N fertilization of grass pasture increased from less than 1 ton/ha where no lime was used to over 40 tons at the highest rate of liming (Abruña and Vicente-Chandler, 1967). While this represented extreme conditions, with soil pH ranging from about 3.8 in the unlimed plots to only 4.8 where 20 tons/ha of lime had been applied 7 years earlier, there was a straight-line relationship between yield and soil pH over this range. Exchangeable Al essentially disappeared at the highest liming rate, but yield appeared to decrease with each increase in exchangeable Al throughout the range occurring in these treatments. Neither foliar composition nor sucrose content of the cane were affected by liming.

In still another study (Abruña et al., 1970) yields of cured tobacco on 3 Ultisols in Puerto Rico increased with liming up to somewhere around pH 5.0, and there was a highly significant relationship between yield and exchangeable Al. Tobacco yield on an Oxisol increased sharply with the first increment of lime but very little beyond that, even though soil pH was still well below 5.0. Only traces of exchangeable Al were found in this soil even at the original pH of 4.4. However, leaf composition indicated that Mn toxicity was probably responsible for the depressed yields at the lowest pH levels. With the exception of Mn content, foliar composition did not seem to be appreciably affected by lime treatment of any of the soils. In an intensive study of one of the Ultisols evidence was obtained that tobacco root development at pH levels below about 5.8 was restricted by Al toxicity and below pH 5.0 additional restrictions due to Ca deficiency appeared.

The purpose of this paper is to present recent observations of the effect of soil acidity on yield and foliar composition of corn and beans growing on Ultisols and Oxisols in Puerto Rico believed to be typical of vast areas of the humid tropics.

II MATERIALS AND METHODS

Some soil characteristics at the beginning of the experiments are show in Table 1. All the soils had pH's below 5.0 and several were extremely acid ranging in pH from 3.9 to 4.3. Such low pH values were the result of past fertilization with $(NH_4)_2SO_4$. The Oxisols had much lower CEC values than the Ultisols. Also, exchangeable Al amounted to only around 1 me or less per 100 g in all 3 Oxisols whereas it ranged from 7 to 10 me/100 g in the Ultisols. Easily reducible Mn was very high in both clay members of the Oxisol group.

One crop each of corn and beans were grown in that order on each soil. With corn satisfactory experiments were carried out at each of the 8 sites, but with beans extreme drouth conditions on the Piñas sand and disease problems in the Catalina clay experiment invalidated results. For this reason data for only 6 bean experiments are reported.

Experimental sites were divided into 30 to 60 plots of 4 x 4 meters arranged in a completely randomized design. Increments of an agricultural grade of calcitic limestone were added as required to provide the desired range in soil acidity, and the limestone was thoroughly mixed with the upper 15 centimeters of soil. The soil in all plots was sampled for analysis 6 months after liming. Twelve cores were taken in each plot at

Table 1.—Some characteristics of the soils at 8 liming experiment sites.

Soil type	Classification	Easily reducible Mn	O.M. content	Soil reaction	CEC	Σ cations	Exch Al
		ppm	%	pH	me/100 g	me/100 g	me/100 g
Humatas clay	Typic Tropohumult	120	3.0	3.9	15	9.4	6.3
Corozal clay	Aquic Tropudult	210	4.0	4.3	19	14.2	9.9
Corozal clay	(level phase)	1/	4.7	4.6	19	15.4	5.5
Corozal clay	(eroded phase)	1/	2.5	4.2	16	11.0	6.9
Los Guineos clay	Epiaquic Tropohumult	40	8.1	4.3	16	9.6	4.5
Coto clay	Tropeptic Haplorthox	700	2.0	4.2	5	3.3	1.1
Catalina clay	Typic Haplorthox	638	2.3	4.8	11	5.0	0.9
Piñas sand	Typic Haplorthox	144	0.5	4.6	2	1.0	0.4

1/ Not determined.

0 to 15 cm depths, composited, air dried and passed through a 20 mesh sieve. Cation exchange capacity was determined by the NH_4OAc extraction procedure and by sum of cations. Calcium and Mg were determined by versenate titration, K was determined by flame photometer and Mn was determined colorimetrically after oxidation with periodate. Exchangeable Al was extracted with normal KCl and determined by the titration method (McLean, 1965). Easily reducible Mn was determined by reduction with hydroquinone as described by Adams (1965). Soil pH was measured with a glass electrode pH meter using 1:1.5 soil-water suspension.

The corn variety used, Pioneer X-306, was developed specifically for the humid tropics and appears to have a yield potential of about 6,500 kg/ha. Green beans of the Bountiful variety was used. The crops were managed in accordance with the intensive management techniques recommended by the Puerto Rico Agricultural Experiment Station and were harvested at the optimum stage of maturity. Leaf samples were taken in each plot using accepted methods of sampling for the specific crop and analyzed for P, K, Ca, Mg and Mn using standard procedures.

Yields were related by regression analysis to the several measured soil properties and to foliar composition.

III RESULTS

Soils

Results for several of the soils presented in Figure 1 show that percent base saturation calculated from CEC determined by NH_4OAc increased from around 20% at pH levels below 4.0 to near 100% as pH approached 5.5. This is consistent with known behavior of Al, which essentially disappears from exchange positions as soil pH is raised to around 5.5. The more highly weathered Coto and the Corozal soils tended to have lower percentage base saturations at pH levels between 4.0 and 5.0 than the Humatas.

Considerable variation was observed between the sum of exchangeable cations and CEC by NH_4OAc among plots in the same experiment due to effect of pH dependent charge. As suggested by Coleman and coworkers (1959) a more satisfactory basis for reporting percentage base and Al saturation seems to be the use of sum of exchangeable cations. Although a definite and relatively close relationship exists between values for Al saturation based on CEC by sum of exchangeable cations and by NH_4OAc for a given soil, the slope of the lines may be considerably different for different soils, as indicated by Figure 2. Data for percent Al saturation used in this paper are, therefore, based on sum of cations.

The close relationship between soil pH and percent Al saturation in all the soils of this study is shown in Figure 3. Al made up about one half the exchangeable cations in these soils when pH was around 4.5 and there were still readily measurable amounts of Al in some of the soils at pH levels as high as 5.4. These characteristics are in agreement with those reported by Brenes and Pearson (1973) for similar soils.

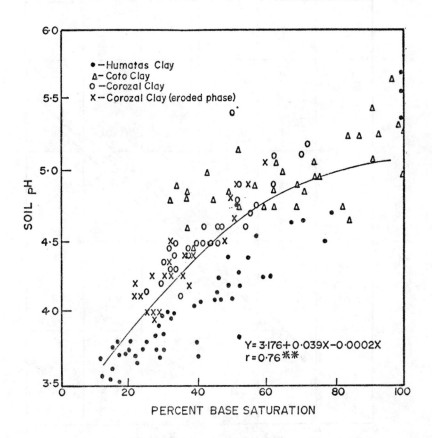

Figure 1. Relationship between soil pH and percent base saturation based on CEC by NH₄OAc. Each point represents an individual field plot.

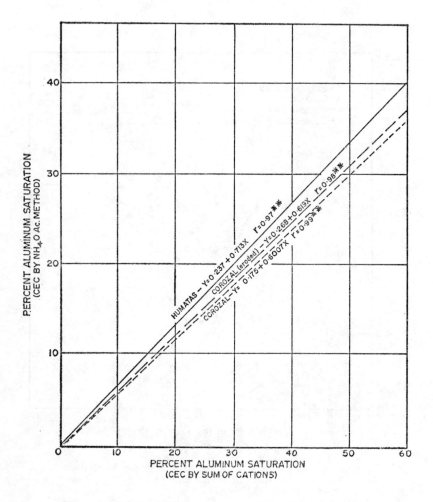

Figure 2. Relationship between percent Al saturation determined by 2 methods.

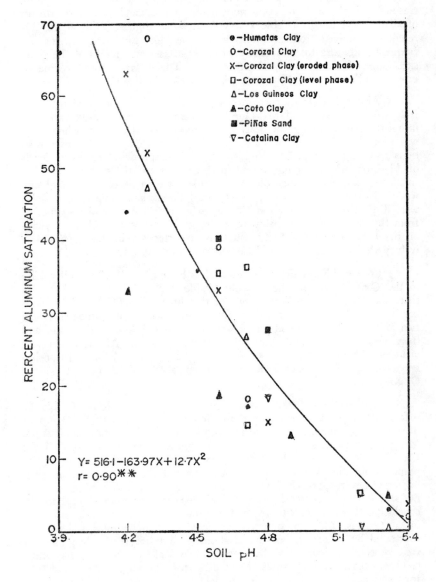

Figure 3. Relationship between soil pH and percent Al saturation in 8 Puerto Rican soils.

Corn.—Despite the lack of an adapted, high-yielding hybrid, reasonably high yields of corn were made in adequately limed treatments of all the experiments (Table 2 and Figure 4). Highest yields at the different sites ranged from 2.79 tons/ha on the Piñas sand where water was frequently limiting to 5.34 tons on the Humatas clay. Yields at the other sites ranged from about 3.7 to 4.8 tons/ha. The striking effect of lime on growth and appearance of the corn is illustrated in Figure 5.

Although yield of corn growing on the Ultisols increased progressively with increasing soil pH (Fig. 6), there were rather wide variations in relative yield among the soils for a given pH. However, when yield was plotted against percent Al saturation of the soils a much closer relationship emerged (Fig. 7). Yields decreased sharply with increasing levels of Al throughout the range found in these soils and the presence of even small amounts of exchangeable Al coincided with a decrease in yield and when Al accounted for as much as 15% of the exchangeable cations yields were distinctly reduced for the Ultisols as a group. As would be expected from the reciprocal relationship of exchangeable bases and Al, corn yields on the Ultisols varied directly with this characteristic, increasing progressively with increasing percent base saturation ($r=0.77$).

Corn yield was depressed much less by a given level of soil acidity in the Oxisols than in the Ultisols (Table 2 and Figure 8). Although there was a response to lime in two of the three soils (Piñas and Coto) it barely reached the level required for significance at .05 probability. In two of the three soils good yields were made at pH levels below 5.0, and there was no significant relationship between percent Al saturation and yield on the Oxisols as a group. Thus, there was no clear relationship between any of the measured soil characteristics and corn yield on the Oxisols.

Composition of corn leaves at the various soil pH levels (Table 2) offers little help in rationalizing the difference in hehavior of the 2 groups of soils. Magnesium, P or K did not vary consistently with lime application. Manganese was present at less than 20 ppm in corn leaves from all the Ultisols except Corozal clay (level phase) where it approached only 100 ppm. While the Mn content of plants from the Oxisols was somewhat higher it never approached values generally associated with phyto-toxicity, nor did it vary consistently with soil pH. These observations lead to the conclusion that Mn toxicity was not a primary cause of acid-soil infertility in the Oxisols. Calcium content was related to yield within a soil type, as illustrated by Figure 9, but the relationship did not hold when all sites were considered simultaneously. For example, leaf-Ca content at maximum yield was 0.57% for Humatas clay, 0.47% for Corozal (eroded) and 0.33 for Catalina clay. Further, maximum yield was made on Catalina at a lower Ca content than minimum yield on Humatas clay. Thus, it appears that the data at hand are not adequate for rationalization of the observed differences in yield response of corn to soil pH variation in Oxisols as compared to Ultisols.

Table 2.—Effect of soil acidity on corn grain yield and leaf composition.

Soil pH	Al saturation	Corn yield	Composition of corn leaves				
			Ca	Mg	P	K	Mn
	%	ton/ha	%	%	%	%	ppm
		Humatas clay					
3.9	66	1.15	.36	.11	.34	1.78	—
4.2	44	2.80	.42	.11	.35	1.85	—
4.5	36	4.09	.49	.12	.37	1.89	20
4.7	17	4.42	.51	.10	.36	1.95	—
5.3	3	5.34	.57	.11	.36	2.00	—
		Corozal clay					
4.3	68	0.42	.33	.10	.42	1.94	—
4.6	39	2.23	.41	.09	.49	1.66	—
4.7	18	2.91	.41	.09	.48	1.64	20
5.4	2	4.17	.48	.10	.46	1.37	—
		Corozal clay (level phase)					
4.6	35	2.35	.28	.07	.47	2.16	97
4.7	14	3.14	.28	.12	.45	2.13	98
5.2	5	3.79	.31	.10	.47	2.03	92
		Corozal clay (eroded phase)					
4.2	63	0.65	.33	.12	.41	1.85	—
4.3	52	0.95	.33	.11	.37	1.75	—
4.6	33	2.25	.40	.10	.43	1.75	20
4.8	15	2.55	.41	.10	.43	1.68	—
5.4	4	3.57	.47	.10	.43	1.35	—
		Los Guineos clay					
4.3	47	1.77	.27	.12	.43	2.87	40
4.7	27	2.65	.28	.12	.46	2.77	35
5.3	—	3.73	.30	.11	.44	2.68	31
		Coto clay					
4.2	33	4.05	.39	.10	.19	1.89	114
4.6	19	4.15	.40	.09	.21	1.84	75
4.9	13	4.50	.39	0.9	.21	1.83	85
5.3	5	4.79	.39	.09	.21	1.73	69
		Piñas sand					
4.6	40	1.71	.41	.15	.42	1.96	121
4.7	36	2.76	.48	.14	.45	2.06	121
4.8	28	2.95	.55	.15	.42	1.90	103
5.5	—	2.79	.58	.16	.44	2.00	80
		Catalina clay					
4.8	18	4.40	.29	.09	.42	2.12	104
5.2	—	4.95	.30	.08	.41	2.07	66
5.3	—	5.15	.33	.08	.42	2.14	86
5.6	—	4.58	.33	.10	.43	2.23	74

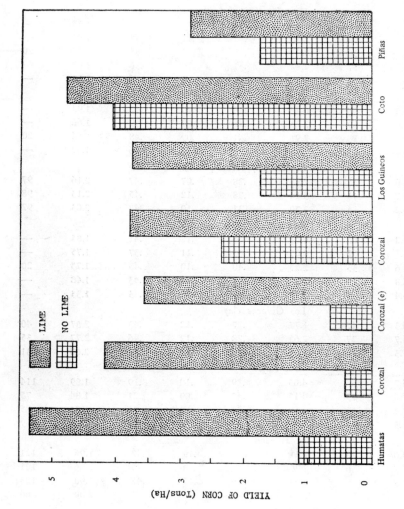

Figure 4. Effect of adequate lime application on corn yield on 5 Ultisols and 2 Oxisols.

Figure 5. Effect of liming a very acid Ultisol (Humatas clay) on corn growth. Plot in foreground had 66% Al saturation as compared with only about 3% for plot in background.

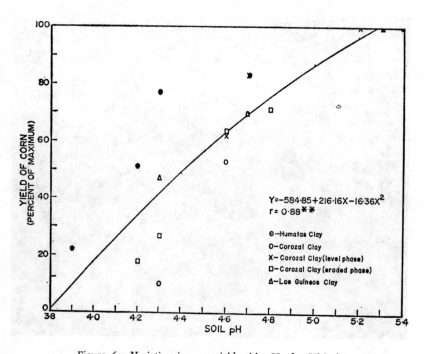

Figure 6. Variation in corn yield with pH of 5 Ultisols.

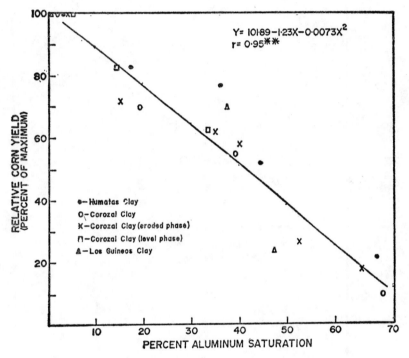

Figure 7. Relationship between percent Al saturation and relative corn yield on 5 Ultisols.

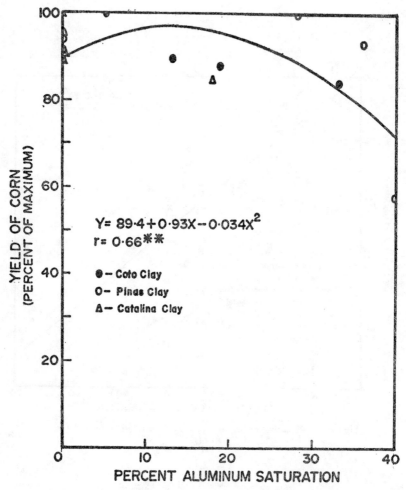

Figure 8.   Relationship between corn yield and percent aluminum
saturation on 3 Oxisols.

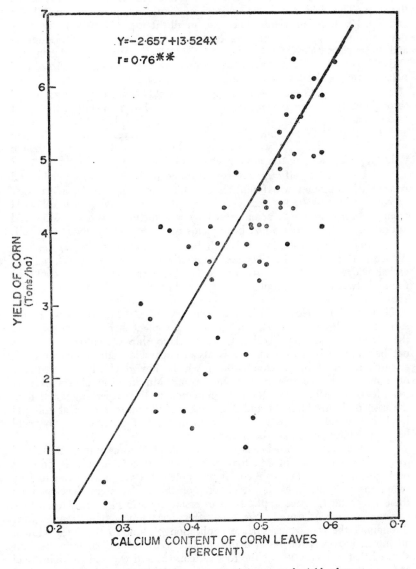

Figure 9. Variation in Ca content of leaves and yield of corn on Humatas clay.

Bean Yield.—Snap beans were grown on 6 of the experiment sites following corn. Beans were not grown on Piñas sand because its poor moisture holding capacity made this soil especially unsuitable for beans. Catalina was not included because of a severe rust infestation that killed the crop. The yield and foliar composition results are presented in Table 3 and Fig. 10. Excellent yields were made in all the experiments with adequate rates of lime application, ranging from around 7 tons/ha on the Humatas and Coto clays to nearly 14 tons on the Los Guineos clay. Again, the Oxisols gave the smallest response to lime even though the unlimed soil pH was among the lowest of the entire group of soils.

The progressive increase in bean yield as soil pH was raised throughout the range covered in this study is shown in Fig. 10. The r value of 0.91 is clear indication of the close relationship over this range, and the shape of the individual soil response curves indicated that, in general, maximum yield was approached by about pH 5.3, even though yield was increased by the last increment of lime.

A highly significant inverse relationship between bean yield and percent Al saturation was found, as illustrated in Fig. 11. As in the case of corn yield, only more clearly defined, any increase in exchangeable Al from the zero level was accompanied by a reduction in yield. When Al saturation reached about 50%, bean yields were reduced by about one half.

Foliar composition varied with lime application in several respects. As with corn, Ca content increased regularly with increasing soil pH but varied widely among the different soils. No clear relationship could be found between leaf-Ca content and yield, but when the ratio of Ca:Mn, expressed in terms of chemical equivalents, is considered together with yield a strikingly close relationship emerges (Fig. 12). In view of the extremely wide range in easily reducible Mn content among these soils and the differences in exchangeable Ca, the relationship shown in Fig. 13 is not believed to be fortuitous. It is also comparable with results of other research reviewed by Jackson (1967) which showed clearly the existence of a reciprocal relationship between Ca and Mn in plant shoots even at toxic levels of Mn. Thus, the data presented in this paper suggest that in the case of beans both Al and Mn were yield-limiting factors at soil pH levels below 5.0 and that a Ca:Mn ratio in the leaf of around 225 would be required for maximum bean yield.

These results with beans on soils such as Coto appear to be related to earlier observations of Mn toxicity and its correction in coffee growing on high-Mn soils in Puerto Rico. It was noted that very severe Mn toxicity symptoms resulting even in defoliation of the coffee trees developed on these soils after repeated applications of residually acid N sources when lime was not concurrently used. Yet even after development of extreme acidity throughout the root zone, surface application of lime to the trees without attempted incorporation resulted in complete recovery. Actual measurements showed that at least 90% of the root system was still exposed to highly acid soil and therefore to high concentrations of soluble Mn. Also, leaf analysis indicated little change in Mn content after liming even though the toxicity symptoms had disappeared. It thus appears that the presence of adequate levels of available Ca is in itself effective in overcoming deleterious effects of excess Mn in plants.

Table 3.—Effect of soil acidity on bean yield and leaf composition.

Soil pH	Al saturation	Bean yield	Composition of corn leaves				
			Ca	Mg	P	N	Mn
	%	ton/ha	%	%	%	%	ppm
			Humatas clay				
3.9	66	1.81	1.10	.23	.49	6.55	210
4.2	44	3.42	1.26	.21	.36	5.95	190
4.5	36	4.87	1.49	.21	.44	5.94	160
4.7	17	5.61	1.56	.25	.34	5.76	160
5.3	3	6.93	1.83	.27	.36	5.75	110
			Corozal clay				
4.3	68	4.31	.95	.27	.32	6.70	184
4.6	39	8.13	1.45	.24	.31	6.32	169
4.7	18	8.89	1.57	.29	.30	6.11	152
5.4	2	11.17	2.18	.34	.35	5.87	121
			Corozal clay (level phase)				
4.6	35	5.56	2.44	.25	.20	5.76	266
4.7	14	8.40	2.92	.25	.18	5.37	234
5.2	5	9.12	3.08	.24	.21	5.29	165
			Corozal clay (eroded phase)				
4.2	63	3.63	.88	.25	.30	6.78	157
4.3	52	5.54	1.07	.24	.30	6.25	150
4.6	33	8.76	1.34	.27	.30	6.28	132
4.8	15	9.83	1.61	.36	.32	6.14	123
5.4	4	11.70	2.00	.33	.31	5.97	122
			Los Guineos clay				
4.3	47	10.12	1.34	.46	.16	5.58	149
4.7	27	12.76	1.72	.40	.16	5.62	124
5.3	—	13.60	2.39	.31	.17	5.79	50
			Coto clay				
4.2	33	4.69	1.63	.29	.30	5.28	267
4.6	19	5.73	1.77	.33	.30	5.13	263
4.9	13	6.51	1.90	.30	.31	5.09	245
5.3	5	6.89	2.12	.30	.32	5.14	211

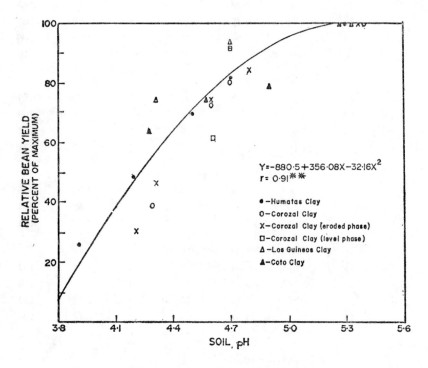

Figure 10. Effect of pH on relative yield of green beans.

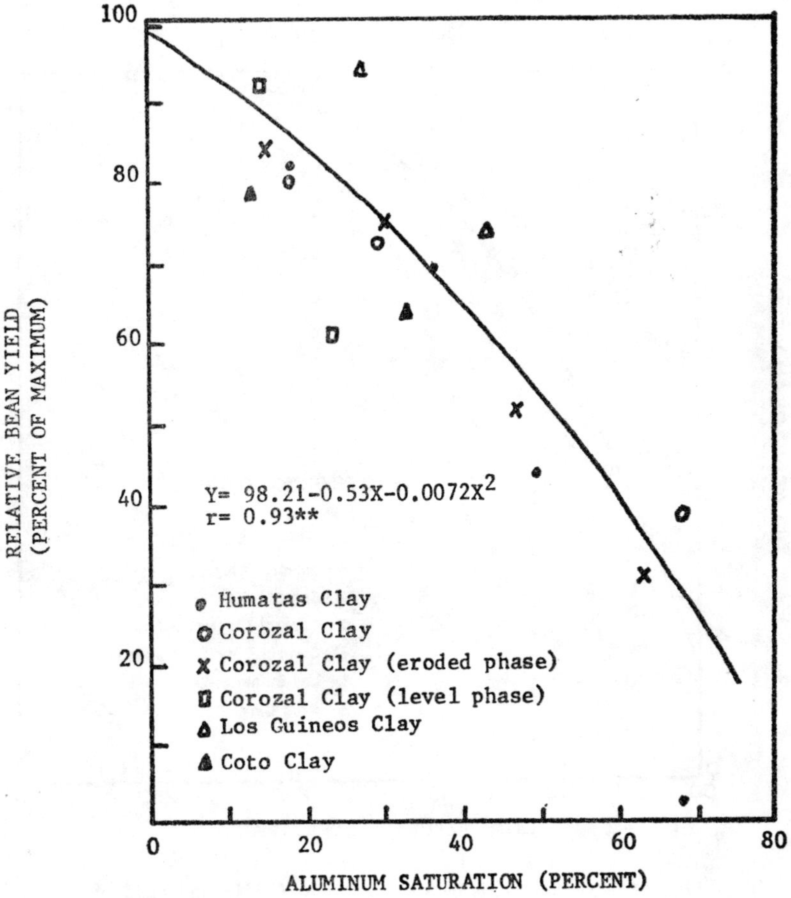

100
80
60
40
20
0
20
40
60
80
RELATIVE BEAN YIELD
(PERCENT OF MAXIMUM)
ALUMINUM SATURATION (PERCENT)
Y= 98.21-0.53X-0.0072X2
r= 0.93**
Humatas Clay
Corozal Clay
Corozal Clay (eroded phase)
Corozal Clay (level phase)
Los Guineos Clay
Coto Clay

Figure 11. Relationship between percent aluminum saturation and relative yield of green beans.

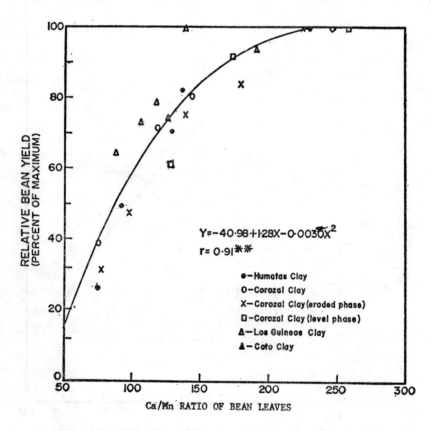

Figure 12. Relationship between the ratio Ca:Mn and yield of green beans.

IV SUMMARY

There was a strong corn yield response to lime application on 5 Ultisols in contrast to the weak response obtained on Oxisols, which was significant at only 1 of 3 sites.

The Ultisols contained on the average around 10 times as much exchangeable Al as the Oxisols, but the percent Al saturation at a given pH level was similar in the 2 soil categories.

There was a close relationship between corn yield and percent Al saturation of the Ultisols, but no apparent relationship in the Oxisols. Al toxicity was most likely the primary cause of acid soil infertility in the Ultisols.

Foliar composition gave no clear evidence of a specific cause of lime response by corn. Ca content increased with increasing yield, probably reflecting increasing root system extent and effectiveness as Al level in the soil decreased. However, Ca deficiency was not likely at the leaf levels found. Mn toxicity was not indicated by foliar composition.

There was a marked response of green beans to lime in the 5 Ultisols and 1 Oxisol included in this series of experiments. In contrast to the results with corn there was a close relationship between yield and both soil pH and percent Al saturation in the Oxisol as well as the Ultisols.

There was a close relationship between Ca:Mn ratio and bean yields among all the soils, maximum yield occurring at a ratio of around 225 on a chemical equivalent basis.

Thus, yield of both corn and green beans on 5 Ultisols of beans on 1 Oxisol was clearly related to percent Al saturation over the entire range studied (0-68%). Liming to a pH of 5.0 to 5.5 on these soils satisfied the needs of both crops with regard to Ca requirements and correction of Al and Mn toxicities. There was no indication of overliming injury even though many times the amount of lime theoretically required to neutralize exchangeable Al was applied in a number of the experiments.

V ACKNOWLEDGEMENT

This report covers work carried out cooperatively between the Agricultural Research Service, USDA and the Agricultural Experiment Station, Mayaguez Campus, University of Puerto Rico, Río Piedras, P. R. This work was partially funded by the U.S. Agency for International Development under research contract csd-2490.

VI REFERENCES

ABRUÑA, F., PEARSON, R. W., and ELKINS, G. 1958. Quantitative evaluation of soil reaction and base status changes resulting from field applications of residually acid nitrogen fertilizers, Soil Sc. Soc. Am. Proc. 22:539-42.

ABRUÑA, F., and VICENTE-CHANDLER, J. 1967. Sugarcane yields as related to acidity of a humid tropic Ultisol, Agronomy J., 59:520-31.

ABRUÑA, F., VICENTE-CHANDLER, J., BECERRA, L., and BOSQUE-LUGO, R. 1965. Effects of liming and fertilization on yields and foliar composition of high yielding sungrown coffee in Puerto Rico, J. Agr. Univ. P. R. 49:413-428.

ABRUÑA, F., VICENTE-CHANDLER, J., and PEARSON, R. W. 1964. Effects of liming on yields and composition of heavily fertilized grasses and on soil properties under humid tropical conditions, Soil Sci. Soc. Am. Proc. 28:657-61.

ABRUÑA-RODRIGUEZ, F., VICENTE-CHANDLER, J., PEARSON, R. W. and SILVA, S. 1970. Crop response to soil acidity factors in Ultisol and Oxisols - Tobacco, Soil Sci. Soc. Am. Proc. 34:629-35.

ADAMS, F. 1965. Manganese. In Methods of soil analysis, Part 2, C. A. Black (ed.) Am. Soc. of Agronomy. pp. 1011-1018.

BERGER, J. 1972. Maize production and the manuring of maize, Centre d'Etude de l'Azote N° 5. Geneva.

BRAMS, E. A. 1971. Continuous cultivation of West African soils: Organic matter diminution and effects of applied lime and phosphorus. Plant and Soil 35: 401-414.

CARO-COSTAS, R., VICENTE-CHANDLER, J., and ABRUÑA, F. 1972. Effect of four levels of fertilization on beef production and carrying capacity of Pangola grass pastures in the humid mountain region of Puerto Rico. Jour. Agr. Aniv. P.R. 56:219-222.

COLEMAN, N. T., WEED, S. B., and McCRACKEN, R. J. 1959. Cation exchange capacity and exchangeable cations in Piedmont soils of North Carolina. Soil Sci. Soc. Amer. Proc. 23:146-149.

JACKSON, W. A. 1967. Physiological effects of soil acidity In Soil acidity and liming, R. W. Pearson and F. Adams (ed.) Am. Soc. of Agronomy.

McCOLLUM, R. E. and VALVERDE, C. 1968. The fertilization of potatoes in Perú: I. A summary and interpretation of data from field experiments completed from 1959 through 1964 in the Sierra, N. C. Agr. Expt. Sta. Tech. Bull. 185.

McLEAN, E. O. 1965. Aluminum. In Methods of soil analysis, Part 2, C. A. Black (ed.) Am. Soc. of Agronomy. pp. 978-998.

MIKKELSEN, D. S., FREITAS, L. M. M. DE and McCLUNG, A. C. 1963. Effects of liming and fertilizing cotton, corn and soybeans on Campo Cerrado soils, State of São Paulo, Brazil. IRI Research Inst. Bull. 29.

PEARSON, R. W., ABRUÑA, F., and VICENTE-CHANDLER, J. 1961. Effect of lime and nitrogen applications on downward movement of calcium an magnesium in two humid tropical soils of Puerto Rico. Soil Sci. 93:77-82.

PRATT, P. F., and ALVAHYDO, R. 1966. Cation exchange characteristics of soils of São Paulo, Brazil. IRI Research Inst. Bull. 31.

REEVE, N. G., and SUMNER, M. E. 1971. Cation exchange capacity and exchangeable aluminum in Natal Oxisols. Soil Sci. Soc. Amer. Proc. 35:38-42.

16 Liming Soils of the Brazilian Cerrado

WILSON V. SOARES, EDSON LOBATO, ENRIQUE GONZALEZ
and GEORGE C. NADERMAN, Jr

I INTRODUCTION

The predominant vegetation covering the great plateau of Central Brazil is known as "cerrado". This vegetation has a xeromorphic appearance with tortuous trees and shrubs distributed in varying densities over a covering of grasses and small woody and herbaceous plants. Eiten (1972) has reported that cerrado vegetation occurs only in upland areas on soils which have excellent internal drainage, in marked contrast with the majority of natural savannas in the northern part of South America.

According to Camargo (1969), cerrado occurs only in moist climates with at least one relatively hot, tropical or subtropical rainy season. Continuous occurrence of this vegetation from the northern part of Maranhao (5°S) to within proximity of the Tropic of Capricorn (23°S) has been observed. Within this area the annual rainfall ranges from 900 to 1600 mm, mostly occurring during the months of October through April, and with mean annual temperatures varying from 19° to 26°C.

Maps and soil survey reports produced by the Ministry of Agriculture (Equipe de Pedología e Fertilidade do Solo, 1966; Divisão de Pedologia e Fertilidade do Solo, 1966; Jacomine, 1969) have revealed that latosolic soils predominate under cerrado vegetation. Two great groups within the Brazilian soil classification system are especially important because of area of occurrence: Dystrophic Dark Red Latosol, and the Dystrophic Red-Yellow Latosol. Each of these categories would include members of the great groups Haplustox and Acrustox in the U.S. system of soil taxonomy (Cline and Buol, 1973).

These soils are usually deep, and frequently with clay or medium texture. They have strong, granular structure making them very porous. In general, the cerrado area has gently rolling terrain which is favorable to development of mechanized and intensive agriculture, and much of this area is already served by a reasonably good system of roads.

Cerrado vegetation occupies an approximate area of 1.8 million square kilometers, which represents nearly one-fifth of the country (Ranzani, 1971). This vast expanse of land is situated between the well developed and populous south-central part of Brazil and the unpopulated Amazon region with the Federal Capital located almost at its geographic center,

Events in recent years have given increased importance to the cerrado area. The construction and growth of Brasília has been accompanied by significant development of the infrastructure, especially roads and transportation facilities. With increasing agricultural and industrial demand for land, land prices in the southern part of the Brazil are extremely high. The potential of the cerrado area for agriculture, and the incentives offered by the government have induced companies from the south to move to the central states. This could transform, perhaps in the near future, an area presently characterized by extensive ranching into a great area of intensive agriculture.

It is thus imperative to intensify research efforts and identify the problems of this agricultural frontier in order to offer more adequate solutions to the farmers who propose to cultivate the extensive area presently covered by cerrado.

The objective of this paper is to summarize results of lime experiments conducted in the vicinity of Brasília from 1966 to the present. This work was done at the Brasília Experiment Station and at other cooperating institutions within the Federal District.

II CHEMICAL CHARACTERISTICS OF THE SOILS

In a review of characteristics of cerrado soils, Ranzani (1971) concluded that in these Latosols the pH increases with depth, ranging from 4.0 to 5.0 in the surface horizons and 5.0 to 6.5 in deeper horizons. He also found that cation exchange capacity decreases with depth, ranging from 3.0 to 13.0 meq/100 g of soil in the surface horizons and being less than 4.0 meq/100 g in deeper horizons. The base saturation is generally less than 20%.

Analytical data for three soils of the Brasília Experiment Station are given in Table 1. The levels of exchangeable bases and available P are very low (only about one-tenth of probable critical levels). The soils are highly acid and generally have more than 70% aluminum saturation. A useful comparative study of several varieties of cerrado soils was recently reported by Cline and Buol (1973).

The effects of various rates of lime application upon pH, exchangeable Al, and the sum of exchangeable Ca and Mg have been studied. Recommendations for lime rates in Brazil have varied somewhat in recent years. Until bout 10 years ago, lime recommendations were designed to attain certain pH levels. A network of laboratories for analysis of farmers' soil samples was established by the Ministry of Agriculture in cooperation with the International Soil Fertility Evaluation and Improvement Program of North Carolina State University. These laboratories changed the method of lime recommendations to that based upon exchangeable Al as described by Kamprath (1967). Because of the high aluminum saturation and low exchange capacity of these soils, this appears to be a reasonable method.

Based upon these concepts, a pot experiment to study the effects of liming was conducted at the Brasília Experiemnt Station with the three soils described in Table 1. Six levels of analytical grade $CaCO_3$ were applied to each of the soils. These levels consisted of the quantity of $CaCO_3$ chemically equivalent to the exchangeable Al in the respective soils multiplied by factors of 0, $\frac{1}{2}$, 1, 2, 3, and 4, with the lime rates expressed in tons per hectare. An application of $CaCO_3$ chemically equivalent to 1 meq

Table 1.—Some chemical characteristics of three soils at the Brasilia Experiment Station. The soils are Dark Red Latosol of clay texture (LE), Red-Yellow Latosol of clay texture (LV), and Red-Yellow Latosol of medium texture (LVm). Analytical procedures by Vettori (1969).

Soil identification	pH	Al	Ca + Mg	K	P	Al Sat'n
	1:2.5		meq/100 g		ppm	%
LE	4.2	1.9	0.3	25	1	86
LV	5.2	0.7	0.3	29	1	70
LVm	5.2	0.9	0.3	28	1	75

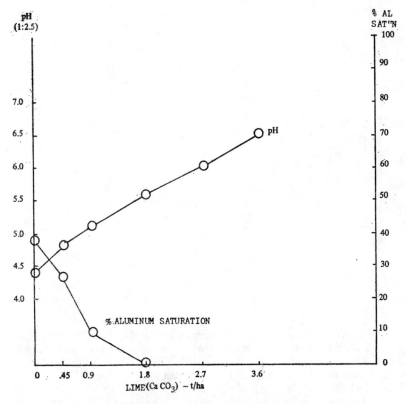

Figure 1. Relationships of pH and percent aluminum saturation to lime rate for surface soil of the Red-Yellow Latosol of medium texture at the Brasilia Experiment Station.

of exchangeable Al/100 g corresponded to 1 ton/ha. Pots with 2 kg of soil were used with four replications. A basal fertilization including P, K. Mg, and micronutrients was also added, and corn was grown in the pots for nearly two months. At that time soil samples were taken from the pots and analyzed. The results for each soil are summarized in Figures 1, 2, and 3.

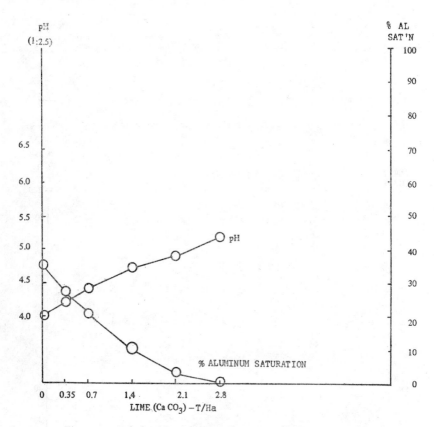

Figure 2. Relationships of pH and percent aluminum saturation to lime rate for surface soil of the Red-Yellow Latosol of medium texture at the Brasilia Experiment Station.

The Red-Yellow Latosol of medium texture (LVm) shown in Figure 1 has a weak buffering capacity in comparison with the other soils (Figures 2 and 3). At the rate of 3.6 tons/ha of $CaCO_3$ (4 x Al) the pH reached 6.5. At the rate of 1.8 tons/ha (2 x Al) the exchangeable Al decreased to zero which resulted in a pH of about 5.5.

For the Red-Yellow Latosol of clay texture (LV) the rate of 2.8 tons/ha (4 x Al) reduced the exchangeable Al in the soil to zero but only raised the pH to 5.2 (Figure 2).

The Dark Red Latosol of clay texture (LE) required the highest rate of CaCO₃ to eliminate exchangeable Al. For the pot experiment, the rate of 6 tons/ha (3 x Al) reduced exchangeable Al to zero and produced a pH of 5.5 (Figure 3). Similar results from a field experiment on the same soil are also shown in Figure 3. The analyses of samples taken from the field experiment almost five years after a single limestone application indicate that the rate of 5 tons/ha was sufficient to maintain the aluminum saturation at less than 10%.

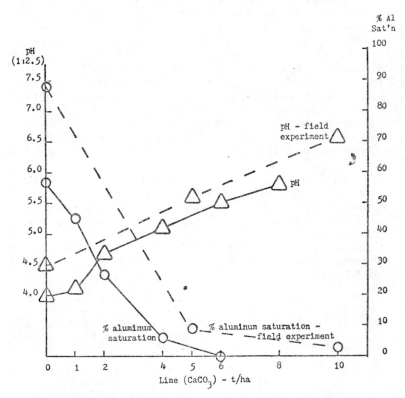

Figure 3. Relationships of pH and percent aluminum saturation to lime rate for surface soil of the Dark Red Latosol of clay texture at the Brasilia Experiment Station. Analytical data are also given for soil samples taken nearly five years after limestone applications in a field experiment on this soil (E. J. Kamprath, 1971, unpublished data).

The general conclusion may be drawn from Figures 1, 2, and 3 that aluminum saturation may be reduced to less than 10%, a condition which is satisfactory for the majority of cultivated plants, by the application of 1.5, 2, and 4 t limestone/ha (equivalent to 1.5, 3, and 2 times exchangeable Al) for the LVm, LV, and LE soils, respectively.

III CROP RESPONSES TO LIMING

Preliminary studies with cerrado soils in São Paulo and Goiás reported by McClung et al., (1958), revealed the special importance of liming the soil for certain legumes. Freitas et al., (1963) found that yields of cotton, corn, and soybeans were strikingly increased by limestone additions, with cotton showing the geratest response in three soils in the state of São Paulo, Verdade (1971) summarized the reports of various workers and reported a response to liming in cotton, peanuts, sweet potato, sugar cane, beans, corn, and soybeans. For rice, wheat, and potatoes, however, the responses were inconsistent.

Field experiments conducted in five localities within the Federal District were reported by Freitas et al., (1971). The soils at the experimental sites have not yet been mapped but these are possibly varieties of the Dark Red Latosol. The Mg content of the limestone used in these early trials was not known. Therefore, the basic fertilization applied to all plots in these experiments included Mg in the form of $MgSO_4$ to avoid yield limitations due to Mg deficiency, and to assure that the measured response was due to the effects of $CaCO_3$. Some of the results of these experiments are summarized and presented in Tables 2, 3, and 4, and in Figures 4 and 5.

From Tables 2, 3, and 4 it is apparent that the rate of 5 tons/ha of lime was sufficient to raise the pH to the range of 5.7 to 6.4. Figure 4 shows that this intermediate rate coincided with the best corn grain yields. Within this pH range all of the exchangeable Al was probably eliminated. The latter supposition is reinforced by the conclusions of a more recent experiment shown in Figure 3 in which 5 tons/ha of limes was sufficient to reduce the aluminum saturation to less than 10% and raised the pH between 5.3 and 5.6.

Table 2.—Effects of lime applications on certain soil chemical characteristics and corn grain yields at the Colegio Agricola de Brasilia. (Freitas et al., 1971).

Limestone	pH	Ca	Mg	Shelled corn yields at 16% moisture	
				Kg/ha	
(t/ha)	(1:2.5)	meq/100 g soil		1965/66	1966/67
0	4.3	0.5	0.08	4.517	4.895
5	5.9	6.0	0.69	5.560	6.207
10	6.5	10.4	1.32	4.940	5.769
Linear effects	* *	* *	* *		
Quadratic effects	* *	n.s.	n.s.		

— 288 —

Table 3.—Effects of lime on certain soil chemical characteristics and yields of corn and soybeans at the Torto farm in the Federal District in 1965-66 (Freitas *et al.*, 1971).

Limestone	pH	Ca	Mg	Shelled corn 16% moisture	Soybeans
(t/ha)	(1:2.5)	meq/100 g soil		Kg/ha	
0	4.9	1.1	0.16	4.732	3.003
5	6.4	4.8	0.64	6.652	3.221
10	6.8	7.3	0.90	6.232	3.196
Linear effects	n.s.	n.s.	n.s.		
Quadratic effects	* *	* *	n.s.		

Table 4.—Effects of lime on certain soil chemical characteristics and yields of corn and soybeans at Vargem Bonita, in the Federal District 1965-66. (Freitas *et al.*, 1971).

Limestone	pH	Ca	Mg	Shelled corn 16% moisture	Soybeans
ton/ha	1:2.5	meq/100 g soil		Kg/ha	
0	4.5	0.5	0.12	3.205	714
5	5.7	4.5	0.62	3.740	1.253
10	6.3	6.8	0.73	3.142	1.503
Linear effects	* *	* *	* *		
Quadratic effects	n.s.	n.s.	n.s.		

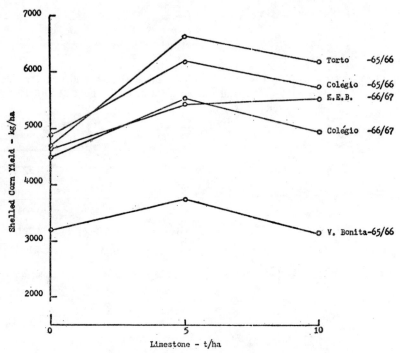

Figure 4. Responses of shelled corn yield (16% moisture) to limestone rates at several locations and different years in the Federal District.

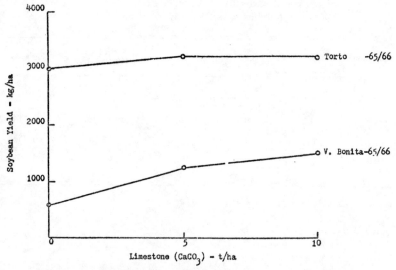

Figure 5. Responses of soybean yield to limestone rates at two locations in the Federal District.

Table 5.—Influence of lime and phosphorus applications on corn yields for a Dark Red Latosol clay texture at the Brasilia Experiment Station in 1966-67.

(kg/ha)	Limes (tons/ha)		
	0	5	10
P_2O_5	Corn yields (Kg/ha)		
0	—	—	—
150	3578	4225	4380
300	3990	5020	4990
450	4665	5440	5550

1sd (.05) = 428.

1d (.01) = 606.

Table 6.—Response of grain sorghum to limes and phosphorus applied during the previous crop year, on a Dark Red Latosol of clay texture at the Brasilia Experiment Station in the 1967-68.[1]

Phosphorus applied in previous year	Limestone (tons/ha)[3]		
	0	5	10
(kg P_2O_5/ha)[2]	Kg/ha		
0	294	1294	1600
150	1619	3294	3666
300	1675	3508	3850
450	1480	3536	3916

lsd (.05) = 314

lsd (.01) = 430

1/ Grain sorghum was planted to follow the corn crop reported in Table 5.

2/ In addition to the residual phosphorus from the previous crop, three levels of banded P were applied for the sorghum crop. The original plots were subdivided with applications of 75, 150, and 225 kg P_2O_5/ha in bands below the seed. Since there was no significant difference due to the banded applications, the yields above are means for the three levels of banded phosphorus.

3/ All limestone was applied during the previous crop year.

On the other hand, it should be noted that yields tended to decrease when lime applications increased to 10 tons/ha. The exception to this is shown by the curve identified as EEB-66/67 in Figure 4 in which the corn yield increased slightly, though not significantly, as the lime application increased to 10 tons/ha. Although these yield decreases with the highest limestone rate, these yield changes were generally not significant, the consistency of this occurrence suggests the possibility that for the soils studied there was some ed trimental effect from the application of 10 tons/ha of lime (which produced a pH of 6.3 to 6.8). For example, a reduction in available Zn, B, Fe, Mn, or Cu could have occurred under such circumstances.

The soybean crop did not benefit as greatly from liming as did corn (Figure 5). On one site there was a small but significant response to 5 tons/ha, with no further response at 10 tons/ha. In the other case, there was a yield response to 5 tons/ha with a slight additional response to 10 tons/ha, although in the latter case all the yields were relatively low, suggesting that other uncontrolled factors may have been involved. These results agree with those obtained by Freitas et al. (1963) in which soybeans responded less than did cotton or corn to limestone applications.

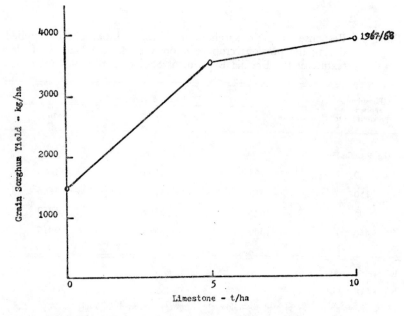

Figure 6. Response of grain sorghum yield to limestone rates at the Brasilia Experiment Station.

Figure 6 indicates the response of grain sorghum to limestone in a Dark Red Latosol at the Brasília Experiment Station. The grain yields increased from 1480 in the control to 3536 and 3916 kg/ha as the rate was increased to 5 and 10 tons/ha, respectively. This yield increase from the addition of 5 tons/ha was significant at the 1% level, while the additional yield response to 10 tons/ha was significant at the 5% level of probability.

We may conclude from the results discussed above that for the soils in the Federal District, the application of 5 tons/ha of lime increased grain sorghum yields by 140% and increased corn yields from 15 to 40%. For soybeans, the yield increase in response to 5 tons/ha was only about 7% with yields of about 3 tons/ha, but was about 75% with lower yields around 1 tons/ha.

The information given in Figure 7 and Table 7 present the results of an experiment with *Stylosanthes guyanensis* at the Brasília Experiment Station. For the first three cuttings there was a significant increase in dry matter in response to the application of 5 tons/ha and there tended to be a reduction in yield at 10 tons/ha. In the fourth and fifth cuttings the dry matter yields tended to be greater with the original application of 10 tons/ha than with 5 tons/ha, altough this yield increase was not significant by the Duncan test. A review of this experiment, however, has suggested the possibility that this apparent response to 10 tons/ha was caused by a yield limitation due to K deficiency because of greater total K uptake at the lower limestone rate. Several preliminary observations by the authors have indicated that K nutrition in this species may readily become limiting under these conditions. Nevertheless, for the total dry matter production over the five cuttings, there was a reduction in yield associated with a lime application of 10 tons/ha in comparison with the rate of 5 tons/ha.

A combination of the information mentioned above with the analytical results from samples taken by Kamprath from the above field experiment (Figure 3) supports the conclusion that for these soils, a limestone application designed to reduce exchangeable Al to about 10% saturation (pH of 5.6) is a more reasonable approach than an application to attain a pH of 6.6. Furthermore, it was observed that the application of 5 tons/ha increased the concentration of Ca in the plant tissue by nearly 30%, while there was practically no further increase in Ca concentration when the rate was raised to 10 tons/ha. It is thus apparent that satisfactory Ca nutrition for *Stylo* plants is supplied by the intermediate level of 5 tons/ha. This conclusion is also in agreement with the data discussed previously for other crops.

IV IMPORTANCE OF DEPTH OF LIME PLACEMENT

Experiments conducted in the state of São Paulo and reported by Mikkelsen *et al.,* (1963) showed a favorable response to the incorporation of limestone to greater depth. The application of 2 tons/ha of lime incorporated to 10 cm by disking resulted in only 20% of the yield of cotton obtained by incorporation of the same quantity of limes to 25 cm depth. This latter incorporation was achieved by applying half the limestone prior to plowing with the remainder applied after plowing and incorporated by disking.

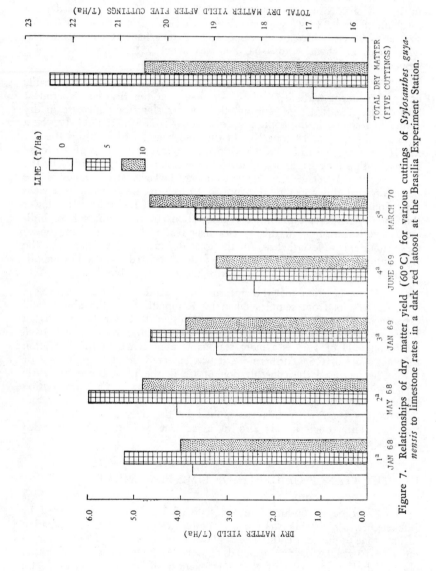

Figure 7. Relationships of dry matter yield (60°C) for various cuttings of *Stylosanthes guyanensis* to limestone rates in a dark red latosol at the Brasilia Experiment Station.

Table 7.—Influence of lime on dry matter yields from five cuttings of *Stylosanthes guyanensis* on a Dark Red Latosol of clay texture at the Brasilia Experiment Station.

Lime	First cut Jan. 68	Second cut May 68	Third cut Jan. 69	Fourth cut June 69	Fifth cut March 70	Total of five cuttings
t/ha			Kg/ha			
0	3700[a] [1]	4100[a]	3236[a]	2400[a]	3404[a]	16840
5	5210[b]	5980[b]	4637[bc]	3013[a]	3650[a]	22490
10	4010[a]	4810[a]	3886[ac]	3187[a]	4637[a]	20530

[1] Mean yields followed by the same letter do not differ significantly at the level of 5% probability.

In Central Brazil the occurrence of dry periods, known as "veranicos", during the rainy season is common. A recent review of rainfall data for a period of 40 years from a city near Brasília indicates that ,on the average, in every other year there will be at least 10 continuous days without rain during the rainy season.[1] Although less probable, periods without rain may extend to more than 15 days.

A severe "veranico" during the 1970-71 crop year caused the loss of nearly all grain production in a series of corn experiments at the Brasília Experiment Station. In these experiments the lime had been incorporated only to a depth of 15 cm. Observations of root depth and soil moisture status were made during the dry period while the plants were severely wilted. It was noted that the root system was limited to the zone of lime incorporation. The available moisture had been exhausted from this root zone, although considerable moisture was apparent below this depth. These observations led to the decision to study the relationship between depth of lime incorporation and root development as an approach to better utilization of soil moisture.

Experimental work to study this problem was recently initiated at the Brasília Experiment Station on a Dark Red Latosol of clay texture. The work forms part of the North Carolina State University (AID/csd 2806) - Cornell University (AID/csd 2490) program at Brasília.

In these studies lime was incorporated at two depths by a technique involving disking and rotovation. The effectiveness of this incorporation was shown by soil sampling, estimations of root length per unit of soil volume, moisture extraction patterns, and corn production. The results of three crops have indicated significant yield increases of corn in response to line incorporation to approximately 30 cm depth as compared with appli-

[1] J. M. Wolf, personal communication.

cation to about 15 cm depth. It has been observed that even with limestone incorporation to 30 cm deph, the roots of a vigorous corn crop at the tasseling stage are almost completely limited to 45 cm depth. The incorporation of limestone and elimination of toxic levels of aluminum saturation to 30 cm depth approximately doubled root growth per unit of soil volume in the depth range of 15 to 30 cm. This additional root development permits more effective moisture and nutrient absorption at that depth.

An additional treatment including Mg as a nutrient without limestone showed a great response of corn yield to the presence of this element. This indicates that Mg fertilization by some means is also very important.

Although this experiment has provided evidence of the need for Al neutralization to greater depth, no practical method is known to achieve this to depths greater than 25 to 30 cm. Natural downward movement of liming materials in soils of this type would be most helpful. Very little information exists, however, regarding the redistribution of Ca and Mg applied as liming mateirals to these kinds of soils. Gargantini (1972) worked with soils from the state of São Paulo and concluded that Ca and Mg movement occurred to a maximum depth of 40 cm. He attributed the changes in Ca and Mg levels within the profile to applications of liming mateirals to the plots five years before the samples were taken. He noted that the movement of Ca and Mg was more pronounced in the more coarse-textured soil as compared with a clayey soil.

V AVAILABILITY OF LIMESTONE

Reports of detailed studies of limestone reserves of the cerrado region of Central Brazil have not been found. However, the existence of numerous deposits in nearly 30 municipalities of the states of Minas Gerais and Goias has been reported (Ministry of Agriculture - USAID, 1964). Within the Federal District there are two limestone deposits currently being exploited. For a large portion of this region, at least, limestone is now readily available commercially, although the material is most frequently calcitic.

VI IMPLICATIONS FOR DEVELOPMENT

Considering that the soils associated with cerrado are generally acid with levels of aluminum saturation toxic to many crops, that limestone is available in much of this area, and that the development of a modern and more intensive agriculture in this region is likely to occur, the use of limestone should become increasingly common and important.

Research results to date have given valuable information. More work involving rates and methods of limestone application, similar to the study recently initiated at the Brasília Experiment Station, is needed. Studies regarding the quality of limestone from various sources should be initiated. Economic levels of limestone application for the crops considered to have high priority in the development of cerrado regions should be sought through persistent, long-term research, under the various environmental conditions of Central Brazil.

VII SUMMARY

The dominant vegetation of Central Brazil is known as "cerrado" and has certain xeromorphic aspects. This vegetation covers nearly 20% of the country.

The soils associated with cerrado vegetation are generally deep and well drained, with very low (less than 20%) base saturation, high (greater than 50%) aluminum saturation and very low available P. These soils are classified as latosols in the Brazilian system and would be members of the great groups Haplustox and Acrustox in the Soil Taxonomy.

Studies with three of these soils have shown that the application of limestone based upon neutralization of exchangeable Al is a reasonable approach. However, the quantities required to achieve this may be influenced by soil texture, organic matter, and the nature of the mineral fraction.

The quantities of $CaCO_3$ which could be recommended for the Red Yellow Latosol of medium texture (LVm), the Dark Red Latosol of clay texture (LE), and the Red Yellow Latosol of clay texture (LV) are chemically equivalent to 1.5, 2, and 3 times the exchangeable Al in the respective soils. These rates are approximately equal to 1.4, 3.8, and 2.1 tons $CaCO_3$/ha-20 cm for the soils studied. For the LE soil, the above rate has given satisfactory production of sorghum, corn, soybeans, and *Stylosanthes*.

Field experiments with several crops grown on Dark Red Latosols at five locations in the Federal District showed that a rate of 5 tons/ha of limes resulted in the following benefits:

1. Aluminum saturation was reduced to less than 10%, and the soil pH was increased to the range of 5.3 to 5.6.

2. The production of grain sorghum was increased by 140%, corn by 15% to 40,% and soybeans by 7% to 75%. The principal causes of variability were related to different experimental sites.

In comparison with the rate of 5 tons/ha, the application of 10 tons/ha of tended to decrease corn yields slightly. In each of the first three cuttings of a long-term field experiment with *Stylosanthes guyanensis* on the LE soil, the dry matter yields from 10 tons/ha lime were less than from the rate of 5 tons/ha. There was some response of soybeans to the application of 5 tons/ha of lime and in one experiment with grain sorghum there were yield responses to both rates of 5 and 10 tons/ha.

It appears advisable to incorporate lime as deeply as possible for non-irrigated crops sensitive to water stress. In an experiment presently underway at the Brasilia Experiment Station, lime incorporated by rotovation to 30 cm reduced exchangeable Al to this depth and resulted in the development of a root system which was effective in absorbing more water during occasional periods of dry weather. These effects were reflected in greater corn yields as compared with incorporation to 15 cm depth.

The existence of limestone deposits in much of the cerrado region is an important resource for development, since the soils of this area require liming for production of many crops. Further studies should include comparisons of quality of limestone from various sources. The Mg content of limestone applied to these soils is an important consideration in view of the high cost of adding other Mg fertilizers.

Further studies are needed regarding economic benefits of various methods of limestone incorporation. Additional studies of possible interactions of acidity, limestone applications, and nutrient availability with plant species and varieties should also be encouraged.

VIII ACKNOWLEDGEMENTS

The authors wish to thank Mr. James M. Wolf for valuable suggestions and preparation of the figures, and Mrs. Patricia Naderman for typing the manuscript.

IX REFERENCES

CAMARGO, A. P. DE. 1969. Problema climático inexiste. Coopercotia 26(232): 21-25.

CLINE, M., and S. W. BUOL. 1973. Soils of the Central Plateau of Brazil. Agronomy Mimeo 73-13. Cornell University, Ithaca, New York.

DIVISÃO DE PEDOLOGÍA E FERTILIDADE DO SOLO. 1966. Mapa esquemático de solos das Regioes Norte, Meio Norte e Centro Oeste de Brasil. Escala 1:5.000.000. DPEA — Ministerio de Agricultura, Brasil.

EITEN, G. 1972. The cerrado vegetation of Brazil. The Botanical Review 38(2). The New York Botanical Garden, Bronx, N. Y.

EQUIPE DE PEDOLOGÍA E FERTILIDADE DO SOLO. 1966. Levantamento semidetalhado dos solos de áreas do Ministério da Agricultura no Distrito Federal. Bol. Técnico Nº 8. Escritório de Pesquisas e Experimentação. Ministério da Agricultura.

FREITAS, L. M. M. DE, D. S. MIKKELSEN, A. C. McCLUNG and W. L. LOTT. 1962. Agricultura no cerrado. In Simpósio sobre o cerrado, p. 323-357. Editora da Universidade de São Paulo.

FREITAS, L. M. M. DE, E. LOBATO, and W. V. SOARES, 1971. Experimentos de calagem e adubação em solos sob vegetação de cerrado do Distrito Federal. Pesq. Agropc. Bras. (Ser. Agron.). 6:81-89.

GARGANTINI, H. 1972. Efeito da calagem no pH e nos teores de cálcio mais mágnésio e alumínio em perfis de solos de cerrado. Tese Escola Superior da Agricultura "Luiz de Queiroz". Piracicaba, SP, Brasil.

JACOMINE, P. K. T. 1969. Descrião das características morfológicas, físicas, químicas e mineralógicas de alguns perfis de solos sob vegetação de cerrado. Bol. Técnico Nº 11. Escritório de Pesquisas e Experimentação Ministério da Agricultura.

KAMPRATH, E. J. 1967. A acidéz do solo e a calagem. International Soil Testing Project. Bol. Técnico Nº 4 N. C. State University, Raleigh.

KAMPRATH, E. J. 1970. Exchangeable Al as a criterion for liming leached mineral soils. Soil Sci. Soc. Amer. Proc. 24:252-254.

KAMPRATH, E. J. 1971. Potential detrimental effects from liming highly weathered soils to neutrality. Soil Crop Sci. Soc. Fla. Proc. 31:201-203.

LOBATO, E., W. V. SOARES, C. W. FRANCIS and J. D. DOWNES. 1967. Análise economica de experimentos de adubação de milho e soja em solos de cerrado do Distrito Federal. Mimeografado - Estação Experimental de Brasilia - DF - Brasil.

McCLUNG, A. C., L. M. M. DE FREITAS, J. R. GALLO, L. R. QUINN, and G. O. MOTT. 1958. Alguns estudos preliminares sobre possíveis problemas de fertilidade em solos de diferentes campos cerrados de São Paulo e Goiás. Bragantia 17:29-44.

MIKKELSEN, O. S. L. M. M. DE FREITAS, and A. C. McCLUNG. 1963. Efeitos da calagem e adubação de algodão, milho e soja em tres solos de campo cerrado. Instituto de Pesquisas IRI, Bol. Nº 29.

MINISTÉRIO DA AGRICULTURA — USAID — BRASIL — CONTRATO 1a. — 152. 1964. Estudo técnico económico sobre a exequibilidade de aumento na fabricação e uso de fertilizantes, calcário e sais minerais no Brasil — Livraria Freitas Bastos, S. A. — Rio de Janeiro.

RANZANI, G. 1971. Solos do cerrado no Brasil. In III Simposio sôbre o cerrado, pp. 26-43. Editora E. Blucher Ltda. & Editora Univ. de São Paulo.

VERDADE, F. G. 1971. Agricultura e silvicultura no cerrado. In III Simposio sobre o cerrado, p. 65-76. Editora E. Blucher & Editora Univ. São Paulo.

VETTORI, L. 1962. Métodos de analise do solo. Bol. Técnico Nº 7. Equipe de Pedología e Fertilidade do Solo — EPE — Ministerio da Agricultura — Brasil.

17 Residual Effets of Liming a Latosol in Sao Paulo, Brazil

LUIZ M. M. DE FREITAS and BERNARDO VAN RAIJ

I INTRODUCTION

Liming is a mandatory agricultural practice for the extensive areas of soils covered by cerrado vegetation in the central part of Brazil.

Examples of positive effects on crop production due to liming acid soils of the cerrado can be found in the papers of Freitas et al., (1971); McClung et al., (1961); Mikkelsen et al., (1961) and in a review paper by Kamprath (1972).

The effect of liming acid soils is expected to last for several years. The question is: how many years will lime last in highly weathered soils of the humid tropics?

In the temperate regions, leaching of applied lime should be of less importance than in humid tropical areas. In a review by Weeks and Lathwell (1967), they describe results of Griffith, Feuer and Musgrave in a rotation experiment with alfalfa (Medicago sativa) trefoil (Lotus corniculatus) and timothy (Phleum pratense). The residual effect of only 2 tons/acre lime was still appreciable 14 years after application.

As an example on the other extreme, in a tropical region, Mahilum et al., (1970) found that 5 tons/ha were almost completely lost 5 years after application to a volcanic ash soil of Hawaii.

A long-term liming experiment in Brazil was established by Schraeder (1959). Using from 10 to 30 tons/ha shell-lime on a lowland soil, an important residual effect was detected in all levels of lime applied, 11 years after application.

In this paper, the results of a liming trial conducted during 6 years on a Red Yellow Latosol are presented, with emphasis on residual effects.

II MATERIALS AND METHODS

The experimental site was located in the Matão farm of the IRI Research Institute, in the State of São Paulo, Brazil. The soil, Red Yellow Latosol with a sandy clay loam texture with about 25% clay and 1% organic matter in the surface horizon, was originally covered with "cerrado" vegetation.

The experiment consisted of four rotation systems x four fertility treatments. The rotation systems consisted of continuous corn, corn-soybean rotation, soybean-corn rotation, and corn-soybean-cotton-peanut rotation. The treatments consisted of liming to pH 6, fertilization, liming and fertilization and a control without liming and fertilization.

Large size plots of 35 m x 20 m were used to permit the use of ordinary farm implements and to minimize contamination between plots. Each rotation system was arranged as a block with four treatments. The three replications were planted in consecutive years and are represented by the letters A, B, and C. For example, the first replication of the continous corn was started in 1962, the second in 1963, and the third in 1964. It was expected that variations due to climatic conditions would influence less the interpretation of the residual effects.

Dolomitic limestone was applied once at a rate of 10 tons/ha, an amount found to be adequate to bring the pH the soil up to about 6. The fertilizer applied yearly at planting time, in kg/ha, was 10 of N, 100 of P_2O_5, 50 of K_2O, 50 of S, 5 of Zn, 1 of B, and 0.1 of Mo. For corn and cotton, 75 kg N/ha was sidedressed about six weeks after planting.

The experiment was initiated in 1962 and was planned for 10 years. However, for financial reasons it was discontinued in 1967.

Soil samples were taken periodically. In 1964, foliar samples of corn, soybeans, and cotton were analyzed for macro and microelements.

III RESULTS AND DISCUSSION

The yields of the four crops obtained with fertilization and liming plus fertilization (Table 1) are considered very good, being of the order of 2 to 3 times the Brazilian average. Liming in the absence of fertilizer had little effect on yields and for this reason the results are not presented.

Yield increases due to liming in the completely fertilized plots, are given in Table 2. They were not very high during the first years of the experiment, but increased with time.

The reason for the small responses to lime during the initial years of the experiment may perhaps be found in the satisfactory aluminum saturation, of the order of 30%, for the unlimed soil (Table 3). Evans and Kamprath (1970) obtained yield increases due to lime for corn when Al saturation was greater than 70% and for soybeans when it was greater than 30%. During the latter years of the experiment, Al saturation of the unlimed plots increased and this was probably the reason for the larger differences between yields of the limed and unlimed plots (Table 3).

No conclusion was drawn on the influence of the rotation systems upon the effect of liming. Neither was it possible to establish if the yields obtained were at the maximum of the response curve due to liming, since this practice might depress yields. In fact, Kamprath (1971) warns against the potential detrimental effects from liming highly weathered soils to neutrality and recommends liming to neutralize exchangeable aluminum only. However, there is large difference between liming to neutralize the aluminum only and liming soils to neutrality. For example, Reeve and Sumner (1970) found that the amount of lime necessary to neutralize exchangeable aluminum in Natal Oxisols was approximately one-sixth of the amount required to raise the soil pH to 6.5. When the experiment described here was started, the criteria of liming to pH 6 was used, which would be somewhere between liming to neutralize aluminum and liming to neutrality.

Table 1.—Effect of fertilizers and initial lime application upon yields of corn, soybeans, cotton and peanuts grown on a Red Yellow Latosol in rotation systems.

Rotation	Planting year	Replication A			Replication B			Replication C		
		Control	Fertilizer	Lime + Fertilizer	Control	Fertilizer	Lime + Fertilizer	Control	Fertiliz.	Lime + Fertilizer
		Kg/ha			Kg/ha			Kg/ha		
Continuous corn	1962	600	4185	4890	—	—	—	—	—	—
	1963	70	3310	3670	95	3020	2480	—	—	—
	1964	20	4980	5915	50	4720	4750	1890	6550	6095
	1965	30	3615	3735	150	3210	2880	1280	4800	5275
	1966	0	2845	3900	30	3070	3530	830	4810	5280
	1967	15	4470	5675	50	3240	4445	440	5170	5950
Corn-soybeans-	1962	330	4280	4695	—	—	—	—	—	—
	1963	190(s)	1255	1515	30	2690	3055	—	—	—
	1964	60	4660	5795	.70(s)	1805	1980	1000	5930	5300
	1965	0(s)	1575	2665	100	3555	3710	510(s)	1415	1670
	1966	0	3155	4760	35(s)	1360	1610	970	5445	5230
	1967	70(s)	1840	2720	70	3150	4935	70(s)	1335	1640
Soybeans-corn	1962	190(s)	1230	1310	—	—	—	—	—	—
	1963	410	3345	3775	Lost(s)	Lost	Lost	—	—	—
	1964	180(s)	2150	2515	640	5874	6370	305(s)	1400	1640
	1965	170	3080	3450	300(s)	2145	2655	620	4130	4460
	1966	100(s)	1730	2825	450	4160	4275	170(s)	1180	1565
	1967	40	2750	5405	25(s)	2435	2740	585	6510	6650
Corn soybeans-cotton-peanuts	1962	310	3795	4540	—	—	—	—	—	—
	1963	Lost(s)	Lost	Lost	260	3365	3570	—	—	—
	1964	0(c)	1415	2220	350(s)	1850	2310	110	4195	5490
	1965	560(p)	2560	3200	380(c)	1380	1715	240(s)	1320	1730
	1966	50	4065	4970	720(p)	2925	3470	10(c)	1720	1880
	1967	45(s)	2090	2785	590	4740	5265	590(p)	3490	3405

(s), (c) and (p) stand respectively for soybeans, cotton and peanuts.

Table 2.—Yield increases obtained during the 6-year rotations due to application of lime in the first year. The results, given in kg/ha, correspond to completely fertilized plots.

Sequence of crops	Year	Repl.	Corn only	Corn-soybean rotation		Soybean-corn rotation		Corn-soybean-cotton-peanut rotation			
				Corn	Soybean	Soybean	Corn	Corn	Soybean	Cotton	Peanut
First year crops	1962	A	705	415				745			
	1963	B	—540	365				205			
	1964	C	—460	—630				1295			
		Average	—98	50				748			
Second year crops	1963	A	360		260	80	430		Lost		
	1964	B	30		175	Lost	495		460		
	1965	C	475		255	240	330		410		
		Average	288		230	160	418		435		
Third year crops	1964	A	935	1135		365				805	
	1965	B	—330	155		510				335	
	1966	C	470	—215		385				160	
		Average	358	358		420				433	
Fourth year crops	1965	A	120		1090		370				640
	1966	B	460		250		115				545
	1967	C	780		305		120				—85
		Average	435		548		202				367
Fifth year crops	1966	A	1055	1605		1095		905			
	1967	B	1205	1785		305		525			
		Average	1130	1695		700		715			
Sixth year crops	1967	A	1205		880		2655		695		

Table 3.—Effect of lime on soil characteristics. The results are average values for samples taken before planting time, from plots of the four rotation systems.

Year	Repl.	Soil with fertilizer			Soil with lime + fertilizer		
		pH	Al	Ca + Mg	pH	Al	Ca + Mg
			meq/100 ml			meq/100 ml	
1962	A	5.7	0.6	1.4	—	—	—
1964	A	5.1	0.8	1.2	6.2	0.1	2.4
	B	5.3	0.7	2.2	6.5	0.0	3.7
1965	A	5.4	0.8	1.1	6.5	0.1	2.9
	B	5.5	0.6	2.0	6.4	0.0	3.7
	C	5.9	0.3	2.4	6.6	0.0	4.1
1967	A	4.5	1.3	0.7	5.7	0.0	3.0
	B	4.7	1.0	1.4	5.6	0.0	3.4
	C	4.9	0.8	1.9	5.7	0.0	3.7

Ten tons per hectare may be considered a very high rate for a Latosol with only 25% clay and 1% organic matter. However, the results reported here show that with adequate fertilization including microelements, high amounts of lime for similar types of soils may not be detrimental. Microelements need to be included in fertilization of soils of the cerrado as shown by Mikkelsen et al., (1961).

Analysis of leaf samples in 1964 showed that manganese, zinc and molybdenum were affected by liming, and other elements were not (Table 4).

It is certain that aluminum played a role in the negative effect of soil acidity in this experiment. This can be seen in Figure 1, showing the relationship between corn yields and exchangeable aluminum for plots that received fertilizers but not lime. Productions were lower for higher Al contents in the soil.

Besides the residual effect of liming on yields shown in Table 1, the results of Table 3 clearly point out a definite residual effect of lime in the soil, 6 years after the application. The results also indicate that the residual effect would probably last for several more years, if the experiment had continued.

It is hard to arrive at accurate values for leaching losses of lime from the results of Table 3. Considering the unlimed plots, the losses of Ca+Mg are of the order of 0.25 meq/100 g each year for the years between 1964 and 1967. This would amount to about 250 kg calcium carbonate per hectare per year, a conservative figure, considering it to be similar to the minimum losses estimated for British soils (Cooke, 1967). Furthermore, the figures given in Table 3 for the limed plots are far too low to account for the 10 t/ha lime that was applied, leaving the suspicion that considerable leaching has occurred. To complicate the analysis, part of the lime was still reacting during the last years of the experiment, as is shown by the almost steady values of Ca + Mg for differente years, which hindered any further attempt to calculate leaching losses of the divalent cations.

Thus, two opposite aspects seem to be involved. First, intensive leaching must have occurred, removing part of the lime applied. Rapid leaching of lime in few years have been demonstrated to occur in soils of the humid tropics by Amaral et al., (1965) and by Mahilum et al., (1970). Second, part of the leached divalent cations were at least partially replaced by cations dissolved from the unreacted lime. The slow reaction of lime lasting several years, expected for soils of temperate region (Adams and Pearson, 1967), also occurs in soils of the tropics, especially for the coarser particles.

It may be concluded that lime will have a significant residual effect for many years in highly weathered soils of tropical regions, and this should be taken into account in economic considerations. Leaching losses of applied lime do occur and are important, but quantitative and phenomenological detailes on the process are lacking.

Table 4.—Leaf nutrient composition of corn, soybean and cotton as effected by liming. Samples were taken from crops planted in 1964.

Element	Corn		Soybean		Cotton	
	Fertil.	Lime + Fertil.	Fertil.	Lime + Fertil.	Fertil.	Lime + Fertil.
N, %	2.27	2.29	4.18	4.28	3.25	3.39
P, %	0.185	0.190	0.227	0.253	0.233	0.248
K, %	1.87	1.65	1.99	2.02	1.47	1.46
Ca, %	0.38	0.47	0.60	0.68	1.05	1.24
Mg, %	0.21	0.38	3.30	0.36	0.29	0.39
Fe, ppm	115	105	91	94	62	57
Mn, ppm	51	27	87	47	196	54
Cu, ppm	7.5	8.3	9.4	10.9	5.6	3.3
Zn, ppm	26	22	67	44	54	22
B, ppm	20	20	79	78	57	54
Mo, ppm	0.09	0.38	0.16	0.25	0.05	0.12

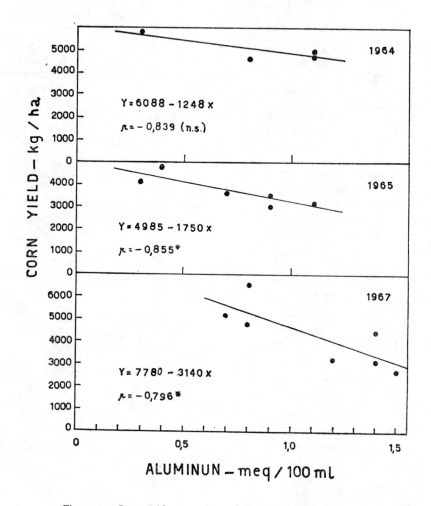

Figure 1.   Corn yields vs exchangeable aluminum levels in the soil as a function of time.

IV SUMMARY

In a six-year experiment, a positive effect of the application of 10 t/ha lime to a Red Yellow Latosol with a sandy clay loam texture was obtained for corn, soybeans, cotton and peanuts in four rotation systems.

With time, the difference of yields between the limed and unlimed plots tended to increase. This was explained by the gradual acidification of the unlimed plots, in which exchangeable aluminum increased with time.

Six years after the application of lime, the content of exchangeable Ca+Mg was about 1 meq/100 g higher than the value of Ca+Mg+Al of the unlimed soil, indicating that the residual effect of liming would probably last for several years more.

V REFERENCES

ADAMS, F., and PEARSON, R. W. 1967. Crop response to lime in the Southern United States and Puerto Rico, *In* R. W. Pearson and F. Adams (ed.), Soil acidity and liming. Agronomy Monographs 12:161-206.

AMARAL, A. Z., VERDADE, F. C., SCHMIDT, N. C., WUTKE, A. C. P., and IGUE, K. 1965. Parcelamento e intervalo de aplicação de calcário. Bragantia 24:83-96.

COOKE, G. W. 1967. The control of soil fertility. Crosby Lockwood, London. 526 p.

EVANS, C. E., and KAMPRATH, E. J. 1970. Lime response as related to per cent Al saturation, solution Al, and organic matter content. Soil Sci. Soc. Amer. Proc. 34:893-896.

FREITAS, L. M. M., LOBATO, E., and SOARES, W. V. 1971. Experimentos de calagem em solos sob vegetação de cerrado do Distrito Federal. Pesc. Agrop. Bras., Sér. Agron. 6:81-90.

KAMPRATH, E. J. 1971. Potential detrimental effects from liming highly weathered soils to neutrality. Soil Crop Sci. Soc. Fla. Proc. 31:200-203.

KAMPRATH, E. J. 1973. Soil acidity and liming, p. 126-137. *In* P. A. Sánchez (ed.), A review of soils research in tropical Latin America. North Carolina Agr. Exp. Sta. Tech. Bull. 219.

MAHILUM, B. C., FOX, R. L., and SILVA, J. A. 1970. Residual effects of liming volcanic ash soils in the humid tropics. Soil Sci. 109:102-109.

McCLUNG, A. C., FREITAS, L. M. M., MIKKELSEN, D. S., and LOTT, W. L. 1961. A adubação do algodoeiro em solos de campo cerrado no Estado de São Paulo. São Paulo, Brasil. Bull. 27, IRI Research Institute, New York. 35 p.

MIKKELSEN, D. S., FREITAS, L. M. M., and McCLUNG, A. C. 1961. Efeitos da calagem e adubação de algodão, milho e soja em três solos de campo cerrado. São Paulo, Brasil. Bull. 29, IRI Research Institute, New York. 29 p.

REEVE, N. G., and SUMMER, M. E. 1970. Lime requirements of Natal Oxisols based on exchangeable aluminum. Soil Sci. Soc. Amer. Proc. 34:595-598.

SCHRAEDER, O. L. 1959. O emprego do calcário na correção dos solos ácidos da baixada de Sepetiba. Anais 5º Congr. Bras. Ciência do Solo. Pelotas, Brasil, 1955. p. 260-266.

WEEKS, M. E., and LATHWELL, D. J. 1967. Crop response to lime in the Northeastern United States, *In* R. W. Pearson and F. Adams (ed.), Soil Acidity and Liming. Agronomy Monograph 12:233-259.

18 Differential Species and Varietal Tolerance to Soil Acidity In Tropical Crops and Pastures

JAMES M. SPAIN, CHARLES A. FRANCIS,
RHEINHARDT H. HOWELER and FABIO CALVO

I INTRODUCTION

Most acid and infertile soils of humid tropics can be readily modified with lime and fertilizers and made quite productive for any climatically adapted crop.

Many of these soils have excellent physical properties, are well drained and are found in land-scapes characterized by smooth to gently rolling topography. None the less, agricultural production in such soil areas continues at a low level and they contribute very little to the development process in Latin America. This is doubtless due to many geographical, historical, cultural, social and above all, economic factors. The costs of fertilizer and lime on the farm are high and crop prices are low because of distance to market and lack of adequate transportation arteries. Inputs will always be costly until market infrastructures are developed.

How can the ever increasing demand for land and employment; for more and better food for rural tropical families and exploding urban populations be met? One approach to the problem of low soil productivity which does not require excessive lime and fertilizer is through the selection of species which are better adapted to the native soil environment and require a minimum of high cost inputs. Many species are well adapted to extremely acid soil conditions and are also efficient at absorbing native soil nutrients. Mango, citrus, cashew, brazil nut and rubber are among the more acid tolerant tree crops. There are many acid tolerant forage grasses and legumes and a number of long season, starchy food crops such as cassava, tropical yams and certain plantains. Tropical farmers have made use of these species for centuries, both for subsistence and commercial production. There is, however, a general shortage of cereal grains and food legumes as a basis for adequate diets.

In recent years a number of annuals, including cereals and legumes, have been shown to vary markedly between varieties and cultivars in regard to acid soil tolerance. However, no systematic effort has been made to screen tropically adapted species for agronomically acceptable material nor for sources of germ plasm for crop improvement programs. There is no other region in the world where such varietal and species differences could be more important than in the humid tropics of the Americas.

The CIAT soils program in cooperation with CIAT commodity programs initiated a screening program in 1971 at Carimagua, an ICA

(Instituto Colombiano Agropecuario) experiment station in the savannah covered eastern plains of Colombia. The Station is located at 4°30'North latitude and 71°30'West longitude, at an elevation of 150-175 meters above sea level. The mean annual temperature is estimated at 27°C. The rainfall distribution from June of 1972 to September, 1973 is shown in Figure 1. The trials, including cassava, field beans, maize, rice, and cowpeas have been conducted on an Oxisol with the characteristics shown in Table 1.

Large plots were established with lime levels of 0, 0.5, 2, and 6 tons/hectare. The 0.5 ton level is sufficient to supply calcium and magnesium as nutrients but does not greatly alter pH nor exchangeable Al levels. The 6 ton level is sufficient to neutralize most of the Al and raise the pH to approximately 5.3. The intermediate level neutralizes 30-35% of the Al, while raising the pH to 4.7 (Figure 2).

In addition to annual crops a number of forage grasses and legumes are under study as part of a search for economically feasible solutions to the problem of extremely low levels of livestock production on natural savannahs under present management. There is no doubt that the majority of the allic[1] soils of the tropics will remain in pastures for a long time to come, thus justifying much greater efforts than are at present being made in the area of pastures and livestock management in the tropics.

II METHODS AND RESULTS

The methodology of the first year of screening for acid soil tolerance are summarized in Figure 3. There was sufficient genetic variability in most species screened to warrant further trials. The results of these trials have been summarized for 1972 and 1973 and are presented below for maize, rice, grain legumes, cassava and forage species. Other species including peanuts and sorghum have received only limited attention and are not included in this report.

III RESULTS WITH MAIZE

Initial screening of maize at Carimagua was carried out at all four lime levels. There was little or no production without lime, and near-normal growth with 6 tons/ha. The extremes were eliminated in succeeding tests and the 0.5 tons/ha level is now used to indicate tolerance to low pH and high aluminum levels, and the 2 tons/ha level to show genetic potential at about the highest economically feasible lime treatment for this zone, given present freight costs and crop prices.

The step-wise selection procedure is based on open-pollination, partial selection pressure on the male pollinators, and a minimum input or profesisonal time due to the distance of the Carimagua experiment station from CIAT's headquarters in Palmira. Two hundred lines, varieties, hybrids, or single ear selections are planted each season under the two lime levels in the introduction phase, with no replication (Phase 1). These include new introductions from outside, progeny from the CIAT or other

---

1/ Allic soils are those in which aluminum is the dominant exchangeable cation.

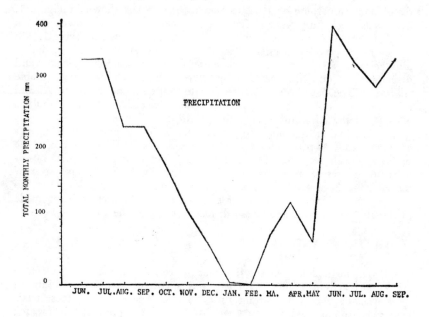

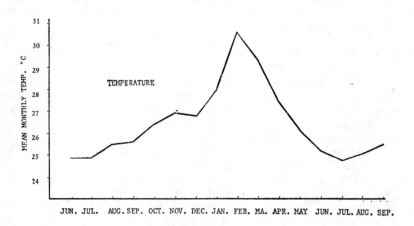

Figure 1. Precipitation and temperature in Carimagua from June
1972 to September 1973.

Table 1.—Characteristics of an Oxisol from Carimagua, Llanos Orientales, Colombia (0-20 cm).

pH	O.M.	Bray II P	Al	Ca	Mg	K	ECEC	Texture
	%	ppm			meq/100			
4.3	5	3	3.5	0.5	0.3	0.08	4.5	Clay loam

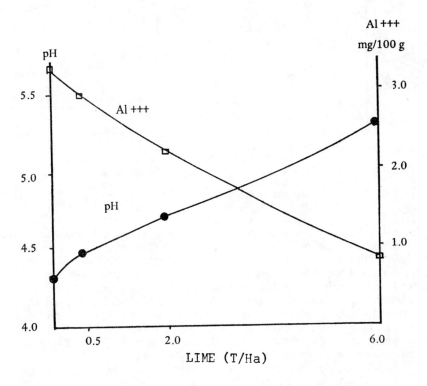

Figure 2. The effect of lime on pH and Al^{+++} in the Carimagua Oxisol.

breeding programs, or single ears selected from the previous cycle in Carimagua. Fifty of the best among these introductions are planted in the following season in single-row plots, two replications, at the 2 tons/ha lime level (Phase 2). From this replicated yield trial, the five best entries are selected for semi-commercial testing (1/10 ha) on the station at 2 tons/ha lime level (Phase 3). The best white and best yellow variety from this semi-commercial test are distributed in the zone as experimental materials for on-farm testing of yield potential. (Phase 4).

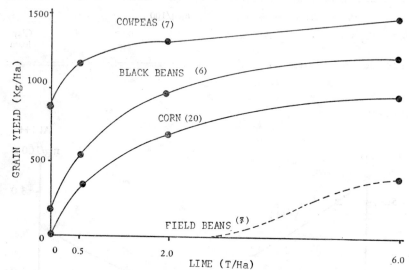

Figure 3. The effect of lime on the grain yields of species screened in 1971 at Carimagua. The number in parenthesis indicate the number of entries of each species.

Selection criteria in each phase include vigor and plant growth potential on these soils, resistance to cutworm *(Spodoptera sp.)* and stalk borer *(Diatraea spp.)*, resistance to foliar and ear diseases, and final yield. Where possible, selection pressure is placed on all fields by detasseling undesirable individual plants previous to anthesis, to prevent their genetic contribution to the next generation. Seed for each phase is harvested from selected plants in selected rows or plots, even though there is no hand control of pollination. Orientation of plots in the field relative to prevalent winds assures pollen flow from more selected material (Phase 3) toward the introductions (Phase 1).

These four selection steps are carried out concurrently in each season; 2 cycles per year, with germ plasm moving through the four steps as quickly as possible. During the second season of 1973, for example, the varieties selected from phase 1 to plant in phase 2 ranged in yield from 3.3-6.0 tons/ha, based on the single row plots (2.8 m²). The best yellow and white varieties selected in phase 2 for planting in phase 3 produced about 3.7 tons/ha (plot size 28 m²). The best yellow variety in phase 3 during the second semester produced 3.2 tons/ha, in a semi-commercial field of 500 m². Seed of this variety will be tested on farms as an experimental material and compared to the white brachytic selected and distributed after the 1972 tests in Carimagua. (Figures 4 and 5).

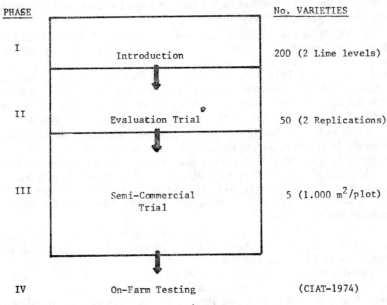

PHASE		No. VARIETIES
I	Introduction	200 (2 Lime levels)
II	Evaluation Trial	50 (2 Replications)
III	Semi-Commercial Trial	5 (1.000 m²/plot)
IV	On-Farm Testing	(CIAT-1974)

Figure 4. Crop improvement scheme.

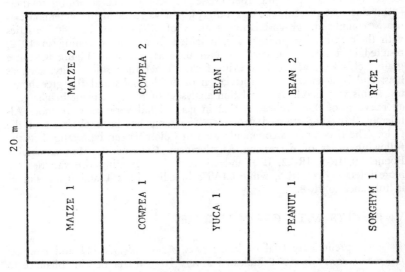

Figure 5. On-farm testing of several food crops.

IV RESULTS WITH RICE

In 1972, two semidwarf varieties, (CICA-4 and IR-8), and two traditional, tall varieties, (Monolaya and Blue Bonnet-50), were seeded in a lime x phosphorus experiment at Carimagua. The tall varieties responded to the first increment of 0.4 tons/ha lime, but there was no positive response to higher lime applications.

Yields of the semidwarf varieties were essentially nil without lime. There was a very marked response to 0.4 and 4 tons/ha and slight response to 16 tons/ha. (Figure 6). Figure 7 summarizes the results of a similar trial conducted in 1973 with Colombia 1 and IR-5 replacing Monolaya and CICA-4. IR-5 is mucho more resistant to blast under Llanos field conditions than CICA-4 or IR-8. The negative effect of higher levels of lime on yields of Colombia 1 is due primarily to increased lodging and bird damage.

In order to identify Al-tolerant varieties, nearly one thousand lines from the IRRI collection and CIAT's advanced breeding lines were screened in the field at Carimagua in 1973 at lime levels of 0.5 and 6 ton/ha, while nearly 40% of the varieties were also screened at 0 and 2 tons/ha. At about 6 weeks of age they were visually evaluated for resistance to soil acidity and blast, *(Pyricularia oryzae)*. One replication was harvested at maturity for grain yield.

Since field screenings are time consuming and their final results are affected by soil variations, differential resistance to blast and bird damage, a rapid greenhouse screening test for Al-tolerance was developed. Rice seedlings are grown in nutrient solutions at two Al-levels of 3 and 30 ppm. At three weeks of age, root lengths are measured, and the ratio of root length at 30 ppm Al ove rthat at 3 ppm Al is used as an indication of Al-tolerance. This ratio is called relative root length (RRL). The varieties were grouped into four classes of Al-tolerance according to their RRL-value. At present, the screening of 850 varieties in the greenhouse is nearly completed. A correlation analysis of RRL-values of 240 varieties with their respective grain yields, obtained in a field screening in 1972, resulted in a correlation coefficient of 0.64 as shown in Figure 8. Since grain yields were affected by many factors other than soil acidity, such as blast and bird damage, the correlation of field results and the greenhouse test seems very good. A correlation analysese of RRL vs. plant height gave an $r=$value of 0.49 indicating that in general tall varieties were more Al-tolerant than short-strawed varieties. The same has been observed in the field. The rice varieties commonly used in Colombia can be arranged in the following order of decreasing Al-tolerance: Colombia-1, Monolaya, Blue Bonnet-50, IR-5, IR-22, IR-8 and CICA-4. The floating rice varieties are more tolerant than IR-5, while CIAT's breeding lines 1 and 8 are similar in tolerance to IR-8.

V RESULTS WITH GRAIN LEGUMES

A preliminary trial of beans *(Phaseolus vulgaris L.)* and cowpeas *(Vigna sinensis)* in 1971 indicated a very large difference in tolerance to soil acidity between cowpeas and beans and between black and non-black

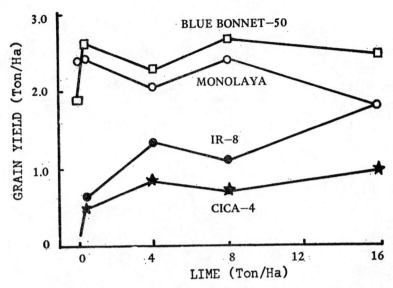

Figure 6. The effect of lime applications on the grain yields of four rice varieties grown under upland conditions in Carimagua in 1972.

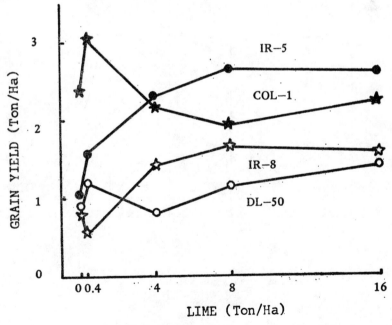

Figure 7. The effect of lime applications on the grain yields of four rice varieties grown under upland conditions in Carimagua in 1973.

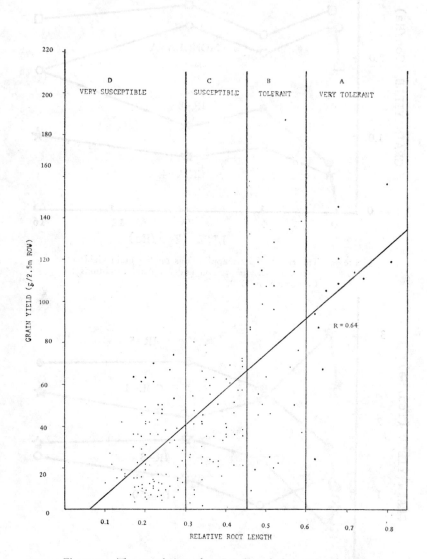

Figure 8. The correlation of RRL values (relative root length) determined in greenhouse solution culture trials and grain yields obtained in field trials of 340 lines and varieties of rice at Carimagua.

beans. Figure 3 summarizes the results. Following this lead, a collection of 50 varieties of black beans, 2 soybeans,, and 20 cowpeas were screened in 1972. The collection was seeded at the same four lime levels of 0, 0.5, 2 and 6 tons/ha.

Figure 9 shows the average response of the species to lime applications, It is clear that all species responded to liming, but the black beans and soybeans responded up to 6 tons/ha, while the cowpeas responded significantly only to the first increment of 0.5 tons/ha.

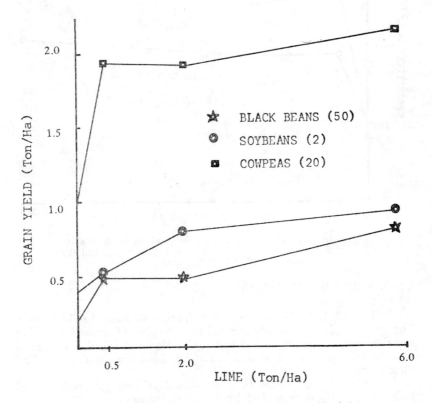

Figure 9. The effect of lime applications of grain yield of three legume species grown in Carimagua. Number in parentheses indicate number of collections tested.

A collection of 100 non-black beans, 125 black beans and 45 cowpeas was screened in Carismagua at 0.5 and 2 tons/ha lime levels during 1973. The results of the harvest, just completed, are very similar to the 1971 and 1972 results. Very few entries of non-black beans show any promise of aluminum tolerance.

Cowpeas are of special interest as a source of high quality protein (dry grain) for human and small animal diets as an excellent vegetable. In addition to their tolerance to soil acidity, they have a high yield potential. Several cultivars have yielded over 2.5 tons/ha in small plots; one cultivar yielded over 3.0 tons. Figure 10 compares the yield of an outstanding black cowpea of Indian origen to the average of 20 entries.

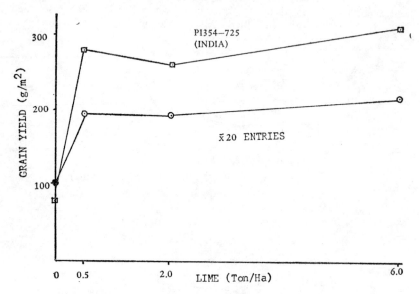

Figure 10. The effect of lime on Cowpea Grain yields at Carimagua, showing the average for 20 entries and the
highest yielding individual entry.

VI RESULTS WITH CASSAVA

In 1972, 138 cultivars were screened, primarily for acid soil tolerance. The entire field was seriously affected by a number of diseases including super elongation, cercospora, and bacteriosis. However, initial development was normal and plants remained essentially disease-free during the first three months.

The following observations were made during this early period before differences were masked by disease symptoms:

1. Most of the cultivars responded visually to lime up to 2 tons/ha.

2. Some cultivars performed equally well at 0, 0,5, and 2 tons/ha.

3. Most of the cultivars were very adversely affected by the 6 ton level of lime and some even by the 2 ton level; this was thought probably due to lime induced micronutrient deficiencies. There were, however, exceptions; some cultivars were not affected by the high level of lime, perhaps indicating differential varietal tolerance to low micronutrient levels.

At four months after planting, samples of the first fully expanded leaves were taken from four cultivars, two of which were severely affected by lime levels of 2 and 6 tons/ha and two of which were apparently unaffected by the higher levels of lime. It was though that leaf content of nutrients would help identify the cause of the negative lime effect observed.

The results of foliar analysis showed a very marked effect of lime on mineral content of leaves. The very large positive effect of the first increment (0.5 tons/ha) on Zn, Cu, Mn and K was followed by an even larger negative effect at levels of 2 and 6 tons. The role of lime at low application rates appears to be more as a fertilizer than as a soil amendment; a source of calcium and magnesium. At higher levels, its effect as a soil amendment becomes evident as pH is increased and leaf content of Mn, Zn, Cu, and K is decerased. These results are different from those observed with forage legumes in the greenhouse primarily at the first level of lime where Zn and Mn content of forage was lowered even at 150 kg/ha level of lime. This can be seen by comparing Figures 11 and 13.

The final root yields of most cultivars in the 1972 trial were low because of disease. However, the effect of lime was very marked as can be seen in Figure 12. It is interesting to note that each of the four varieties sampled for foliar analysis responded in a different way to lime. CMC 169 responded to lime like many other crops, with maximum yield at 6 tons/ha. CMC 198 responded very little to lime at any level, CMC 87 responded slightly to the first increment but yields dropped to essentially mil with six tons/ha. CMC 128 yielded almost nothing without lime; responded very markedly to 0.5 tons/ha after which yields dropped to the original level at 2 tons/ha and there was no yield at 6 tons/ha.

VII   RESULTS WITH FORAGE LEGUMES AND GRASSES

A series of greenhouse experiments was conducted in 1973 at CIAT, Palmira to determine optimum levels of lime for four legumes and three grasses on a Carimagua Oxisol. Lime levels were 0, 150, 1000, 2000 and 4000 kg/ha of $CaCO_3$ equivalent, using the oxides of Ca and Mg and maintaining the same Ca:Mg ratio (10:1) used in most of our liming experiments. Figure 13 shows the results of the first cut for the four legumes. Maximum yield was achieved for all four at 150 kg lime/ha. The shape of the curves is most unusual; probably reflecting various functions of lime. The first response is likely a nutrient response to Ca and/or Mg. The effects of lime treatment on the Mn, Zn, P and K contents of the forage are shown in Figure 14. The effect of 150 kg equivalent of $CaCO_3$ on Zn and Mn is surprisingly large.

The depression in yield at 1000 and in some cases 2000 kg/ha is similar to results obtained on the same soil with cassava in 1972. The high yields at 4,000 kg/ha are difficult to explain.

The negative effects on dry matter yield of the 1,000 and 2,000 kg/ha lime applications were not observed in the second cutting. As in the first cutting, maximum, or nearly maximum yields, were achieved with 150 kg/ha. Figure 15 shows the effect of lime on dry matter yield of the four legumes averaged for all harvests.

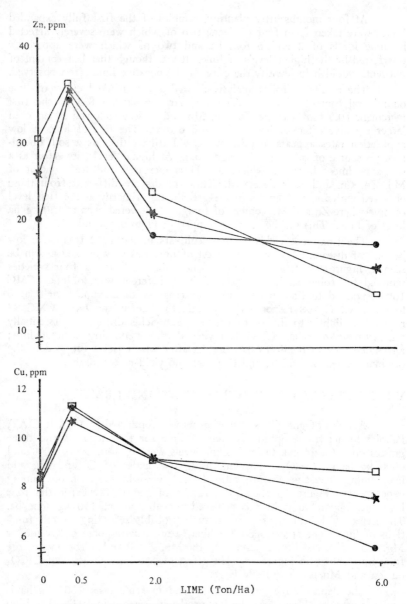

AVERAGE OF FOUR VARIETIES
AVERAGE OF TWO VARIETIES LEAST AFFECTED BY 6 Ton LIME/Ha
AVERAGE OF THE TWO VARIETIES MOST AFFECTED BY 6 Ton LIME/Ha

Figure 11. The effect of lime applications on the Zn, Cu, Mn,
Ca and K content of cassava leave samples four
months after planting.

Figure 11. (Cont.).

Mn, ppm

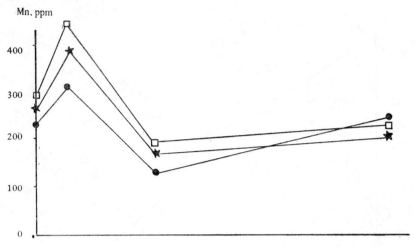

Ca, %

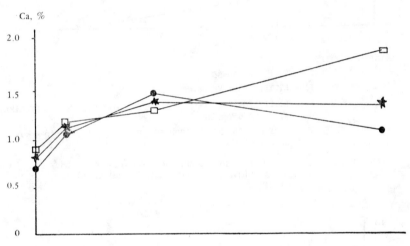

K, %

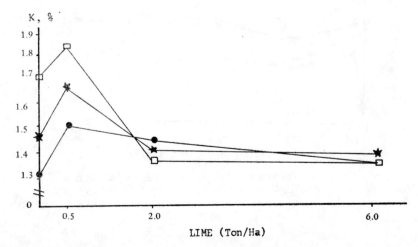

LIME (Ton/Ha)

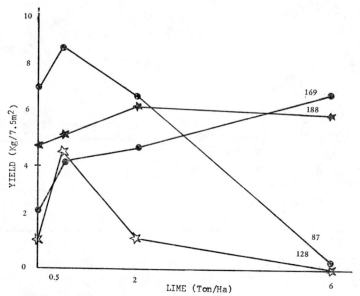

TYPE I   - NORMAL RESPONSE

TYPE II - LITTLE POSITIVE OR NEGATIVE RESPONSE

TYPE III- LITTLE POSITIVE RESPONSE, MARKED NEGATIVE EFFECT OF LIME AT 2 AND 6 Ton/Ha

TYPE IV - VERY MARKED INITIAL RESPONSE FOLLOWED BY DRASTIC NEGATIVE EFFECT OF LIME

Figure 12.   The effect of lime applications on fresh root yields cassava cultivars 9 months after planting. Carimagua, 1972.

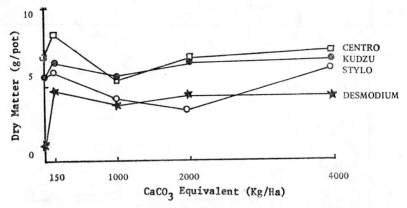

Figure 13.   The effect of lime on dry matter production of four legumes grown in a Carimagua Oxisol; first cuting.

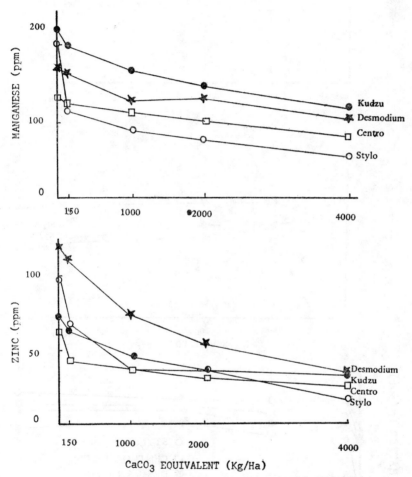

Figure 14. The effect of lime on forage composition of four legumes grown in an Oxisol from Carimagua; first cutting.

Figure 14. (Cont.).

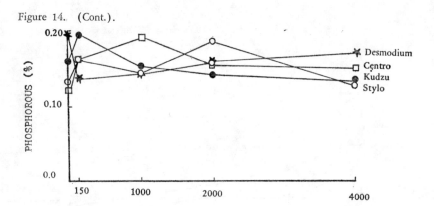

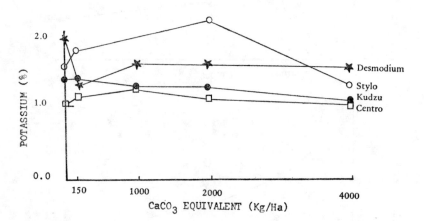

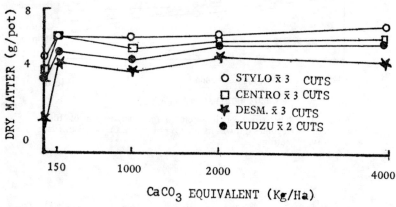

Figure 15. The effect of lime on dry matter production of four legumes, Carimagua soil, average of 2 and 3 cuts as indicated.

— 324 —

The response curves for grasses are quite different from those observed for legumes for the first cutting but quite similar for the subsequent cuttings as can be observed in Figures 16 and 17.

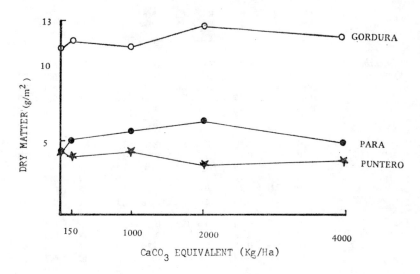

Figure 16.   The effect of lime on dry matter production of three grasses grown in a Carimagua oxisol, first cutting.

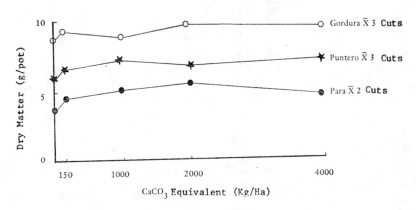

Figure 17.   The effect of lime on dry matter production of three grasses, average of 2 and 3 cuts as indicated.

The effect of liming on the chemical composition of the four legumes and three grasses is shown in Table 2. It is clear that the effect is much less pronounced with the grasses than with the legumes.

Table 2.—The effect of lime applications on forage nutrient content of four tropical legumes and three tropical grasses, grown in an oxisol from Carimagua, Colombia, 1st harvest.

Species	Lime level	N %	P %	K %	Ca %	Mg %	Mn ppm	Zn ppm	Cu ppm	B ppm
Stylosenthes	0	2.6	0.13	1.5	1.2	0.29	213	103	5.0	24
guyanensis	150	2.3	0.16	1.8	1.5	0.26	119	65	6.0	28
La Libertad	1000	2.6	0.14	1.9	1.6	0.26	90	38	7.3	24
	2000	3.3	0.19	2.2	1.9	0.24	79	38	8.7	20
	4000	2.4	0.13	1.3	2.1	0.30	57	17	4.7	21
	x̄ 2.6		0.15	1.7	1.7	0.27	112	52	6.3	23
Centrosema	0	2.3	0.12	1.0	0.8	0.17	136	63	5.7	16
pubescens	150	1.4	0.16	1.1	1.1	0.17	126	43	9.8	20
	1000	2.0	0.19	1.2	1.2	0.18	115	39	10.7	22
	2000	1.8	0.16	1.1	1.3	0.18	104	32	10.7	23
	4000	2.0	0.15	1.0	1.4	0.20	83	26	10.9	24
	x̄ 1.9		0.15	1.1	1.2	0.18	113	41	9.6	21
Pueraria	0	2.6	0.16	1.4	0.9	0.22	222	70	6.7	33
phaseoloides	150	1.9	0.20	1.4	1.4	0.25	201	63	7.0	41
	1000	1.8	0.15	1.3	1.4	0.20	170	47	6.0	33
	2000	2.6	0.14	1.3	1.3	0.21	147	37	6.7	30
	4000	2.0	0.13	1.1	1.5	0.29	120	32	6.0	29
	x̄ 2.2		0.15	1.3	1.3	0.23	172	50	6.5	33
Desmodium	0	3.3	0.20	2.0	1.0	0.29	172	120	4.0	21
intortum	150	2.2	0.14	1.3	1.3	0.28	167	110	3.3	22
	1000	2.6	0.15	1.6	1.3	0.29	127	72	3.7	21
	2000	2.5	0.16	1.6	1.4	0.26	134	52	3.3	21
	4000	2.7	0.17	1.5	1.5	0.28	107	35	4.0	21
	x̄ 2.7		0.16	1.6	1.3	0.28	141	78	3.7	21
Hyperrhenia	0	1.8	0.09	1.0	0.4	0.29	166	35	7.1	16
rufa	150	1.8	0.10	1.4	0.4	0.19	115	28	7.6	14
	1000	1.5	0.08	1.3	0.5	0.24	136	23	6.6	16
	2000	1.9	0.10	1.4	0.6	0.21	126	21	8.0	12
	4000	2.1	0.10	1.1	0.6	0.22	114	19	8.0	11
	x̄ 1.8		0.09	1.2	0.5	0.23	131	25	7.5	14
Melinis	0	1.1	0.07	0.6	0.3	0.27	110	73	8.0	7
minutiflora	150	0.9	0.07	0.7	0.3	0.30	108	58	6.9	7
(leaves only)	1000	1.0	0.07	0.6	0.3	0.34	113	49	6.7	7
	2000	1.0	0.07	0.7	0.3	0.33	97	47	6.0	7
	4000	1.0	0.07	0.6	0.4	0.45	106	48	5.0	8
	x̄ 1.0		0.07	0.6	0.3	0.34	107	55	6.5	7
Brachiaria	0	0.9	0.08	0.5	0.1	0.07	31	41	10.7	5
mutica	150	0.7	0.08	0.4	0.2	0.08	33	44	10.0	5
	1000	0.7	0.08	0.5	0.2	0.11	42	33	9.3	5
	2000	0.7	0.09	0.6	0.2	0.12	44	34	9.3	2
	4000	0.8	0.08	0.5	0.3	0.15	34	35	10.7	5
	x̄ 0.8		0.08	0.5	0.2	0.10	37	38	10.0	4

It appears that lime is required primarily as a source of Ca and/or Mg for the tropical forages included in these trials. Many trials reported in the literature use 1 ton of lime as a first increment. It may be that the most beneficial range of lime applications has often been completely bypassed.

In practice, sufficiente calcium as a nutrient may well be applied in the form of phosphate fertilizers. Simple super phosphate contains about 20% Ca; triple super phosphate about 15%. Colombian basic slag (from Paz del Rio) contains 45-60% $CaCO_3$, equivalent to 18-24% Ca. In all trials involving low levels of lime or calcium, a non-calcium source of P has been used.

VIII   CONCLUSIONS

High quality food crops can be economically produced on many allic soils with minimum lime requirement.

Cowpeas appear to be the most tolerant food legume; black beans are intermediate while the non-black beans (both are *Phaseolus vulgaris*) are the poorest. Rice is the most promising cereal grain crop. Within each species there is considerable genetic variability as regards acid soil tolerance. In the case of upland rice, there are traditional varieties such as Monolaya that barely respond to the first increment of lime while many of the new semi-dwarf varieties respond strikingly to lime and produce practically nothing in its absence under upland conditions. Soil acidity is normally not a problem with flooded rice since pH increases markedly as the soil is reduced.

Crops that are tolerant to soil acidity are also likely to be more efficient at recovering applied as well as native plant nutrients than susceptible crops even when the latter are grown on limed soils. It is almost impossible to effectively lime the subsoil; as a result, susceptible crop roots are often limited to the plow layer even after liming. Tolerant crops can develop wider and deeper root systems and thus exploit a larger volume of soil for needed nutrients and moisture.

The response of many species to small applications of lime when grown on Oxisols emphasizes the importance of Ca and Mg as nutrients in soils with high exchangeable Al levels relative to exchangeable Ca and Mg. The calcium content of phosphorus fertilizers may be sufficient to meet the nutrient requirements of many crops.

It is clear that some cultivars of crops that have evolved in the tropical allic soil environment are extremely sensitive to over-liming. Most of the 138 cassava cultivars screened at Carimagua were adversely affected by 6 tons of lime/ha and the yields of many were depressed by only 2 tons of lime. It has also been observed that liming of cashew trees may be very detrimental at rates as low as 1 ton lime/ha. However, most acid soil tolerant species and cultivars we have observed are surprisingly tolerant to a wide range of lime rates (up to 16 tons/ha).

A tentative listing of food crops suitable for allic soils is given in Table 3, along with lime requirements for the more tolerant cultivars. All indications are based on experience at Carimagua on an Oxisol with the characteristics shown in Table 1. The list is not meant to include all acid soil tolerant tropical species. It is drawn from personal experience and observations of CIAT's staff, primarily in the American tropics.

Table 3.—Food crops suitable for allic soils with minimum lime requirement. Lime requirement figures are for acid soil tolerant cultivars.

CROP	LIME REQUIREMENT
Upland rice	⅓-½ T
Cassava	¼-½ T
Plantain (topocho)	½-2 T*
Cowpeas (vegetable)	½ 1 T
Cowpeas (grain)	½ 1 T
Peanuts	½-2 T
Corn (vegetable)	1-2 T
Corn (grain)	1-2 T
Black beans	2 T
Sesame	2 T*
Sorghum	1-2 T
Fruits and tree crops	
Mango	¼-½ T*
Cashew	¼-½ T*
Citrus	¼-½ T*
Pineapple	¼-½ T*

* Tentative.

The most promising forage species for acid soils include stylosanthes (*S. guyanensis*), desmodium, kudzu and centrosema among the legumes and molases grass (*Melinis minutiflora*), puntero (*Hypharrhenia rufa*), brachiaria (*B. decumbens*) and pasto negro (*Paspalum plicatulum*) among the grasses.

The results of our work, although preliminary in nature, clearly emphasize the importance of teams of researchers made up of breeders, physiologists and soils specialists working together on problems of low crop and pasture productivity on the acid soils of the humid tropics in order to affect a more efficient and rational development of these regions.

IX SUMMARY

The differential tolerance to soil acidity of various important food crops and pastures was studied. Many species and crop varieties were screened for acid tolerance and results are given for maize, rice, grain legumes, cassava and some forage species. Maize varieties doing best with a 2 tons/ha lime treatment produced over 3 tons/ha in semi-commercial fields. Traditional rice varieties responded only to 0.4 tons/ha of lime while the semidwarf varieties responded markedly up to 4 tons/ha, A greenhouse method is proposed to test rice varieties for Al tolerance by measuring root growth in nutrient solutions with different Al concentrations, and comparing values for 3 and 30 ppm Al.

It is reported that while field beans and soybeans responded up to 6 t/ha of lime, cowpeas only responded significantly to 0.5 tons/ha.

For cassava very large differences between cultivars were observed. However, most of them responded visually to lime up to 2 tons/ha and were adversely affected by 6 tons/ha. Foliar mineral content was strongly influenced by liming even at the lowest lime rates.

For grasses lime apparently is required primarily as a Ca source with positive results for 150 kg lime/ha and yield depressions can occure already at 1 ton/ha.

19 Micronutrient Limitations in Acid Tropical Rice Soils

FELIX N. PONNAMPERUMA

I INTRODUCTION

Micronutrient problems in tropical soils were recently reviewed by Cox (1972) and Drosdoff (1972). The wider aspects of micronutrients in agriculture were extensively covered in a recent publication (Morvedt, Giordano and Lindsay, 1972). But these publications hardly mention rice, which is widely grown under both upland and lowland conditions on tropical acid soils.

The main micronutrient limitations to the growth of rice on acid tropical soils, as we know them, are iron deficiency and manganese toxicity on upland (aerobic) soils, iron toxicity in submerged (anaerobic) soils, and zinc deficiency in continuously wet soils.

II IRON

Iron deficiency

Iron deficiency was one of the first micronutrient disorders of rice to be recognized. In solution cultures, it was corrected by acidifying the solution (Gile and Carrero 1916), by frequent addition of Fe (Gericke 1930), or by adding a complexing agent (Lin 1946). In fact, as early as 1930, rice was known to be more susceptible to Fe deficiency than other cereals, and its apparent Fe requirement was known to be greater than that of other plants. Submerging the soil (Gile and Carrero 1920) or raising the water table (IRRI 1962, 1963) prevented Fe deficiency.

The content of water-soluble Fe in most aerobic soils is so low that it is almost chemically undetectable. Plant roots extract Fe by first reducing insoluble Fe^{3+} to the more soluble Fe^{2+} form (Brown, Holmes, and Tiffin 1961; Ambler, Brown, and Gauch 1971). Because in mesophytes the flux of oxygen decreases from the bulk of the soil to the root surface, their rhizosphere tends to be reducing. This facilitates the uptake of Fe. The rhizospheres of both upland and lowland rice, however, are oxidizing because oxygen flows from the shoots to the roots (van Raalte 1944; Arikado 1959; Armstrong 1970), and the greater the flux of oxygen, the smaller is the uptake of Fe (Armstrong 1971). This explains why the apparent Fe requirement of rice is higher than that of other plants, and why rice suffers from Fe deficiency in well-drained upland soils. The severity of Fe defi-

— 330 —

ciency increases with the pH of the soil (IRRI 1963), so Fe deficiency is the most serious limiting factor on aerobic neutral and alkaline soils that are not under water stress. But if the redox potential (Eh) of an upland soil falls below 0.2 v at pH 7 because of temporary waterlogging, or if the subsoil is saturated and anaerobic, Fe deficiency many not occur even in alkaline soils.

Acid tropical soils, except perhaps bleached sands, are well supplied with Fe, so Fe deficiency is rare in upland crops with their reducing rhizospheres. But rice can suffer from Fe deficiency on aerobic soils with pH levels as low as 4.7, as we found in greenhouse and field experiments.

In one greenhouse experiment with two soils (Table 1), we studied how flooding the soil or adding certain chemicals such as iron chelate, dicalcium phosphate, and silicic acid, affects the growth, foliar symptoms, yield, and iron content of the plant. The soils were mixed with 50 ppm N, P, and K as ammonium sulfate, triple superphosphate, and muriate of potash . The chemical treatment consisted of adding 50 ppm extra P as $CaHPO_4$, and 250 ppm Si as silica gel with the fertilizer, followed after planting by the daily addition of 5 ml of a solution of FeEDTA containing 5 ppm Fe. The soils were placed in 16 liter pots fitted with drainage tubes. In the aerobic treatments, the soils were brought to field capacity and mainatined at this moisture level by daily frequent watering with demineralized water; in the others they were submerged to a depth of 2 cm. The treatments were replicated four times. Two-week-old seedlings of the rice vairety Chianung 242 were planted in each pot. At panicle primordia initiation, the pots were topdressed with an additional 50 ppm N.

In Luisiana clay (an Oxisol) the addition of the chemicals and submerging the soil prevented Fe deficiency and markedly increased the yield of grain. It raised the Fe content, but depressed the manganese content of the active center leaf (Table 2). In Maahas clay (an Inceptisol), Fe-EDTA was apparently ineffective, for it did not increase the Fe content of the leaf, nor did it prevent iron deficiency.

The late appearance of the symptoms (Table 2) suggested either that the rice plant was more susceptible to Fe deficiency and manganese toxicity in the reproductive stage of its development, or that the availability of these elements in the soil had changed. If aerobic soils go through a period of intense biological activity during the first 10 weeks after moistening (during which organic Fe ligands are probably formed), followed by a lull that persists, then Fe deficiency could be due to reduced availability of Fe in the soil, rather than to the plant's inability to extract sufficient Fe.

To settle this question, we conducted another experiment. Ten-kilogram portions of air-dry Luisiana clay were treated with 0.15 percent of a 1:1 mixture of chopped straw and Glyricidia sepium, along with 50 ppm each of N,, P, K, as ammonium sulfate, triple superphosphate, and muriate of potash. The soils were moistened and kept at field capacity for 12, 8, 4, and 0 weeks. A parallel set of soils was similarly treated and kept flooded for comparison. During the growth of the rice plants, the premoistened soils were kept at field capacity and the presubmerged soils were kept flooded. All pots received 50 ppm N as urea at 8 weeks after transplanting.

— 331 —

Table 1.—Soil properties.

Soil	pH.[a/]	C	N	CEC[b/]	Exch. bases	Active Fe[c/]	Active Mn[c/]
		(%)	(%)	(meq/100 g)		(%)	(%)
Luisiana clay	4.7	1.9	0.13	25.3	9.7	3.3	0.048
Maahas clay	6.6	1.2	0.19	29.7	23.1	2.2	0.163
Oxisol (Taiwan)	4.8	0.9	0.09	9.7	1.5	2.1	0.012
Oxisol (Colombia)	4.5	2.2	0.17	11.6	0.9	1.3	0.005
Sulfaquept soil (A)	4.3	1.7	0.17	30.1	17.8	1.1	0.006
Sulraquept soil (B)	3.6	5.6	0.27	23.0	8.1	0.08	0.001
Sulfaquept soil (C)	3.4	3.3	0.18	30.3	12.3	1.9	0.040

a/ 1:1 in water.

b/ Cation exchange capacity.

c/ By the method of Asami and Kumada (1959).

Table 2.—Influence of chemicals and the water regime on the yield, and Fe and Mn contents of the active center leaf, and on the foliar symptoms of Chianung 242.

Treatment	Straw	Grain	Fe	Mn	Foliar symptoms
	(g/pot)		(ppm)		
Luisiana clay (pH, 4.7; organic matter, 3.2%)					
Field capacity (FC)	87	21	79	7770	Fe def.[a/] Mn toxicity[b/]
FC + Fe + P + Si	132	91	109	4570	Mn toxicity[b/]
Submerged	55	45	125	1240	None
Maahas clay (pH, 6.6; organic matter, 2.0%)					
Field capacity	79	43	63	53	Fe def.[a/] [b/]
FC + Fe + P + Si	95	67	58	46	Fe def.[a/] [b/]
Submerged	143	131	100	856	None

a/ At panicle initiation.

b/ At flowering.

Premoistening of the soil markedly depressed vegetative growth but did not appreciably affect grain yield (Table 3). The plants at field capacity with no pretreatment produced excellent vegetative growth: the yield of 149 g/pot was, in fact, the highest among all treatments. This means that both water and nutrients were adequate and injurious substances were absent during the first 8 weeks after the soil was moistened and the rice seeds were planted. Why then was the grain yield so low (36 g compared with 100 g for the same soil flooded) and no different from that of the premoistened treatments in which vegetative growth was so poor? Figures 1, 2, 3, and 4 show that low pH and high concentrations of nitrate and Mn retarded growth in the premoistened soils. These retarding factors, which operated throughout the period of growth began to exert themselves in the non-premoistened treatment only 8 weeks after transplanting. Low pH brought about by nitrification and absorption of NH_4^+ from fertilizer $(NH_4)_2SO_4$ made Mn more soluble compared to iron. This increased the concentration of Mn and depressed that of Fe in the plant (Table 3). The high concentrations of NO_3^- probably enhanced the uptake of Mn and further depressed that of Fe (Table 3). Tanaka, Patnaik, and Abichandani (1959) and Senewiratne and Mikkelsen (1961) have shown that NO_3^- increases the uptake of Mn by rice, and Drosdoff (1972) has referred to

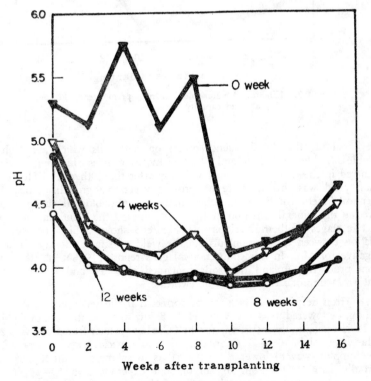

Figure 1. Kinetics of pH in premoistened Luisiana clay at field capacity.

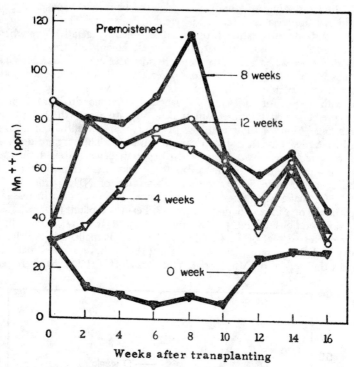

Figure 2. Kinetics of water-soluble Mn in premoistened Luisiana clay at field capacity.

the possibility that Fe deficiency occurs on acid soils which are high in soluble Mn. Fe deficiency and Mn toxicity, as well as aluminum toxicity, occurred in the non-premoistened soil only after the 10th week. Hence the grain yield was low in spite of prolific vegetative growth. Apparently chemical kinetics of the soil, rather than some physiological change which affected the mineral nutrition of the plant, injured the plants in the reproductive stages of their development. Figure 5 shows a high positive correlation between the Fe content and the yield of straw; the correlation is negative for Mn. In this connection Nagai's report (1958) that the straw from productive upland rice soils contained more Fe and less Mn than that from unproductive soils is noteworthy.

Iron deficiency in rice can be corrected if the redoc potential of the soil can be lowered to < 0.2 V at pH 7. Below this potential the availability of Fe is dramatically increased, for $Fe_3O_4.nH_2O$ which forms below 0.2 V is far more soluble than $Fe_2O_3.nH_2O$, the stable species above this potential. The simplest way to lower the potential is to submerge, saturate, or even partially saturate, the soil. In an outdoor experiment in 55-gal. drums, Luisiana clay with the water table 20 cm below the surface yielded as much straw and almost as much grain as did the submerged soil (Table 4).

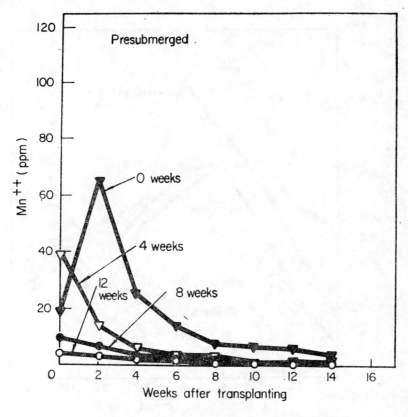

Figure 3. Kinetics of water-soluble Mn in submerged Luisiana clay.

Table 3.—Influence of duration of premoistening before planting on the yield and the Fe and Mn contents of IR 5 on Luisiana clay.

Weeks premoistened	Straw	Grain	Fe	Straw content Mn
	(g/pot)	(g/pot)	(ppm)	
8	71	30	28	3170
4	95	37	41	2950
0	149	36	57	2660
Flooded	133	100	254	980

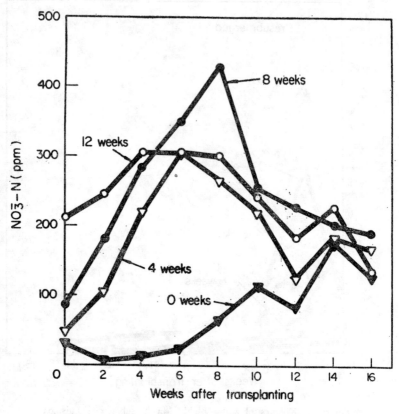

Figure 4. Kinetics of NO_3^- in premoistened Luisiana clay at field capacity.

Table 4.—Influence of depth of water table on the yield of rice on Luisiana clay.

Depth from surface	Mean yield for 2 seasons	
	Straw	Grain
(cm)	(g/drum of 4 hills)	
—10	382	398
+20	381	359
+40	344	245

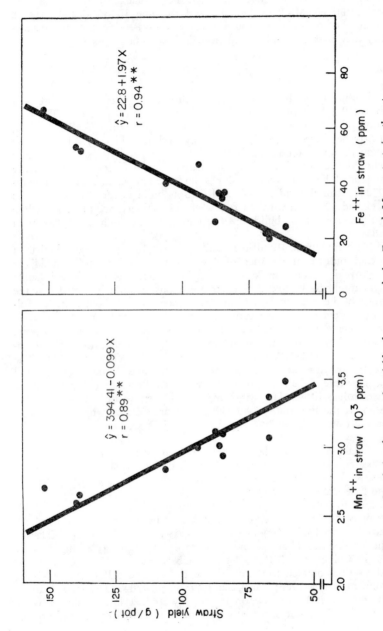

Figure 5. Correlation between the yield of straw and the Fe and Mn content in the straw in Luisiana clay at field capacity.

Since little water control is possible on upland soils on which rice is grown, the use of varieties that resist Fe deficiency may be the only practical solution. Ml-48, CAS 209, and the line IR1561-228-3 may be good sources of resistance to iron deficiency while Peta (one of the parents of IR8) may pass susceptibility to iron deficiency on to its progeny.

Iron toxicity

Within a few hours of flooding, the redox potential of most soils falls below 0.2 V at pH 7, and Fe comes into solution as Fe^{2+}. The concentration of Fe^{2+} in the soil solution increases with time, reaches a peak, which may be sharp or broad, and usually declines (Fig. 6). The rate of formation of water-soluble Fe^{2+}, the peak height, and the subsequent rate of decline depend on pH, the organic matter content of the soil, the nature and content of Fe (III) oxide hydrates, and the temperature (Ponnamperuma 1972). Strongly acid Ultisols and Oxisols build up Fe^{2+} concentrations which exceed 300 ppm within a few weeks of submergence (Fig. 7), while acid sulfate soils may build up concentrations as high as 5,000 ppm (Fig. 8).

Ponnamperuma, Bradfield, and Peech (1955) suggested that a widespread nutritional disorder of lowland rice known as "Mentek" in Java, "Penyakit Merah" in Malaya, and "browning disease" in Sri Lanka (Ceylon) might be Fe toxicity. Their greenhouse studies indicated that the symptoms of Fe toxicity —reddish brown spots on the older leaves followed by the entire leaf first turning reddish brown and then drying up— appeared when the concentration of Fe in the soil solution exceeded 350 ppm. Later work showed that the symptoms varied with the variety (Ponnamperuma and Castro 1972) and the soil (Tanaka and Yoshida 1970). The discoloration of the leaves ranges from light orange, through orange and brown, to purple. The leaves of some varieties rolled markedly while those of others rolled little. The symptoms varied even within the same cross. For example, the line IR759-79-2 had light-orange leaves while IR759-54-2 had purple leaves; IR790-28-5 showed severe leaf scorch while IR790-54-1 exhibited severe bronzing.

Tanaka and Yoshida (1970) in their survey of Fe toxicity in Asia reported that the symptoms varied with the variety and location. Some of the soil factors involved were the potassium and phosphorus contents and the base status of the soil.

Iron toxicity is now recognized as one factor which limits the yields of rice on strongly acid Oxisols and Histosols in the tropics. It has been recognized in Sri Lanka (Ponnamperuma 1959), India, Thailand, Malaysia, and the Philippines (Tanaka and Yoshida 1970) and, according to some reports, in Colombia (IRRI 1971) and Liberia as well.[1] It is also considered a serious obstacle to the growth of rice on acid sulfate soils (Nhung and Ponnamperuma 1966; Tanaka and Yoshida 1970). The main features of soils on which Fe toxicity occurs are low pH, a low cation exchange capacity, a low base status, a low supply of Mn, a high content of organic

---

1/   Ou. S. H. Personnal communication.

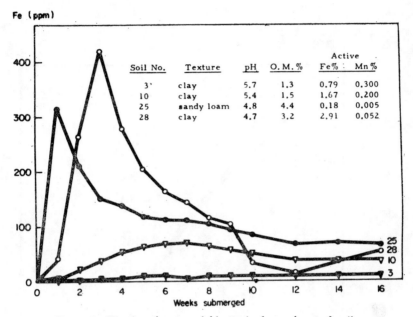

Figure 6. Kinetics of water-soluble Fe in four submerged soils.

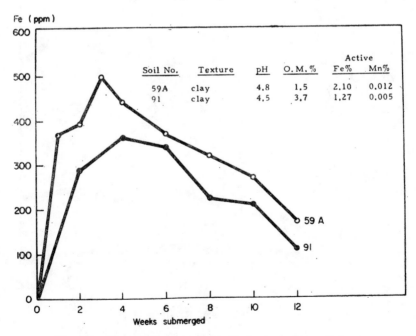

Figure 7. Kinetics of water-soluble Fe in two submerged iron-toxic oxisols.

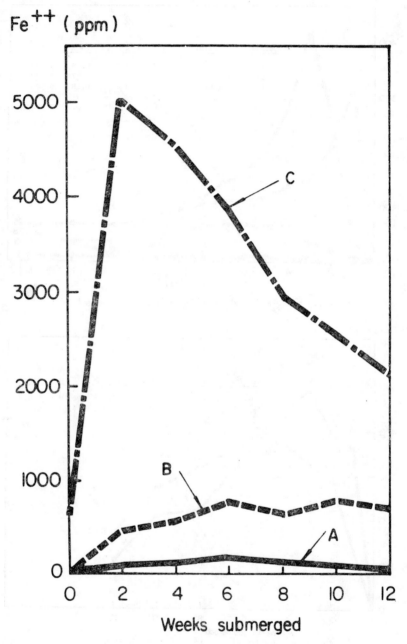

Figure 8. Kinetics of water-soluble Fe in three submerged sul-
faquepts.

matter, and poor drainage. In such soils, Fe concentrations exceeding 400 ppm in the soil solution persist for several weeks (Figs. 7 and 8). Plants which grow exposed to high concentrations of Fe contain more than 800 ppm Fe in the straw, compared with about 150 ppm for normal plants.

Among the treatments that have alleviated Fe toxicity in pot cultures are liming, drainage, presubmergence, late submergence, midseason soil drying, application of manganese dioxide, and avoidance of organic matter (Ponnamperuma, Bradfield, and Peech 1955; Nhung and Ponnamperuma 1966; IRRI 1970). Of these, only liming has been tested under field conditions and it was found to be satisfactory (Ponnamperuma 1959; Tanaka and Yoshida 1970). Since liming may not often be economically feasible, the use of varieties that resist iron toxicity is desirable. In pot test, Cadung Phen R-92, Cadung Go Gung 1601, H4, Pokkali, and Pelita $\frac{1}{2}$ resisted iron toxicity while many upland varieties succumbed to it.

III MANGANESE

Manganese deficiency

Although Mn is much less abundant than Fe in soils, Mn deficiency in acid tropical soils (except, perhaps, bleached sand) is uncommon. This is because the concentration of Mn in the soil solution of normal oxidized acid soils is always higher than that of Fe, its closest nutritional competitor; besides, its uptake is favored by NO_3^-. When a soil is submerged, large amounts of Mn (with larger amounts of Fe) enter the solution phase. Thus Tanaka and Yoshida (1970), in their survey of nutritional disorders of rice in Asia, observed no symptoms of Mn deficiency. But they did not exclude the possibility of Mn deficiency on bleached sandy soils and on soils producing plants low in P and high in Fe.

Manganese toxicity

Plants growing on aerobic acid soils may suffer from Mn toxicity. Rice is no exception. We have shown that Mn toxicity is one factor retarding the yield of rice on aerobic acid soils (IRRI 1963, 1966, 1970). Submerging the soil prevented Mn toxicity, in Luisiana clay apparently by depressing the concentration of Mn and increasing that of Fe in the plant (Table 2).

The symptoms of Mn toxicity in rice are similar to those in other ceerals. But in our experiments, the symptoms appeared in the reproductive phase of the plant's growth. Chemical kinetics of the soil (see section on iron deficiency) suggested that it may be due to the increase in the concentration of water-soluble Mn in the soil brought about by soil acidification, combined with the presence of NO_3^- derived from the nitrification of fertilizer N (Figs. 2 and 3). But because Al toxicity symptoms appeared before Mn toxicity symptoms, we investigated the effects of acidity on manganese toxicity.

Luisiana clay was terated with the appropriate amounts of dilute H_2SO_4 or $Ca(OH)_2$ to give the following pH levels: 3.5, 4.0, 4.5, 5.0, and 5.5 (the actual pH ranges are in Table 5). Two weeks later[a] the soils were mixed with 50 ppm each of N, P, and K and six germinated seeds of each of three varieties (IR8, M1-48, and Peta) were planted in the moist aerobic soil in each pot. The soil solutions (obtained by displacement with water) were analyzed for pH as well as for Al and Mn contents.

Three weeks after seeding, symptoms of Al toxicity appeared in all plants at pH 3.5 and 4.0, they were mildest in M1-48. A week later, half of the IR8 and Peta plants at pH 3.5 were dead. The concentration of Al in the soil solution at this time was 39 ppm. The Al concentration then declined (Table 5) and the surviving plants recovered. But there were no symptoms of Mn toxicity in spite of high concentrations of Mn in the soil solution in the seedling stage (Table 6). Only at flowering did the symptoms begin to develop, and only in one variety. IR8. At this stage the Mn content of the plant was 3,090 ppm (Table 7). Either Al was retarding the uptake or Mn became toxic through a cumulative process, as suggested by Vlamis (1953).

Table 5.—Influence of pH on the kinetics of water-soluble Al in soil solutions of Luisiana clay at 0 to 12 weeks after seeding.

Soil solution (pH)	Al (ppm) in soil solution						
	0 wk	2 wk	4 wk	6 wk	8 wk	10 wk	12 wk
3.4 to 3.8	46	32	39	40	19	17	14
3.8 to 4.5	1.9	2.0	6.7	5.5	5.1	1.6	0.8
4.3 to 5.0	0.3	1.2	0.6	0.1	0.2	0.1	0.1
4.8 to 5.2	0.3	1.0	0.7	0.1	0.1	0.1	0.0
4.6 to 5.3	0.2	0.6	0.4	0.1	0.2	0.0	0.0

Table 6.—Influence of pH on the kinetics of water-soluble Mn in soil solutions of Luisiana clay at 0 to 12 weeks after seeding.

Soil solution (pH)	Mn (ppm) in soil solution						
	0 wk	2 wk	4 wk	6 wk	8 wk	10 wk	12 wk
3.4 to 3.8	415	384	390	482	262	278	226
3.8 to 4.5	131	134	122	112	124	27	17
4.3 to 5.0	51	79	47	7.3	1.8	2.3	2.1
4.8 to 5.2	38	58	48	4.0	0.5	1.1	0.6
4.6 to 5.3	21	31	15	1.3	0.2	0.2	0.1

The Mn content of the plants growing on the non-flooded acid soils was extraordinarily high (Tables 2, 3, and 7). Apparently rice can tolerate large amounts of Mn in the plant. It can also tolerate high concentrations of Mn in the soil solution if the concentration of Fe is also high (Nhung and Ponnamperuma 1966; Tanaka and Yoshida 1970). But about 20 ppm Mn, in the absence of a detectable amount of Fe, proved toxic to rice (see section on Fe deficiency).

Table 7.—Influence of pH on the Mn content of three rice varieties at two intervals after seeding.

pH	IR8		MI-48		Peta	
	4 wk	12 wk	4 wk	12 wk	4 wk	12 wk
	Mn (ppm) in plant					
3.4 to 3.8	n.d.	2450	1890	1440	2100	2080
3.8 to 4.5	1550	3090	1400	2170	1700	2250
4.3 to 5.0	1660	2590	1580	1720	1700	1700
4.8 to 5.2	n.d.	1825	1430	1140	1600	950
4.6 to 5.3	11.80	1250	1400	700	1200	750

In their survey of nutritional disorders of lowland rice in Asia, Tanaka and Yoshida (1970) found no Mn toxicity. They attributed this to the high resistance of rice to excess Mn.

Manganese toxicity of acid soils can be adverted by liming (Abruña-Rodríguez et al., 1970), by submerging the soil (IRRI 1963), or by using resistant varieties (Ponnamperuma and Castro 1972). We have found that some varieties grow better than others on acid aerobic Oxisols. Such varieties apparently resist Fe deficiency and Al and Mn toxicities. Among them are MI-48, Monolaya, Colombia 1, IR24, IR127-80-1, IR661-1-170, IR1008-14-1, and CAS 209.

IV ZINC

Zinc deficiency

Zinc deficiency was one of the earliest micronutrient deficiencies to be recognized and was at first associated with high pH soils and soils high in organic matter. There is evidence now of Zn deficiency in corn, cotton, and coffee on the highly weathered acid Oxisols of Brasil (Igue and Gallo 1960; McClung et al., 1961), Puerto Rico (Hernández and López 1969), and in rice on continuously wet soils, regardless of pH, in the Philippines (Katyal and Ponnamperuma 1974).

Zinc deficiency has not been reported in upland rice. But it is regarded as a major facstor limiting the yield of lowland rice on about 2 million hectares in Asia.[1] Lowland rice is more susceptible to Zn deficiency because flooding a soil depresses the availability of Zn (IRRI 1968, 1970). Organic matter aggravates the deficiency (Yoshida and Tanaka 1969; IRRI 1970).

The symptoms of Zn deficiency in lowland rice are stunted growth, interveinal chlorosis of the emerging leaf, a reddish brown speckling or discoloration of the older leaves, delayed maturity, low yield, and, in severe cases, death within 4 to 6 weeks after transplanting. Zinc deficiency symptoms were observed when the available zinc concentration (by the method of Trierweiler and Lindsay 1969) was 1.5 ppm or less, and when the Zn content in the dried 50-day-old plant was less than 15 ppm (Katyal and Ponnamperuma 1974).

Although Zn deficiency is usually associated with high-pH soils, we observed deficiency symptoms on continuously submerged soils with air-dry pH values as low as 4.8 (IRRI 1970). The application of $ZnCl_2$ corrected the deficiency.

We observed marked varietal differences in resistance to Zn deficiency. IR5, IR20, and H4 survived on a Zn-deficient soil on which 29 other varieties died (IRRI 1971). Upland varieties suffer more than lowland varieties in submerged soils that are deficient in Zn (IRRI 1973).

Zinc deficiency in transplanted rice is easily corrected by dipping the roots of the seedlings in a 2% suspension of ZnO in water before planting. In direct-seeded rice, the application of 50 kg/ha of $ZnSO_4.7H_2O$ has prevented zinc deficiency.

Zinc toxicity

Zinc toxicity has not been encountered on acid tropical soils but it is common in Japan on soils contaminated with acid mine wastes. Flooding the soil alleviates Zn toxicity.[1]

V   COPPER, MOLYBDENUM, BORON

Information on the effects of Cu, Mo, and B on rice on acid tropical soils is meager. Yamasaki (1964) has reviewed work in Japan, but much of it is with solution cultures.

Our studies on the kinetics of Zn, Cu, Mo, and B in submerged soils indicate that the concentrations of Zn and Cu in the soil solution decrease, the concentration of Mn markedly increases, while the concentration of B remains more or less constant (Table 8).

1/   Yoshida, S.   Personal communication.

Table 8.—Kinetics of water-soluble Cu, Zn, B, and Mo in submerged Luisiana clay.

Micronutriente	Concentration (ppm) in soil solution				
	0 wk	1 wk	2 wk	3 wk	4 wk
Zn	029	0.20	0.25	0.10	0.05
Cu	0.14	0.12	0.09	0.04	0.03
B	0.24	0.22	0.24	0.27	0.25
Mo	0.01	0.02	0.18	0.39	0.47

VI ACKNOWLEDGEMENT

I am grateful to Oscar C. Reyes, Antonio C. Tianco, and Ruby Castro for their valuable help.

VII SUMMARY

The literature on micronutrients limiting rice production in acid tropical soils was reviewed. For iron, one of the most limiting elements, deficiency and toxicity problems were also studied in the greenhouse. It was shown that the deficiency is a complex phenomenon and that many factors like Mn and NO_3^- concentration, contribute to the development of this deficiency. The literature on the minor element problems in field condition in Asia is also presented. A short discussion of Mn deficiency is given followed by a review of its more common toxicity. For Zn literature of its deficiency is reviewed, and work on other minor elements is indicated.

VIII REFERENCES

ABRUÑA-RODRIGUEZ, F., J. VICENTE-CHANDLER, R. W. PEARSON and S. SILVA. 1970. Crop response to soil acidity factors in ultisols and oxisols: 1. Tobacco. Soil Sci. Soc. Amer. Proc. 33:478-479.

AMBLER, J. E., J. C. BROWN, and H. G. GAUCH. 1971. Sites of iron reduction in soyabean plants. Agr. J. 63:95-97.

ARIKADO, H. 1959. Comparative studies on the development of the ventilating system between lowland and upland rice plants grown under flooded and upland soil conditions. Bull. Fac. Agric. Mie Univ. Tsu, Japan. N° 19.

ARMSTRONG, W. 1970. Rhizosphere oxidation in rice and other species: A mathematical model based on oxygen flux component. Physiol. Plant. 23:623-630.

ARMSTRONG, W. 1971. Oxygen diffusion from the roots of rice grown under non-waterlogged conditions. Physiol. Plant. 24:242-247.

ASAMI, T. and K. KUMADA. 1959. Comparison of several methods of determining free iron in soils. Soil Sci. Pl. Nutr. 5:179-183.

BROWN, J. C., R. S. HOLMES, and L. O. TIFFIN. 1961. Iron chlorosis in soyabean as related to genotype of rootstalk: 3. Chlorosis susceptibility and reductive capacity at the root. Soil Sci. 91:127-132.

COX, F. R. 1972. Micronutrients. In: P. A. Sanchez, ed. A review of soil research in tropical Latin America, Soil Science Depth. North Carolina State Univ., Raleigh. pp. 244-254.

DROSDOFF, M. 1972. Soil micronutrients. In Soils of the humid tropics. Nat. Acad. Sci., Washington, D. C. pp. 153-162.

GERICKE, W. F. 1930. Plant food requirements of rice. Soil Sci. 29:207-227.

GILE, P. L. and J. O. CARRERO. 1916. Assimilation of iron by rice from various nutrient solutions. J. Agric. Res. 7:503-528.

GILE, P. L. and J. O. CARRERO. 1920. Cause of lime induced chlorosis and availability of iron in the soil. J. Agric. Res. 20:33-62.

HERNANDEZ, M. E. and M. A. L. LOPEZ. 1969. Effect of minor elements and magnesium upon the growth development, and yield of plantains. J. Agric. Univ. Puerto Rico. 52:33-40.

IGUE, K. and J. ROMANO GALLO. 1960. Zinc deficiency of corn in São Paulo. Bull. N° 20, IBEC Research Institute, New York.

IRRI. 1962. Ann. Rep. Int. Rice Res. Inst., Los Baños, Philippines.

IRRI. 1963. Ann. Rep. Int. Rice Res. Inst., Los Baños, Phillipines.

IRRI. 1966. Ann. Rep. Int. Rice Res. Inst., Los Baños, Philippines.

IRRI. 1967. Ann. Rep. Int. Rice Res. Inst., Los Baños, Philippines.

IRRI. 1968. Ann. Rep. Int. Rice Res. Inst., Los Baños, Philippines.

IRRI. 1970. Ann. Rep. Int. Rice Res. Inst., Los Baños, Philippines.

IRRI. 1971. Ann. Rep. Int. Rice Res. Inst., Los Baños, Philippines.

IRRI. 1973. Ann. Rep. Int. Rice Res. Inst., Los Baños, Philippines.

KATYAL, J. C. and F. N. PONNAMPERUMA. 1974. Zinc deficiency: a widespread nutritional disorder of rice in Agusan del Norte. Phillipine Agriculturist (in press).

LIN, CH'WAN-KWANG. 1946. Effect of oxygen and sodium thiogleycollate on growth of rice. Plant Phys. 21:304-318.

McCLUNG, A. C., L. M. M. DE FREITAS, D. S. MIKKELSEN, and W. L. LOTT. 1961. Cotton fertilization on Campo Cerrado soils, state of São Paulo. Bull. N° 27, IBEC Research Institute, New York.

MORTVEDT, J. J., P. M. GIORDANO and W. L. LINDSAY eds. 1972. Micronutrients in Agriculture. Soil Sc. Soc. of Am., Inc., Madison Wisconsin. 666 p.

NAGAI, I. 1959. Japonica Rice. Yokendo, Tokyo.

NHUNG, M. T. and F. N. PONNAMPERUMA. 1966. Effects of calcium carbonate, manganese dioxide, ferric hyldroxide, and prolonged flooding on chemical and electrochemical changes and growth of rice in a flooded acid sulfate soil. Soil Sci. 102:29-41.

PONNAMPERUMA, F. N. 1959. Lime as a remedy for a physiological disease of rice associated with excess iron. IRC Newsletter 7(1):10-13.

PONNAMPERUMA, F. N. 1972. The chemistry of submerged soils. Adv. Agron. 24:29-96.

PONNAMPERUMA, F. N., R. BRADFIELD, and M. PEECH. 1955. Physiological disease of rice attributed to iron toxicity. Nature 175:265.

PONNAMPERUMA, F. N. and R. U. CASTRO. 1972. Varietal resistance to injurious soils. In Rice Breeding. The Int. Rice Res. Ins., Los Baños, Laguna, Philippines. pp. 677-684.

RAALTE, M. H. VAN. 1941. On the oxygen supply of rice roots. Annals. Bot. Gard. Buitenzorg. 51:43-57.

SENEWIRATNE, S. T. and D. S. MIKKELSEN. 1961. Physiological factors limiting growth and yield of Oryza sativa under unflooded conditions. Plant and Soil 14(2):127-146.

TANAKA, A., S. PATNAIK, and C. T. ABICHANDANI. 1959. Studies on the nutrition of the rice plant (Oryza sativa L.) Part V. Comparative effect of ammonium and nitrate uptake by the rice plant. Proc. Indian Acad. Sci. Sect. B, 49(6):386-396.

TANAKA, A. and S. YOSHIDA. 1970. Nutritional disorders of the rice plant in Asia. The Int. Rice Res. Ins. Los Baños, Laguna, Phillipines. 51 p.

TRIERWEILER, J. F. AND W. L. LINDSAY. 1969. EDTA ammonium carbonate soil test for zinc. Soil Sci. Soc. Amer. Proc. 33:49-53.

VLAMIS, J. 1953. Acid soil infertility as related to soil solution and solid phase effects. Soil Sci. 75:383-394.

YAMASAKI, T. 1964. The role of microelements. In The Mineral Nutrition of the Rice Plant. pp. 107-122. Johns Hopkins, Baltimore, Maryland.

YOSHIDA, S. and A. TANAKA. 1969. Zinc deficiency in the rice plant in calcareus soils. Soil Sci Plant Nutr. 15(2):75-80.

SECTION V

SOIL MANAGEMENT SYSTEMS

20 Management Implications of Soil Mineralogy in Latin America

GORO UEHARA and JOHNNY KENG

I INTRODUCTION

Minerals which commonly occur in soils can be categorized into two distinct groups. The first group includes those minerals in which surface charge density (and therefore cation exchange capacity) is a constant and permanent quantity. The second group of minerals includes those whose surface charge density and the sign of the surface charge are pH-dependent. Most soils contain mixtures of minerals from both groups.

In general, inorganic soils of the temperate regions contain minerals from the first group. Smectite, vermiculite, illite, and chlorite posses permanent, negative surface charge which arises from ion substitution in lattice interior. For soils containing minerals which are predominantly of this group, well-established soil management parameters, based on surface charge, and ion exchange, have been developed and applied successfully.

However, as we move from the northern latitudes, where the bulk of soil research has been conducted and tested, to regions near the equator, we discover that minerals from both groups occur with about equal frequency. In the tropics, one can no longer assume that soil minerals will be of the permanent charge type. The tropical Black Earths (Vertisols), for example, represent soils which contain minerals which are predominantly of the permanent charge (smectite) group. On the other extreme, the Oxisols contain minerals whose surface charge density is almost entirely pH-dependent.

Vertisols and Oxisols are frequently heavy textured, but the physical and chemical behavior of these extreme mineralogical end members are markedly different. Use of Vertisols is rendered more difficult because of poor soil physical conditions. In Oxisols this is generally not the case and the limiting agronomic variable is most frequently soil fertility. The Mollisols, Inceptisols, Alfisols, and Ultisols have soil management requirements which are intermediate between Vertisols and Oxisols.

In the Soil Taxonomy developed by the United States Department of Agriculture, mineralogy appears in the family level of soil classification. The soil family, which also includes information on soil temperature and texture, is the category which explicitly provides soil management information.

The purpose of this paper is to present a brief summary of the properties of soils containing minerals whose surface chemistry is pH-dependent . In order to characterize soils with these minerals, it is hepful to use several descriptive equations. The first is the Gouy-Chapman equation

$$\left(\sigma_0 = \frac{2n\varepsilon kT}{\pi} \right)^{1/2} \quad senh \left(\frac{ze\psi_0}{2kT} \right) \qquad (1)$$

in which σ_0 is the surface charge density, n is the concentration of the equilibrium solution in number of ions per cm^3, z is the valence of the counter ion, ε is the dielectric constant of the medium, k is the Boltzman constant, T is the absolute temperature, and ψ_0 is the surface potential.

For low surface potentials ($\psi_0 << 25$ mV), equation 1 reduces to

$$\sigma_0 = \frac{K\varepsilon}{4\pi} \psi_0$$

where K is the reciprocal of the double layer thickness, and depends on salt concentration.

For minerals with permanent charge, such as montmorillonite, addition or removal of salt from the soil solution (change in K) causes a proportionate change in ψ_0 since surface charge σ_0 (cation exchange capacity) is a fixed value.

For minerals with pH dependent charge, the same variations in salt concentration will bring about changes in σ_0, if surface potential is held constant. Examples of minerals which respond in this manner are the crystalline and non-crystalline oxides and hydrous oxides of iron, aluminum, titanium and manganese, quartz, amorphous silica, kaolinite, halloysite, allophane, and organic matter. For these materials the potential ψ_0 can be held constant by holding pH constant.

The relationship between surface potential ψ_0 and hydrogen ion concentration H^+ for these minerals is:

$$\psi_0 = \frac{RT}{F} \ln \frac{H^+}{H^+_0} \qquad (3)$$

where R is the gas constant, T is absolute temperature, F is the Faraday constant and H^+_0 is the hydrogen ion concentration at which $\psi_0 = 0$.

Equation 2 and 3 can be combined to give

$$\sigma_0 = \frac{K\varepsilon}{4\pi} \cdot \frac{RT}{F} \ln \frac{H^+}{H^+} = \frac{K\varepsilon}{4\pi} (0.059) (ZPC - pH) \qquad (4)$$

where $\log \dfrac{1}{H^+_0}$ is the pH at the zero point of charge (ZPC). Equation 4

describes the dependence of cation or anion exchange capacity (σ_0) on pH. Figure 1 illustrates how σ_0 will vary as K (salt concentration) and pH are changed.

From equation 4 or Figure 1, one can readily see that when $H^+ = H^+_0$ or ZPC = pH, $\sigma_0 = 0$. This situation is represented by the intersection of the σ_0 — pH curves. When a soil is at this pH, σ_0 and pH are independent of salt concentration.

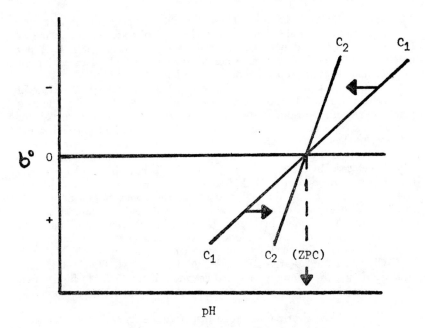

Figure 1. Relationship between surface charge o_0, salt concentration C, and equilibrium pH for colloids for which H^+ and OH^- are potential determining ions. When o_0 is positive, pH increases with increasing salt concentration ($C_2 > C_1$). The reverse is true when o_0 is negative.

In some subsoils samples from Oxisols, the pH measured in water and in N KCl is the same. The field pH of such a material is equal to the zero point of charge. This material has low affinity for monovalent ions such as NH^+_4 or Cl^-. Leaching losses of fertilizer can be a serious problem in such situations.

A few ZPC values of soil materials have been measured, and they generally fall between pH 4-5. In most cases the pH at the zero point of charge shifts to higher values in the subsoil.

It follows from equation 3, that if the soil pH is higher than the pH corresponding to the ZPC, the soil material will have a net negative charge (cation exchanger) and the pH in N KCl will be lower than that in water. The reverse will be true when the soil pH is on the acid side of the ZPC, and the soil is an anion exchanger. When a soil material is an anion exchanger, the pH in N KCl will be higher than the pH in water.

The cation exchange capacity determined with N NH_4OAc at pH 7 is clearly not as useful in soils with pH-dependent charge minerals as it is in other soils. The useful soil management parameter for soils with pH-dependent charge minerals is the ZPC. ZPC's can be determined by a method described by van Raij and Peech (1972). The method involves addition of acid (HCl) or base (NaOH) to soil suspended in 1.0, 0.1,

0.01 and 0.001N NaCl solution. The pH of these suspensions are measured after a prescribed equilibration period and the results are plotted as me of H^+ or OH^- adsorbed per gram of soil as a function of pH. It is not necessary and probably preferable not to wash the sample with acid prior to ZPC analysis as was done by van Raij and Peech.

Figures 2 and 3 shows results of this type for a Dark Red Latosol and a Yellowish Red Latosol from the Central Plateau of Brazil. The zero points of charge correspond to the pH's were the titration curves for several electrolyte concentrations intersect. The shift in ZPC to higher pH values with depth is, in part, related to decreasing organic matter content. In most horizons the curves intersect at a common point and a well-defined ZPC is evident. In the surface horizon of the Yellowish Red Latosol and the deepest horizon of the Dark Red Latosol, the curves for the highest electrolyte concentration do not intersect at the common point. This is related to displacement of adsorbed aluminum ions and exposure of surface charge formerly balanced by them. Under acid soil conditions, adsorbed aluminum ions can effectively block negative charge sites.

If a soil is washed free of extractable aluminum with N NaCl, N $CaCl_2$ or N Na_2SO_4 the ZPC shifts to lower pH's (Figure 4). This clearly indicates that strongly adsorbed cations shift the ZPC to higher pH. Strongly adsorbed anions, on the other hand, shift the ZPC to more acid pH's.

It should be clearly understood that neutral salts can generate charge on oxide surfaces even when the oxide has no permanent charge. A neutral salt which does not affect the ZPC of a material is called an indifferent electrolyte. Sodium and potassium nitrate or chloride are examples of indifferent electrolytes. When NaCl causes the ZPC to shift as in Figure 4, it is doing so by displacing strongly adsorbed aluminum ion and thus exposing permanent charge.

Salts such as $CaCl_2$ and $NaSO_4$, on the other hand, are not indifferent. They will shift the ZPC of oxide systems (Breeuwsma, 1972).

Analyses of pH-dependent charge on soils from the Llanos of Colombia are presented in Figure 5. Quite clearly, the linear plot in Figure 1, which comes about from the use of equation 4, does not occur in real soils. Fortunately, the experimental σ_0 — pH curves are quite linear in the range (pH 4 to 6) which is most common to these soils, so that equation 4 may in fact be more useful than is expected.

II CEC OF MINERALS WITH pH-DEPENDENT CHARGE

There are two factors which cause low CEC in soils. Low CEC is most commonly associated with coarse textured soils. A low CEC in heavy textured soil is another matter. If CEC of a heavy textured soil is determined at a pH value very near the ZPC of the soil material, the CEC value will be low. If, on the other hand, the pH is adjusted to some value much higher than the ZPC, the CEC will be correspondingly higher. The change in CEC with increasing pH differs among soils depending on texture and mineralogy. The higher the clay content (higher surface area) and the greater the oxide content, the greater will be the increase in CEC for a unit change in pH above the ZPC. For most soils with pH-dependent charge

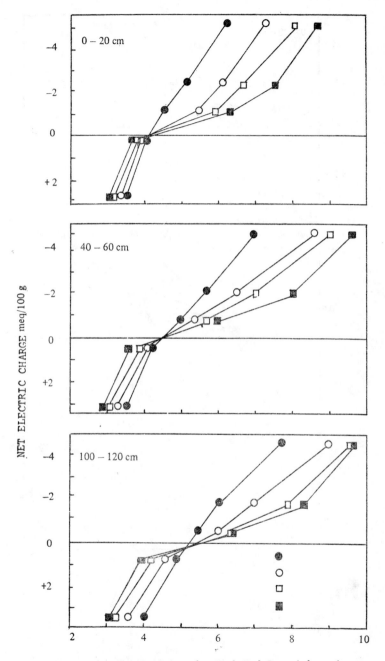

Figure 2. Net electric charge of a Dark Red Latosol from the Central Plateau of Brazil as a function of electrolyte (NaCl) concentration and equilibrium pH.

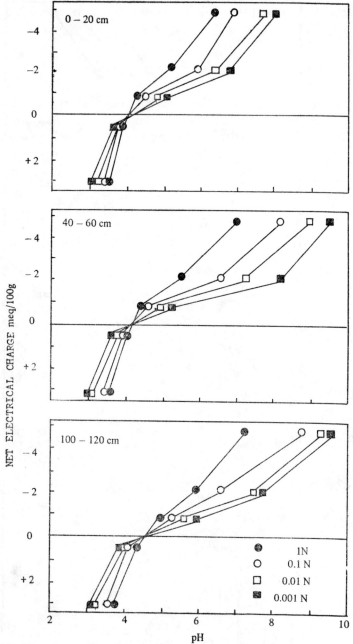

Figure 3. Net electrical charge of a Yellowish Red Latosol from the Central Plateau of Brazil as a function of electrolyte (NaCl) concentration and equilibruim pH.

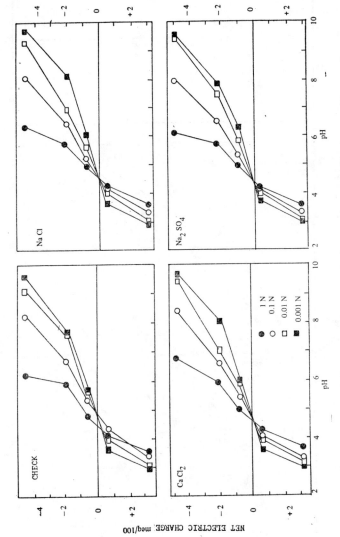

Figure 4. The effect of removing extractable aluminum with NaCl, NaCl₂ or Na₂So₄ on the net electric charge of a Dark Red Latosol from the Central Plateau of Brazil as a function of electrolyte (NaCl) concentration and pH.

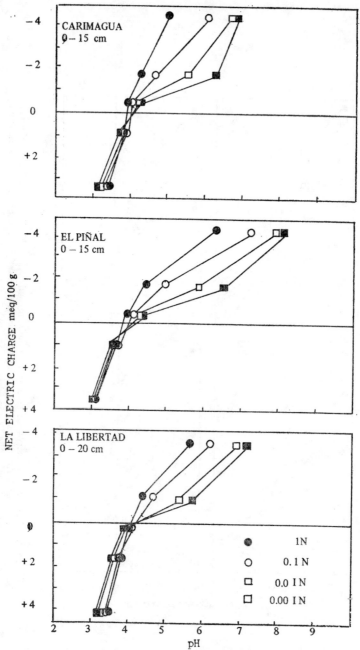

Figure 5. Net electric charge of three surface horizons of soils
from the Llanos of Colombia as a function of electrolyte (NaCl) concentration and equilibrium pH.

minerals, the increase in CEC per unit change in pH is greater when the pH is far away (on alkaline side) from the ZPC (see Figure 2 to 5). In addition, at a given pH above the zero point of charge, more calcium ions will be adsorbed than sodium or potassium ions (Keng and Uehara, 1973; Tardos and Lyklema, 1969).

It is also clear from equations 1, 2 or 4 that when CEC is determined at a given pH, the charge and therefore CEC will decrease as excess salt is removed, and will decrease even more if the excess salt is removed with a solvent of low dielectric constant such as alcoholl (van Raij and Peech, 1972).

Before laboratory ion exchange determinations can be used as soil management parameters, the laboratory method must take into account the effect not only of pH, but the additional effects related to changes in salt concentration and dielectric constant. The method described by van Raij and Peech (1972) for determining net charge on soil colloids is recommended for soils which are known to contain significant amounts of pH-dependent charge minerals.

III LIMING AND SOIL pH

In some heavy textured soils, particularly in Oxisols and Ultisols, an inordinate quantity of lime is required to raise soil pH from an initial value near 5 to a final value of 7. In such soils, lime is consumed to develop surface charge. The crystalline and non-crystalline oxides and hydrous oxides of silicon, iron and aluminum can develop very high surface charge densities (Breeuwsma, 1972; Tardos and Lyklema, 1969).

The slopes of the σ_0 — pH curves give a good indication of the buffering capacity of a soil. If σ_0 is expressed as me/100 gram soil, the slopes will be steeper as percent clay increases. For a given clay content, the slopes will be steeper as the oxide content increases.

Soils with step σ_0 — pH curves and ZPC values below pH 5, generally do not need to be limited above pH 6. As acid tolerant crops are selected or bred for the tropics, it may become possible to grow crops under very acid conditions, but the pH should be maintained at values higher than the ZPC to reduce leaching losses of nutrient cations.

IV SUBSOIL ACIDITY

In Oxisols it is frequently noted that the pH is higher in the subsoil than in the topsoil; yet root development is severely restricted in the subsoil. This is often associated with subsoils high in aluminum, low in calcium, and pH very near or below the zero point of charge. Such a subsoil will adsorb only trace amounts of calcium, magnesium, or potassium because of low negative charge density.

When lime is added and mixed with the topsoil, most of the lime is consumed to create negative charge. The negative charges in turn are balanced by calcium ions at the site of lime applications, so that very little lime moves to the subsoil. Correcting subsoil acidity remains a serious problem in the tropics.

V ANION EFFECTS ON ZPC

In addition to lime, the other major limiting agronomic factor is phosphorus nutrition. Phosphorus and lime, in some ways, have similar effects on soils. Both increase net negative charge, and precipitates aluminum ions. Lime increases net negative charge by increasing pH, and phosphorus increases net negative charge by lowering the pH corresponding to the ZPC. Each millimole of adsorbed phosphorus increases CEC by about 0.8 m.e. (Mekaru and Uehara, 1972).

Calcium silicates, in some cases, may be superior to calcium carbonate as a liming material. Calcium silicate not only increases pH and adds calcium and soluble silica to the soil, but can also lower the ZPC through anion adsorption effects. In most instances, however, calcium silicate, even when it is the waste product (slag) of industry, is too expensive and frequently not as effective as ordinary limestone.

In any case, lime experiments in Latin America should include calcium silicate as one of the test materials. When possible basic slag from local industry should be tested.

The strong amendment effects of anionic fertilizers, especially phosphate fertilizers, often result in unexpected field results. In high oxide soils, better crop response to phosphorus fertilizer is sometimes obtained when P is broadcast than when it is banded.

VI REDUCING LEACHING LOSSES

It is common practice to apply nitrogen fertilizers in several applications over a period of time. In heavy textured soils with soil pH very near the zero point of charge, it may be practical to apply potassium fertilizer in the same way. While frequent, light applications of fertilizer reduce leaching losses, this practice required additional labor which may render it uneconomical. Leaching loss of potassium can be reduced by using potassium sulfate. Ayers and Hagihara (1953) showed that while potassium applied as KCl leached rapidly from high oxide soils, leaching was significantly reduced by using the sulfate or phosphate salt of potassium. Strongly adsorbed anions tend to increase net negative charge in soils with pH-dependent charge minerals. Potassium silicate may have the same effect as a slow release potassium fertilizer. The same arguments should apply to magnesium and calcium.

VII ORGANIC MATTER

The shift in ZPC to higher pH in subsoils (see Figures 2 and 3) is partly related to decreasing organic matter content with depth (van Raij and Peech, 1972; Keng and Uehara, 1973). Increasing organic matter content of the subsoil through increased root proliferation is desirable, but the unfavorable environment of the subsoil makes this difficult.

Even when nitrogen fertilizer is inexpensive and soil physical conditions are ideal, green manures can benefit high oxide soils by increasing cation retention capacity.

VIII   DEEP PLOWING

Soil physical conditions are not mayor limiting factors in infertile, through deep tillage. Deep tillage has a pronounced beneficial effect when lime, fertilizer or organic matter is incorporated into the subsoil. The beneficial effect is related more frequently to improved chemical environment and less often to improved soil physical conditions.

The effect of deep plowing with incorporation of nutrients and amendments to the subsoil is most pronounced in dry seasons. Soils which permit deep root proliferation can help a crop weather periods of drought. Subsoil management should be an integral part of the total management program and should be viewed as a means to enlarge the efefctive rooting volume. Results of planting density and irrigation trials can be expected to be strongly influenced by subsoil conditions.

IX   SOIL-WATER RELATIONS

The soil-water relation of well-aggregated kaolin-oxide soils can be markedly different from that in soils with permanent charge minerals. Heavy textured kaolin-oxide soils have moisture release curves, which in some respects, resemble those of sandy soils (Sharma and Uehara, 1968).

In aggregated Oxisols for example, water can reside in large inter-aggregate pores and fine intra-aggregate pores. Water in the large pores moves rapidly under gravitational forces, and field capacity is attained at low tensions, generally between 0.1 and 0.15 bars. Field capacity is attained at this low tension because the hydraulic conductivity at this tension is very low, much like that of a sandy soil.

The water in the fine, intra-aggregate pores is, for the most part, immobile and can be extracted only when extremely high tensions (>100 bars) are applied.

From an agronomist's standpoint, the water content-tension relation between zero and two bars is of interest. Water held at tensions much above two bars in aggregated kaolin-oxide soils is limited in availability to plants because of its low mobility (conductivity).

X   SOIL STRUCTURE

The redeeming feature of infertile ,acid soils with pH-dependent charge minerals is soil structure. The high aggregate stability of these soils has been frequently attributed to the presence of free iron oxide. Recent high resolution electron microscope examination of soils (Jones and Uehara, 1973) shows that coatings of amorphous substance on soil particles, which act as cementing agents, may be another cause of soil aggregation. These amorphous coatings probably play a major role in determining the physical and chemical behavior of soils.

Water dispersible clay in Oxisols attains minimum values in a soil profile at a point corresponding to the depth at which net electric charge on the soil colloid is zero. In equation 4, this is the situation when $\sigma_0 = 0$ and ZPC = pH. The percent water dispersible clay increases rapidly on either side of the ZPC. This feature of oxidic soils is clearly shown in the Nipe series (Acrorthox) of Puerto Rico. The data are reproduced in Table 1. Similar results are suggested from data compiled for soils from the Central Plateau of Brazil (Cline and Buol, 1973).

In Table 1, data on soil depth, organic carbon, pH in N KCl (pH KCl), pH in water (pH H_2O), the difference between these two pH values ($\triangle pH$), and percent water dispersible clay are presented.

Table 1.—Relation between the sign and magnitude of the electrical charge on % water dispersible clay in the Nipe (Acrorthox) soil.

Depth in inches	Organic Carbon (%)	pH KCl	pH H_2O	$\triangle$ pH	Water dispersible clay (%)
0-11	6.04	4.3	5.1	—0.8	22
11-18	2.09	4.4	5.0	—0.6	33
18-28	1.33	4.7	5.0	—0.3	37
28-38	0.86	5.7	5.2	+0.5	2
38-48	0.72	6.1	5.5	+0.6	42
48-62	0.56	5.4	5.7	+0.7	32
62-70	0.19	6.7	5.8	+0.9	34

(Source: Soil Survey Investigation Report Nº 12. SCS, USDA in cooperation with Puerto Rico Agr. Expt. Sta.).

The sign of the $\triangle pH$ value corresponds to the sign of the net electric charge of the soil material. Note that water dispersible clay contents approach minimum values as the absolute value of $\triangle pH$ approaches zero.

In many cases water dispersible clay attains zero value even when $\triangle pH$ is near —0.5. This occurs when adsorbed aluminum blocks permanent negative charge sites. N KCl will displace exchangeable aluminum and the computed $\triangle pH$ will be negative, but in water or low electrolyte solutions, the net charge is near zero. This is the case in the deepest sample from the Dark Red Latosol (Figure 2). In that sample, the σ_0 — pH curve for the highest (1N) salt concentration intersects the other curves on the acid side of the "effective" ZPC. The "effective" ZPC, which determines water dispersible clay content, corresponds to the intersection of the low salt concentration σ_0 — pH curves.

Application of lime to oxidic soils can result in flocculation or dispersion depending on whether liming changes "effective" surface charge from positive to zero values (flocculation) or from zero to negative values (dispersion). In general lime does not disperse kaolin-oxide soils because, while lime is an efficient generator of surface charge, it does not necessarily develop "effective" charge (Lyklema, 1968). Calcium (divalent) ions, to some extent, act in the same manner as aluminum (trivalent) ions. Both are adsorbed on the oxide surface (specific adsorption) and can block negative charge site, but this occurs to a much lesser extent with calcium.

XI SUMMARY

A discussion of the surface charge characteristics of the minerals for which this is a pH-dependable property is presented (systems where sesquioxides are important). The zero point of charge (ZPC) is proposed as the characteristic by which many management practices as e.g. liming should be guined. A method for the determination of ZPC is suggested and the effect of a serias of factors on this property are discussed. The interaction between ZPC and soil physical properties as the water retention of tropical soils and their structure is presented also. Examples from Brazil and Colombia are given to illustrate the importance of the ZPC.

XII REFERENCES

AYERS, A. S. and H. H. HAGIHARA. 1953. Effect of Anion on the Sorption of Potassium by Some Humic and Hydrolhumic Latosols. Soil Sci. 75:7-17.

BREEUWSMA, A. and J. LYKLEMA. 1971. Interfacial Electrochemistry of α Hematite (αFe_2O_3). Dis. Faraday Soc. 52:324-333.

BREEUWSMA, A. 1973. Adsorption of Ions on Hematite (αFe_2O_3). Ph. D. Thesis, Agricultural Univ., Wageningen, The Netherlands.

CLINE, M. G. and BUOL, S. W. 1973. Soils of the Central Plateau of Brazil. Agronomy Mimeo 73-13. Cornell University.

JONES, R. and G. UEHARA. 1973. Amorphous Coatings on Mineral Surfaces. Soil Sci. Soc. Amer. Proc. 37:792-798.

KENG, J. and G. UEHARA. 1974. Chemistry, Mineralogy, and Taxonomy of Oxisols and Ultisols. Proc. Florida Soil Crop Sci. Soc. 33:119-126.

LYKLEMA, J. 1968. The Structure of the Electrical Double Layer on Porous Surfaces. J. Electroanal. Chem. Interf. Electrochem. 18:341-348.

MEKARU, T. and G. UEHARA. 1972. Anion Adsorption in Ferruginous Tropical Soils. Soil Sci. Soc. Amer. Proc. 36:296-300.

SHARMA, M. L. and G. UEHARA. 1968. Influence of Soil Structure on Water Relations in Low Humic Latosols. I. Water Retention. Soil Sci. Soc. Amer. Proc. 32:765-770.

SHARMA, M. L. and G. UEHARA. 1968. Influence of Soil Structure on Water Relations in Low Humic Latosols. II. Water Movement. Soil Sci. Soc. Amer. Proc. 32:770-774.

TARDOS, TH. F. and LYKLEMA, J. 1969. Electrical Double Layer on Silica in the Presence of Bivalent Counter-Ions. J. Electroanal. Chem. Interf. Electrochem. 22:1-7.

VAN RAIJ, B. and M. PEECH. 1972. Electrochemical Properties of Some Oxisols and Alfisols of the Tropics. Soil Sci. Soc. Amer. Proc. 36:587-593.

21 Management Properties of Oxisols in Savanna Ecosystems

ARMAND VAN WAMBEKE

I INTRODUCTION

Oxisols under savanna may be looked upon as having two sets of properties. The first set would be related to processes which are determined by the vegetation and the present climate acting upon the organic components of the soil. The second set of properties is the result of the strong weathering of the mineral materials from which the oxisols have developed.

Both groups of properties interact to form soils, the management of which has requirements and limitations, and which present problems when attempts are made to integrate them into a modern market economy.

II PROPERTIES RELATED TO ORGANIC MATTER

Frankart (1960) studied the composition of A_1 horizons in comparable soils under savanna and the rainforest in North Eastern Zaire. Under tropical grassland the top horizons are usually darker, and finely divided coal produced by burning may be partly responsible for it. They also contain less nitrogen than the forest soils, and this is attributed to the annual fires which return much N to the atmosphere. Much sulfur is also lost. McClung et al., (1959) report that 75% of the sulfur contained in gramineae may be volatilized by burning.

There is normally no litter layer and as in other parts of the world, grasses distribute carbon more evenly with depth than trees. Roots of grasses do not pump up nutrients as efficiently and concentrate them in the top layers as well as a forest vegetation would do. The results of Frankart are summarized in Table 1.

There have been several explanations for the common low chemical fertility of Oxisols under savanna. Some of them which are related to the particular climate and vegetation are briefly recalled:

a) Under seasonal wetting and drying, normal not severely eroded soils produce high amounts of nitrates at the beginning of the rains, when most crops have not yet developed a suitable rooting system capable of preventing excessive leaching of bases. Not only major elements would be removed from the profile, but zinc would be lost mainly as a nitrate. The surge in nitrate production would be shortlived, and depends on the length of the dry season, during which the formation of ammonium and readily nitrifiable materials continues.

Table 1.—Nutrient distribution in soils in different ecosystems. (Frankart 1960).

Parameter	Rainforest	Forest Zone Fallow	Crop	Savanna	Savanna Area Fallous	Crop
C/N in A_1	8.6	9.0	8.6	13.3	13.7	12.4
C tons/ha/m	86	88	83	107	121	85
N tons/ha/m	10.1	11.3	10.6	8.9	8.5	7.1
pH in A_1	6.6			5.4		
pH in A_3	5.6			5.2		
pH in C	5.3			5.3		
V% in A_1	91			23		
V% in A_3	47			13		
V% in C	27			19		

b) Savanna has apparently only a low effiicency in recycling phosphorus. Enzewor and Albeore (1966) found in Nigeria that the total phosphorus content in the upper horizons was almost twice as high in forest soils as under savanna. Seventy - two percent of the total P was organic under forest, whilst only 17-29% under savanna.

c) Soil under savanna are not protected by vegetation at the beginning of the rainy season, and most losses of nutrients are due to truncation of the surface layers. Fire further decreases the normal supply of N and S by destroying the aereal parts of plants.

Accelerated erosion is one of the major processes which causes deterioration of Oxisols, not only by removing nutrients, but also by bringing stone lines, plinxphite or other physically unfavorable layers closer to the surface.

d) Some types of savanna contain less nitrifying bacteria than forest soils. Meiklejohn (1962) found that nitrite oxidezers were almost absent in savanna soils even after the start of the rainy season. In this case a shortage of available N would be due to the absence of bacteria able to oxidize nitrates to nitrate. The growth of nitrifying bacteria would be suppressed by toxins secreted by some tropical (Boughey et al., 1964).

In a certain sense savanna grassland associations seem to autoprotect themselves against invasion by other plants. partly by preventing formation of nitrates from ammonium which they can more easily absorb than other species, partly by being more stronger competitors than legumes for sulfur which is normally in short supply under savanna.

III PROPERTIES RELATED TO THE PARENT MATERIAL

Oxisols are mineral soils which have an oxic horizon within two meter of the soil surface, without a plaggen epipedon, having no argillic or a natric horizon that overlies the oxic horizon. Soils with an aquic moisture regime which have plinthite that forms a continuous phase within thirty centimeter of the surface are also included in the same order (Soil Survey Staff, 1973).

The present discussion will be limited to the suborders Ustox and Orthox, not considering the soils of cool tropical climates, or those which are poorly drained.

The definition given above leaves sample margins for variation; it is nevertheless possible to point out some specific management properties.

Soil Physics

Structure: Oxic horizons have strong very fine ($<$0.5 mm) granular or crumb structure the aggregates of which pile up to form massive fragments or to build weak subangular blocks. Oxic horizons are normally very porous, although, the porosity of the granules or crumbs is still under discussion. Cultivation mainly affects the macropores (larger than 50 microns). It is assumed that virgin Oxisols have sufficiently wide channels and voids for root penetration. After several years of cropping the reduced amount of large pores, however, could become limiting if biological activity in the surface horizons has diminished for some reason.

Morel and Quantin (1964) found in virgin soils under savanna instability indexes of 0.4 (Hénin *et al.,* 1955), or approximately 70% of stable aggregates. Sandy topsoils degraded after two years cropping; medium textured soils after four years, reaching indexes of 1.5 (only 40% stable). Longer cropping resulted in indexes of 2.0 (33% stable). Restoration of soil structure by fallows usually only gives temporary improvement. (Pereira *et al.,* 1954). Soil structure is seldom a primary limiting factor in Oxisols, however, and nutritional disorders are usually the first to depress yields.

Soil Water: Oxic horizons can only hold small amounts of water between the conventional limits of permanent wilting point (15 bars) and field capacity (0.33 bars). It is generally accepted that they cannot store more than 10 mm of available water per 10 cm of soil.

This low figure makes Oxisols particularly sensitive to drought especially for crops with shallow rooting habits, or in profiles where the soil volume in which roots can develop is reduced.

Water movement in the soil is equally important to plant growth as water storage. Infiltration rates are rapid in oxic horizons and most reports mention 8 cm/hour after one hour of continuous flooding.

Water conductivity in Oxisols changes markedly with water content. The greatest release of water takes place at tensions below one bar. When the soil becomes drier the conductivity of moisture decreases abruptly. Sharma and Uehara (1968) found that it falls below 10^{-5} cm/sec at tensions of 60 cm of water.

With respect to water, most Oxisols behave as sandy soils. Medium and clayey textured oxic horizons, however, are physiologically dry at considerably higher water contents than sands. The water which is present in the microaggregates is available as a source of vapour which may move to the rooting zone by distillation effects directed towards cooler areas that can be cerated for example by mulching.

Walton (1962) contends that in hot climates dry soil does not form a protective barrier and that evaporation from deep layers is not negligible. He found that water was lost from soil horizons between 30 and 60 cm. depth, even when the surface layers had dried out completely.

IV   ION EXCHANGE PROPERTIES

Oxic horizons may have by definition as much as 16 meq. cation exchange capacity (NH_4OAc, pH 7) per 100 g clay, with a maximum of 10 meq/100 g clay, due to permanent charges. (Soil Survey Staff, 1973). These limits have been selected in order to reflect the strong weathering of the materials in which the soils are formed, characterized by the dominance of kaolinite in the clay fraction.

In the U.S. Soil Taxonomy (Soil Survey Staff, 1973) a further subdivision is made at lower categorical level which sets apart great groups which are named Acrusthox and Acrorthox. These "acric" properties were singled out in order to group the soils which have almost completely lost the ability to retain bases, and which normally have a net positive charge. These soils obviously require special management practices and more accurate diagnostic techniques are still to be devised for their identification. At present a sum of bases plus aluminum of less than 1.5 meq./100 g. clay is used as a criterion to identify then.

The separation of the acric great groups, which have practically no cation exchange capacity, makes the distinction of the other great groups, as the Eutrusthox and Eutrorthox more meaningful, since base saturation can be used as a diagnostic property both for genetic classification purposes and fertility appraisal.

At still a lower level, Soil Taxonomy distinguishes tropeptic and ultic subgroups, which frequently have a higher permanent charge than the modal concept of an oxisol would normally accept (typic subgroups).

It is only possible to mention some consequences of this subdivison. Acric and oxic horizons have usually water dispersible clay, and may suffer deterioration of structure when limed (Schuffelen and Middelburg, 1954). Specific adsorption of calcium and blocking of exchange site, is possible in these soils (Uehara, Swindale and Jones, 1972). In the other great groups aluminum becomes a major problem in the ultic and tropeptic subgroups when leaching of bases reduces pH at values below 5.2. The typic subgroups have usually less aluminum, but present more manganese toxicities when leached.

V CHEMICAL PROPERTIES

Analytical data published by Westin and de Brito (1966) suggest that phosphorus is more rapidly converted into occluded forms in climatic regimes having a dry season. Oxic horizons are not the strongest phosphorus fixers among the tropical soils, although, quite a range of intensities and capacities occurs between acric and tropeptic groups. The latter may contain more amorphous hydrated oxides which are known to have high fixation capacities (Fox et al., 1968).

Freshly precipitated iron and aluminum phosphates in Oxisols are as available to plants as the phosphorus from the fertilizer itself (Landelout, 1959). Residual effects in Oxisols have been reported among others by IRI (1967).

Oxic horizons by definition contain only traces of weatherable minerals, and they are consequently poor in potassium included in the crystal lattice of soil particles. Only when chloritized expansible layer silicates are present, some retention of K may be expected (Oliveira et al., 1971). Leaching of Oxisols, however, occurs mostly at the expense of calcium and magnesium, and potassium deficiencies are rater late in becoming limiting in the sequence of nutritional disorders which affect crop production in Oxisols.

Calcium depletion of subsoil horizons is known from Oxisols in Brazil (Mikkelsen et al., 1963). It restricts root development and may in this way reduce the soil volume from which plants may extract water, and thus increase drought hazards.

VI MANAGEMENT PRACTICES

It is not surprising that soils which are developed in poor mineral materials and are covered by plant communities which are burnen periodically, present adverse conditions that have to be corrected when they are put into production. Since economic and social factors come into play, only very general statements about management requirements can be made.

Tillage practices should essentially aim at increasing the water intake capacity of the soil in order to take maximum advantage of rainfall, reduce runoff, and control erosion. If necessary, plowing and sowing should always be on the contour. Pereira, Hosegood, and Dagg (1967) proposed a system of tied ridges which consists of furrows tied at intervals to form basins. In some years it increased yields by 40% relative to those from fields cultivated on the flat. (Dagg and McCartney, 1968).

Ridging of Oxisols which are not exposed to erosion is not necessary because it has been found that at start of the growing season the moisture available in the topsoil is less under ridged than under flat land. The danger of water strain may than be lessened by planting on the side of the ridge, or by ridging after the establishment of the crop (Walton, 1962).

Maintenance of soil fertility of Oxisols in savanna regions calls for a number of practices the choice of which depends on local economic condition. As a rule natural savannas on deep Oxisols only slowly succeed in creating suitable environments for restoring soil productivity by fallows. There have been attempts to improve their efficiency, and most of them include the control of fires. Jurion and Henry (1969) report increases of 170 kg/ha seed cotton and 350 kg/ha corn in a two years rotation following spontaneous grass fallows protected against fire on Eutrorthox in Zaire. Replacement of natural regrowth by other species on the same soil was considered adequate. *(Setaria sphacelata, Brachiaria ruziziensis).*

In Oxisols with low base status no short term benefits from fallows could be demonstrated, without addition of fertilizers, effective erosion control and limitation of fires.

Grazing of grass leys which are included in a crop-fallow rotation in savanna areas may have beneficial effects upon the subsequent arable crop. The action is particularly noticeable just at the opening of the arable cycle. Stobbs (1969) assumes that most benefits result from the gerater quantity of nitrogen which accumulates in the grazed land. There is usually some transference and concentration of fertility by moving animals from surrounding permanent grassland into the fallow area. Defoliation is thought to stimulate plant growth, and to increase the efficiency of bringing up cations from lower layers into surface horizons.

Grass fallows have also been used to restore physical properties, and the experimental results seem to indicate that natural plant communities which include deeply rooted erect grasses are the most suitable. They improve the ability of the soil to accept rainfall and to transmit water, primarily by increasing the volume of freely draining very large pores and channels corresponding to 20 cm water tension, (Pereira et al., 1954). In Oxisols they do not affect the distribution of finer pores, for example those which are filled at field capacity. The influence of grasses on structure is mainly one of improving soil aeration. According to Pereira et al., (1954), they do not confer continuing advantages, and the soils return to their unfavorable state after the first year of cropping. This is probably due to the fact that the better physical conditions are essentially the result of an increase in the amount of the large pores which are necessarily the most fragile.

Natural grass fallows, however, are very demanding on soil moisture and a dry season may deplete a three meter deep profile of all available water. Pereira et al., (1958) report that soils kept bare during the same time still contained 230 mm of available water. Such severe water deficits have deleterious effects on the following crops, especially if the rainfall distribution at the beginning of the growing season is erratic.

Bare fallowing which would restore available water is a dangerous technique, too however, to be recommended when soils have at the same time to be protected against erosion. Natural fallows which are composed of plant species have usually deep rooting systems which exhaustively extract water from the entire profile. Introduced grasses with shallow rooting habits when properly sown may suppress volunteer regrowth and afford some protection against erosion, without depleting the available water in deeper horizons (Pereira et al., 1958).

In intensive management systems correction of nutritional deficiencies by fertilizers is necessary. It is beyond the scope of this paper to discuss the economics of the chemical fertilization of savanna Oxisols. In many areas, however, it is felt that the most suitable utilization for most of the types of land which are considered here will be livestock production.

There is however, only little consistent information on the capacity of pastures to support permanent types of settlements on Oxisols. Long term reseacrh on pasture management is needed, particularly in adapting plant species to adverse soil conditions, weed control, the appraisal of rotational grazing and burning, and the carrying capacity on specific soil families. Methods of correction of fertility levels and the protection against erosion will have to be evaluated, in order to determine the optimal use of savanna Oxisols which have to be integrated into the development process in tropical areas. Precise information on the kind of soil at the most detailed categorical level, where the experimental work has been conducted, will greatly increase the possibilities for transferring knowledge to the farm level.

VII SUMMARY

The main factors responsable for the formation of the Oxisols of savannas are discussed with special emphasis on the influence of these factors on soil management practices.

Attention was given to the properties related to soil organic matter content, to parent materials, to soil physical properties, to ion exchange behaviour and other aspects of soil chemistry. Management practices are suggested in accordance with soil properties and the intensity of soil use.

VIII REFERENCES

BOUGHEY, A. S., MUNRO, P. E. and MEIKLEJOHN et al. 1964. Antibiotic reaction between African savanna species. Nature, London 203, 1302-1303.

DAGG, M. and MACARTNEY, J. C. 1968. The agronomic efficiency of the NIAE tied ridge system of Cultivation. Exp. Agric. 4, 279-294.

ENZEWOR, W. O., and MOORE, A. W. 1966. Phosphorus status of some Nigerian Soils. Soil Science 102(5):322-328.

FOX, R. L., PLUCKNETT, D. L. and WHITNEY, A. S. 1968. Phosphate requirements of Hawaiian latosols and residual effects of fertilizer phosphatus. 9th Int. Cong. Soil Sci. 2:301-310.

FRANKART, R. 1960. Carte des sol et de la vegetation du Congo Belge et du Ruanda-Burundi : 14 : VELE Notice explicative 128 pp. Publication INEAC, Bruselles.

HENIN, S., ROBICHET, O., and JONGERIUS, A. 1955. Principes pur l'evaluation de la stabilité de la Structure de sol. Ann, Agron. 6:537-557.

IRI. Research Institute, 1967. Semi-annual report. June 1967. Mimeographed 95 pp. New York.

JURION, F. and HENRY, J. 1969. Can primitive be modernized. Publication INEAC. Mors série. 457 pp. Bruselles.

LAUDELOUT, H. 1959. Principes de l'utilisation des engrais minéransc an Congo - Belge, Agricultura 7:451-457. Lenven, Belgium.

McCLUNG, A. C., MARTINS, L. M. and DE FREITAS, L., 1959. Sulfur deficiencies in soils from Brazilean campos. Ecology 40(2):315-317.

MEIKLEJOHN, J. 1962. Microbiology of the nitrogen cycle in some Ghana soils. Emp. J. Exp. Agric. 30:115-126.

MIKKELSEN, D. S., DE FREITAS, L. M. M. and McCLUNG, A. C. 1963. Effects of liming and fertilizing cotton, corn and soybeans on campo cerrado soils. State of São Paulo, Brazil. IRI Research Institute, Bull. Nº 29.

MOREL, R., and QUANTIN, P. 1964. Following and soil regeneration under the Sudan-Guinea climate in Central Africa. Agron. Trop. 19:105-136.

OLIVEIRA, V., LUDWICK, A. E. and BEATY, M. T. 1971. Potassium removed from some southern Brazilian soils by exhaustive cropping and chemical extraction methods. Soil Sci. Soc. Am. Proc. 35(5):763-767.

PEREIRA, H. C. 1954. Soil structure criteria for tropical crops. Trans. V Intern. Congr. Soil Sci. II:59-64.

PEREIRA, H. C., CHENERY, E. M. and MILLS, W. R. 1954. The transient effects of grasses on the structure of tropical soils. Emp. J. Exp. Agric. 22:148-160.

PEREIRA, H. C., HOSEGOOD, P. H. and DAGG, M. 1967. Effect of tied ridges. terraces and grass leys on a lateritic soil in Kenya. Exp. Agric. 3:89-98.

PEREIRA, H. C., WOOD, R. A. and BRZOSTOWSKI et al. 1958. Water conservation by fallowing in semi-arid tropical East Africa. Emp. J. Exp. Agric. 26:213-228.

SCHUFFELEN, A. C., and MIDDELBURG, H. A. 1954. Structural deterioration of lateritic soils through liming. Trans. V Int. Cong. Soil Sc. 2:158-165.

SHARMA, M. L., and UEHARA, G. 1969. Influence of soil structure on water relations in low humic latosols, I. Water retention, II. Water movement. Soil Sc. Soc. Am. Proc. 32(6):765-774.

SOIL SURVEY STAFF. 1973. Soil taxonomy. A basic system of soil classification for making and interpreting soil surveys. U. S. Dept. of Agr., SCS, Washington, D. C.

STOBBS, T. H. 1969. The effect of grazing resting land upon subsequent arable crop yields. E. Afr. Agr. For. J. 35:28-32.

UEHARA, G., SWINDALE, L. D., and JONES, R. C. 1972. Mineralogy and behavior of tropical soils. Mimeo 13 pp. Seminar on tropical soil research, Ibadan, Nigeria.

WALTON, P. D. 1962. The effect of ridging on the cotton crop in the eastern province of Uganda. Emp. J. Exp. Agric. 30(117):63-76.

WESTIN, F. C., and DE BRITTO, J. G. 1969. Phosphorus fractions of some Venezuelan soils as related to their stage of weathering. Soil Sci. 107:104-202.

22 Soil management problems and possible solutions in Western Nigeria

RATTAN LAL, B. T. KANG,
F. R. MOORMAN, ANTHONY S. R. JUO and JAMES C. MOOMAW

I INTRODUCTION

The International Institute for Tropical Agriculture (IITA) studies on soil management problems have been mainly carried out at the IITA experimental station (7°30'N, 3°54'E), but a start has been made with outreach work, mainly in the Western State, but also in the humid forest areas in south and southeast Nigeria, in Ghana and in Liberia.

Climate

The Western State lies essentially in a zone of transition between the humid and sub-humid tropics. The northern and western areas of the Western State are sub-humid (CA'w of Thornthwaite) whereas the southern and southeastern part is humid (BA'w of Thornthwaite). The vegetation of the uplands in the northern part of the State is wooded savannah (Southern Guinea Zone and derived savannah), while in the Southern and southeastern area, moist lowland forest (semi-deciduous) dominates.

The rainfall has a characteristic bi-modal distribution with peaks in June and September. The dry season is from November to March, with minimal rainfall in December and January. Annual temperatures range from an average minimum of about 20-21°C to a corresponding maximum of 31-32°C, with slightly decreasing fluctuations from north to south.

Parent Materials

Parent materials in the northern part of the State have been derived mainly from Pre-Cambrian basement complex rocks. A smaller portion of these rocks is igneous (mainly granites and syenites), but they are predominantly metamorphic; paragneisses, micaschists, quartzites and some amphibolites. The upland soils are mainly formed on autochthonous weathered rocks, but the upper horizons have developed in allochthonaus pediment materials in which a stone line frequently presents a prominent feature. Lower slope soils and depression soils are formed on colluvium and alluvium.

In the southern part of the state, parent materials are sedimentary in origin, the surface strata being mainly formed by late Tertiary to early Pleistocene unconsolidated coastal sediments (continental terminal).

At IITA, the basement complex is dominantly composed of medium and coarse grained biotite-plagioclase-hornblende paragneiss, with intrusions of granitic-orthogneiss, and strata of quartzites and quartz schists. This intricated pattern, combined with variations in thickness and composition of the covering pediment, colluvial and alluvial materials cause a great variability over short distance in the soils of IITA.

Soils

In Table 1, the approximate correlation between the FAO (1970), USDA (1970) and ENSA (1967) classification systems for modal upland soils in Southern Nigeria is given. The correlation is not exact, since important diagnostic criteria vary between systems. Thus, some Alfisols with a base saturation of less than 50% in the argillic horizon will be Acrisols in the FAO system.

Table 1.—Approximative correlation of the FAO, USDA and the ENSA classification of major upland soils in Southern Nigeria.

FAO (1970)	USDA (1970)	ENSA (1967)
LUVISOLS		
Ferric	Paleustalfs, and (Rhodustalfs')	Sols ferrallitiques faiblement desatures, sous-groupes remanies et rajeunis, and (sols ferrallitiques lessives) (sols ferrugineux tropicaux)
NITOSOLS		
Eutric	Paleustalfs	Sols ferrallitiques faiblement desatures sous groupes typiques et appauvris
Dystric	Paleustalfs, and (Paleudults)	Sols ferrallitiques moyennement et fortement desatures sous groupes typiques et appauvris
ACRISOLS		
Ferric	Paleustalfs, and (Rhodustults) (Paleudults) (Rhodudults) (Tropudults)	Sols ferrallitiques moyennement et fortement desatures, sous groupe remaine, and (sols ferrallitiques lessives) (sols ferrugineux tropicaux)

NOTE: Less important units are indicated between brackets.

Of importance to note is the great extent of Alfisols in areas with an annual rainfall of approximately 1600 mm or less ,and the virtual absence of Oxisols (Ferrasols of the FAO classification) not only in Nigeria, but throughout the humid part of West Africa.

In Western Nigeria, soils over basement complex rocks mostly have a moderately deep solum, though the regolith is generally several meters deep. In the southern sedimentary areas, solums are very deep; frequently over 10 meters in the well drained upland positions.

II SOILS UNDER TRADITIONAL SYSTEMS OF MANAGEMENT

Particle Size Distribution, Structure and Root Penetrability

Most of the upland soils in Western Nigeria, particularly those derived from basement complex, are predominantly coarse textured in the surface soils horizons. A gravelly horizon, immediately below the surface horizon, is a characteristic feature of most soils on basement complex. The depth of the surface soil above the gravel horizon varies roughly between 0 and 40 cm, depending on the location of the profile in the catena. The gravels, usually a combination of quartz and concretions, are imbedded in clayey to sandy clay materials forming a rigid matrix. The layer immediately beneath the gravel horizon is predominantly clayey in texture.

The surface horizons of most of the upland soils are poorly graded, with a small amount of organic and inorganic colloidal fraction to bind the primary particles together (Figure 1). The surface horizons have a sand content ranging from 56 — 80 percent (mean of 70), silt content from 11 to 19 percent (mean of 13) and clay content from 9 to 25 percent (mean of 17). The concentration of gravel in the sub-soil horizon varies from 0 (for soils in the lower catena or those derived from sedimentary parent material) to 70 percent (Figure 2).

The structural stability to raindrop impact for most of these soils is extremely low (Figure 3). One of the causes of this low stability is the predominance of the coarse fraction in the surface horizon. Even though the potential infiltrability is high, the formation of soil crusts in the exposed surface soil as a result of splash, reduces the actual infiltrability of the soil. This crust forming, though is minimal under the extensive traditional agricultural system.

The rigidity of the matrix in the gravel horizon may be one of the reason for inhibited root penetrability, particularly of cereal crops. Field experiments have indicated that the depth of maximum root penetration in these soils is governed by the depth of this compact gravelly horizon (Figure 4). The frequent wilting of maize and upland rice, a few days after heavy rains, may be attributed to the direct and indirect effects of these gravelly horizons causing insufficient water supply to the roots. One of the indirect effects could also be a decreased available water holding capacity of the soil.

Moisture Release Characteristics and Available Water Holding Capacity

Moisture release characteristics of the surface horizon of some soil series of Western Nigeria indicate the predominance of macropores (Figure 5), as shown by a relatively small change in moisture retention beyond 2 bar suction. The data in Table 1 show that the available water holding capacity of these soils is low.

In Tables 3 and 4 are given the simple and multiple correlations of the moisture content at 0, 0.1 and 0.3 bar suction with soil constituents. It is obvious, that the organic matter content has arelatively low contribution

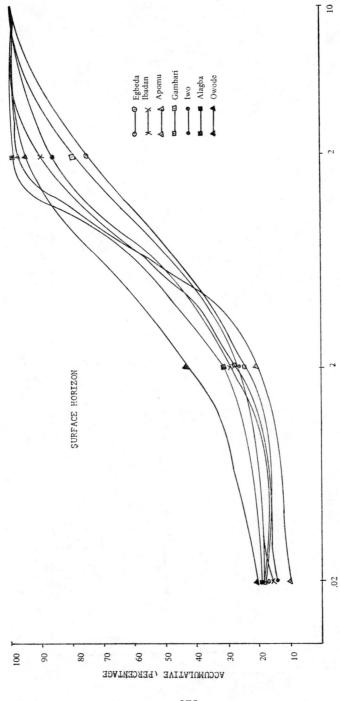

Figure 1. Particle size distribution of the surface horizon of different soil series.

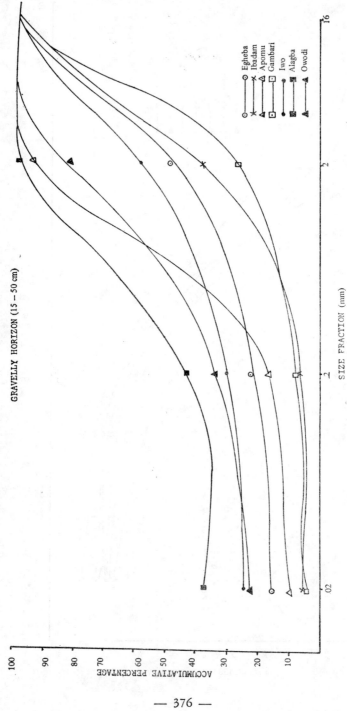

Figure 2. Particle size distribution of the gravelly horizon for different soil series.

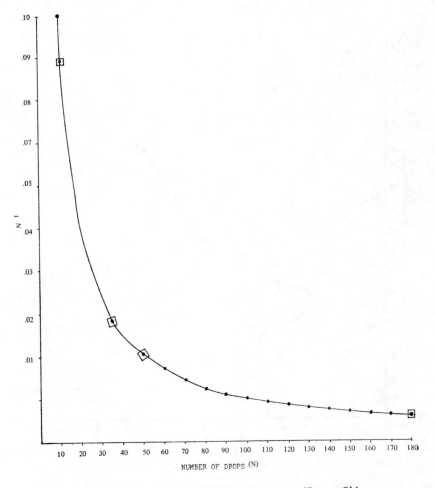

Figure 3. A generalised erodibility rating curve (Bruce, Okine and Lal, 1973).

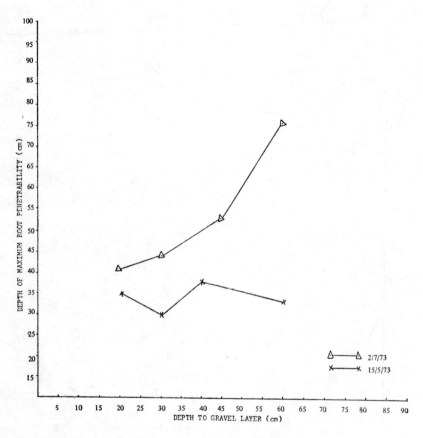

Figure 4. Effect of depth of gravel layer on depth of maize root penetration.

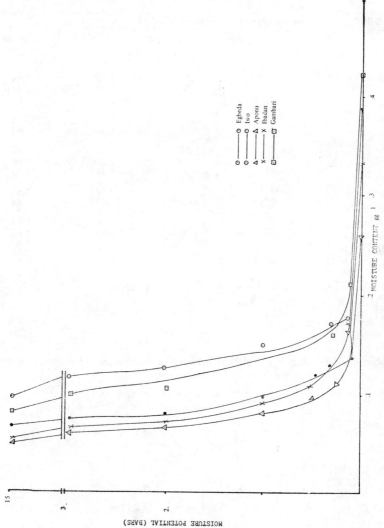

Figure 5. Moisture release characteristics of the surface horizons of some soil series.

Table 2.—Available water holding capacity of some Western Nigerian soils.

Soil Series	Horizon Depth (cm)	Organic C %	Available Water holding Capacity (cm)	
			Uncorrected	Corrected*
Egbeda	0—15	1.50	1.57	1.34
	15—22	0.76	0.89	0.52
	22—50	0.28	2.59	1.08
Ibadan	0—25	1.30	4.12	3.74
	25—50	0.44	2.50	1.40
Iwo	0—15	1.54	1.12	0.97
	15—28	1.66	0.98	0.60
	28—45	0.49	1.63	0.96
Apomu	0—9	2.48	0.67	0.65
	9—36	0.30	1.69	1.64
Alagba	0—13	1.10	0.68	0.68
	13—36	0.70	1.66	1.66
Nifor	0—35	1.2	0.91	0.91
	35—74	0.7	1.11	1.11

* Corrected for stone concentration.

Table 3.—The simple correlation between soil moisture retention at 0, 0.1 and 0.3 bar and soil constituents.

Soil Constituents	Correlation Coefficients for Moisture Retention at		
	0 bar	0.1 bar	0.3 bar
Sand (%)	—0.433**	—0.813**	—0.710**
Silt (%)	n.s.	0.553**	0.367*
Clay (%)	0.487**	0.647**	0.680**
O.C.(%)	0.305*	n.s.	n.s.

towards the available water holding capacity of these tropical soils. The clay and sand content, on the other hand, are most significantly correlated with moisture retention at 0.1 and 0.3 bar, the former positively and the latter negatively.

Table 4.—Multiple correlation for moisture retention at various suctions.

Dependent Variable	R^2	Regression Equations
		0.1 BAR
Clay, organic carbon (O.C.)	0.72**	$Y = 0.082 + 0.016$ (C.O.) $+ 0.004$ (clay)
Silt, O.C.	0.29	$Y = 0.151 - 0.035$ (C.O.) $+ 0.007$ (clay)
Sand, O.C.	0.64**	$Y = 0.367 + 0.016$ (C.O.) $- 0.003$ (sand)
Clay, O.C., silt	0.76**	$Y = 0.057 + 0.010$ (C.O.) $+ 0.003$ (clay) $+ 0.003$ (silt)
		0.3 BAR
Clay, O.C.	0.48**	$Y = 0.065 + 0.01$ (C.O.) $+ 0.003$ (clay)
Silt, O.C.	0.18	$Y = 0.131 - 0.034$ (C.O.) $+ 0.005$ (silt)
Sand, O.C.	0.41**	$Y = 0.307 + 0.008$ (C.O.) $- 0.003$ (sand)
Clay, O.C., silt	0.49**	$Y = 0.49 + 0.005$ (C.O.) $+ 0.003$ (clay) $+ 0.002$ (silt)

Nutrient Variability in the Soil

The variability in physical soil properties and nutrient status over short distances within plots or between plots of the same soil series, results in uneven growth of the crop, with adjacent patches of good and poor growth. This soil heterogeneity has also a practical implication, making soil sampling and the use of plots for fertility investigations complicated. Observations at IITA have indicated, that this lack of uniformity can, to a large extent, be related to human and other biogenetic parameters, active prior to clearing and after clearing while preparing the land for cropping.

Effect of Pre-clearing Vegetation: A study on the effect of pre-clearing vegetation on the nutrient variability of an Egbeda soil series, (Oxic Paleustalf), has shown very distinct differences in nutrient status and variability of the various plant nutrients resulting from the previous vegetation. The data presented in Table 5, are averages of 77 samples each collected at distances of 2 m apart from three adjacent plots after clearing the land. The three plots previous to clearing were respectively under secondary forest, 4-5 years old secondary thicket regrowth, and a cassava crop. Under secondary forest, the soil shows the best nutrient status, this is followed by thicket regrowth. However, after cassava, which is usually the last crop planted before bush fallow, the nutrient status is clearly lower. In terms of soil heterogeneity, the forest plot shows more variability than the other two plots especially as regards soil organic matter. This is due to the presence of various shrubs and trees, particularly palm trees *(Elaeis guineensis)* and piles of decomposing wood under the forest vegetation. The soils under palm trees tend to show a higher nutrient status. After cropping as indicated by the cassava plot, the soil is more homogeneously poor in nutirents.

Table 5.—Effect of preclearing vegetation on some chemical properties of surface soil of Egbeda soil series, at the IITA site. (Oxic Paleustalf).

Preclearing vegetation	pH	Organic C (%)	Exch. K (ppm)	Exch. Ca (ppm)	Available P (Bray 1) (ppm)
Secondary forest	5.75±0.36	1.50±0.28	97.4±49.1	544.9±214.5	2.62±0.98
Thicket 3-4 years	5.60±0.38	1.21±0.11	80.3±29.1	491.3±185.7	1.66±0.80
Cassava crop	5.81±0.31	0.89±0.09	75.7±30.8	420.8±138.5	2.10±1.00

Effect of Burning: Burning is one of the most important steps in land preparation for cropping after clearing for the traditional farmers. Univen burning causes uneven distribution of ash and plant nutrients thereby increasing the already high nutrient variability in soil. The data presented in Table 6, illustrate the effect of light burning of a secondary thicket regrowth on the nutrient status of an Apomu soil series (Ustorthent). As seen from the data, burning has a very significant effect in raising soil pH, the amount of exchangeable cations and available soil phosporus. The rise in pH after burning on the soils at the IITA is shown to have a deleterious effect on upland rice. On spots with concentrated burning the subsequent upland rice crop showed severe symptoms of iron deficiency.

Effect of Termite Activity: The activity of the mound building termites *(Macrotermes bellicosus* and *Macrotermes subhylinus),* also contribute significantly to the soil variability. At the IITA site, the distribution of termite mounds is found to be related to soil drainage. They are mode abundant on the well drained soils but larger on poorly drained soils. The number of termite mounds is estimated to run as 60 active and abandoned mounds per hectare. These termite mounds consisting mainly of subsoil materials, contain less organic matter and have a higher clay content. (Table 7). Because of the lower nutrient and high clay content, poor soil structure results in reduced emergence and stunted growth of maize.

Table 6.—Effect of burning on some chemical properties of surface soil of Apomu soil series (Oxic Paleustalf) at the IITA Site.

Treatment	pH-H₂O	Organic C. (%)	Exch. K (ppm)	Exch. Ca (ppm)	Exch. Mg (ppm)	Available P (Bray 1) (ppm)
Before burning	7.0	0.75	93.6	626.0	111.6	5.2
After burning	7.5	0.90	230.1	818.0	135.6	11.8

Table 7.—Some properties of termite mound soil and surrounding surface soil (mean of 10 samples) at IITA site.

Soil sample	Mechanical Analysis (%)			pH	Organic C (%)	Exch. K (ppm)	Exch. Ca (ppm)
	Sand	Silt	Clay				
Termite mound (outer casing)	57.3	8.3	34.4	6.3	0.80	180.0	570.0
Surface soil	63.6	14.8	21.6	6.4	1.40	170.0	660.0

III PROBLEMS ENCOUNTERED WITH INTRODUCTION OF INTENSIVE AND PERMANENT FARMING SYSTEMS

Soil Erosion and Changes in Soil Structure

Because of the low structural stability of the surface soil, and high climatic erodibility, the potential erosion hazard particularly for the soils derived from the basement complex parent material is high. The erosion problem is further aggravated if large scale mechanized farming is introduced. While the erosion is negligible for the soils under the cover of native vegetation, the soil loss can reach as much as 115 tons/ha/year for unprotected plowed land (Figure 6). Considering the shallow depth of the surface horizon and the poor root penetrability into the sub-soil, the yield reduction by crop due to 2.5 cm of soil removal can be as much as 40 to 50 percent (Figure 7). The addition of fertilizer is no substitute for the loss of surface soil. The soil erosion is accompanied by drastic changes in soil properties i.e. organic matter, clay content and soil structure (Table 8). In addition, the initial high infiltration rate declines rapidly after forest clearing and following cultivation. The water intake rate was decreased by 40 and 70 percent, respectively, under maize and bare fallow after one year of land clearing. Surface encrustation due to cultivation results in this drastic decrease in soil infiltrability.

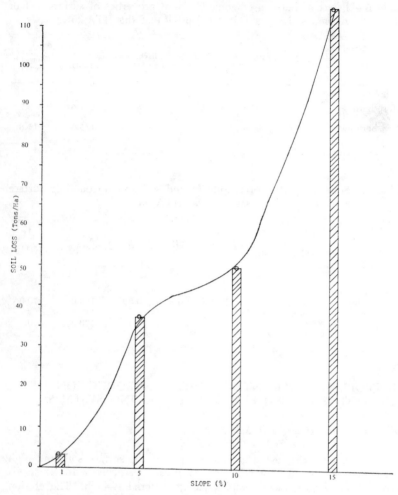

Figure 6. Soil erosion as effected by slope.

Table 8.—Effect of erosion on particle size distribution slope (5%).

Soil separate %	1971		1972		1973	
	Bare fallow	Maize	Bare fallow	Maize	Bare fallow	Maize
Clay	22.5	20.8	14.5	16.1	12.6	12.9
Silt	13.6	13.8	15.7	16.1	11.7	13.0
Sand	59.9	50.6	60.2	61.4	52.5	48.4
Gravel	4.0	15.0	9.5	6.4	23.2	25.7

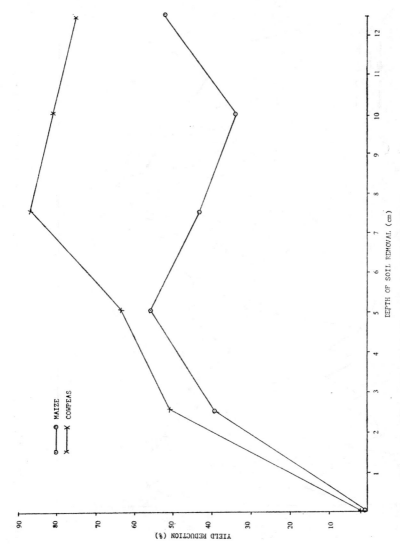

Figure 7. Effect of surface soil removal on yield reduction.

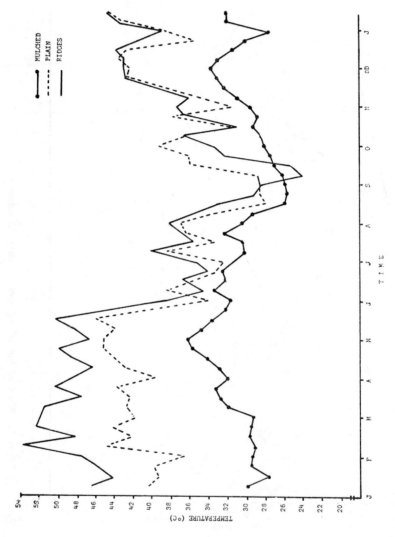

Figure 8. Effect of seed bed preparation on the maximum soil temperature (1971 at 3.00 pm).

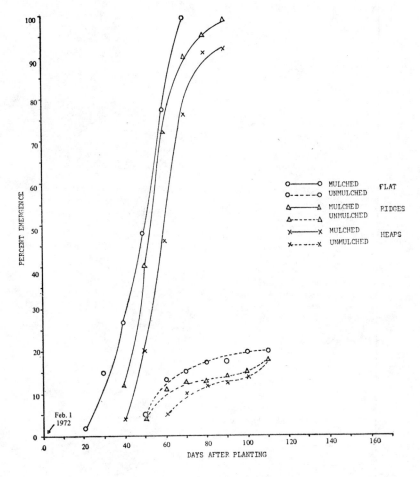

Figure 9. Time of yam emergence as affected by mulching and seed.

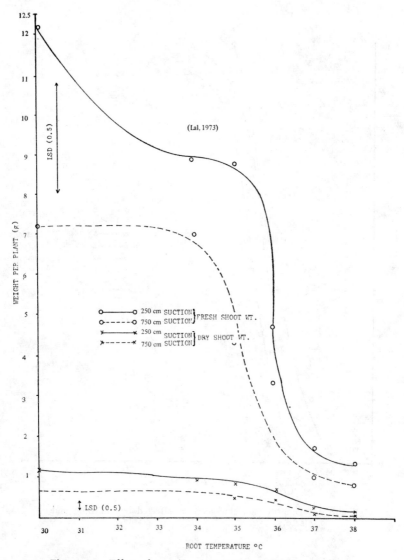

Figure 10. Effect of root Zone temperature on Maize seedlings.

Soil Temperature

Forest clearing and the methods of seed bed preparation significantly influence the soil thermal regime. Vegetation removal increases the heat flux density into the ground. The effect of vegetation removal on soil temperature measured at 5 and 10 cm depth is shown in Figure 8. The diurnal fluctuations in soil tehmperature as a result of land clearing, can be of the magnitude of 20 to 30°C.

Germination, emergence, seedling growth, nutrient and water absorption and yield potential are significantly affected by the soil thermal regime. Supraoptimal temperature significantly influenced yam *(Dioscorea sp.)* emergence on unmulched plots (Figure 9). Growth of maize (Figure 10) and soybean seedlings is virtually stopped by soil temperatures above 35 to 38°C. Nutrient absorption and translocation (Table 9) and water absorption (Table 10) are adversely affected by supra-optimal temperature conditions.

Table 9.—Effect of high soil temperature on nutrient uptake by maize seedlings (shoot).

Soil Temperature	N (mg/g)	P (mg/g)	K (mg/g)	Zn (mg/g) Shoot	Zn (mg/g) Root	B (μg/g)
30	46.1	7.2	68.1	0.19	0.42	3.1
34	43.9	6.3	62.5	0.26	0.35	3.5
35	41.7	4.7	58.6	0.21	0.30	3.0
36	40.3	4.0	49.5	0.32	0.25	3.4
37	46.1	4.6	40.8	0.19	0.24	3.6
38	47.1	7.0	33.4	0.26	0.24	3.9
LSD (.05)	2.6	2.4	23.8	0.09	0.17	1.2

Decline in Chemical Fertility of the Soil

The question of decline in chemical fertility of the soil under traditional systems of cropping has been widely discussed and review (Nye and Greenland, 1960; Vine, 1965). There are indications that the decline in soil fertility which is associated with a decline in soil organic matter is often more marked under forest than under savannah conditions. The decline in the ability of the soil to supply plant nutrients under subsequent cropping can be measured by (1) changes in chemical soil properties, and (2) crop yield. These measurements however have several limitations especially under traditional systems of agriculture due to variations in climate, type of management etc. as discussed recently by Ahn (1973). For a better appraisal of the problem of the soil fertility changes under continuous cropping a number of me-

Table 10.—Effect of root temperature and soil moisture potential on transpiration rate of maize seedlings (Time in seconds per miliamp).

Soil Temperature °C	10.30 a.m.		1.30 p.m.	
	250 cm Suction	750 cm Suction	250 cm Suction	750 cm Suction
35	4.76	1.53	2.30	1.54
36	2.38	1.45	2.02	1.15
37	1.04	0.90	0.88	0.66

dium term experiments are being carried out at the IITA site and at an outstation site. These studies are primarily designed to see the effect of crop and soil management on the speed and extent of changes in the fertility status of the soil with continuous cropping. Preliminary data obtained from one of these trials conducted at IITA site on an Egbeda soil series (Oxic Paleustalf) (Table 11) clearly shows the significant effect of crop husbandry and fertilizer use on the long term yield of maize. Although it is realized that this sequential measurement of yield is very much affected by climatic variations, the data obtained show some interesting differences. Without fertilizer application and no weeding, the maize yield on this soil shows a clear decline after the second year of cropping. With good husbandry (weeding) the yield decline is more gradual, and even after four years of cropping has not apparently reached the equilibrium level. While with good husbandry and fertilizer use the yield of maize is less variable and can apparently be maintained at approximately 6.5 tons/ha. It also appears from the present data that the influence of fertilizer application on yield is greater than that of weed control. Chemical soil measurements have indicated a significant increase in the organic matter content, total nitrogen and available posphorus and potassium in the fertilized plots. The unfertilized plots show a decline in these parameters. However, the differences between the weeded and unweeded but unfertilized treatments are very small at the third year after cropping.

Table 11.—Grain yield IITA maize composite A x B from maximum yield plots at IITA (Egbeda Soil Series) 1971-1973* (Moormann & Kang, 1973).

Year/treatments	Grain yield Kg/ha (%)		
	1 9 7 1	1 9 7 2	1 9 7 3
1. No fertilizer, no weeding	4960(92)	1486(22)	1736(26)
2. No fertilizer, weeding	5829(108)	4556(66)	3519(53)
3. Fertilizer, no weeding	5724(107)	5828(86)	4700(71)
4. Fertilizer, weeding	5384(100)	6785(100)	6619(100)

* Plots cleared in 1970 and subject to uniformity trial with maize in that year.

** Fertilizer rate 120 N- 40 P - 50 K - 4 Zn kg/ha per crop.

IV RECOMMENDED SOIL MANAGEMENT PRACTICES

Role of Surface Mulch in Soil and Water Management

Surface mulch of 4 to 6 tons/ha reduces the soil erosion and runoff losses to a minimum and these losses are comparable to those from soils under forest (Table (12). The decrease in surface soils temperature by mulching can be as much as 8°C (Figure 11) accompanied by an increase in soil moisture storage due to reduction in evaporation losses (Figure 12). Experiments conducted at IITA have also indicated an increase in the availability of NO_3^- N and phosphorus under the mulch layer. Maintenance of yield levels over a period of time by mulching can be attributed to the aforementioned factors (Figure 13). Mulching stimulates the earthworm activity and thus maintains the infiltration rate of the soil, and enhances a favorable tilth.

Mulch Farming Technique

Surface mulch can either be produced in situ by establishing a low growing crop preferably a legume such as *Pueraria phaseoloides, Stylosanthes humilis* etc. or by using the previous crop residue by mulch tillage techniques. Mulch tillage techniques are based on the zonal tillage concept (Larsen, 1962) and involve leaving the crop residue on the surface with a minimum disturbance of the soil. Only the seedling environment zone is disturbed to plant seed and place fertilizer, leaving the inter-row areas undisturbed with with mulch cover to conserve soil and water and to produce a favourable thermal regime. The soil erision losses under minimum tillage are negligible (Figure 14) while the soil moisture

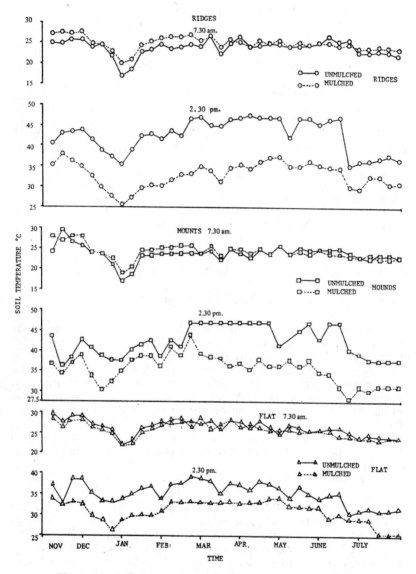

Figure 11. Soil temperature as affected by mulching and tillage.

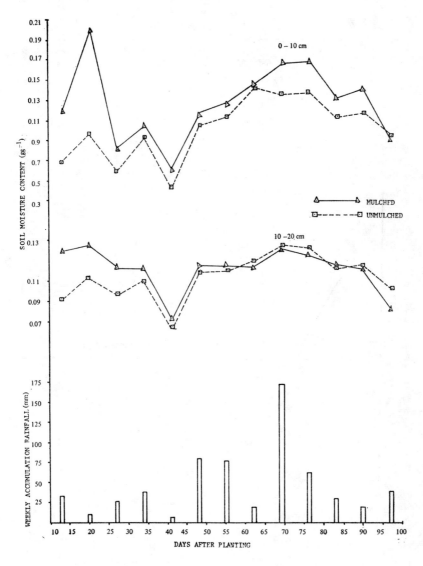

Figure 12. Effect of mulching on soil moisture regime under maize.

Table 12.—Effect of mulching on runoff losses (% of rainfall).

Slope (%)	Under Maize Unmulched	Mulched	Forest cover
1	6.4	2.0	1.7
5	40.3	7.7	1.3
10	42.7	5.7	1.7
15	17.6	1.9	2.0

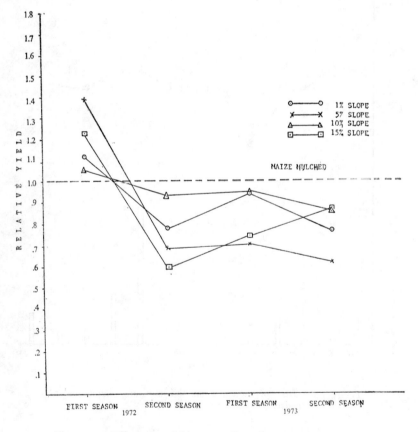

Figure 13.   Effect of mulching on soil productivity.

content is higher (Figure 15) and the soil temperature regime is more favourable (Figure 16). The germination of soybeans is considerably improved. Yields equivalent to those on plowed plots are obtained for a variety of crops during normal rainy periods. Significantly higher yields have been obtained by the use of this technique during the peirods of severe drought stress (Table 13). Due to favourable soil temperature and moisture regime, the biological activity, particularly of earth worms, under mulch tillage plots is maintained as under forest. No-tillage plots with crop residue retained on the soil surface also maintained their organic matter content.

Table 13.—Comparative crop yield with minimum and conventional tillage.

| | Grain Yield (kg/ha) | |
Crop	Minimum Tillage	Conventional Tillage
Maize	4,500.00	3,000.00
Cowpeas	784.80	639.20
Soybeans	846.00	1,066.00
Sweet potatoes	22,000.00	17,750.00
Pigeon peas*	26,250.00	25,000.00

* Total dry matter produced.

Changes in Soil Chemical Properties Under Different Vegetation

Changes in soil chemical properties under different vegetation using no-tillage technique show that organic matter content, total nitrogen, C/N ratio and CEC are maintained under maize with crop residue left on the surface like that under Pigeon Peas, Guinea Grass or bush fallow rotation (Table 14).

Retuning maize residue is, therefore ,equally as effective as bush fallow and other cover crops in maintaining soil organic matter and CEC level of the soil. Yield data of two years clearly demonstrated that maize yield levels were maintained as a result of returning crop residue as surface mulch. While removing maize residue resulted in decline of both grain and dry matter production. (Table 15).

Soil and Water Management for Irrigated Crops

The frequent drought stress is one of the serious limiting factors for crop growth in 'Western Nigeria. The yield of rice and maize is significantly affected by soil moisture stress. Rice yield was significantly decreased by a low level of soil moisture stress i.e. 25 to 50 cm of soil water suction (Figure 17). The effect of soil moisture stress on the leaf

Table 14.—Effect of cropping on soil properties after one year as compared to continued natural bush regrowth.

	Treatment	Organic C (%)	Total N (%)	C/N	CEC me/100g	Total plant residue Returned tons/ha
A	Bush Regrowth	140	.136	10	5.72	Litter fall
C	Guinea Grass	150	.178	8	8.63	30.4 (3 cutting)
D	Lucaena leucophyla	1.56	.141	11	6.15	Litter fall/Ratoon
E	Pigeon Pea	1.40	.143	10	5.73	Litter fall/Ratoon
H	Maize (Return Residue)					16.4 (2 crops)
G	Maize (Remove Residue)	1.04	.115	9	4.64	Removed
F	Soybean (Return Residue)	0.96	.099	10	4.00	3.2 (2 crops)
B	Maize/cassava mixed crop Return Residue	1.24	.140	9	5.73	8.2/Litter fall

Soils sampled in February, 1973 (0-15 cm and 20 composite samples per plot).

Data reported are average value of three replications.

CEC determined by summation of all exchangeable cations.

Table 15.—Effect of crop residue on grain yield.

Treatment	Grain Yield* ton/ha		Dry Matter Yield* ton/ha	
	1972	1973	1972	1973
Maize, Return Residue	7.32	8.35	16.4	16.8
Maize, Remove Residue	6.68	5.71	14.3	10.4
Soybean, Return Residue	2.71	1.85	3.2	1.5

* Total yield of two crops per year.

Data presented are average value of three replications. Plot size: 100 m².

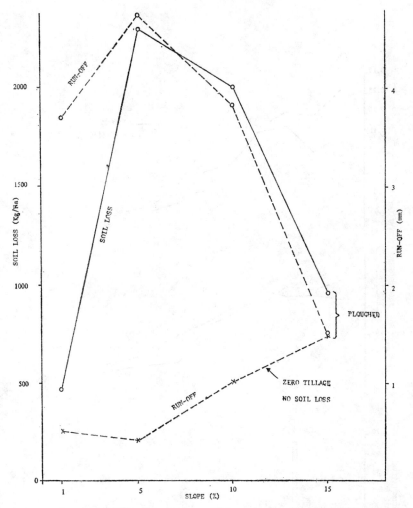

Figure 14. Effect of minimum tillage and conventional plowing on soil erosion and run of losses under maize.

moisture potential of IR-20 and OS6 rice varieties indicates that OS-6, in general, has higher leaf moisture potential (less negative) than IR-20 at the same soil moisture stress. Similarly, maize grain yields were of the order of 6:2.7:1 for maize grown under continuous soil moisture suction of 0.3, 2.0 and 10.0 bar respectively, maintained at 15 cm depth (Figure 18). At the silking stage (of maize growth), the average ear leaf moisture potential was 8, 10, and 12 bar, respectively, for soil moisture suction values of 0.3, 2.0 and 10 bar. The flag leaf moisture potential however, varied from 8 to 13, 11 to 21 and 12 to 43 bars for the three soil moisture regimes, (Figures 19 and 20).

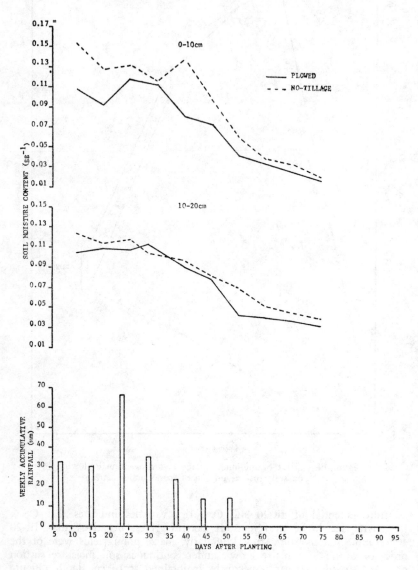

Figure 15. Soil moisture storage under minimum and conventional tillage (1972 2nd season).

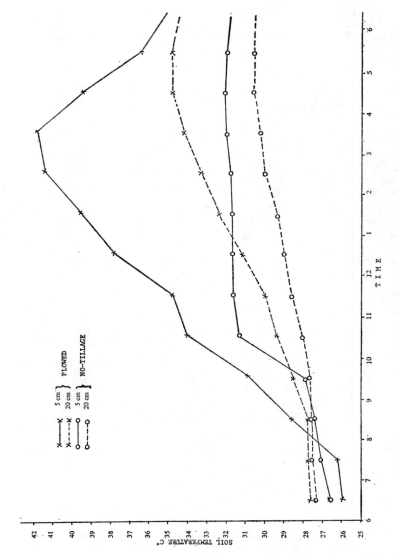

Figure 16. Effect of minimum tillage on soil temperature.

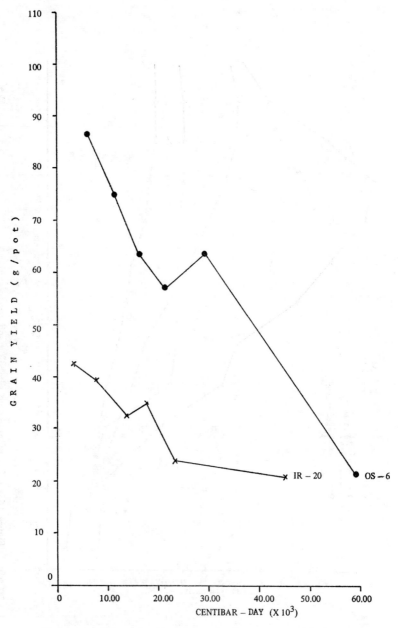

Figure 17. Effect of soil moisture stress on grain yield of two rice varieties.

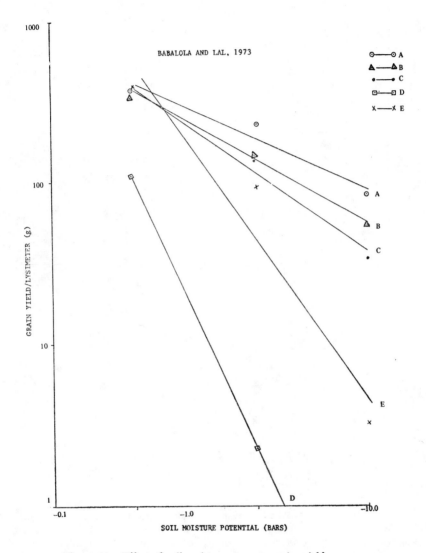

Figure 18. Effect of soil moisture stress on maize yield.

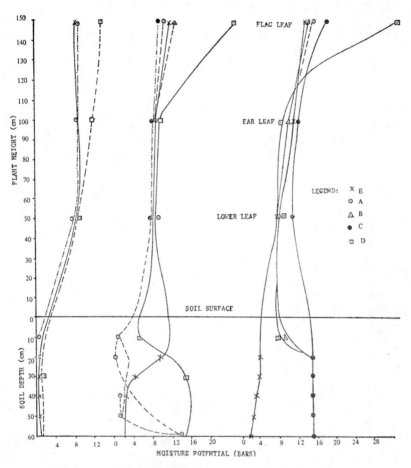

Figure 19. The distribution of water potential in the soil-plant system at 0800 hours. Relative Humidity = 85.0%, temperature = 23.9°C, and M_1, M_2 and M_3 are moisture treatments.

Management of Hydromorphic Soils

In most areas of West Africa, but more especially in the areas with less than 1500-1700 mm rainfall with an unreliable distribution, the occurrence of drought stress is one of the main production limiting factors. In hydromorphic soils, i.e. soils which, due to their situation in depressed terrain, receive supplementary water from surface flow and from interflow, this limiting factor is less severe or, in the most favourable cases, not present at all. Poor drainage is, under condition of tropical West Africa less of a restraint than in the temperate zones since crops are available (especially rice) which can be grown under waterlogged conditions and since in the dry season even poorly drained hydromorphic soils dry to such an extent that they are suitable for crops other than rice. Excluding major river valleys and deltas, hydromorphic soils occupy, according to physiography, from 5 to 20 percent of the landscape in West Africa, and are usually not intensively used.

Studies are under way at IITA on the appropriate land use and on intensified cropping on these soils, in relation to the degree and duration of hydromorphic conditions. Intensive cropping systems, with three crops a year on a sustained basis appear possible; for instance very early maize, rice, soybeans or a vegetable crop. Such systems are impossible on adjacent uplands.

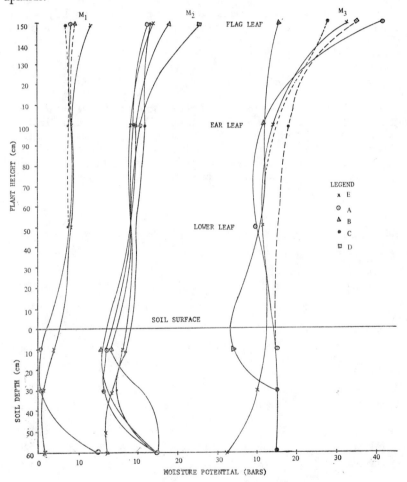

Figure 20. The distribution of water potential in the soil-plant system at 1500 hours during the silking stage. M_1, M_2 and M_3 are moisture treatments. Relative humidity $= 56\%$ temperature $= 32.5°C$, global radiation $= 189.6$ CAL cm d^{1-}.

Fertilizer Management

Of the many factors that need to be considered in the development of better farming systems in the humid tropics, use of fertilizers has been recognized to play a significant role. Despite the importance that fertilizer can play in increasing and maintaining soil fertility, too little attention has been devoted to the fertilizer management problems in the tropics. Many of the parameters determining fertilizer efficiency and, in particular, the long term effects of fertilizer are little known. Most of the fertilizer trials conducted in the area in the past have primarily dealt with studies of N, P and K response using low yielding varieties. In order to obtain more basic data on fertilizer effectiveness and their medium —and long— term effects on soils and crop yield several experiments are carried out at the IITA site and at several other locations. Some of the results obtained are summerised below.

Response to Major Plant Nutrients

Only responses to nitrogen and phosphorus are observed at the IITA site. These responses differ with soil series. Data presented in Table 16 indicate that the Egbeda soil series (Oxic Paleustalf) shows a significant response to phosphorus, and only a small response to nitrogen even in the second year of cropping. The sandy Apomu soil series (Ustorthent) shows a significant response to nitrogen and less response to phosphorus. No response to potassium was observed on both soil series.

Table 16.—Response of Maize to N, P, K (Grain Yield, tons/ha).

Treatment	1972*		1973	
	Egbeda Series	Apomu Series	Egbeda Series	Apomu Series
$N_0P_2K_1$	2.6	1.1	6.2	2.9
$N_1P_2K_1$	2.4	1.9	6.6	5.8
$N_2P_2K_1$	2.9	2.2	7.4	6.9
$N_2P_0K_1$	1.5	2.1	4.0	5.6
$N_2P_1K_1$	2.1	2.4	6.2	6.4
$N_2P_2K_0$	2.6	2.0	6.7	6.3
$N_2P_2K_2$	2.6	1.7	6.9	5.9
LSD 0.05	0.6	0.6	0.9	1.4

* Crop affected by drought.

N_1 = 60 kg N/ha: P_1 = 30 kg N/ha: K_1 = 40 kg K/ha.

Responses to Secondary and Micronutrients:

Of the secondary nutrients tested, only sulfur was found to be frequently deficient, particularly on the sandy soils. A survey in the region has indicated that frequency and degree of sulfur deficiency is more pronounced in the savannah than in the forest zone. This is also shown by the results of the field experiment conducted with maize (Table 17). Significant responses are obtained with low rates of sulfur, while high sulfur rates in certain locations have the tendency of depressing the yield.

Table 17.—Grain yield response of maize varieties composite A x B and NS-1 to S application (tons/ha).

| S. Rate Kg/ha | Ibadan | | Oyo | Ogbomosho* | Ikoyi | Kishi |
	Egbeda Series (Paleustalf)	Apomu Series (Ustorthent)	Apomu Series (Ustip-samment)	Apomu Series (Ustip-samment)	Apomu Series (Ustip-samment)	Omo Series (Paleustalf)
0	2.3	2.3	2.4	1.8	3.3	5.9
7.5	2.1	2.7	3.0	2.4	3.9	6.9
15.0	2.4	2.8	2.7	2.8	3.8	6.2
30.0	2.5	3.0	3.0	3.5	4.3	6.7
60.0	2.4	2.7	3.2	3.2	4.1	6.8
LSD 0.05	NS	0.5	0.5	0.9	0.5	0.9

* Variety NS-1.

Among the micronutirents, zinc deficiency was found to be a major problem in some of the sandy soils in the savannah region. In a recent field experiment with maize, it was observed that with application of Zn at 1 to 2 kg/ha, yield increases of 1,750 kg/ha of maize grain was obtained.

Residual Effects of Fertilizers

The residual effect of application of single superphosphate was studied on an Egbeda soil series (Oxic Paleustalf). Despite the fact that a fresh dressing of phosphorus gave better yields (Figure 21), there is a significant effect of the residual phosphorus on maize yield. Soil analysis indicated very little movement of phosphorus from the surface horizon.

The residual effect of sulfur application was also studied on an Apomu soil series. (Ustorthent). One year after application of sulfur as ammonium sulfate, no significant response to S was noticed on the maize yield. Soil analysis indicated that after one growing season, even at an application rate of 60 kg S/ha most of the sulfur had migrated to the lower horizons below 30 cm depth.

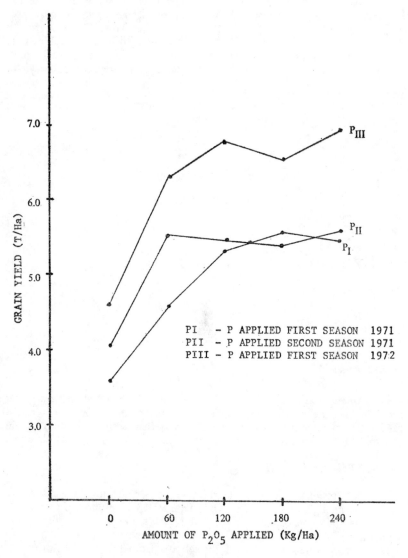

Figure 21. Influence of fresh dressing and residual phosphate on grain yield of IITA maize composite A x B, first (Main) growing season 1972.

V CONCLUSIONS

The data presented supports the following conclusions:

1. Soil management problems forming major restraints for the introduction of continuous cultivation in Western Nigeria are soil erosion, high soil temperature, low water and nutrient holding capacity, poor root penetrability, decreasing organic matter content and low nutrient status.

2. Soils at IITA, and in most of Western Nigeria are as a rule very heterogeneous, leading to extreme soil microvariability. Some biogenetic causes for microvariability are described, e.g. burning, termites, differential influence of vegetation and land use.

3. Preliminary data has indicated that the decline in soil fertility under traditional farming systems depends on the intensity of managements.

4. Mulching and mulch-tillage techniques offer one of the ways to manage the highly erodible soils. In addition, the available water holding capacity is increased and the maximum soil temperature decreased by mulching. Enhanced earthworm activity stimulated by mulch improves the soil tilth.

5. Judicious management of crop residue can maintain soil organic matter content at the same level as under bush fallow or cover crop. Removal of crop residue (by burning or grazing and incorporating into the soil by plowing) hastens depletion of the organic matter content. Crop yields were maintained by retaining the crop residue while sharp decline was observed with residue removal over a two year period.

6. Slight soil moisture stress can result in low leaf moisture potential (more negative) of maize and rice and a sharp decline in yields. A greenhouse technique of growing rice varieties at a soil moisture potential of 50 to 100 cm of water suction at 15 cm depth can be used to screen varieties for their drought tolerance.

7. Hydromorphic soils offer a good potential to produce satisfactory yields even during periods of drought stress.

8. Nitrogen, phosphorus, sulfur and zinc have been identified as important limiting nutrients in Western Nigeria.

9. With good crop husbandry and fertilizer application a high level of yield can be maintained with continuous cropping.

VI SUMMARY

The climatic, geological and soil conditions at IITA are presented.
The soil management problems hindering the introduction of continuous cultivation techniques are discussed and solutions to overcomme the problems presented.
Data are presented explaining the declive in soil fertility under traditional agriculture and methods are suggested to reduce these problems.

Nitrogen, phosphorus, sulfur and zinc are identified as limiting nutrients and their correction by adecuate fertilization is proposed. Methods of soil water imanagement adequate for conditions in Nigeria are proposed.

VII REFERENCES

AHN, P. M. 1973. Some observations on basic and applied research on shifting cultivation. FAO/SIDA Seminar on Shifting Cultivation and soil conservation in Africa. Ibadan July 2-21, 1973.

BABALOLA, O. and R. LAL. 1973. Neutron moisture meter and beta gauging technique to study plant-water relation of maize. Proc. Symp. on Radiation and Isotope Technique in Soil Physics Res. IAEA (in press).

BRUCE-OKINE, E., and R. LAL. 1975. Soil erodibility as determined by rain drop technique. Soil Science (in press).

LAL, R. 1973. Effect of seed bed preparation and time of planting on maize in Western Nigeria. Expl. Agri. 9(4):1973. pp. 303.

LAL, R. 1974. Soil moisture, soil temperature and maize yield from mulched and unmulched tropical soils. Plant and Soil 40:129-143.

LAL, R. 1974. No-tillage effects on soil properties and maize production in Western Nigeria. Plant and Soil 40:321-331.

LAL, R. 1974. Effects of constant and fluctuating soil temperature on growth, development and nutrient uptake by maize seedlings. Plant and Soil 40: 586-606.

LARSON, W. E. 1962. Tillage requirements for corn. J. Soil and Water Conservation 17:3-7.

MOORMANN, F. R. and B. T. KANG. 1973. Agricultural bench mark sites, a methodology and some initial results. Second meeting of the West African soil Correlation Sub-Committee for Soil Evaluation and Management. Jos, Nigeria.

NYE, J. H. and D. J. GREENLAND. 1960. The soil under shifting cultivation. Tech. Com. N° 51 Comm. Bureau of Soils, Harpenden. England.

VINE, H. 1968. Development in the study of soil and shifting agriculture in Tropical Africa. In: Soil Resources of Africa. B. P. Moss. Ed. Cambridge Univ. Press. pp. 89-119.

23 Intensive Management of Pastures and Forages in Puerto Rico

JOSE VICENTE-CHANDLER

I INTRODUCTION

Millions of hectares of rolling to steep lands in the hot humid tropics are not suited to mechanized cropping and, furthermore, the soil requires the protection that well-managed grasslands can afford. Since pastures can be fertilized and limed from the air and cattle do their own harvesting, efficient production together with conservation is feasible on these lands.

Efficient grassland farming in the humid tropics must increasingly be based on heavy fertilization and intensive management. High- yielding tropical grasses (Figure 1) growing throughout the year and often producing more than twice as much forage as grasslands in the temperate region have high nutrient requirements. In Puerto Rico, Vicente-Chandler et al., (1964), found that moderately fertilized grasses removed about 350 kg of N, 70 kg of P, 400 kg of K, 110 kg of Ca, 70 kg of Mg, and 80 kg of S/ha/year. These high nutrient requirements contrasts sharply with the low nutrient supplying power of Ultisols which, in Puerto Rico, supply an average o fabout 70 kg of N, 15 of P, and 60 of K/ha/year to grasses on a long-term basis (Vicente-Chandler et al., 1972).

Also, land in the humid tropics is often expensive and must, therefore, be utilized to its full capacity. Although remote tracts can be purchased for a few dollars per hectare, clearing and providing the necessary roads, housing, health and educational facilities can cost hundreds of dollars per hectare.

As demand increases, fertilizer prices in the tropics should drop to levels similar to those in temperate regions. At the same time, beef prices are rising and meat is becoming an increasingly important export and source of foreign exchange for underdeveloped countries in the humid tropics. Also, local demands for meat and milk are increasing with rising standards of living in these areas. Under these conditions the cost benefits of fertilizing and managing pastures intensively should become increasingly favorable.

The experiments discussed in this paper, unless otherwise indicated, were conducted under the following conditions typical of much of the humid tropics. Annual rainfall averaged 1,600 mm, with lowest precipitation from December through March. Mean monthly temperatures ranged from 21° to 27°C, with seasonal variations of about 5°C, and highest daily temperatures seldom exceeding 33°C. The soils were deep, porous Ultisols on 30 to 50% slopes. These soils had a pH of 4.8 to 5.2 and 4 to 8 meq of exchangeable bases/100 g of soil.

Figure 1. Sixty-day-old, heavily fertilizer Napier (elephant) grass ready for cutting. This field yielded about 300 tons/ha of green forage (50 tons of dry forage) enough to feed about 10 cows.

II FERTILIZING CUT GRASSES

Nitrogen

The effects of N fertilization, with all other nutrients provided in abundance, on yields and composition of seven grasses have been evaluated in numerous experiments in Puerto Rico by Caro, Abruña, and Figarella (1972), Caro, Vicent-Chandler and Figarella (1960), Vicente-Chandler, Figarella, and Silva (1961), Vicente-Chandler and Pearson (1960), Vicente-Chandler, Silva and Figarella (1959) and Vicente-Chandler *et al.*, (1972).

Yields of Guinea, Pangola, Para, Star and Congo (Figure 2) grasses increased sharply with N levels up to 448 kg/ha/year, then rose at a slower rate with higher N levels. Yields of Napier grass increased rapidly with N rates up to 896 kg/ha (Figure 2). Molasses grass did not respond to N applications above 224 ka/ha/year. The grasses produced an average of about 30,000 kg/ha/year of dry forage when fertilized with 448 kg/ha/year of N.

Crude protein content of all the grasses increased with N rates up to the highest rates tested, averaging about 10% for 60-day-old grass receiving 896 kg/ha/year of N (Figure 3). Only traces of nitrate were found in the forage even at the highest N levels. The grasses recoveerd about 50% of the fertilizer N.

Phosphorus content of all the grasses dropped from 0.36 to 0.19% in 60-day-old grass as annual N rates increased from 0 to 896 kg/ha. Lignin conetnt increased somewhat with N fertilization. Nitrogen fertilization had no consistent effect on the Ca, K or Mg contents of the grasses.

More forage was produced per kilogram of fertilizer N as length of harvest interval increased (Figure 4), but protein content of the forage decreased with length of harvest interval.

The grasses responded much more strongly to N fertilization during seasons of fast growth than during the drier, cooler winter months (Vicente-Chandler et al., 1972). Protein content of the forage, however, was higher during seasons of slow growth, owing to the concentrating effect of lower yields in the presence of an equal supply of N.

Vicente-Chandler, Silva and Figarella (1962) found that yields were highest and more of the fertilizer N was recovered in the forage when N was applied immediately after each cutting, which is also the easiest practice.

Studies by Vicente-Shandler and Figarella (1962) on the effects of five N sources applied at the rate of 672 kg/ha/year of N in six equal applications on yield and protein content of Napier grass showed that the N sources did not significantly affect P, Ca, K or Mg content of the forage or yields. However, urea and ammonium hydroxide resulted in lower yields of crude protein.

The relative efficiency of different N sources put on in six equal applications yearly to a dense Pangola grass sod on a Ultisols and harvested by simulated grazing was determined by Figarella, Abruña, and Vicente-Chandler (1972) over a 2-year period. The five N sources differed little in their effect on Pangola grass (Table 1). Also, the various N sources have no effect on the P, K, Ca or Mg content of the forage.

Mixing urea or ammonium nitrate with lime did not affect their efficiency as N sources (Table 1); however, the lime did maintain desirable levels of soil acidity (Table 2). Ammonium sulfate applications over a 2-year period sharply increased soil acidity.

Potassium

The effects of K fertilization on yields and composition of other-wise well- fertilized grasses growing on an Ultisols were determined by Vicente-Chandler, et al., (1962). Yields and K content of all grasses increased rapidly with K rates up to 448 kg/ha/year, (Figure 5). Potassium contents of about 1.5% were associated with high yields. Recovery of fertilizer K in the forage ranged from 65 to 77% at the 448 kg/ha K rate. Ca and Mg contents of the forage decreased with increasing K rates.

Vicente-Chandler et al., (1972) found that KCl and K_2SO_4 were equally effective suppliers of K to Star grass growing on an Ultisol and that liming increased the efficiency of K fertilization as indicated by uptake of this nutrient by the grass.

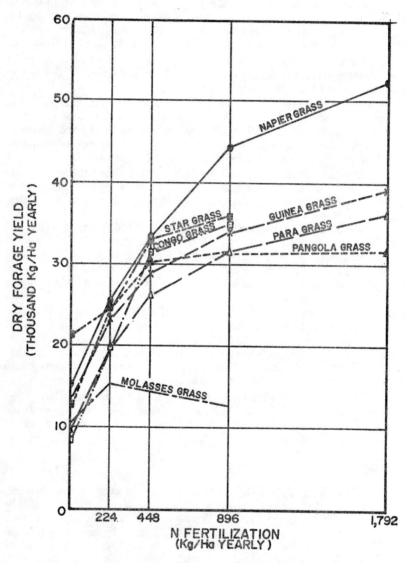

Figure 2.   Effect of N fertilization on yields of 7 grasses harvested by cutting every 60 days.

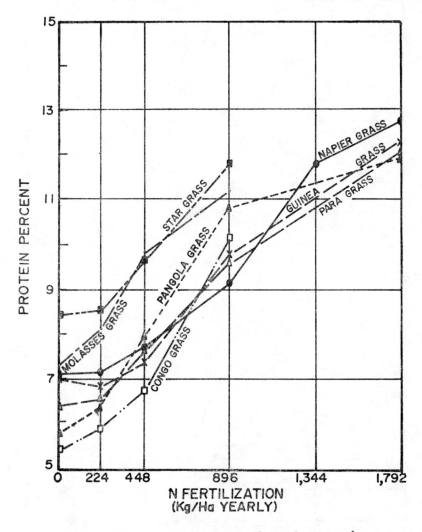

Figure 3. Effect of N fertilization on crude protein content of 7 grasses harvested by cutting every 60 days.

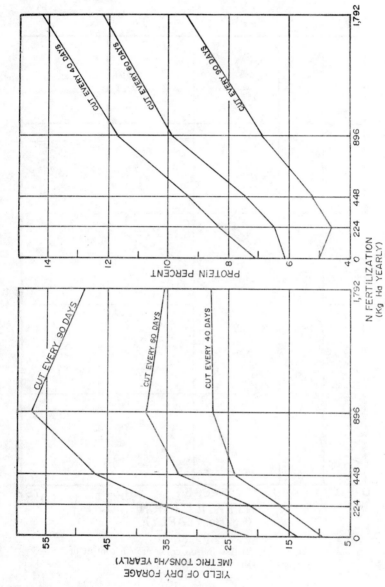

Figure 4. The effect of frequency of cutting on the response of intensively managed tropical grasses to N fertilization.

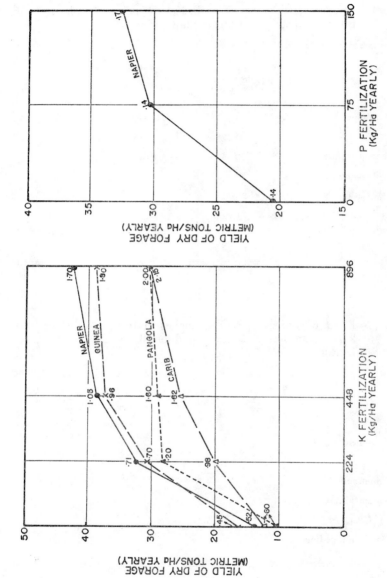

Figure 5. The response of tropical grasses to fertilization with P and K on a typical Ultisol. Numbers show percent K and P content of forage on a dry-weight basis.

Table 1.—Effect of five N sources applied at the rate of 550 kg/ha/year on productivity of a Pangola grass sod.

N Source	N Source Yield of dry forage kg/ha/year	Protein content of forage, %	Recovery of fertilizer N, %
No N applied	5,468	6.2	—
Urea	20,255	8.9	40.8
Ammonium sulfate	20,836	10.2	49.7
Ammonium nitrate	20,480	9.6	46.1
Urea + CaCO$_3$	20,707	8.8	44.9
Ammonium-nitrate-lime	21,291	9.3	45.8
L.S.D. 0.05	NS	0.6	8.8

Table 2.—Effect of various N sources applied at the rate of about 560 kg/ha/year over a 2-year period on the acidity of a typical Ultisol.

N source	pH	Exchangeable Ca + Mg (me/100 g of soil)
No N applied	5.5	9.3
Urea	4.8	7.2
Ammonium sulfate	4.5	5.1
Ammonium nitrate	4.9	7.3
Urea + CaCO$_3$	5.2	10.2
Ammonium nitrate-lime	5.5	11.0

Vicente-Chandler *et al.*, (1972) determined the long-range K-supplying power of the major soils of the humid region of Puerto Rico. Four hundred jars, each containing 11.4 kg of soil from different locations representing 30 soils, were planted to Pangola grass. The grass was heavily fertilized, irrigated as required, and cut every 60 days. Yields and K extracted in the forage over a 4-year period were determined.

Figure 6 shows that the soils released rather large, varying quantities of K during the first year or so, but, thereafter, with the exception of soils from the semiarid region, provided a fairly uniform 40 to 80 kg/ha/year of K to the grass. Therefore, on a long-term basis K fertilization of grasslands should be roughly the same for all these soils typical of large areas of the tropics.

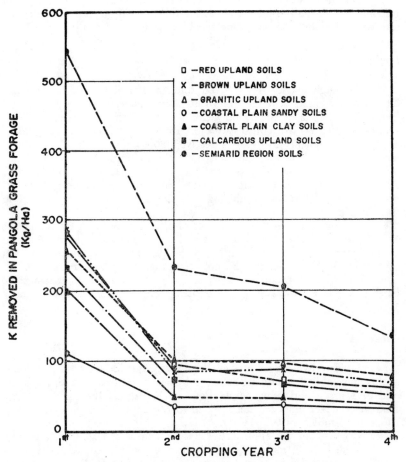

Figure 6. Potassium uptake by Pangola grass from 50 different soils over a 4-year period of continuous cropping in pots.

Phosphorus

Ultisols are naturally low in P and, furthermore, can react with fertilizer P to render it relatively unavailable to plants. The effects of P fertilization on yields and composition of grasses growing on two Ultisols with all other nutrients provided in abundance, were determined by Figarella, *et al.,* (1964).

Napier grass responded strongly to applications of 75 kg/ha/year of P on a soil that had received little previous P on a soil that had received little previous P fertilization, and P content increased with P rates up to 150 kg/ha/year (Figure 5). A content of about 0.17% P in 60-day-old grass was associated with high yields. This rather low P content may be partly the result of heavy N fertilization as mentioned previously.

On the other hand, Napier, Guinea and Pangola grasses did not respond in yield or P content to P applications during 4 years on a Fajardo clay which had been in sugarcane fertilized with P for many years.

Liming

Although grasses are relatively tolerant of soil acidity, heavy applications of residually acid fertilizers can rapidly increase acidity to harmful levels. The effects of liming on yields and composition of well fertilized grasses growing on two Ultisols were determined by Abruña *et al.,* (1964).

On both soils the grasses received 800 kg/ha/year of N as ammonium sulfate responded strongly in yield to application of limestone up to about 3 tons/ha/year, and the response was related to exchangeable Al content of the soil (Figure 7). Applying limestone to the soil surface produced as good results as mixing it with the upper 20 cm. of soil in this experiment.

Liming increased the Ca content of all the grasses. A Ca content of about 0.40% in 60-day-old Napier and Pangola grasses and of 0.60% in Guinea grass was associated with high yields. Liming decreased the Mn content of all the grasses but did not affect their P or Mg content.

Yields were maximum when soil pH was above 5.0, exchangeable bases exceeded 8 meq/100 g, and exchangeable Al was less than 3 meq/100 g.

Other Nutrients

Intensively managed grasses take up large quantities of Mg, and losses of this nutrient by leaching are increased by heavy fertilization with residually acid N sources, and heavy applications of K depress the uptake of Mg However, Napier grass did not respond to Mg applications on two Ultisols (Vicente-Chandler *et al.,* 1964). Although Mg content of the forage increased when Mg was applied, the grass contained at least 0.25% of Mg, which is adequate to meet livestock requirements and needs of the grass.

Serious deficiencies of S occur in some areas. In Brazil, McClung and Quinn (1960) found that grasses responded strongly to applications of this nutrient. Some Ultisols contain very little S in the root zone, whereas others have high contents either naturally or as a result of fertilization.

With continued heavy fertilization of the acid, leached soils of the tropics, it is very likely that micronutrient deficiencies will eventually occur.

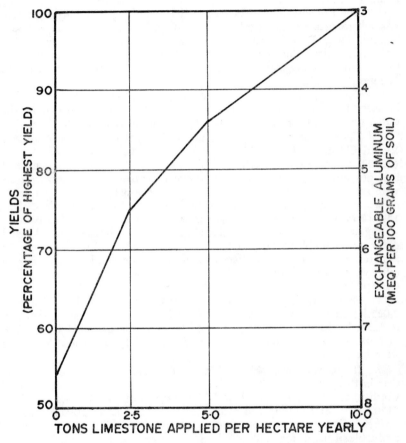

Figure 7. Effect of liming on yields of heavily fertilized Napier grass growing on a Ultisol as related to exchangeable aluminum content of soil. Eight hundred kg/ha/year of N were applied as ammonium sulfate.

III FERTILIZING GRASS PASTURES

Fertilizer requirements of pastures differ from those of cut grasses, since only about half as much forage and hence less nutrients are taken from the land by pastures. Although about 80 percent of the N, P and K consumed are excreted, grazing animals are not very effective in maintaining soil fertility because of poor distribution of the excreta (Peterson, Woodhouse and Lucas (1956). Because of heavy losses by leaching, N fertilization of tropical grasslands should not be decreased counting on buildup of N from excreta, but much of the applied P and over 20% of the K fertilization can be built up in the soil under heavy stocking and intensive management with consequent economies in fertilization (Vicente-Chandler et al., (1972).

The response of grasses harvested by plucking to simulate grazing, was determined by Caro-Costas, Vicente-Chandler and Figarella (1960). Guinea, Para, Pangola, and Napier grasses respond well only to the 224-kg/ha N level during the winter but strongly to the 448-kg level during the remainder of the year. Protein content of all the grasses increased with N rates.

Grazed pastures, however, may respond differently to fertilization because of variations in nutrients removed in the forage consumed by the cattle, trampling effects, and return of nutrients in the excreta.

Three separate grazing experiments were carried out by Caro and Vicente-Chandler (1961, 1972) and Caro, Vicente-Chandler and Abruña (1972), to determine the effect of fertilizer rates on carrying capacity and beef produced by Napier, Pangola, and Star grass pastures. The experiments were carried out on steep Ultisols limed to about pH 6.0. Fertilizer treatments were replicated four times with individual 0.4 hectare plots. The 15-5-10 fertilizer was applied in four equal applications yearly. The pastures were grazed in rotation by young cattle initially weighing about 175 kg and receiving no supplementary feed. A new group of cattle were put on the pastures every year. Total digestible nutrients consumed by the grazing cattle were calculated following the recommendations of the Pasture Research Committee (1943).

As fertilization of the Napier grass pasture increased from 675 to 2,025 kg/ha/year over a 2-year period, beef production increased from 638 to 1,201 kg/ha/year, T.D.N. consumed by the cattle increased from 4,720 to 7,500 kg/ha/year, and carrying capacity moved from 3.5 to 5.5, 273-kg steer/ha (Table 3).

It was very profitable to increase fertilization up to 2,025 kg/ha/year in this experiment. The additional 563 kg of liveweight produced is worth about $338, compared with increased fertilizaiton costs of about $120. Costs of handling and caring for the additional cattle are offset by savings in investment in land, fencing, etc. Such fertilization is even more profitable if used for milk production. Increasing fertilization to 3375 kg/ha/year did not significantly increase productivity of the pastures in this experiment.

Pangola grass pastures responded in terms of beef production and carrying capacity to applications of up to 2,688 kg/ha/of 14-4-10 fertilizers, but did not respond to heavier fertilization (Table 3). With 2,688 kg/ha of fertilizer the Pangola grass pastures produced 976 kg/ha/year of gain in weight and carried the equivalent of 5-273-kg steers/ha with daily gains per head of 0.6 kg.

Star grass pastures responded in terms of beef gains to the application of up to 3,136 kg/ha of 15-5-10 fertilizer (Table 3). The pastures produced an average of 1,032 kg/ha of gain in weight with 1,793 kg/ha of fertilizer, compared to 1,382 kg/ha worth about $663 with 3,136 kg/ha of fertilizer. The additional 350 kg of beef worth $210 was produced as a result of applying 1,343 additional kilograms of fertilizer worth $121. Daily gains per head averaged 0.6 kg at all fertilizer rates. With 3,136 kg/ha of fertilizer the Star grass pastures produced over 11,000 kg/ha of T.D.N., equivalent to a carrying capacity of 6.5-273 kg steers.

Table 3.—Effect of fertilizer rates on the productivity of various tropical grass pastures on a steep Ultisol.

14-4-10 fertilizer applied kg/ha/yr	Gains in weight kg/ha/yr	Carrying capacity 273 kg steers/ha[1]/	T.D.N. consumed by cattle kg/ha/yr[2]/
		NAPIER	
675	638	3.5	4,820
2,025	1,201	5.5	7,500
3,375	1,333	6.3	9,070
		PANGOLA	
448	398	1.9	2,630
1,344	633	3.4	4,560
2,688	976	5.0	6,980
3,808	1,054	6.0	8,250
		STAR	
1,792	1,032	5.0	6,900
3,136	1,382	6.5	9,210
4,480	1,603	8.6	11,320

1/ One 273 kg steer = 3.86 kg T.D.N. daily.

2/ Calculated from body weights, days of grazing, and gains in weight, folloowing recommendations of the Pasture Research Committee (1943).

IV MEAT AND MILK PRODUCTION FROM INTENSIVELY MANAGED GRASSLANDS

The productivity of intensively managed Guinea, Pangola, Napier, Para and Molasses grass pastures on a steep Ultisol was determined by Caro, Vicente-Chandler and Figarella (1965) in a 4-year grazing experiment using previously described experimental techniques. Five head were kept per hectare at all times on the Pangola, Guinea, and Napier grass pastures, but only 3.3 head could be kept on the Para and Molasses grass pastures during the winter season.

The Para and Molasses grass pastures produced much lower gains in weight, an average of 712 kg/ha/year, less T.D.N., and had a lower carrying capacity than did Pangola, Guinea, or Napier grasses (Table 4).

Pangola, Guinea, and Napier grass pastures produced similar yields, averaging 1,181 kg/ha/year of gain in weight, 8,466 kg/ha/year of T.D.N. with a carrying capacity of 6.1-273-kg steers/ha, and daily gains of 0.6 kg/head.

Consumption of dry forage by the cattle averaged 15,700 kg/ha/year. An average of 7.2 kg of T.D.N. or 12.6 kg of dry forage were required to produce 1 kg of beef.

Quality of the forage consumed by the grazing cattle was excellent (Table 4), with protein contents averaging 18.1% and varying little with species or season of the year.

The productivity of Star and Pangola grass pastures on a steep Ultisol was compared by Caro, Abruña, and Vicente-Chandler (1972). Pastures received 2,200 kg/ha/year of 15-5-10 fertilizer.

Star grass (Figure 8) produced an average of 1,514 kg/ha of gain in weight yearly with average daily gains of 0.6 kg/head as compared to 1,062 kg/ha of gain in weight and daily gains of 0.49 kg for Pangola grass (Table 5). Star grass had a carrying capacity of 7.4, 273-kg steers/ha compared to 6.5 for Pangola grass. Calculations from dry forage and T.D.N. consumption indicate a digestibility of about 55% for these grasses. Star grass had a higher dry matter content than Pangola grass at all times of the year and protein content of the forages ranged from 11.3 to 18.5%.

Caro and Vicente-Chandler (1969) determined the productivity of intensively managed pastures of Guinea, Napier, Star, and Pangola grasses on a steep Ultisol in terms of milk produced by Holstein cows receiving no suplementary feed. Eight to ten cows were carried on 4 hectares of grasslands fertilized and managed as previously described. The pastures had shade, water, salt, and ground bonemeal available. Protein content of the forage consumed by the cows ranged from 16.3 to 19.1% throughout the year.

The cows on this all-grass ration produced an average of more than 10 liters of milk daily (Table 6) for a total of over 3,000 liters per lactation. Butterfat content of the milk averaged 3.8%. Calving interval averaged about 13.5 months over the 5 years of experimentation.

V GRASSLAND MANAGEMENT FOR BETTER UTILIZATION

Although it is expensive to fertilize too frequently, heavy rates put on in only one or two applications/year can cause burning, rapid growth immediately after application to the detriment of subsequent yields, and higher nutrient losses.

The effects of frequency and rates of fertilization on Guinea grass harvested by simulated grazing were determined by Vicente-Chandler, Silva and Figarella (1962). Treatments consisted of applying 1,500, 4,500, and 6,000 kg/ha/year of 14-4-10 fertilizer in 2, 4, or 8 applications/year.

Figure 8. Cattle grazing intensively managed, heavily fertilized star grass pastures on a steep Ultisol. These pastures produce over 1,000 kg/ha of beef or over 6,000 kg/ha of milk yearly without supplementary feeds under conditions typical of much of the tropics where dietary protein deficiencies are widespread. With cattle doing their own harvesting and fertilizer applied aerially, grasslands can constitute an efficient "mechanized" operation together with conservation on steep lands with few alternative uses.

Table 4.—Productivity of well-fertilized[1] pastures of five grasses on a steep Ultisol.

Grass	Gain in weight, ka/ha/yr	T.D.N. consumed by cattle kg/ha/yr[4]	Carrying capacity, 273-kg steers/ha[2]	Dry, weight composition of forrage consumed by the cattle[3] Crude protein, %	Lignin, %
Guinea	1,319	8,941	6.5	18.2	7.6
Napier	1,110	8,140	5.8	19.3	7.8
Pangola	1,124	8,316	6.0	16.9	9.0
Pará	781	6,434	4.5	—	—
Molasses	644	4,838	3.5	—	—

1/ 2.5 tons of 14-4-10/ha/yr in four equal applications.

2/ One 273 kg steer/day = 3.86 kg of T.D.N.

3/ Average of samples taken every 10 days by plucking to simulate grazing.

4/ Calculated from body weights, days of grazing, and gains in weight, following recommendations of the Pasture Research Committee (1943).

Table 5.—Comparative productivity of intensively managed Star and Pangola grass pastures on a steep Ultisol.

Grass	Gains in weight, kg/ha/yr	Average daily gains per head, kg	TDN consumed by cattle, kg/ha/yr	Carrying capacity, 273 kg steers/ha	Yields of dry forage, kg/ha/yr
Star	1,514	0.60	10,380	7.4	19,240
Pangola	1,062	0.49	9,200	6.5	17,000
L.S.D. 05	288	0.11	987	0.7	—

Table 6.—Milk produced per lactation by Holsteins on an all-grass ration from steep, intensively managed grass pastures with 2.2 cows/ha.

	1968	1969	1970	1971	1972
	8 cows in their 4th and 5th lactations	10 cows in their 4th and 5th lactations	9 first lactation cows	9 second lactation cows	9 third lactation cows
	(liters)	(liters)	(liters)	(liters)	(liters)
	3,232	2,872	2,181	2,941	4,242
	3,383	2,512	2,162	2,710	4,120
	3,158	3,258	1,812	3,166	4,016
	2,276	2,771	1,925	4,050	3,980
	2,354	2,941	1,914	4,171	3,538
	2,211	3,430	2,591	3,985	3,840
	2,911	2,320	2,093	3,317	3,610
	2,430	3,440	1,808	3,570	4,360
	—	2,633	3,034	3,455	4,012
	—	2,772	—	—	—
Average	2,744	2,895	2,169	3,485	3,968
Average daily production (litters)	10.2	10.7	8.0	12.6	14.4
Average lactation = 275 days					

The number of fertilizer applications did not strongly affect annual yields or protein content of the forage, both of which increased sharply with fertilization. However, when the fertilizer was applied in only two applications, yields and protein content were higher over the next two yield periods, then lower during the subsequent two yield periods. Four applications were just as effective as the more expensive eight applications in reducing these undesirable fluctuations in yield and composition.

The effect o ftwo grazing heights on yields of a Pangola grass pasture were determined by Vicente-Chandler, Silva, Rodríguez and Abruña (1972). Higher yields were obtained when the grass was grazed down to about 15 cm from the ground than with closer grazing; 14,407 vs. 10,647 kg/ha/year of dry forage, respectively.

However, the situation is often very different when the grasses are harvested by cutting. Table 7 from the work of Caro and Vicente-Chandler

(1961 and 1971) and Vicente-Chandler et al., (1972) shows that Napier, Pangola, Para, Star and Congo grasses produced higher yields when cut to 0-8 cm from the ground than with higher cutting. On the other hand, yields of Guinea grass were not affected by cutting height and those of Molasses grass were drastically reduced by cutting close to the ground.

Table 7.—Effect of two cutting heights on yields of seven well-fertilized grasses harvested every two months over a 2-year period.

	Yields of dry forage	
Grass	Cut high (18.25 cm)	Cut low (0 - 8 cm)
	kg/ha/yr	
Molasses	13,300	4,300
Guinea	27,700	27,100
Napier	25,500	30,700
Pangola	21,900	32,200
Pará	21,700	27,200
Star	26,700	32,600
Congo	26,000	32,500

Also, Caro et al., (1960, 1971) and Vicente-Chandler et al., (1959, 1960, 1961, 1962, 1964, and 1972) found that yields of well-fertilized Napier, Guinea, Para, Pangola, Star and Congo grasses increased as cutting intervals increased from 30 to 90 days (Figure 4 and Table 8). However, digestibility, protein and mineral contents of the forage decreased and lignin content increased with length of harvest interval (Table 8), so that it was best to cut these grasses about every 40 days during seasons of fast growth and every 60 days during periods of slow growth.

Grass yields in Puerto Rico are little more than half as high during the winter months as during the remainder of the year (Figure 9) due to drier weather, slightly shorter days, and cooler temperatures (Vicente-Chandler et al., 1964). On the other hand, composition of the grasses harvested by simulated grazing was not markedly affected by season of the year (Table 9).

This seasonal variation in growth poses an obvious management problem which can be partly solved by storing excess forage as silage or hay for use during the "winter" season; producing "carry-over" forage for the winter by timely fertilization and management; supplementary concentrate feeding during winter; or applying more fertilizer and using a longer harvest or grazing interval during winter.

Table 8.—Effect of Frequency of Cutting on the Yield and Composition of 4 Well-Fertilized[1]/ Grasses Over a 2-Year Peirod.

Grass	Interval Between Cuttings	Yields of Green Forage Yearly	Yields of dry forage Yearly	(calculated[2]/) digestible Dry-Matter Yearly	Dry-Matter Content of Forage	Proportion of leaf Blades	Composition of Forage on a Dry-Weight Basis				
							Protein (Nx6.25)	Phosphorous	Calcium	Magnesium	Lignin
	days	kg/ha	kg/ha	kg/ha	%	%	%	%	%	%	%
Napier	40	157,400	22,700	15,000	14	55	9.9	0.24	0.35	0.30	6.9
	60	240,800	41,100	23,100	17	42	7.9	0.18	0.28	0.19	8.8
	90	258,100	63,300	26,400	25	30	5.4	0.13	0.23	0.19	11.1
Guinea	40	127,200	26,700	17,600	21	63	9.0	0.27	0.88	0.49	8.2
	60	135,500	32,700	18,400	24	53	7.0	0.22	0.78	0.38	9.4
	90	129,900	41,300	17,200	32	36	5.6	0.16	0.64	0.33	11.4
Carib	40	93,100	19,100	12,700	21	—	9.2	0.25	0.39	0.27	7.5
	60	113,800	26,600	15,000	23	28	7.2	0.21	0.35	0.20	8.4
	90	117,264	36,800	15,500	31	24	4.8	0.15	0.29	0.15	9.4
Pangola	30	141,200	21,600	15,200	19	38	12.5	0.22	0.43	—	8.1
	45	152,300	25,600	16,200	24	39	9.6	0.22	0.36	—	8.8
	60	164,600	33,400	18,800	28	40	8.0	0.17	0.34	—	9.2
Star	30	86,800	18,900	13,300	22	53	14.6	0.31	0.47	0.29	7.6
	45	99,900	24,100	16,000	24	52	11.1	0.26	0.50	0.23	8.4
	60	119,200	33,600	18,800	28	50	9.7	0.19	0.50	0.21	10.0
	90	123,100	35,800	15,000	29	—	7.7	0.15	0.52	0.27	10.4
Congo	30	95,600	20,900	14,800	22	32	9.8	0.36	0.60	0.19	6.8
	45	120,100	28,300	18,800	24	32	8.7	0.28	0.64	0.23	7.5
	60	128,800	30,900	17,400	24	35	6.4	0.19	0.62	0.28	8.1
	90	166,900	49,800	20,800	30	33	5.1	0.14	0.51	0.26	10.3

1/ About 3.5 tons of 15-5-10/ha/year.

2/ Assuming a 0.48 percent decrease in digestibility per day increase in harvest interval
, starting with 85 percent digestibility for very young grass (MacDonald 1964).

Table 9.—Dry-weight Composition (Percent) of Forage of Five Well-fertilized Grasses Harvested by Simulated Grazing at Orocovis[1] as Affected by Season of the Year.

Months	Pangola				Guinea				Napier				Star			Congo		
	Protein	Lignin	Ca	P	Protein	Lignin	Ca	P	Protein	Lignin	Ca	P	Protein	Ca	P	Protein	Ca	P
Jan.-Feb.	18.1	9.39	0.32	0.19	19.8	7.18	0.67	0.19	20.7	7.20	0.30	0.20	23.8	0.51	0.20	22.3	0.61	0.21
Mar.-Apr.	16.4	9.02	0.33	0.20	17.5	7.73	0.67	0.23	18.6	7.90	0.30	0.25	19.9	0.54	0.18	22.8	0.59	0.24
May-June	14.9	7.95	0.35	0.21	16.8	7.78	0.65	0.23	16.8	8.02	0.29	0.25	17.2	0.44	0.19	15.6	0.53	0.21
July-Aug.	16.7	8.93	0.35	0.18	16.6	7.62	0.60	0.20	18.7	7.68	0.29	0.24	17.3	0.41	0.21	13.3	0.45	0.21
Sept.-Oct.	18.3	7.20	0.35	0.25	18.9	8.30	0.53	0.21	20.0	7.73	0.28	0.25	16.3	0.50	0.25	10.3	0.53	0.21
Nov.-Dec.	17.3	11.45	0.37	0.20	19.5	7.16	0.58	0.51	20.9	8.10	0.30	0.25	24.4	0.55	0.27	19.9	0.58	0.23
Average	16.9	8.99	0.35	0.21	18.2	7.63	0.62	0.21	19.3	7.77	0.29	0.24	19.8	0.49	0.22	17.3	0.55	0.22

1/ Values shown are averages of samples taken at intervals of 10 days by plucking so as to simulate grazing.

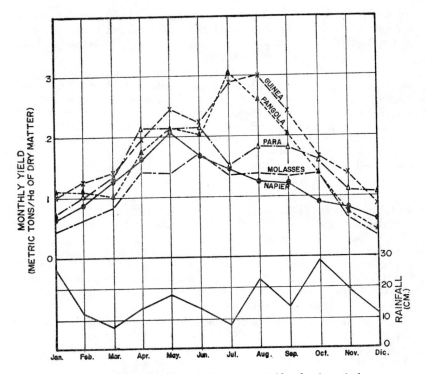

Figure 9. Effect of season of the year on yields of 5 intensively managed grasses harvested by simulated grazing.

The latter measure however, decrease the quality of the forage since cattle fed on cut grass ingest more stems which are much lower in protein, calcium and phosphorus content and higher in lignin than are the leaves. Vicente-Chandler *et al.*, (1973), found that young cattle fed on Pangola or Napier grass pastures gained an average of 0.6 per head daily, whereas those fed on cut Pangola or Napier gained only 0.3 kg/head.

Heavy N fertilization without liming can rapidly increase deep profile acidity in Ultisols (Abruña, Pearson and Elkins, 1958; Abduña *et al.*, 1964; and Pearson, Abruña and Vicente-Chandler, 1962) which is later difficult to correct and can seriously limit plant growth.

In these experiments exchangeable Al in two Ultisols was rapidly increased by heavy fertilization alone, but this increase was prevented by surface liming. Base content of the soil profiles was decreased by fertilization alone, but was increased when fertilization was preceded by surface liming. The massive movement of bases deep into these porous Ultisols suggests a method for correcting subsoil acidity.

The effect of heavy stocking and consequent trampling on a Ultisol stocked with 5 head/ha for 4 consecutive years was studied by Vicente-Chandler and Silva (1960). Undisturbed soil cores from the various pastures showed little compaction of the surface soil under Pangola or Napier

— 429 —

grasses, but some compaction with Guinea-grass where animal traffic is concentrated between clumps. However, densities did not exceed 1.1 g/ml and soil permeability remained excellent. Loosening the surface soil not increase subsequent yields of these grasses.

The possibility that heavily fertilized Napier grass could be toxic to cattle under some conditions was investigated by Morris, Cancel and González (1958). Analyses of Napier grass from numerous locations revealed no Se, As ,o rotehr heavy metals, toxic organic acids or toxic levels of cyanides. Oxalic acid content of the forage ranged from 1 to 4% in 8-week-old grass, decreasing rapidly with age. Such levels of oxalic acid were not toxic because this compound was destroyed in the rumen. About three-quarters of the N in 6- to 8-week-old Napier grass was protein N and the remainder was mostly water-soluble amino acids.

Morris, Cancel and González Más (1958) also conducted feeding trials to determine the toxicity of nitrates or nitrites to cattle. Pregnant, nonlactating milk cows as well as eight lactating cows suffered no ill effects from consuming large quantities of herbage containing 1.8% of potassium nitrate on a dry-weight basis, and yearling bulls suffered no apparent ill effects from consuming large quantities of herbage containing 3% of either potassium nitrate or potassium nitrite. In these latter tests potassium nitrate or nitrite was added to the forage as in form of a compound to attain the desired levels in the ration.

Much can be done through the judicious use of fertilizers to bring forage production into line with farm needs. %hen required, a heavy application of fertilizer can quickly increase the supply of forage during the favorable weather usually present in the humid tropics. On the other hand, forage production can be cut back by reducing fertilizer applications during slack seasons.

A marked advantage of heavily fertilized, properly managed grassland is that it has few weeds. Also, observations over many years show that manure spots are not a serious problem in heavily fertilized, intensively managed grasslands on Ultisols under humid tropical conditions. Under these conditions the grasses apparently grow almost as rapidly throughout the pasture as in the manure spots, thus tending to equalize their palatability.

VI SUMMARY

On steep lands in the humid region of Puerto Rico, typical of vast areas in the humid tropics, grasses growing on Ultisols and harvested by cutting, responded strongly in yield to applications of 400 to 800 kg/ha/year of N and about 50% of the applied N was recovered in the forage. Best results were obtained when N was applied immediately after each cutting and there was little difference in effectiveness betwen N sourcs.

Grasses responded to applications of about 400 kg/ha/year of K and about three-quarters of the applied K was recovered in the forage. They also responded to applications of 75 kg/ha/year of P on previously unfertilized Ultisols. Grasses often responded to liming and maximum yields were obtained when soil pH was above 5.0 and Al saturation was less than around 20%.

Pastures of Napier, Pangola, and Star grasses on steep Ultisols responded strongly to the application of 2 to 3 tons of 15-5-10 fertilizer/ha/year. With 2.5 tons/ha of fertilizer, pastures of Guinea, Pangola, Star, and Napier grasses carried 6 steers/ha with no supplementary feed and produced over 1,000 kg/ha of gain in weight or 2.5 cows producing over 7,000 kg/ha/year of milk with no concentrate feed.

VII REFERENCES

ABRUÑA, F., PEARSON, R. W. and ELKINS, C. 1958. Quantitative evaluation of soil reaction and base status changes resulting from field applications of residually acid-forming nitrogen fertilizers, Soil Sci. Soc. Amer. Proc. 22: 539-542.

ABRUÑA, F., VICENTE-CHANDLER, J., PEARSON, R. W., and FIGARELLA, J. 1964. Effects of liming on yields and composition of heavily fertilized grasses and on soil condition under humid tropical conditions, Soil Sci. Soc. Amer. Proc. 28:657-661.

ANONYMOUS. 1943. Report on pasture investigation techniques, Joint Committee of the American Dairy Society, American Dairy Science Association, and American Society of Animal Production, J., Dairy Sci. 26:353-369.

CARO-COSTAS, R., ABRUÑA, F., and FIGARELLA, J. 1972. Effects of nitrogen rates, harvest interval and cutting heights on yield and composition of Stargrass in Puerto Rico, Jour. of Agric. Univ. of P.R. 56:171-186.

CARO-COSTAS, R., ABRUÑA, F. and VICENTE-CHANDLER, J. 1972. Comparison of heavily fertilized Pangola and Star grass pastures in terms of beef production and carrying capacity in the humid mountain region of Puerto Rico, Jour. of Agri. Univ. of P.R. 56:104-109.

CARO-COSTAS, R., and VICENTE-CHANDLER, J. 1961. Effect of fertilization on carrying capacity and beef produced by Napier grass pastures, Agron. J. 53:204-205.

CARO-COSTAS, R., and VICENTE-CHANDLER, J. 1961. Effect of two cutting heights on yields of five tropical grasses, J. Agri. Univ. of P.R. 45:46-49.

CARO-COSTAS, R., and VICENTE-CHANDLER, J. 1969. Milk production with all-grass rations on steep intensively managed tropical pastures, J. Agr. Univ. of P.R. 53:251-258.

CARO-COSTAS, R., and VICENTE-CHANDLER, J. 1972. The effects of heavy rates of fertilization on beef production and carrying capacity of Napier grass pastures over five consecutive years of grazing under humid tropical conditions, J. Agr. of the Univ. of P.R. 56:223-227.

CARO-COSTAS, R., VICENTE-CHANDLER, J., and ABRUÑA, F. 1972. The effect of 4 levels of concentrate feeding on milk production by Holstein cows grazing intensively managed tropical grass pastures, J. of Agr. Univ. of P.R. 56:97-103.

CARO-COSTAS, R., VICENTE-CHANDLER, J., and ABRUÑA, F. 1972. The effect of four levels of fertilization on beef production and carrying capacity of Pangola grass pastures in the humid mountain region of Puerto Rico, J. of Agr. of Univ. P.R. 56:219-22.

CARO-COSTAS, R., VICENTE-CHANDLER, J. and ABRUÑA, F. 1972. The effect of four levels of fertilization on beef production and carrying capacity of Pangola grass in the humid mountain region of Puerto Rico. J. Agr. Univ. of P.R. 56:219-222.

CARO-COSTAS, R., VICENTE-CHANDLER, J., and FIGARELLA, J. 1960. The yield and composition of five grasses growing in the humid mountains of Puerto Rico as affected by nitrogen fertilization, season and harvest procedure, J. Agr. Univ. of P.R. 44:107-120.

CARO-COSTAS, R., VICENTE-CHANDLER, J., and FIGARELLA, J. 1965. Productivity of intensively managed pastures of five grasses on steep slopes in the humid mountains of Puerto Rico, J. Agr. Univ. P.R. 49:99-111.

FIGARELLA, J., VICENTE-CHANDLER, J., SILVA, S., and CARO-COSTAS, R. 1964. Effect of phosphorus fertilization on productivity of intensively managed grasses under humid tropical conditions in Puerto Rico, J. Agr. Univ. P.R. 48:236-242.

FIGARELLA, J., ABRUÑA, F., and VICENTE-CHANDLER, J. 1972. The effects of five nitrogen sources applied at four rates to Pangola grass sod under humid tropical conditions, J. of Agr. Univ. P.R. 56:410-416.

McCLUNY, A. C., and QUINN, L. R. 1964. Sulphur and phosphorus responses of Batatais grass (Paspalum notatum), IBEC, Research Institute Bull N° 18 New York, N.Y.

MORRIS, M. P., CANCEL, B., and GONZALEZ-MAS, A. 1958. Toxicity of nitrate and nitrites of dairy cattle, J. Dairy Sci. 41:694-696.

PEARSON, R. W., ABRUÑA, F., and VICENTE-CHANDLER, J. 1962. Effect of lime and nitrogen applications on downward movement of calcium and magnesium in two humid tropical soils of Puerto Rico, Soil Sci. 93:77-82.

PETERSEN, R. S., WOODHOUSE, W. W., and LUCAS, H. L. 1956. The distribution of excreta by freely grazing cattle, and its effect on pasture fertility, II, Effect of returned excreta on the residual concentration of some fertilizer elements, Agron. J. 48:444-448.

VICENTE-CHANDLER, J., ABRUÑA, F., CARO-COSTAS, R., FIGARELLA, J., SILVA, S. and PEARSON, R. W. 1972. Intensive Grassland Management and Utilization in the Humid Tropics of Puerto Rico, Technical Bull. 226, Agr. Expt. Station, Mayaguez Campus, University of P.R., Río Piedras, P.R.

VICENTE-CHANDLER, J., CARO-COSTAS, R., PEARSON, R. W., ABRUÑA, F., FIGARELLA, J., and SILVA, S. 1964. The intensive management of tropical forages in Puerto Rico, Univ. of P.R., Agr. Exp. Sta. Bul. 187, p. 152.

VICENTE-CHANDLER, J., and FIGARELLA, J. 1962. The effect of five nitrogen sources on yield and composition of Napier grass, J. Agr. Univ. P.R. 56: 102-106.

VICENTE-CHANDLER, J., FIGARELLA, J., and SILVA, S. 1961. Effects of nitrogen fertilization and frequency of cutting on the yield and composition of Pangola grass in Puerto Rico, J., Agr. Univ. P.R. 45:37-45.

VICENTE-CHANDLER, J., and PEARSON, R. W. 1960. Nitrogen fertilization, of hot climate grasses, Soil Conserv. Mag. 25:269-272.

VICENTE-CHANDLER, J., PEARSON, R. W., ABRUÑA, F. and SILVA, S. 1962. Potassium fertilization of intensively managed tropical grasses under humid tropical conditions Agron. J. 54:450-453.

VICENTE-CHANDLER, J., and SILVA, S. 1960. The effect of nitrogen fertilization and grass species on soil physical condition in some tropical pastures, J. Agr. Univ. P.R. 44:77-86.

VICENTE-CHANDLER, J., SILVA, S., and FIGARELLA, J. 1959. The effect of nitrogen fertilization and frequency of cutting on the yield of: I, Napier grass, II, Guinea grass, and III Para grass, J. Agr. Univ. P.R. 43:215-248.

VICENTE-CHANDLER, J., SILVA, S. and FIGARELLA, J. 1959. The effect of nitrogen fertilization and frequency of cutting on the yield and composition of three tropical grasses, Agron. J. 51:202-206.

VICENTE-CHANDLER, J., SILVA, S., and FIGARELLA, J. 1962. Effect of frequency of application on response of Guinea grass to nitrogen fertilization, J. Agr. Univ. P.R. 46:342-349.

VICENTE-CHANDLER, J., SILVA, S., ABRUÑA, F., and RODRIGUEZ, J. 1972. The effect of two cutting heights, four harvest intervals and five nitrogen rates on yield and composition of Congo grass under humid tropical conditions, J. Agr. Univ. of P.R. 56:280-291.

VICENTE-CHANDLER, J., SILVA, S., RODRIGUEZ, J., and ABRUÑA, F. 1972. The effects of two heights and three intervals of grazing on the productivity of a heavily fertilized Pangola grass pasture, J. 9gr. Univ. of P.R. 56:110-114.

24 Management of Legume Pastures in a Tropical Rainforest Ecosystem of Peru

K. SANTHIRASEGARAM

I INTRODUCTION

The main characteristics of tropical rainforest ecosystems are low altitude with uniform high temperature and rainfall, supporting high evergreen forest with little or no ground vegetation on leached soils which are acidic and high in aluminium. Large areas of such ecosystems exist in Central and South America, South Asia, Central Africa and North Australia. Considerable literature has accumulated during the past twenty years on the development of tropical pastures, but very few deal with rainforest ecosystems, and even those are almost exclusively pure grass swards with some use of nitrogenous fertilizers. While a large number of grass species have been in use in this ecosystem for some time now, legume usage is relatively new and data is scarce indeed.

The use of legumes in pastures is to provide protein to the grazing animal and nitrogen to the associated grasses. The legume is expected to reduce or eliminate the need for protein supplementation to the animal and nitrogen fertilizer to the grass; thus reduce the cost of animal production.

Recent research has shown that the amount of nitrogen fixed by the legumes is linearly related to its dry matter yield (Jones, 1971) and the productivity of animals is also linearly related to the content of legume herbage in the pasture (Norman, 1970). Tropical legumes in general are slow growing compared to the grasses; their persistence and performance depend on their competitive relationship with the associates and relative palatability to the grazing animal. With these considerations in mind, the paper presents the experience the author had during the past three years at Pucallpa, Peru. Hutton (1970) has presented a comprehensive review of tropical pastures in general and Jones (1972) has dealt with the place of legumes in tropical pastures, in particular.

II THE ENVIRONMENT IN PUCALLPA

Pucallpa is at 8°S, 75°W, with a mean altitude of 270 m. The climax vegetation and the climatic conditions generally conform to that of a rainforest ecosystem. The soil is aluvial developed from sedimentary deposits of varying depth on an undulating topography. It has been described as Ultisols, which is acidic, high in aluminium content and capable of high phosphate adsorption, by Estrada (1971). The nutrient status of the virgin forest soil is not known, but areas which were under grass pasture

— 434 —

for four to five years, after the forest has been felled and burnt, were found to be deficient in nitrogen, phosphorus and sulphur (Santhirasegaram and Morales, 1971).

There are about 50,000 hectares of cleared land in the Pucallpa region. Forest is traditionally felled by hand, burns and *Hyperrhenia rufa* sown into the ash. The resulting pasture growth is good and usually supports 2 to 3 cows/ha, but within 4 or 5 years it declines, due to loss of fertility and poor management. The sown species is replaced by *Paspalum virgatum, P. conjugatum, Homeolepis aturensis* and *Axonopus compressus* and in extreme cases by *Pseudo elephantopus spicatus*. There is also considerable shrub invasion and soil compaction. In this state the carrying capacity is less than one cow per hectare. The cattle suffer protein and phosphorus deficiencies resulting in low calving and growth rates with calves seldom reaching 300 kg liveweight even after four years of age.

The FAO sponsored pasture research programme at IVITA, Pucallpa is exclusively aimed at improving these pastures to correct protein and phosphorus deficiencies at least cost. Preliminary economic considerations indicated that for general beef production from cow/calf operations the incorporation of legumes with supplemental use of phosphorus in what is called "Semi-intensive Pasture Systems" would be in harmony with the socio-economic conditions and level of technology practicable in the region for quite some time to come (Santhirasegaram and Aldunate, 1972).

The key to economic success of legume based pastures is the selection of legumes adapted to the environment and capable of persisting under grazing when nutrient deficiencies are corrected.

III SELECTION OF LEGUMES

The high acidity and aluminium content of the soil usually lead researchers to consider these conditions as abnormal and accept their correction as prerequisite for crop and forage growth. Santhirasegaram et al., (1972) consider these conditions as normal under tropical conditions and looked for legumes that would grow and persist without soil ammendment. They are of the opinion that it would truly be amazing if one could not find and acid, aluminium and manganese tolerant species for every other condition, among the wealth of tropical flora, with the aid of present day techniques of plant breeding and selection. Norris (1958 and 1967) studying the origin of legumes concluded that they are essentially a tropical group and the present members in the tropics would show very little improvement in growth due to addition of lime to increase pH. He further showed that the type of *Rhizobia* associated with them exude alkaline substances that need to be neutralized by soil acidity for their proper functioning. It has also been demonstrated that high soil pH would reduce nodulation of *Pueraria phaseoloides* (Loustalot and Telford, 1948). *Centrosema pubescens* and *Stylosanthes guyanensis* (Odu, Fayemi and Ogunwale, 1971). In Hawaii, *Desmodium intortum* in association with *Digitaria decumbens* did not respond to lime in soils of pH 4.8 (Young et al., 1964). Jones (1972) is of the opinion that the response of tropical legumes to lime reported from Puerto Rico may be attributed to reduced uptake of manganese and release of molybdenum, and in the case of the claim from Brazil, using dolomite, a response to magnesium, in soils deficient in that nutrient. Rios *et al.*, (1968) studying the effect of lime on acidity, aluminium and iron in some soils of Panama concluded that "the soils with high exchangeable acidity and aluminium (Latosols and Andosols) required excessive liming to bring the pH to values which are adequate in the temperate zone. This over saturation with Ca would more likely produce Mg, K and minor element deficiencies and other adverse conditions to plants".

Reviewing the problems of liming tropical soils, Martini (1968) concluded that "one should not expect the optimum pH values for tropical crops to be the same as for those of the temperate zone". It may be pointed out that tropical pasture legumes, fortunately, still retrain in them the genetic combinations that make them tolerant of tropical conditions. They sould be bred and selected for the conditions of the environment which must be accepted as normal. The successful exploitation of the humid tropics would depend not on the "mere extrapolation of the experiences from areas with other ecological settings but "through" the use of creative initiative condusive to the creation of rules and standards that may satisfy the demands of our own unique ecology" (Martini, 1968).

Agronomic studies at Pucallpa has shown that *P. phaseoloides*, *C. pubescens* and *S. guyanensis* would grow satisfactorily without the applicatio of lime. A small quantity of phosphorus appear to be optimal for their establishment and early growth. Table 1 gives the dry matter yield of these three legumes to levels of superphosphate and lime application in pot experiments.

IV PHOSPHATE NUTRITION OF PLANTS AND ANIMALS

The soil and hence plant content of phosphorus is low and inadequate for proper growth and reproduction of cattle. The soil is also known to be capable of high phosphate adsorption. Early experiments at Pucallpa used rather high quantities of phosphate fertilizers (Motooka, 1970). Recent studies using species adapted to the enviornment demonstrated that rather small quantities of phosphate (10 kg/ha) would be optimal for establishment and early growth (Santhirasegaram *et al.*, 1972 and Table 1).

These agronomic data are being tested under grazing conditions. It will be seen later that application of 500 kg/ha of single phosphate to *P. phaseoloides* / *H. rufa* pasture actually reduced the growth rate of Nellore type heifers, compared to the control treatment, and that an application of 100 kg/ha super phosphate was only effective for about six months.

When 100 kg/ha superphosphate was applied to *S. guyanensis* / *H. rufa* / *P. conjugatum* pasture, the phosphorus content of the herbage eight weeks after fertilization was not increased (P content of unfertilized grass pasture and fertilized grass/legume pasture were 0.11 and 0.12% P respectively), but dry matter yield was nearly 2.5 times higher in the fertilized plot.

These results may indicate that species adapted to this environment of inherently low phosphate status would have acceptable growth rates with low phosphate contents. This phosphate content however is insufficient for animal performance. It would then appear that satisfactory plant growth could be maintained with frequent small applications of phosphatic fertilizers and animal growth could be further improved by phosphate supplementation. This strategy is both efficient and economical.

Table 1.—Dry matter production of three legumes as affected by super-phosphate and lime applications in pot conditions. (Pineda and Santhirasegaram 1973a, Casas 1974).

Simple superphosphate	Lime (tons/ha)			Means
	0	1	5	
kg/ha		g/pot		
PUERARIA PHASEOLOIDES:				
0	8.00	11.50	10.50	10.10
100	11.00	16.00	17.00	14.67
500	17.50	23.00	15.50	18.67
Mean	12.30	16.83	14.67	—
CENTROSEMA PUBESCENS:				
0	0.58	1.55	1.85	1.32
100	3.30	3.62	2.62	3.18
500	4.88	6.65	3.96	5.16
Mean	2.92	3.94	2.81	—
STYLOSANTHES GUYANENSIS:				
0	0.30	0.69	1.33	0.78
100	3.33	2.66	2.84	2.94
500	4.36	5.08	1.77	3.73
Mean	2.66	2.81	1.99	—

Olsen and Moe (1971) has shown that the phosphate requirement of many tropical legumes would be much lower than that of their temperate counterparts and that they are capable of extracting phosphorus from soil sources which are usually unavailable to many plant species. These combined characteristics are considered to be extremely important by Jones (1972) for the development of the tropics, where phosphate supplies may be limited or costly.

V LEGUME ESTABLISHMENT INTO GRASS SWARDS

Soil physical conditions, fertility, other plant species and seeding rates are usually important factors in establishing legumes into existing grass swards. Our practice has been to graze heavily and the lightly harrow the area and broadcast sow seed along with phosphatic fertilizer. In other attempts seeds were sown into the sward without any soil preparation and results have been very unsatisfactory, particularly when dry weather is experienced soon after seedlings emmerge.

Table 2 gives number of *Stylosanthes guyanensis seedlings*, 4 and 24 weeks after sowing under various treatments into a sward of *Hyperrhenia rufa*. Initially seedling number was linearly related to seeding rate, later however there appear to be a stabilization of number of plants per unit area. Soil preparation had beneficial effect on legume establishment specially at the lower seeding rate. Silva (1974) has further shown that on compacted soil surfaces seed germination is unaffected, but radicle preparation is; unless debris such as other plant material is available to serve as anchorage. Such poorly anchored seedlings fail to establish if the soil is allowed to dry.

Table 2.—Number of seedlings/m^2 of *S. guyanensis*, 4 and 24 weeks after sowing into a sward of *H. rufa* under different treatments, (Silva, 1974).

| | | Seed rate (Kg/Ha) | | | | | | | |
| | | 2 | | 4 | | 6 | | Mean | |
		4 wk	24 wk	4 wk	24 wk	4 wk	24 wk	4 wk	24 wk
	P_0	8.1	4.3	13.5	5.8	21.7	7.4	14.4	5.5
C_0	P+	4.3	4.6	7.2	7.0	19.0	9.0	10.1	6.9
	P_0	9.2	8.3	16.2	8.3	30.2	7.9	18.5	8.1
C+	P+	8.9	8.5	15.4	10.4	19.5	11.8	14.6	10.2
Mean		7.6	6.4	13.1	7.8	22.6	9.4	—	—

C_0 = No cultivation,   C+ = Harrowing

P_0 = No phosphorus,   P+ = 200 Kg/Ha super phosphate

Tables 3 and 4 give the dry matter yield of legume and grass components after 24 weeks of growth. Legume dry matter yield is related to seeding rate. The yield of the grass was not affected by legume or treatments.

It would appear that where soil could be prepared, a seed rate of 2 kg/ha would be sufficient in the case of *S. guyanensis;* higher rates need to be considered where such preparation of compacted clayey surfaces is not possible.

Table 3.—Mean dry matter yield (g/m²) of *S. guyanensis,* 24 weeks after sowing into a sward of *H. rufa* under different treatments (Silva, 1974).

| | | Seed rate (Kg/Ha) | | | |
		2	4	6	Lignin
C_0	P_0	51.50	64.38	112.12	76.00
	$P+$	61.12	124.12	142.50	109.24
$C+$	P_0	203.00	204.12	292.50	233.21
	$P+$	224.25	251.27	289.25	254.94
Mean		135.00	161.00	209.10	—

Table 4.—Mean dry matter yield (g/m²) of *H. rufa,* 24 weeks after sowing of legume under different treatments (Silva, 1974).

| | | Seed rate of legume, (Kg/Ha) | | | |
		2	4	6	Lignin
C_0	P_0	94.50	96.75	93.12	94.74
	$P+$	129.00	107.62	117.00	117.87
$C+$	P_0	82.88	118.50	83.00	94.79
	$P+$	138.12	134.75	128.00	133.62
Mean		111.00	114.40	105.28	—

VI COMPATIBILITY AND BOTANICAL COMPOSITION

The persistence and contribution of the legumes to the feed of the grazing animal become the next important factors. Here, the competitive relationship and relative palatability to the grazing animals of the associates would largely determine these factors. Santhirasegaram *et al.*, (1972) concluded from observations of a large number of legume/grass associations that the promising legumes at Pucallpa would form acceptable swards with errect growing grasses. Reyes (1974) studied the competitive relationships between these three promising legumes and three grasses. His data suggest that with the errect growing grasses, *H. rufa* and *Paspalum pliactulum,* the legumes were not suppressed to any appreciably extent; with the diffuse type of growth of *Brachiaria decumbens* there was again no effect at the early stages, later however the yield of the legumes began to decline, (Figures 1, 2 and 3). With all grasses the gradient of the lime was greatest for *P. phaseoloides,* followed by *C. pubescens,* with *S. guyanensis* recording the lowest. The gradient exhibited by each of the legumes with the three grasses was highest in the case of *H. rufa,* followed by *P. plicatulum* and lowest with *B. decumbens.* The general conclusion to be drawn from this study is that the competitive potential of the species decrease in the following order:

Grasses: *B. decumbens* > *P. plicatulum* > *H. rufa*
Legumes: *P. phaseoloides* > *C. pubescens* > *S. guyanensis*

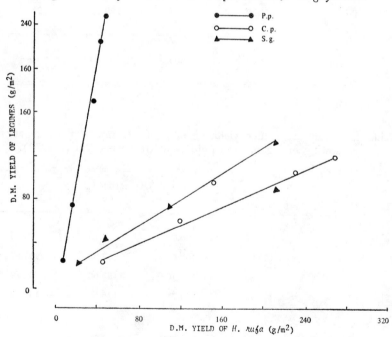

Figure 1.   Relationship between three legumes and *Hyparrhenia rufa* in dry matter yield (g/m²) in association with time (Reyes, 1974).

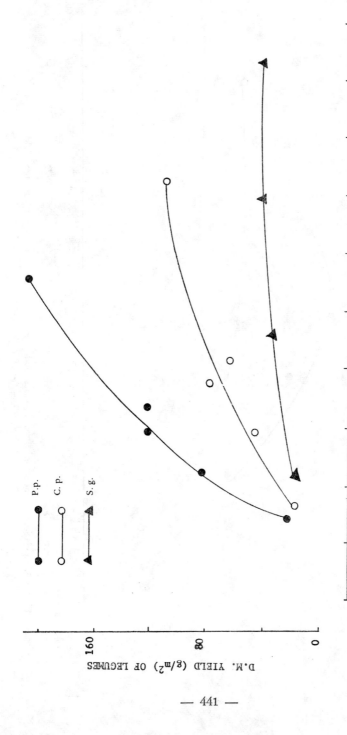

Figure 2. Relationship between three legumes and *Paspalum plicatulum* in dry matter yield (g/m²) in association with time. (Reyes, 1974).

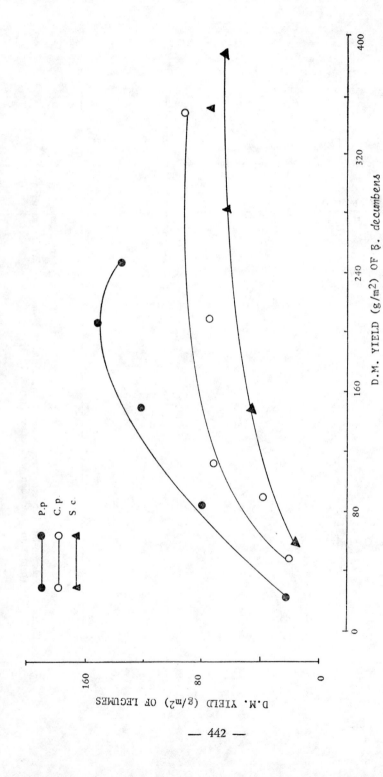

Figure 3. Relationship between three legumes and *Brachiaria decumbens* in dry matter yield (g/m²) in association with time. (Reyes, 1974).

Attempts to establish the shading effect of one associate on the other in relation to composition for light through measurements of height and spread of the species have not been satisfactory due to the diverse growth habits of the species and the bolting of grass tillers to flower.

Pinedo and Santhirasegaram (1973 b and c) examined the percent available herbage of these three legumes in association with different grasses over a range of grazing frequencies and intensities. (Figures 4, 5 and 6). In general *P. phaseoloides* and *C. pubescens* contributed around 25% and *S. guyanensis* about 33% of the available dry matter, once the pastures have attained equilibrium.

Tropical legumes are particularly sensitive to severe defoliation. Twining or scrambling legumes are seriously affected (Jones, 1971 and Whiteman, 1969). Jones (1972) suggests that the behaviour of tropical legumes to defoliation is almost opposite to that of their temperate counterparts (white clover and alfalfa) and goes on to state that "for workers trained in temperate areas it may be difficult to accept this concept. It may also be difficult to appreciate that the close rotational grazing, so effective in maintaining quality and a good legume component in white clover based pastures, may be disastrous on a tropical legume/grass pasture".

Height of cutting and residual leaf area have been found to be important factors in subsequent regrowth of tropical legumes. These were examined by Reyes and Santhirasegaram (1974), where the three promising legumes were cut at five weeks interval either at 5 or 15 cm. height above soil surface and at each height the residual leaves after cutting were either allowed to remain or were removed. Table 5 gives the mean dry matter produced following three successive cuttings. In general the greater the stubble height the better the regrowth. At both stubble heights, presence of residual leaves promoted better regrowth. It is not intended to enter into the controversy over the contribution of reserve photosynthesate and photosynthetic surface to regrowth.

Both *C. pubescens* and *S. guyanensis* are readily eaten by all breeds of cattle, but some unacceptability of *P. phaseoloides* has been noted with pure Nellore types at IVITA, Pucallpa and elsewhere. Associations of this legume with *H. rufa* and *Panicum maximum* were soon dominated by it and within 12 months there were no grass species present, whether the paddocks were rotationaly or continuously grazed, and the animals lost weight inspite of abundance of available legume forage. Whether this is due to the genetic make-up of the animals or to soil and climatic factors is not known.

VII   ANIMAL PRODUCTIVITY LEGUME-GRASS PASTURES

The inclusion of legumes into grass pastures with adequate fertilization of phosphate should increase the quantity and improve the quality of feed avilable to cattle. This should result in higher number of animals supported by unit are a of pasture with improved performance of each animal resulting in 5 to 10 fold increase in animal production (Jones, 1972). Table 6 summarises liveweight gains recorded in legume/grass pastures in some humid tropical areas of the world.

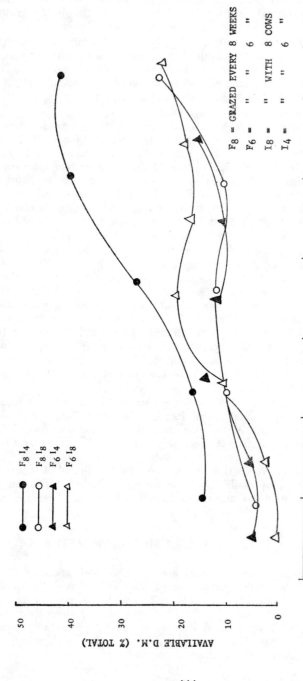

Figure 4. Available dry matter (% total) of *Pueraria phaseoloides* at successive grazings (moving averages in pairs). (Pinedo and Santhirasegaram, 1973 b).

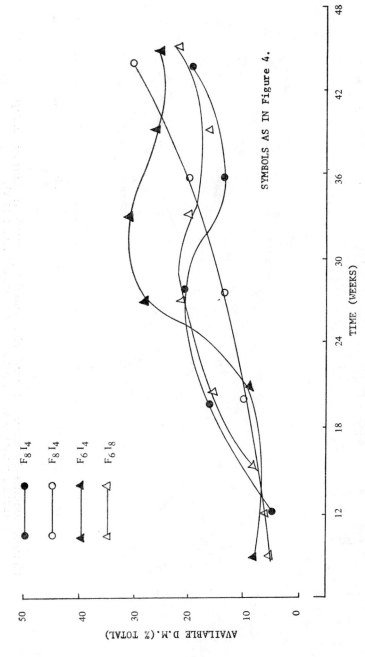

Figure 5. Available dry mater (% total) of *Centrocema pubescens* at successive grazing (moving averages in pairs) (Pinedo and Santhirasegaram, 1973 b).

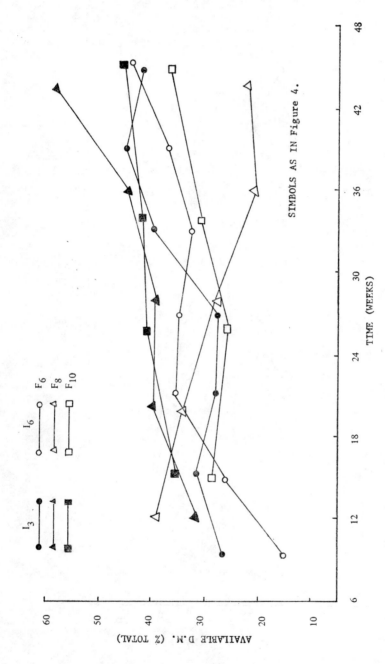

Figure 6. Available dry matter (% total) of *Stylosanthes guyanensis* at successive grazings (moving average in pairs). (Pinero and Santhirasegaram, 1973 c).

Table 5.—Mean dry matter yield (g/plant) of *P. phaseoloides, C. pubescens* and *S. guyanensis* from three successive cuts at two heights and in presence or absence of residual leaves, (Reyes and Santhirasegaram, 1974).

		P. phaseoloides	C. pubescens	S. guyanensis	Mean
H_5	L—	1.23	1.15	2.62	1.66
	L+	2.03	1.31	3.28	2.21
H_{15}	L—	2.55	0.94	2.41	1.97
	L+	3.41	1.52	4.24	3.06

H = height and L = leaves

Table 6.—Annual liveweight gain (kg/ha) from tropical grass/legume pastures in different countries.

Pasture	Country	Weight gain	Sources
P. phaseoloides/ Melinis minutiflora	Puerto Rico	500	Vicente Chandler *et al.,* 1964
C. Pubescens/Cynodon plectostachyus	Nigeria	300	McIlroy, 1972
Desmodium intortum/ Digitaria decumbens	Hawaii	896	Younge and Plucknett, 1965
C. pubescens/ S. guyanensis/H. rufa	Uganda	526	Stobbs, 1965

Echeverría and Santhirasegaram (1974) grazed yearling Nellore heifers on *P. phaseoloides/H. rufa* pastures at a stocking rate of 2 beasts/ha, with different rate of superphosphate application to the soil and mineral lick supplementation (Table 7). Sowing legume alone had very little effect on liveweight gain. Application of 100 kg/ha of superphosphate increased weight gains during the first six months, but was without effect during the second half of the year. Application of 500 kg/ha of superphosphate caused a significant reduction in weight gain compared to no phosphate application during the first six months. Response to phosphate lick was very good at all times; the combination of phosphate lick and application of 100 kg/ha of superphosphate recorded a further 10% increase in weight gain. Nearly all treatments were under stocked with abundant feed available at all times. An interesting observation was that the animals hardly consumed the legume.

Table 7.—Liveweight gain (Kg/Head) of Nellore heifers grazing pastures of *P. phaseoloides/H. rufa* mixtures with different rates of super phosphate application and mineral supplementation, at a stocking rate of 2 beasts/Ha. (Echeverría and Santhirasegaram, 1974).

Management	First 6 moths	Second 6 moths
H. rufa only	37.5	18.0
H. rufa + *P. phaseoloides*	39.9	20.2
Grass + Legume + 100 kg/ha super phosphate	57.7	21.8
Grass + Legume + 500 kg/ha super phosphate	24.8	35.3
Grass + Legume + mineral supplement	84.3	76.1
Grass + Legume + 100 kg/ha super phosphate + Mineral supplement	93.2	83.0

In a comparison of the carrying capacity of *H. rufa* with *H. rufa/S. guyanensis* pasture fertilized with 100 kg/ha superphosphate, Riesco and Santhirasegaram (1974) recorded maximum weight gain from yearling Nellore bull calves during the first six months of grazing at stocking rates of 1.8 and 3.0 beasts/Ha in the grass only and grass/legume pastures, respectively (Table 9), during the second half of the year however, inspite of abundant feed, growth was poor in all treatments, due, probably to inadequate phosphate nutrition.

Table 8.—Total number of heifers (total of two replicates, each with 4 beasts) diagnosed for pregnancy after six weeks of joining with bulls at the end of one years grazing in the experiment of Echeverría and Santhirasegaram (1974) on Table 7.

Management	Positive	Negative
Grass + Legume	2	6
Grass + Legume + 100 Kg/Ha super phosphate	3	5
Grass + Legume + 500 Kg/Ha super phosphate	1	7
Grass + Legume + Mineral supplement	7	1
Grass + Legume + 100 Kg/Ha super phosphate + Mineral supplement	7	1

Table 9.—Liveweight gain (kg/ha) of Nellore bull calves grazing *H. rufa* and *H. rufa/S. guyanensis* pastures at different stocking rates (Riesco and Santhirasegaram, 1974).

Treatment	First 6 mths.	Second 6 mths.
H. RUFA		
1.2 beasts/Ha	41.5	3.0
1.5	83.7	2.1
1.8	116.8	16.2
2.1	77.5	16.3
H. RUFA/S GUYANENSIS		
2.1 beasts/Ha	126.0	29.1
2.4	139.4	41.9
2.7	141.8	7.7
3.0	179.7	24.6

Combining the data from these two experiments Santhirasegaram (1974a) estimated that legume/grass pastures with adequate phosphate application to the soil and supplementation to the animal would carry 3 yearling beasts/Ha with annual liveweight gain of 640 Kg.

In another experiment Riesco and Santhirasegaram (1974) recorded 50 and 100% pregnency of cows grazing grass only and grass/legume pastures, respectively, in Pucallpa. Both groups had access to phosphate licks *ad libitum* and the legume based pasture received 100 kg/ha super phosphate.

Considering these increased carrying capacity, growth rate and fertility, Santhirasegaram (1974 b) estimates that legume based pastures would in general double the carrying capacity, double the calving rate, quadruple the growth rate of bull calves and reduce by half their finishing age.

VIII DISCUSSION

It is becoming increasingly evident that tropical soils and plants differ in some fundamental features from their temperate counterparts. The observations of Martini (1968) and Santhirasegaram *et al.*, (1972) on soil acidity and aluminium content of tropical soils and the capacity of tropical pasture species not only to tolerate but in fact to thrive under these conditions coupled with the assertions of Norris (1958 and 1967) on the origin of legumes and the need for acid soils for the proper functioning of their associated *Rhizobia,* that of Olsen and Moe (1971) on phosphate requirement and absorption capacity of tropical legumes and that of Jones (1972) on the behaviour of these legumes under defoliation, can no longer be dismissed as isolated instances peculiar to particular ecological niches. For the proper development of the humid tropics the salient features of the ecosystem have to be identified and accepted as normal conditions and new concepts and standards should be developed as matters of urgency. If we are not capable of this approach, then it would be far better to leave the rainforest as it is than destroy it and reap the condenation of posterity.

The legume based pasture is the back bone of animal industry in temperate areas. Here in the tropics the potential of similar pastures, even at the present primitive state compares very well indeed. The future potential when the soil, plant and animal characteristics are understood, selected, improved and managed may "bloody well" surpass even the wildest dreams of the late Dr. J. Griffth Davies, who alone amidst great opposition visually the potential of legumes in tropical pastures at the now well known CSIRO Division of Tropical Pastures (Agronomy) in Australia.

IX ACKNOWLEDGEMENTS

The author wishes to thank Ings. O. Casas, C. Reyes and G. Silva for permitting use of their thesis data in advance.

X SUMMARY

The soils in the tropical rainforest ecosystem are generally acidic with high aluminium content and many tropical legumes and grasses would grow satisfactorily under these conditions. Preliminary data indicate that the potential of these pastures compares favorably with those in other regions of the tropics and elsewhere. The success of animal industry in the ecosystem would depend on the development of new concepts and standards for soil and plant management.

XI REFERENCES

CASAS, O. 1974. Reponse of some Tropical Legumes and Grasses to lime and Super phosphate application. Thesis, National Agrarian University, La Molina. (In preparation).

ECHEVARRIA, M., and SANTHIRASEGARAM, K. 1974. Liveweight gain and Fertility of Nellore type heifers grazing *Pueraria phaseoloides/Hyparrhenia rufa* pastures with phosphate fertilization and direct supplementation. (In preparation).

ESTRADA, J. 1971. Mineralogical and chemical properties of Peruvian acid tropical soils, Ph.D. Thesis, Uni. Calif. Riverside 185 p.

HUTTON, E. M. 1970. Tropical Pastures, Advances in Agronomy, 22:1-73.

JONES, R. J. 1972. The place of legumes in tropical pastures, Food and Fertiliser Technology Center, Taiwan, Tech. Bull. 9:1-69.

JONES, R. J. 1971. Tropical legumes - their growth and response to management variables in a sub-tropical environment, Ph.D. Thesis, University of New England, Armidale, Australia.

LOUSTLOT, A. J., and TELFORD, E. A. 1948. Physiological experiments with tropical kudzu, Jour. Amer. Soc. Agron., 40:503-11.

MARTINI, J. A. 1968. Algunas notas sobre el problema del encalado en los suelos del trópico, Turrialba, 18:249-56.

McILROY, R. J. 1962. Grassland improvement and utilization in Nigeria, Outlock Agric, 4:174-179.

MOTOOKA, P. S. 1970. Informe de algunos experimentos realizados en Pucallpa. Miss. Agric. Uni. Carolina Norte. 9 p.

NORMAN, M. J. T. 1970. Relationships between liveweight gain of grazing beef steers and availability of townsville lucerne, Proc. XI Internat. Grassl. Cong., Aust., 829-32.

NORRIS, D. O. 1958. Lime in relation to nodulation of tropical legumes, *In.* Nutrition of the legumes, E. G. Hallsworth, ed. 164-82. Butterworths, London.

NORRIS, D. O. 1967. The intelligent use of inoculants and lime pelleting for tropical legumes, Tropical Grasslands, 1:107-21.

ODU, C. T. I., FAYEMI, A. A., and OGUNWALE, J. A. 1971. Effecct of pH on the growth, nodulation and nitrogen fixation of *Centrosema pubescens* and *Stylosanthes gracilis*, Jour. Sci. Food Agric., 22:57-59.

OLSEN, F. J., and MOE, P. G. 1971. The effect of phosphate and lime on the establishment, productivity, nodulation and persistence of *Desmodium intortum, Medicago sativa* and *Stylosanthes gracilis,* East African Agric. Fores. Jour., 37:29-37.

PINEDO, L., and SANTHIRASEGARAM, K. 1973a. Respuesta de algunas especies de pastos tropicales a la aplicación de fósforo y cal., Proc. IV Reunión Asoc. Latinoamer. Prod. Anim. p. 31.

PINEDO, L., and SANTHIRASEGARAM, K. 1973b. Cambios en el contenido de dos leguminosas postradas asociadas con un pasto natural bajo pastoreo., Proc. IV Reunión Asoc. Latinoamer. Prod. Anim., p. 32.

PINEDO, L., and SANTHIRASEGARAM, K. 1973c. Cambio en la composición botánica de una mezcla de *Hyparrhenia rufa, Paspalum conjugatum* y *Stylosanthes guyanensis* bajo pastoreo; Proc. IV Reunión Asoc. Latinoamer. Prod. Anim. p. 33.

REYES, C. 1974. Compatibility between some tropical legumes and grasses, Thesis, Universidad de la Amazonía Peruana, Iquitos. (In preparation).

REYES, C., and SANTHIRASEGARAM, K. 1974. The effect of cutting height and residual leaves on the regrowth of some tropical legumes. (In preparation).

RIESCO, A., and SANTHIRASEGARAM, K. 1974 . The effect of legumes and phosphate on the growth rate and fertility of beat cattle in Pucallpa, Peru. (In preparation).

RIOS, V., MARTINI, J. A., and TEJEIRA, R. 1968. Efecto del encalado sobre la acidez y el contenido de aluminio e hierro extraíble en nueve suelos de Panamá, Turrialba, 18:139-46.

SANTHIRASEGARAM, K. 1974a. Potentialities of sown pastures in the Amazon region of Peru, Proc. XII Internat. Grassl. Cong. Moscow. (In preparation).

SANTHIRASEGARAM, K. 1974b. Establishment and management of improved tropical grass/legume pastures, Proc. Semi. Potential for increased beef production in Tropical America, CIAT, Cali.

SANTHIRASEGARAM, K., and ALDUNATE, P. 1972. The possible economic consequences of beef production from three pasture systems in Pucallpa., Proc. II Reunión Especialistas Investigadores Pastos Forrage Perú, Arequipa.

SANTHIRASEGARAM, K., and MORALES, V. 1971. Major nutrient status of the red soil at Pucallpa, Proc. I Cong. Inves. Agropec. Peru. Lima.

SANTHIRASEGARAM, K., MORALES, V., PINEDO, L., and DIEZ, J. 1972. Interim Report on Pasture Development in the Pucallpa Region, 1-134, FAO-IVITA, Lima.

SILVA, G. 1974. Seed rate, soil preparation and phosphate fertilization on the establishment of *Stylosanthes guyanensis* into a sward of *Hyparrhenia rufa.* Thesis, National Agrarian University, La Molina.

STOBBS, T. H. 1965. Beef production from Uganda Pastures containing *Stylosanthes gracilis* and *Centrocema pubescens*, Proc. IX Internat. Grassl. Cong., II, 934-42.

VICENTE CHANDLER, J., CARO-COSTAS, R., PEARSON, R. W., ABRUÑA, F., FIGARELLA, J., and SILVA, S. 1964. The intensive management of tropical pastures in Puerto Rico, Uni. P. R., Agric. Expt. Sta. P. R., Bull. 187.

WHITEMAN, P. C. 1969. The effects of close grazing and cutting on the yield, persistence and nitrogen content of four tropical legumes with Rhodes grass at Samford, Southeastern Queensland. Aust. Jour. Exp. Agric. Anim. Husb., 9:287-94.

YOUNGE, O. R., and PLUCKNETT, D. L. 1965. Beef production with heavy phosphorus fertilization in infertile wet lands of Hawaii, Proc. IX Internat. Grass. Cong., II, 959-63.

YOUNGE, O. R., and ROTAR, P. P. 1964. Culture and yield performance of *Desmodium intortum* and *D. canum* in Hawaii, Hawaii Agric. Exp. Sta. Tech. Bull., 59:1-28.

SECTION VI

SOIL FERTILITY EVALUATIONS

25 The Soil Fertility Evaluation Program in Guatemala

J. ANIBAL PALENCIA O., JAMES L. WALKER, LUIS ESTRADA L.

I INTRODUCTION

In Guatemala, the constantly increasing demand for technical information concerning fertilization programs, on a regional as well as at the individual farm level, is the best evidence that soil fertility problems are not only common to all crops but are also of the first order of magnitude in importance among other factors affecting yield in each one of them. This demand, measured in terms of the quantities of soil samples sent to the government soils laboratory accompanied by requests from farmers for recommendations regarding the use of fertilizers and other soil amendments, has increased more than 1180 percent in the last eight years.

The benefits from the rational use of fertilizers and other soil amendments are becoming increasingly recognized but the cost of these products has been rising substantially. Because of this, it is believed that the demand for increased technical assistance on fertilizer inputs will continue to expand as farmers, in attempting to minimize their investment risks, act with increasing caution. As a result, more people will be using this technical assistance and they will surely place more demands on its quality.

This situation, requiring rapid generation of increasing amounts of reliable information about fertilizer use, has resulted in greater interest in improved systems not only for solving soil fertility problems but also for rapidly extending that knowledge throughout the agricultural sector.

This interest has been demonstrated by the efforts made in recent years to implement and develop a soil fertility program (titled PLANT NUTRITION) whose description and most pertainent findings follow.

II PROGRAM DESCRIPTION

The Plant Nutrition Program furnishes scientific technical support to the Crop Production Program of the Agricultural Science and Technology Institute (ICTA) in Guatemala. Therefore, it develops activities directed toward evaluating and improving soil fertility in the principal agricultural areas of the country. Emphasis is placed on those areas which receive attention through the National Development Plan from the Public Agricultural Sector.

Because soil fertility evaluation and improvement is based upon the study of soil-plant relationships, the plant nutrition program focuses its attention on analyses of the correlation between the soil laboratry results and those from greenhouse studies and field trials. In this way, inductive interpretation of the correlation analyses allows decisions concerning the adoption of the best laboratory analytical methods, the definition of critical levels for each plant nutrient and the determination of the optimum levels of application of the most important nutrients in order, finally, to determine the most economical fertilizer requirements for each crop based upon the soil fertility level and the yield goal estimate.

It has been found that this system offers considerable advantages, in arriving with the best probabilities of success as solutions to the soil fertility problems faced by any farmer because, on one hand, the laboratory analytical methodology in addition to being reliable is extremely rapid and inexpensive and, on the other hand, the need for field work is considerably reduced in terms of the number of field trials required, which are inherently costly.

This philosophy has been used in developing the ICTA Plant Nutrition Program activities to attain the following general goals:

a. Obtain the basic information needed for establishing the best recommendations concerning the rational use of fertilizers and other soil amendments on the principal crops included in the National Development Plan (corn, beans, upland rice, wheat, sorghum, and vegetables);

b. Incorporate this important component in the package of technology which low and medium income farmers should use to improve crop productivity; and

c. Promote the use of this technological resource as a basis element in the process of agricultural development.

III PROGRAM ACCOMPLISHMENTS

Installation and Operation of Multiple Analyses Equipment

The idea of using multiple soil analysis laboratory equipment was adopted by the Program in 1966 (5, 11). Since then the Program Laboratory has been using the multiple analysis equipment designed by the International Soil Fertility Evaluation and Improvement Program (ISFEI) described by Perur *et al.*, (9). The use of this equipment has allowed attaining an analytical capacity of 400 samples daily since 1972 when an atomic absorption apparatus (Perkin Elmer 103) was added.

This multiple analysis equipment, in addition to allowing the use of control samples, has clearly met the farmers demands for service analyses which have ungergone substantial annual increases during the past eight years.

Correlation of Analytical Methods

The Cate and Nelson (1) correlation system has been used in evaluating methods for extractable soil phosphorus and potassium.

Based upon the use of this system, the Nelson, Mehlich and Winters method (0.05N HCl + 0.025N H_2SO_4, soil: solution = 1:5) (7), was adopted after obtaining acceptable correlation between the results of analyses of available soil P and K and the percent yield obtained through potted plant trials utilizing sunflower *(Helianthus annus)* as the indicator plant (2, 3).

This correlation study also allowed setting the critical soil analyses levels at 19 ppm P and 140 ppm K, which for phosphorus coincides with the level found in El Salvador (4) and in North Carolina (7).

Recent studies, however, suggest the need to revise these critical levels because they are quite different from thos obtained in correlation studies utilizing field trials.

For example, as can be observed in Figure 1, which is based on the data given in Table 1, the correlation obtained for the Nelson *e tal.,* (7) an dthe modified Olsen (6) methods results in phosphorus critical levels of 7.3 and 6.2 ppm, respectively.

For potassium, a critical level of 60 ppm K is obtained with the Nelson *et al.,* (7) method (Figure 2).

Determination of Appropriate Fertilization Levels

The incorporation of auxiliary field technicians was obtained through a cooperative agreement with the Peace Corps. This permitted a new field research campaign to be launched in 1972. In this new activity, a series of trials were installed in different parts of the country. The interests of both the Program and the farmer cooperator were reflected in the sites chosen.

The objectives of these trials, through which the response of corn, wheat, upland rice, beans, sorghum, and potatoes to various levels of applied nitrogen, phosphorus and potassium were evaluated, were as follows (8):

a. Define the optimum N, P_2O_5 and K_2O needs for the selected crops, determining economic application levels for each nutrient by means of yield functions;

b. Correlate soil analysis results with relative yields obtained at the field level, and;

c. Establish critical soil analysis levels for P and K in order to differentiate between soils with a high or low probability of response to these nutrients.

The response of these crops to N, P and K fertilization was evaluated through the use of a factorial arrangement comparising 12 partial combinations (5x5x4 and 5x4x5) in a completely randomized block design with three replications (Table 2).

The results, summarized in Table 3, were interpreted using the "Linear-Plateau Response" model developed by Waugh, Cate and Nelson which is based on Liebig's Law of the Minimum (12).

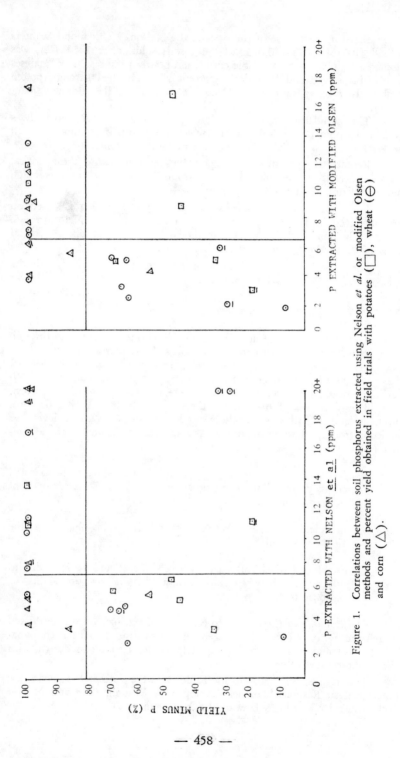

Figure 1. Correlations between soil phosphorus extracted using Nelson *et al.* or modified Olsen methods and percent yield obtained in field trials with potatoes (□), wheat (⊖) and corn (△).

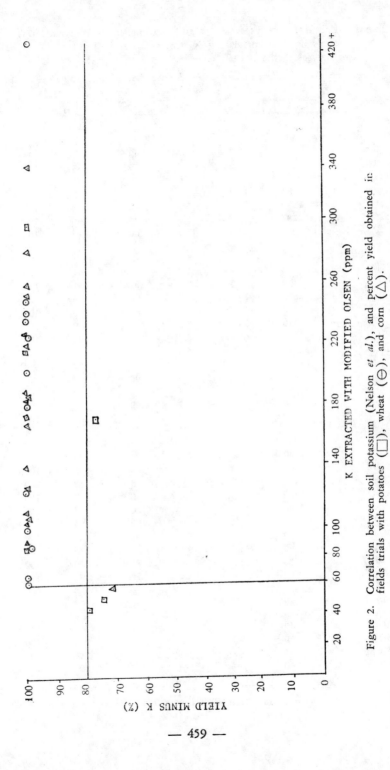

Figure 2. Correlation between soil potassium (Nelson *et al.*), and percent yield obtained in: fields trials with potatoes (□), wheat (⊖), and corn (△).

YIELD MINUS K (%)

K EXTRACTED WITH MODIFIED OLSEN (ppm)

Table 1.—P and K analyses results and percent yields obtained in field trials used in correlating Nelson *et al.* and Modified Olsen soil analyses methods (12, 16).

Trial	Altitude meters above sea level	ppm P		%Y (—P)	ppm K	(—K) %Y
		Nelson	Olsen		Nelson	
P O T A T O						
AHP	3180	7.2	16.7	48.5	50	73.4
ISMP	2850	11.0	3.0	19.3	83	100
CPQ	2350	3.5	5.0	30.3	43	79.2
OQP	2380	10.4	10.1	100	168	75.8
USP	2350	6.0	5.3	68.6	170	100
TSMP	2287	5.4	8.8	45.2	296	100
CMP	1760	13.3	11.5	100	214	100
W H E A T						
PHT	3150	3.1	1.9	7.9	61	100
ISMT	2850	22.6	2.0	27.8	121	100
ISMT	2850	17.0	3.6	100	83	100
SFTT	2610	4.7	5.2	69.3	240	100
TSMT	2570	4.7	3.2	67.3	439	100
TTT	2480	5.7	9.0	100	96	100
FSMT	2440	35.8	6.0	31.6	63	100
OQT	2430	2.4	2.4	64.4	178	100
OQT	2400	10.0	13.0	100	224	100
OQT	2380	11.3	6.8	100	248	100
TCT	2260	7.6	6.9	100	234	100
TCT	2260	5.2	5.2	64.8	207	100
C O R N						
TSMM	2700	7.9	6.3	100	186	100
TSMM	2700	19.2	9.2	100	165	100
CQM	2450	3.7	3.9	100	337	100
OQM	2400	4.8	8.4	100	182	100
OQM	2390	10.8	11.1	100	137	100
SMM	2300	46.1	17.0	100	185	100
SMM	2290	34.1	7.6	100	124	100
TCM	2260	5.6	9.3	100	226	100
TCM	2260	3.5	5.4	85.4	100	100
MAM	1760	5.6	4.4	56.2	87	100
SCM	40	—	—	—	258	100
LMAM	40	—	—	—	108	100
LMAM	40	—	—	—	103	100
LMBM	40	—	—	—	57	70.5
LMBM	20	—	—	—	252	100
LMCM	45	—	—	—	214	100
LMCM	40	—	—	—	280	100

———— = Trials located in are covered by ash from the 1902 eruption of Santa María Volcano.

Table 2.—Treatments Selected from Plant Nutrient Response Field Trials in Guatemala, 1972. Treatment Levels Expressed in Kg/Ha.

Treatment	Corn, Sorghum and Sesame	Wheat, Beans, Upland Rice	Potatoes
$N_1 P_4 K_4$	0—180—180	0— 90—90	0—180—180
$N_2 P_4 K_4$	60—180—180	30— 90—90	60—180—180
$N_3 P_4 K_4$	120—180—180	60— 90—90	120—180—180
$N_4 P_4 K_4$	180—180—180	90— 90—90	180—180—180
$N_5 P_4 K_4$	240—180—180	120— 90—90	240—180—180
$N_4 P_1 K_4$	180— 0—180	90— 0—90	180— 0—180
$N_4 P_2 K_4$	180— 60—180	90— 30—90	180— 60—180
$N_4 P_3 K_4$	180—120—180	90— 60—90	180—120—180
$N_4 P_5 K_4$	180—240—180	90—120—90	
$N_4 P_4 K_1$	180—180— 0	90— 90— 0	180—180— 0
$N_4 P_4 K_2$	180—180— 60	90— 90—30	180—180— 60
$N_4 P_4 K_3$	180—180—120	90— 90—60	180—180—120
$N_4 P_4 K_5$			180—180—240

Since this model postulates a linear response to additions of the principal element limiting plan growth, ceasing completely when some other factor becomes limiting and resuming its linearity when the other limiting factor is removed, the data from each trial were evaluated to determine the regression line in the "response zone" and the line of average maximum yield (yield plateau) in the "non-responding zone".

In each trial, the yield plateau was determined by calculating the average of all the yields except zero nutrient treatments and those treatments significantly different when a l.s.d. of 0.01 p. was applied. The regression line $Y = a + bx$ was calculated using the following equations for a and b:

$$a = \frac{(\Sigma X^2)\ (\Sigma Y) - (\Sigma X)\ (\Sigma XY)}{(N)\ (\Sigma X^2) - (\Sigma X)^2}$$

$$b = \frac{(N)\ (\Sigma XY) - (\Sigma X)\ (\Sigma Y)}{(N)\ (\Sigma X^2) - (\Sigma X)^2}$$

The estimation of the amount of fertilizer required to attain the yield plateau was obtained through solving the regression equations using the a and b values found for each trial.

Table 3.—Guatemala: Field Trials on Plant Nutrient Response, 1972, Yield Plateau and Threshold Response Data.

Experiment and Crop	Altitude (meters)	Threshold Yield (Mt/Ha)	Nutrient Reqd. (Kg/Ha) to Reach Yield Plateau*	Yield Plateau (Mt/Ha)	Slope, b
POTATO, white					
AHP	3180	14.77 (—P)	180P_2O_5	30.43	87.0 (P_2O_5)
		22.33 (—K)	120K_2O		67.5 (K_2O)
ISMP	2850	15.00 (—N)	79N	33.19	230.2 (N)
		6.40 (—P)	151P_2O_5		177.4 (P_2O_5)
CPQ	2350	11.24 (—N)	91N	25.56	157.3 (N)
		7.75 (—P)	102P_2O_5		174.6 (P_2O_5)
		20.24 (—K)	128K_2O		41.5 (K_2O)
OQP	2380	15.39 (—N)	108N	34.53	177.2 (N)
		26.18 (—K)	60K_2O		139.2 (K_2O)
USP	2350	17.65 (—N)	100N	24.85	72.9 (N)
		17.04 (—P)	30P_2O_5		260.4 (P_2O_5)
TCMP	2287	12.15 (—N)	120N	24.10	99.6 (N)
		10.89 (—P)	83P_2O_5		159.2 (P_2O_5)
CMP	1760	15.33 (—N)	91N	25.54	112.2 (N)
WHEAT					
PHT	3150	0.80 (—N)	62N	1.37	9.2 (N)
ISMT	2850	0.44 (—P)	75P_2O_5	1.60	15.3 (P_2O_5)
ISMT	2850	1.22	none	1.22	n.s.
SFTT	2610	1.85 (—N)	83N	2.51	8.0 (N)
		1.74 (—P)	37P_2O_5		21.0 (P_2O_5)
TSMT	2570	1.84 (—P)	33P_2O_5	2.73	27.3 (P_2O_5)
TTT	2400	0.36 (—N)	35N	1.40	29.7 (N)
FSMT	2440	0.72 (—N)	90N	1.01	3.2 (N)
		0.32 (—P)	53P_5O_2		13.0 (P_2O_5)
OQT	2430	1.83 (—N)	41N	3.17	33.0 (N)
		2.04 (—P)	60P_2O_5		18.8 (P_2O_5)

TABLE 3.—(Continued).

Experiment and Crop	Altitude (meters)	Threshold Yield (MT/Ha)	Nutrient Reqd. (Kg/Ha) to Reach Yield Plateau*	Yield Plateau (MT/Ha)	Slope, b
TRIGO					
OQT	2400	2.50	none	2.50	n.s.
OQT	2380	3.11	none	3.11	n.s.
TCT	2260	0.46 (—N)	65N	1.54	16.8 (N)
TCT	2260	0.96 (—N)	73N	1.62	9.0 (N)
		1.05 (—P)	88P$_2$O$_5$		6.5 (P$_2$O$_5$)
UPLAND CORN					
TSMM	2700	1.36 (—N)	118N	3.87	21.2 (N)
TSMM	2700	1.16 (—N)	90N	2.89	30.3 (N)
CQM	2450	2.22 (—N)	131N	6.37	31.7 (N)
OQM	2400	2.71 (—N)	131N	6.49	28.9 (N)
OQM	2390	2.56 (—N)	156N	5.50	18.9 (N)
SMM	2300	1.18 (—N)	180N	6.06	27.1 (N)
SMM	2290	2.86 (—N)	140N	7.64	34.2 (N)
TCM	2260	1.02 (—N)	145N	5.60	31.6 (N)
TCM	2260	5.39 (—N)	227N	6.23	3.7 (N)
		5.32 (—P)	57P$_2$O$_5$		15.8 (P$_2$O$_5$)
MHM	1760	0.66 (—N)	159N	4.32	23.0 (N)
		2.43 (—P)	151P$_2$O$_5$		12.5 (P$_2$O$_5$)
LOWLAND CORN					
EMC	40	2.96	none	2.96	n.s.
LMAM	40	2.01	none	2.01	n.s.
LMCN	40	4.56	none	4.56	n.s.
LMBM	40	1.78 (—N)	180N	3.54	9.8 (N)
		2.50 (K$_2$O)	60K$_2$O		12.5 (K$_2$O)
LMBM	20	2.11	none	2.11	n.s.
LMCM	45	3.45	none	3.45	n.s.
LMCM	40	3.18	none	3.18	n.s.

* $\dfrac{\text{Yield Plateau}}{\text{Slope, b}}$ = Nutrient required to reach yield plateau.

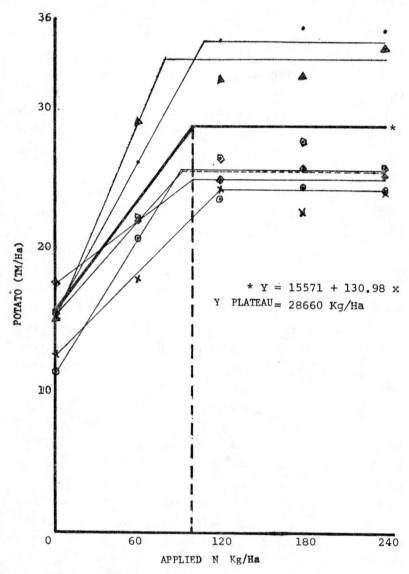

$$* \ Y = 15571 + 130.98 \ x$$
$$Y \ \text{PLATEAU} = 28660 \ \text{Kg/Ha}$$

Figure 3. Response function for potatoes in seven locations on the highlands of Guatemala using increasing levels of N and a linear-response plateau model.

A graphical example (Figure 3) shows nitrogen response functions and corresponding yield plateaus for seven trials conducted in the Guatemalan highlands during 1972.

Technical Assistance

The technical assistance offered by the Program as a final phase in its process of activities is principally carried out by means of the recommendations for rational use of fertilizers and other soil amendments which are, in part, based upon the analyses of composite soil samples sent to the laboratory.

In making these recommendations, "guide sheets" are used. In these, the fertilizer requirements for each crop are indicated for each of the nine fertility levels resulting from the possible combinations depending upon whether P and K are deficient (D), adequate (A) or very high (VH); N is always considered to be deficient: DDD, DDA, DDVH, DAD, DAA, DAVH, DVHD, DVHA, DVHVH.

The quantity of fertilizer recommended is determined by the nutrient applicatiion level necessary to reach the yield plateau in field trials and the soil sample analyses fertility level compared with the critical level for each nutrient.

This procedure is the means through which the increasing demand for technical assistance to solve soil fertility problems is met. This demand has grown (Table 4) from 1566 soil samples analyzed in 1964 to 20,800 in 1973, a trend similar to that shown for fertilizer consumption and cost.

Table 4.—The consumption and estimated value of N + P$_2$O$_5$ + K$_2$O and the number of soil samples analyzed for the purpose of obtaining recommendations for the use of fertilizers in the ICTA Plant Nutrition Laboratory. Guatemala 1964-1973.

Year	N° Samples Analyzed	Apparent Consumption N+P$_2$O$_5$+K$_2$O	Estimated Value of the Apparent Consumption of ($200/Mt nutrient) Fertilizers
1964	1.566	16.8	$ 3.36 millions
1965	1.200	17.4	3.48
1966	2.533	19.2	3.84
1967	6.803	21.6	4.32
1968	8.324	30.3	6.06
1969	10.531	33.0	6.60
1970	13.130	35.0	7.00
1971	16.372	36.5	7.30
1972	22.445	50.5	10.10
1973	20.800	Consumption data not yet available	

IV SUMMARY

The organization and development of a soil fertility evaluation program in Guatemala is presented. The techniques used and the critical levels for P and K identified, are given (7.3 ppm P with Olsen's solution, 60 ppm K). The use of the "Linear-Plateau Response" model is suggested for fertilizer evaluation as it gave satisfactory results in Guatemala.

V REFERENCES

1. CATE, R. B., and NELSON, L. A. 1965. A rapid method for correlation of soil test analysis with plant response data. Technical Bulletin N° 1, International Soil Testing Series. Raleigh. USA. N. C. State University - AID/Washington. 13 p.

2. ESTRADA, L. A. 1973. La disponibilidad de potasio en seis suelos de Guatemala (Tesis de Ing. Agr.). Guatemala, Universidad de San Carlos. 47 p.

3. GONZALEZ, J. A. 1970. Evaluación de la fijación y disponibilidad del fósforo en 14 series de suelos de Guatemala. (Tesis de Ing. Agr.). Guatemala, Universidad de San Carlos. 31 p. (Mimeografiado).

4. GONZALEZ, J. A., and WALKER, J. L. 1967. Suelos de Guatemala: Estado de los Nutrientes Vegetales. Guatemala, DGIEA-Ministerio de Agricultura. s/p. (Mimeografiado).

5. GUATEMALA. 1967. Memoria Anual 1966 de la División de Investigaciones Agropecuarias. Guatemala, Dirección General de Investigación y Extensión Agrícola, Ministerio de Agricultura, 210 p.

6. HUNTER, A. Métodos comúnmente usados para análisis rutinarios de suelo en los países cooperativos. Raleigh USA, ISFEI, SF. 15 p.

7. NELSON, W. L., MEHLICH, A., and WINTERS, E. 1953. The development, evaluation and use of soil test for phosphorus availability. Agronomy 4:153-158.

8. PALENCIA, J. A., and WALKER, J. L. 1972. Evaluación de la respuesta de varios cultivos a la fertilización en diferentes suelos de Guatemala. DIA-DIGESA, Ministerio de Agricultura. 12 p. (Mimeografiado).

9. PERUR, N. G. et al. 1953. Soil fertility evaluation to serve Indian farmers. Bangalore, India, Mysore University of Agricultural Sciences - USA-AID. 124 p.

10. SIMMONS, CH., TARANO, J. M., and PINTO, J. H. 1959. Clasificación de Reconocimiento de los Suelos de la República de Guatemala. Editor: Pedro Tirado Sulsona. Guatemala, José de Pineda Ibarra. 1,000 p.

11. WALKER, J. L. 1971. El análisis de suelos y las recomendaciones para fertilizantes. Guatemala, DIA-DIGESA, Ministerio de Agricultura. 10 p.

12. WAUGH, D. L., CATE, R. B. and NELSON, L. A. 1971. Discontinuous models for rapid correlation, interpretation and utilization of soil analysis and fertilizer respons data Tech. Bull. N° 7. ISFEI N. C. State University. 77 p.

26 New Techniques and Equipment for Routine Soil-Plant Analytical Procedures

ARVEL H. HUNTER

I INTRODUCTION

The foundation of a viable Soil Fertility Evaluation and Improvement Program *is* a laboratory which is capable of analyzing large numbers of soil, plant, and water samples in a reasonably short time and with a reasonably high degree of precision and accuracy. It must, of course, be assumed that the laboratory is using the best available methods for analysis. The results of such methods must be correlated with the soil fertility status of the soils for which the laboratory data is to be used to provide predictive capacity for improving soil fertility and thus crop productivity.

The International Soil Fertility Evaluation and Improvement Project (ISFEI) involving North Carolina State University, USAID, and a number of cooperating Latin American countries, is now entering its tenth year of operation. In such a project there are a number of phases which must be instituted and improved simultaneously for the proper functioning of the project. 1) Sampling techniques and sample logistics. 2) Laboratory methods and systems for production of data. 3) Interpretation of data. 4) Recommendations based on interpretation. 5) Educational extension to initiate and improve the use of available information. 6) Research to provide the basis for integrating all of the other phases into a functioning program.

As stated earlier, the laboratory phase is really the backbone of the overall program because without it, there can be no data generated on which to build the rest of the program.

Information for determining, maintaining, and/or improving soil fertility status comes largely from three main sources: 1) soil analysis, 2) plant tissue analysis, and 3) water analysis.

Each of these sources of information can best be interpreted when used in conjunction with each other. As a rule the peak period of demand for analyses of these three types of samples do not occur during the same time periods. For these reasons and for the obvious economical and operational advantages in establishing and maintaining a single laboratory and in training and efficiently utilizing laboratory technicians it is suggested that the analysis of all three of these types of samples should be done within a single laboratory system.

From its inception, the ISFEI project has been concerned with improving laboratory methods, procedures, equipment, and systems so as to permit the analysis of soil, plant, and water samples in the same lab; to increase the capacity in terms of number of samples analyzed per day; and to improve the accuracy and precision of analytical results.

From the time that a sample is received by the laboratory it must proceed through a number of steps before the data are ready to be compiled and processed for interpretation. For example when a soil sample is received, it must be logged so as to maintain or recover its identity. It must be air dried, crushed, and mixed so as to become a homogeneous whole from which subsamples can be taken for analysis.

Subsamples must be taken, extracting solutions added, sample and solutiion uniformly mixed and agitated. The mixture must be filtered and measured aliquots of the filtrate are then taken and reagents or diluents added to prepare the aliquot for analysis by means of flame photometer, atomic absorption, spectrophotometer, or titration, etc. Each of these various steps requires time for the manipulation of the sample and provides opportunity for introducing error in the final results. If any one of these steps require undue time in relation to the others then the process of analysis will be slowed and the capacity for analysis will be decreased. If any one step allows for introduction of undue error because of loss of sample, improper measurement, contamination, or loss of identity etc. then accuracy and precision of analysis will be decreased.

In service laboratories which are being called upon to provide data for larger and larger numbers of farmers and research samples, capacity and accuracy of analyses are both of vital importance. Under these circumstances neither capacity without accuracy nor accuracy without capacity can be of any great value. It is unfortunate that too often in routine analytical service laboratories accuracy may be sacrificed to increase capacity. Where too much accuracy is sacrificed then we must certainly arrive at a situation in which the inaccurate data is as bad or worse than no data at all because only false or misleading conclusions can result from the interpretation of erroneous data.

The balance of this discussion will be concerned primarily with indicating various procedures, laboratory items, and equipment which have been developed by or for the International Soil Fertility Evaluation and Improvement Project to reach the objectives stated earlier.

II   EQUIPMENT AND PROCEDURES FOR SAMPLE PREPARATION

When a sample is received at the laboratory it is logged on a master sheet which indicates its position in a group of 33 samples. The sample container is then placed in its proper position in a drying and storage tray which has three rows of eleven positions in each row (Figure 1). The eleven spaces provide for ten farmers or unknown samples and one control sample in each row (Figure 2). Control samples are special samples collected in bulk and prepared so as to be homogeneous throughout. These samples are then analyzed numerous times by the laboratory in which they are to be used and preferably by other laboratories using the same procedures. In this manner, the analytical results of the control samples are known to the laboratory director. These samples should be included in each group of samples to be analyzed. For best analytical control, each laboratory should have at least three to six bulk control samples and each row of each group of samples should have a control sample included with it. At least some of the control samples should be located in positions in the

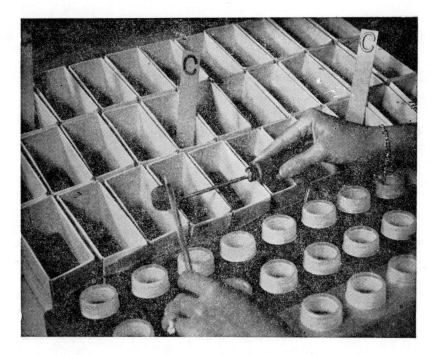

Figure 1. Samples and control samples in drying and storage tray.

group so as to be unknown to the analysts. The inclusion of this control sample is the key to maintaining accuracy and precision control in all analytical procedures. The tray is assigned a group number. Each row in the tray is color coded with the colors appearing on only one end of the tray. The numbering of the sample position in the row begins with number one at the color end of the tray. Each sample container is spaced two inches on center within the row. This same spacing and color coding is used for all of the laboratory bottle racks and carry trays so that the only number carried through the laboratory is the group number which is placed on each tray. All of the analytical apparatus and systems have been designed so as to avoid the necessity of removing any sample from its assigned position in the group during the entire process of analysis.

After logging, the samples are placed in a drying cabinet designed to hold the maximum number of samples which may be analyzed in a day during the peak season. The drying cabinet is constructed so that air is pulled in through vents in the bottom of the cabinet. The air circulates around the sample containers and is exhausted out the top of the cabinet by an exhaust fan. The resulting dried samples are air dried. In some situations it may be found desirable to slightly warm the air passing through the cabinet. This can be done by drawing it over a few light bulbs placed just above the bottom air intake vents.

Figure 2. Drying and storage trays.

From the drying cabinet the soil sample tray is taken to the crushing machine. This soil crusher is constructed of stainless steel and has been designed so as not to break rocks or debri, which may be in the field sample, and to prevent these from passing into the prepared sample. On the average a soil sample can be crushed, mixed, and returned to its box and position in the tray in 15 to 20 seconds. Even the hardest clay samples usually require less than 25 seconds (Figure 3).

After preparation, the tray is placed in position under a sampling table where the subsamples will be measured for processing in the laboratory. All soil samples are measured by volume for analysis. Special sampling spoons have been designed and constructed of polivinyl chloride plastic to avoid any possible contamination of the sample with microelements due to sampling (Figure 4).

The subsamples are placed in a polystyrene plastic bottle which is positioned two inches on center in a styrofoam bottle rack (Figure 5). Styrofoam is used for the botle racks because it is light weight but more important the holes can be drilled so that the bottles fit snugly enough that when the rack is inverted and shaken, the bottles will not fall out. Yet the bottles can be easily removed and replaced when desired. The styrofoam is resistant to most lab chemicals, does not absorb solution, and is easily cleaned (Figure 6). If handled properly they will give several years of

Figure 3. Returning the crushed and screened sample to its container.

Figure 4. Soil sampling spoons for taking volume subsamples.

Figure 5. Bottle racks and carry tray.

Figure 6. Bottle racks can be inverted and shaken without loss
of bottles.

service. For ease of handling, the bottle racks are placed in an aluminum frame type carry tray. These carry trays are light weight and sufficiently sturdy. The aluminum is generally non-corrosive, except where strong hydrochloric acid fumes are present. The frame design is used so that the bottles will dry rapidly when inverted on the carry tray and contamination is avoided where the inverted bottles do not touch the tray.

Laboratory carts have been constructed to carry twelve trays or 360 farmers samples and 36 control samples. The use of these carts to carry the samples from laboratory station to station greatly facilitates the movement of samples through the analytical process. Using the carts in conjunction with "island" dispensing, diluting, and instrument tables also eliminates the necessity of a lot of bench top or horizontal space by utilizing the vertical space of the laboratory (Figure 7).

III EQUIPMENT AND PROCEDURES FOR EXTRACTION AND DILUTION

The subsamples are transferred to the trays on the cart and taken to the dispenser table. The dispenser table is constructed with the space under the top open so that carboys for the various solutions can be rolled in and out of position under the table. The solution carboys are placed on dollies which allow for easy handling of large volumes of solution (Figure 8).

The dispenser table is positioned so as to provide adequate space on all four sides of the table for carts to be brought along side. The trays are placed on top of the cart while the solutions are dispensed into the sample bottles.

Two types of new dispensers have been developed. One dispenser is designed to dispense multiple aliquots of a specific volume of solution (Figure 9). The volumes can easily be changed and calibrated from less than 5 ml to 50 ml. The dispensers are hand operated which simplifies their operation, avoids mistakes in delivery of aliquots to proper sample bottle, and speeds up the process. Aliquots of 25 ml volume can be delivered to each of the 33 bottles in a tray within 35 to 45 seconds. The dispensers require no auxiliary vacuum, pressure or gravity flow for their operation and by means of a quick disconnect coupling, different solutions can be easily and rapidly introduced for dispersing. The solutions come in contact only with plastic or glass tubing so as to avoid contamination. A wide range of types of solutions can be dispensed but the dispensers will not accomodate concentrated sulfuric acid.

The other type dispenser is similar to the first but is designed to dispense three different volumes of a solution, one aliquot at a time, without having to change and calibrate the volume of the volume control syringes. Changing dispensed volume is accomplished simply by manipulation of two valves (Figure 10).

After the extracting solutions are dispensed into the sample bottles ti is necessary to thoroughly mix and agitate this mixture. In the past this agitation has been done by some means of shaking the mixture. In most shaking systems it is difficult to agitate each sample in a uniform manner and with some shakers it is impossible. Because of this and other difficulties encountered in the shaking process, a stirrer was developed which can

Figure 7. Laboratory cart with shelves for 12 trays.

Figure 8. "Island" work tables with cart on each side and with carbody on dolly.

Figure 9.　Three aliquot dispenser.

Figure 10.　One aliquot dispenser for 3 different volumes.

thoroughly mix and agitate each sample in an identical manner. The stirrer is constructed with 33 stirring rods (with paddles) connected by gears and driven by a single motor controlled by a timing device. Thus each rod turns at exactly the same speed as each other and the paddles are positioned so as to keep all soil particles suspended in the solution during agitation. The sample bottles do not need to be closed to prevent loss or contamination of sample from spilling or splashing (Figure 11).

When the samples are removed from the stirrer a washing basin is moved into position around the rods and a spray system automatically washes the rods and paddles. The rods are made of nylon and the paddles of polyvinyl so as to avoid contamination of the sample. A timing device automatically controls the length of time the sample and solution are mixed.

After mixing, the samples are usually filtered to obtain a solution suitable for analysis. We have found that filtering can be accomplished easily and rapidly by placing the filter paper in the bottles of the bottle rack then the samples can be transferred to the filters, eleven at a time, by pouring from the sample bottle rack to the filter bottle rack (Figure 12).

After filtering, the analytical procedure for several of the elements requires that an aliquot of the filtrate be taken for dilution or for receiving reagents. For accomplishing this operation, two types of diluters have been developed. Both of these diluters are hand operated for simplicity, speed, and accuracy. Both diluters are designed so that the sampling probe extends to each sample and delivery bottle. This eliminates the necessity of taking the sample bottle out of its position in the rack and group. The sample aliquot is washed from the probe tube by the reagent or diluent thus eliminating contamination from one sample to the next.

One diluter is designed primarily for taking relatively large sample aliquots and adding equal or larger amounts of reagent or diluent. For example, the determination of 1 N KCl extractable acidity by titration requires that ten ml of water containing a few drops of phenolphthalein be added to a ten ml aliquot of the sample filtrate prior to titration. Using this diluter, about 4 to 5 seconds per sample are required for transferring an aliquot and adding the diluent. For greatest precision, the dilution ratio for this diluter should be kept between 1:1 and 1:15.

The other diluter is designed to make wider dilution ratios with high precision and also has the capability of adding two different reagents at the same time. By the manipulation of two valves and quick disconnects, three different dilution ratios can be obtained without adjusting the volumes of the volume control syringes (Figure 13). The diluter or combination diluter-dispenser was originally designed for use in the phosphorus determination procedure when sodium bicarbonate is used as the soil extracting agent. In this case, the standard type diluters which have an interface in the sample probe tube between the sample aliquot and the reagent or diluent will not function because the acid color reagent reacts at the interface with the sodium bicarbonate to form carbon dioxide gas which causes loss of sample aliquot volume. By using the combination diluter-dispenser, water can be used to wash the sample aliquot from the probe tube and the acid reagent is added through a separate tube. This permits the reaction between sample

Figure 11. Multiple sample stirrer with stirring rods are easily washed by spray nozzles in basin.

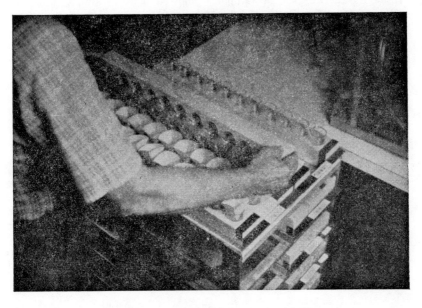

Figure 12. Bottle racks are used for filtering.

and reagent to take place only in the receiving bottle. The entire operation of taking the aliquot, transferring it to the receiving bottle, adding the reagent and mixing requires about 4 to 5 seconds per sample.

Both of the above mentioned diluters provide for a wide range of volume selection for both the sample aliquot and diluents or reagents so that final volumes can be chosen according to the requirements of the analytical method. The diluents or reagents can be placed at bench height position or the carboy can be stored underneath the diluter table. By means of quick disconnects diluents or reagents can be rapidly and easily changed. As with the dispensers, the solutions contact only glass or plastic to avoid contamination.

IV APPARATUS FOR DETERMINATIONS

After dilution or adding reagents the samples are then ready to be taken to the various analytical instruments or stations for analysis. With certain analytical instruments such as most atomic absorption apparatus and some flame photometers the sample can be introduced into the instrument easily and rapidly without the necessity of removing the bottles from their assigned position in the group. However, for spectrophotometric, pH, and titration analysis some auxilliary means of transferring or positioning the sample is needed to reduce the time required for analysis, improve the accuracy or maintain position of sample in the group.

A simple sample changer apparatus has been developed for use with a spectrophotometer or colorimeter which accomplishes all three of the above mentioned requirements (Figure 14). The sample changer operates by vacuum through a waste jar. Constant vacuum is applied to a plunger tube inside a cuvette. When the plunger tube is not in contact with liquid inside the cuvette then the vacuum is transferred to the sample probe tube (Figure 15). When the sample probe tube is immersed in the sample solution, the solution is drawn into the cuvette. The cuvette is filled to the level of the plunger tube and if excess sample is drawn in, it is automatically transferred into the waste jar. To empty the cuvette, the plunger tube is pushed down until its tip reaches the bottom of the cuvette. As this occurs, all the cuvette contents are drawn into the waste jar. The cuvette is fixed in a constant position in the spectrophotometer so that the light path through the cuvette is constant. To avoid sample to sample contamination, the cuvette is washed once with the sample then filled with another portion of the same sample and the reading made. Using this apparatus, each reading requires about 15 seconds.

To simplify pH determinations, an accessory for positioning and washing electrodes and for stirring the sample during measurement has been developed (Figure 16). With this accessory the sample tray is placed in a fixed position in front and to the side of the pH meter. The electrodes and stirrer are fastened to an arm mechanism which permits the electrodes to be positioned in each bottle. As each measurement is completed, the electrodes are then positioned over a wash basin and electrodes and stirrer are automatically washed. With good stable electrodes and pH meter each reading requires about 15 to 20 seconds.

Figure 13. Combination diluter-dispenser for wide dilution ratios or for addition two different reagents or diluents.

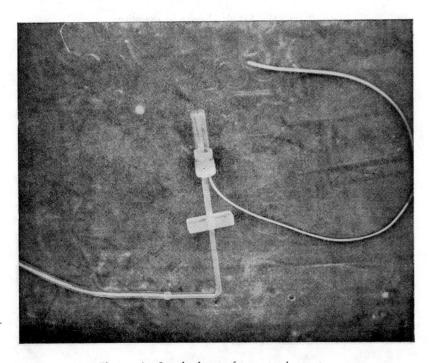

Figure 14. Sample changer for spectrophotometer.

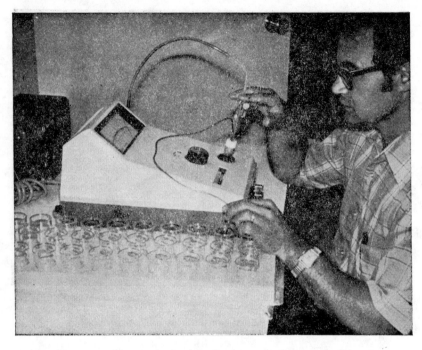

Figure 15. Sample changer in operation.

Figure 16. Accessory for positioning and washing pH electrodes.

At present, 1 N KCl extractable acidity is apparently best measured by means of titration. Standard titration procedures are usually quite time consuming.

A titration apparatus has been developed which permits each of the bottles to be positioned under the burette without removing them out of the tray or out of their group position (Figure 17). In conjunction with the positioner a specially designed device which utilizes vacuum is used for rapidly and easily filling the burette which is then automatically zeroed. The titration apparatus does not affect the accuracy of the measurement but does permit it to be accomplished in a time period comparable to the various other types of measurements that are made.

Finally, after all the analytical procedures have been completed it is desirable to have a means for rapidly washing or cleaning the sample containers. We use a washer which has two rows with eleven spray nozzels

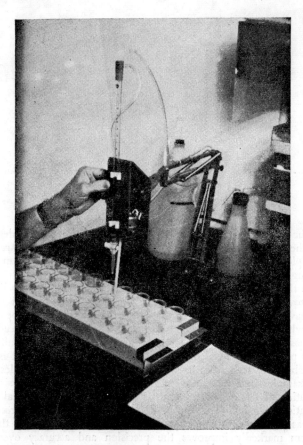

Figure 17. Titration apparatus with semi-autofill and zero.

in each (Figure 18). One row is connected to tap water and the other to distilled water. The valve controlling the water flow is activated by hand pressure as the bottles are placed over the nozzels. One bottle rack at a time can be thoroughly washed with tap water and then quickly rinsed with distilled water. The bottle racks are then returned in an inverted position to the carry trays. This permits rapid drying and prevents contamination by dust etc., as the trays are stored in the lab cart for reuse.

Figure 18. Bottle rack washer.

These various devices and apparatus which have been designed to increase the ease, speed, and accuracy of analysis are sometimes referred to as "multiple unit apparatus" because multiple samples can be handled as a unit throughout the analytical process.

In the control laboratory of the International Soil Fertility Evaluation and Improvement Project, the analytical methods for both soil and plant analysis have been worked out so that the same multiple unit apparatus can be used where applicable for both types of analyses without readjustment of volumes etc. Using these methods and with adequate multiple unit apparatus properly arranged in a good analytical flow pattern, it is possible for one laboratory technician to analyze four groups (132 samples) of soil or plant samples in a regular eight hour work day. This analysis includes determination of ten different elements on each sample or a total of 1,320 determinations per day. This can be done with no sacrifice of precision and occuracy as compared to other systems of analysis. Frequently the use of this system markedly improves the precision and accuracy over systems previously used.

The basic aquipment needed for the analysis of more than 100 samples per day is adequate for the analysis of 1,000 samples per day except for the number of lab carts, bottle racks, and carry trays. Of course, additional lab technicians would be required but more determinations per technician can be accomplished as the number of elements per technician is decreased. Thus six to eight technicians should be able to analyze 1,000 samples per day.

V SUMMARY

A primary concern of every laboratory which has the responsibility of doing routine analysis of soil, plant, and water samples is the ability to analyze large numbers of samples efficiently and economically with good precision.

Described herein are some new techniques and equipment or apparatus which were designed specifically for the purpose of increasing the number of analyses per man hour while at the same time maintaining or improving the precision and accuracy of the results.

27 New Concepts in Biological and Economical Interpretation of Fertilizer Response

DONOVAN L. WAUGH, ROBERT B. CATE, Jr., LARRY A. NELSON,
and AMADO MANZANO

I INTRODUCTION

Most discussions in the literature on fertilizer response are based on field trial interpretation utilizing some version of the Law of Diminishing Returns, i.e., continuous curvilinear functions in which equal additional increments of fertilizer result in steadily smaller responses. The more important curvilinear models in use today are the quadratic, square root, and logarithmic functions. The Mitscherlich model adds constants to the logarithmic function to adjust the interpretation of fertilizer response in accordance with variations in native soil fertility.

With the aid of the computer, many additional factors, which are known to affect yield, have been incorporated into these response models in an attempt to further describe the response to applied fertilizers. Yet, for all the refinement potentially inherent in these complex models their use is impractical in some areas.

There are no established rules for determining which kind of response model is the most appropriate to use in the interpretation of fertilizer response from field trials. If a single experiment is to be evaluated, the researcher may test the data for fit with various linear and curvilinear models and select the one which gives the best R^2 for regression. However, a model which best describes the response data from one experiment may not necessarily be the best for another experiment. This places the user of such a complex model in a difficult position because the whole purpose of soil fertility evaluation is the accurate prediction of relative response to nutrients.

II DIFFICULTIES WITH THE TRADITIONAL FERTILIZER RESPONSE MODEL

In practice a number of problems are encountered in attempting to apply complex fertilizer response models to existing data. Several of these difficulties are summarized below:

Insufficient information available to correctly apply a complex fertilizer response model

Mathematical models which predict yield must either assign a researched value to each of the factors affecting yield or apply some kind of constant in their place when such a value is not available. Most field tirals conducted in the past, and even many currently being carried out, simply do not supply sufficient input information to permit the practical application of a detailed, complex response model.

Bias in the interpretation model

Anderson and Nelson (1) have described in some detail the limitations and difficulties associated with the quadratic model for describing some single nutrient responses. Their study showed that the quadratic is particularly biased when there is a marked response to first increment applications followed by little or no response to higher rates. In these cases ,the quadratic characteristically overestimates the measured yield at the zero rate of applied nutrient, then underestimates the yield at low nutrient rates, and overestimates the yield at high rates. The predictions of fertilizer requirements for maximum yield are, therefore, unrealistically high.

Variability in yield observations obtained at high rates of nutrient application

Most continuous curvilinear response models are very sensitive to fluctuations in yield at these higher rates. If, for example, high application rates cause a fertilizer burn or create a nutrient disequilibrium, there will likely be a yield depression. The quadratic function usually fits this situa- tiou quite well. On the other hand, the same high rates of nutrient in question, if applied in a different cultural practice or in a different configu- ration of nutrient balance, may give yields equal to or higher than inter- mediate rates. The square root or long function usually fits this kind of response better than the quadratic. Unfortunately, factors other than nature of plant growth and nutritional responses are likely to affect the response at high application rates, such that the model which gives the best fit of the data for one experiment may give the poorest fit for another.

Difficulty in practical analysis of complex response models if computers are not available

In many parts of the world, field experiments can be conducted on a year-round basis. The time available for analyzing one set of experiments and planning for another is often very limited. Complex curvilinear res- ponse models are not very practical for fertilizer response interpretation if a computer is not available.

III ALTERNATE MODELS FOR USE IN INTERPRETATION OF FERTILIZER RESPONSE DATA

Swanson (6) has pointed out an alternative model based on Liebig's Law of the Minimum which should be considered for interpretation of fertilizer response data. This model postulates a linear response to the principal limiting element, halting abruptly when another factor becomes limiting but resuming its linear rise when the limitation is corrected. Eventually, the yield is limited by the genetic capability of the plant when all external limiting factors have been removed. An idealized diagram of these responses and limiting factors is depicted graphically in Figure 1.

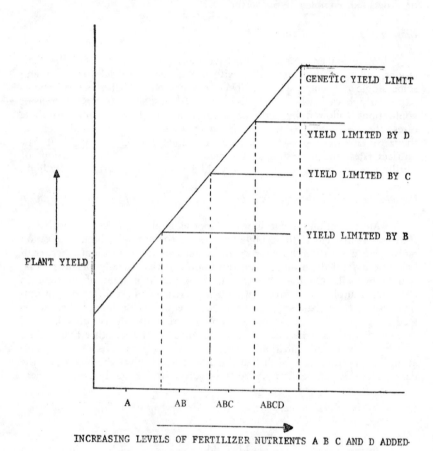

Figure 1. The Linear Response-and-Plateau (LRP) model based on Liebig's law of the minimum.

Boyd (3) has summarized a considerable amount of fertilizer response data covering different crops and has shown that most data fit the Liebig-type model very well. In his study, most of the fertilizer trials could be characterised by a sloping straight line on the ascending portion of the curve (the yield response) and a more or less horizontal line representing maximum yield (the yield plateau).

The purpose of this study was to determine if a linear response-and-plateau (LRP) model results in sufficiently reasonable estimates of nutrient requirements to be used as a rapid method for interpretation of fertilizer response data.

IV EXPERIMENTAL PROCEDURE

The data analyzed were obtained from experiments in Bolivia carried out during the period of 1969-70. The same central composite rotatable design had been used in all of the trials (with the center-point treatment replicated). The center-point treatment for those experiments was coded as 2-2-2 for N-P_2O_5—K_2O applications, respectively, and the range of code levels for each nutrient was 0 to 4. Application rates for P_2O_5 and K_2O were based on soil tests and previous knowledge of crop response. At the time of data summary and analysis, the sites were grouped into soil-crop categories derived by the critical-level technique of Cate and Nelson (4). The treatments and yields for each group are summarized in Table 1.

Preliminary interpretation of the data was done first by regression analysis of individual locations using a conventional quadratic model including terms representing the interaction among the nutrient elements. The results were useful in showing that all three nutrients contributed to the fertilizer response in at least certain experiments, and also that the interaction among the nutrients was significant for a number of the experiments. For example, in soils responsive to both N and P, the response to N could not be studied until sufficient P was supplied so as not to be limiting. Therefore, in order to facilitate subsequent single-nutrient comparisons between models in the absence of interaction terms, the zero treatments of accompanying nutrients had to be deleted from the analysis. Specifically, the 202 (zero P) and 220 treatments (zero K) were deleted when the nitrogen response was being processed. The 1-level of the accompanying nutrients was assumed to be sufficiently high to permit a realistic picture of response to the variaible nutrient being studied. Likewise, the 022 and 220 treatments were deleted in determining the P curve and the 022 and 202 treatments were deleted from the K curve. The 000 treatment was not used in any of the response analyses since its most limiting nutrient cannot be determined.

Regression analyses were then carried out with the computer on the data deck for each of the 37 experiments, using quadratic, square root, and logarithmic models. A further regression analysis was made on the same data deck with two linear response-and-plateau (LRP) models, in one case assuming that treatment levels 0 and 1 were on the response slope while levels 2, 3, and 4 were on the plateau, and in the other case assuming that levels 0, 1, and 2 were on the response slope while levels 3 and 4 were on the plateau. The R^2 for fit was determined as follows:

$$R^2 = \frac{\text{S.S. for regression (2 d.f.)}}{\text{S.S. for treatments (12 d.f.)}}$$

Comparisons were also made between the different models on data from pooled experiments rather than on individual experiments following the same procedure.

Table 1.—Summary of treatments and average yields for each soil-crop category in Bolivia trials.[1]

	Soil-crop categories									
	Potato trials						Wheat trials			
	I Low P — High K[2]		II Low P — High K[2]		III High P — High K[3]		IV Low P — Low K[4]		V Low P — Low K[4]	
Treatment code	Treatment Kg/Ha	Yield T/Ha	Treatment Kg/Ha	Yield T/Ha	Treatment Kg/Ha	Yield T/Ha	Treatment Kg/Ha	Yield T/Ha	Treatment Kg/Ha	Yield T/Ha
000	0- 0- 0	6.8	0- 0- 0	6.0	0- 0- 0	4.8	—	—	—	—
222	120-120-40	18.6	120-40-40	16.3	120-120-120	15.6	120-100-40	1.94	120-100-40	2.06
022	0-120-40	8.5	0-40-40	8.6	0-120-120	7.3	0-100-40	1.12	0-100-40	1.00
202	120- 0-40	11.1	120- 0-40	15.4	120- 0-120	4.8	120- 0-40	0.90	120- 0-40	0.79
220	120-120-0	17.7	120-40- 0	11.7	120-120- 0	10.9	120-100- 0	2.07	120-100- 0	1.63
422	240-120-40	19.7	240-40-40	15.6	240-120-120	12.5	240-100-40	1.94	240-100-40	1.98
242	120-240-40	19.5	120-80-40	16.9	120-240-120	19.4	120-200 40	2.33	120-200-40	2.28
224	120-120-80	19.9	120 40-80	12.7	120-120-240	14.4	120-100-80	1.88	120-100-80	2.33
111	60- 60-20	16.7	60-60-20	14.8	60- 60- 60	13.1	60- 50-20	1.69	60- 50-20	1.68
113	60- 60-60	16.2	60-20-60	13.9	60- 60-180	14.8	60- 50-60	1.78	60- 50-60	1.68
131	60-180 20	16.8	60-60-60	15.2	60-180- 60	15.3	60-150-20	1.74	60-150-20	1.56
311	180- 60-20	18.7	180-20-20	14.3	180- 60- 60	11.5	180- 50-20	1.72	180- 50-20	1.72
133	60-180-60	18.3	60-60-60	15.4	60-180-180	12.9	60-150-60	1.77	60-150-60	1.60
331	180-180-20	20.0	180-60-20	19.5	180-180- 60	16.6	180-150-20	2.56	180-150-20	1.95
313	180- 60-60	18.9	180 20-60	16.4	180- 60-180	9.7	180- 50 60	1.56	180- 50-60	1.70
333	180-180-60	21.5	180-60-60	14.6	180-180-180	18.3	180-150-60	2.01	180-150-60	2.08

1/ Experiments conducted under direction of ISFEI project and Bolivian Ministry of Agriculture. (Categoroies I and II had 8 reps. of treatment 222, while III had 5 reps. and IV and V had 3 reps.).

2/ Original data after Saravia et al., Chinoli Exp. Sta. (14 trials).

3/ Original data after Claure et al., Toralapa Exp. Sta. (3 trials).

4/ Original data after Manzano, Carrera, Iriarte, Luján, Zuleta, Hinojosa et al., Cochabamba and Tarija (11 trils).

V RESULTS AND DISCUSSION

Fertilizer response interpretation at individual locations

The results of the R^2 of regression analysis of the data for each model are given in Table 2 (only those functions which gave significant yield response are shown).

These results, obtained by fitting the response data of individual experiments with the various models, point out the fact that each function fits some data better than others. In some cases, the R^2 for all models is very low due to the fact that there was very little nutrient response. The function which best describes the response in one field trial is sometimes the poorest for describing the response in another. Nevertheless, the linear response-and-plateau (LRP) model did result in the best R^2 fit of the data in 27 out of the 37 significant response functions studied in comparison with 3, 6, and 1 for quadratic, square root ,and logarithmic models, respectively (Table 2). The linear response-and-plateau (LRP) model should be recognized as an appropriate working model for describing and interpreting fertilizer response from individual experiments.

Fertilizer response interpretatiion for pooled locations

The R^2 results for pooled locations are given in Table 3. Whereas the linear response-and-plateau (LRP) model was clearly better than curvilinear models for the majority of the individual locations, there was less difference between models when working with pooled locations. This is probably due to the fact that the averaging together of data from individual sites, whose slope of response and plateau yield are different, will mathematically result in curvilinear average response, even when the individual responses are essentially characterized by the two straight lines of the linear response-and-plateau (LRP) model (3,2).

A plot of the response data for soil-crop category II (N) is given in Figure 2. The plots for the other soil-crop categories gave similar results and are not shown. These plots of the response data use the means of all experiments in the pool of locations, thereby making it easier to see the range of observations and the weighting effect of unequal numbers of observations at each level. The predicted response line is drawn through the points for each response model studied.

The residual of the regression analysis are perhaps even more worthy of mention than the fit of the model to the response function. Ideally, the residuals should be random (i.e., distributed equally on the negative and positive sides of the reference line). However, the curvilinear models showed some consistent residual trends for the individual experiments in this study, indicating a tendency for bias. When the linear response-and-plateau (LRP) model was used, on the other hand, these residual appeared to be appropriately random. The work of Boyd (3) and Anderson and Nelson (1) indicated a similar bias with the quadratic model. An example of the residual plots for all six locations in Group 2, nitrogen, is given in Figure 3. In this example, the quadratic model shows many

Table 2.—Regression analysis R^2 obtained by fitting four response models to potato and wheat field data: by location.

Soil-crop category	Location	Response model			
		Linear response-and-plateau	Quadratic	Square root	Log
		N DATA			
I	7	0.294*	0.307*	0.309*	0.308*
	8	0.909**	0.834**	0.938**	0.911**
	9	0.947**	0.520*	0.720**	0.651**
	10	0.869**	0.855**	0.896**	0.891**
II	4	0.826**	0.616**	0.815**	0.749**
	5	0.754**	0.611**	0.764**	0.712**
III	13	0.775**	0.735**	0.672**	0.712**
	14	0.389*	0.580*	0.523*	0.576*
	15	0.467*	0.351	0.455*	0.424*
IV	25	0.909*	0.888**	0.868**	0.894**
	26	0.340*	0.132	0.107	0.106
	27	0.273*	0.207	0.151	0.180
	28	0.562*	0.264	0.544*	0.440*
V	29	0.370*	0.307	0.347	0.345
	30	0.423*	0.381*	0.390*	0.396*
	32	0.474*	0.454*	0.476*	0.512*
	33	0.625**	0.426*	0.370*	0.413*
	34	0.556*	0.785**	0.454*	0.617*
		P DATA			
I	7	0.345*	0.421*	0.312*	0.363*
	8	0.718**	0.605**	0.716**	0.690**
	9	0.534*	0.522*	0.620*	0.567*
	10	0.552*	0.408*	0.540*	0.488*
III	13	0.348*	0.296	0.292	0.301
	14	0.421*	0.462*	0.503*	0.487*
	15	0.718**	0.690**	0.650**	0.704**
IV	24	0.361*	0.235	0.346	0.305
	25	0.592*	0.487*	0.571*	0.561*
	26	0.376*	0.256	0.311	0.260
	27	0.569*	0.545*	0.518*	0.535*
V	29	0.463*	0.399*	0.346*	0.381*
	30	0.371*	0.258	0.194	0.238
	31	0.300*	0.250	0.190	0.227
	32	0.433*	0.144	0.368*	0.286
	33	0.584*	0.432*	0.524*	0.514*
		K DATA			
III	15	0.401*	0.270	0.212	0.243
V	29	0.342*	0.206	0.306	0.293
	33	0.467*	0.323	0.310	0.321
Total number of experiments in which model gave best R^2		27	3	6	1

negative residual at the 0-and 3-levels and positive residual at the 1-and 4-levels. The residual trends of the square root and log models are not shown, but they appeared to be intermediate between the quadratic and the linear response-and-plateau (LRP) models in nearly all cases.

Table 3.—Regression analysis R^2 obtained by fitting four NPK response models to potato and wheat field trial data pooled into soil-crop categories.[1]

Nutrient response studied	Soil-crop category	Response model			
		Linear response-and-plateau	Quadratic	Square root	Log
Nitrogen	I	0.872	0.813	0.906	0.881
	II	0.737	0.664	0.738	0.730
	III	0.507	0.503	0.468	0.524
	IV	0.642	0.574	0.616	0.630
	V	0.745	0.592	0.625	0.636
Phosphorus	I	0.706	0.617	0.720	0.690
	III	0.698	0.677	0.719	0.715
	IV	0.818	0.744	0.838	0.816
	V	0.745	0.552	0.614	0.630
Potassium	V	0.444	0.157	0.150	0.167

1/ R^2 is based on treatment sum of squares $= \dfrac{\text{S.S. regression (2 d.f.)}}{\text{Total S.S. treatments (12 d.f.)}}$

VI INTERPRETATION OF RESPONSE DATA

Graphical technique for the linear response-and-plateau (LRP) model

Many agronomists have very little time to analyze results from one set of experiments before they begin to plan for a subsequent experiment. A rapid graphical method of interpretation of response data would, therefore, be invaluable for evaluating the yield response and the yield plateau portions of the response function. Similarly, a rapid technique would be useful to those in charge of making fertilizer recommendations based on soil analysis by aiding them in taking new data and readily determining a suitable level of fertilization. The following graphical procedure ultimately produces approximately the same result as the interpretation obtained with the computerized version of the linear response-and-plateau (LRP) model. Each of the steps are illustrated in Figure 4.

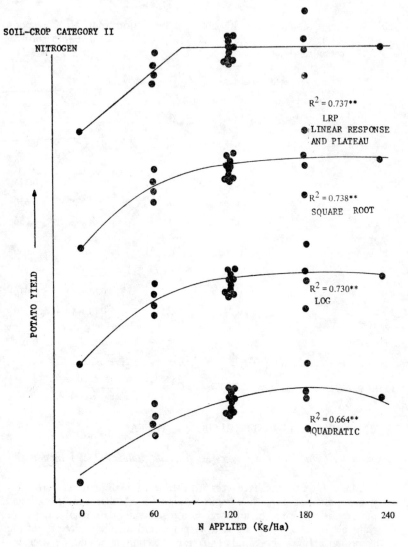

Figure 2. Nitrogen response for potatoes fitted to Linear-Response-and-Plateau (LRP), square root, log, and quadratic models.

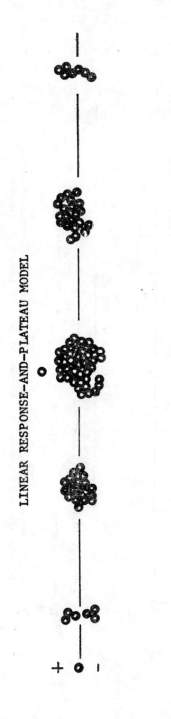

LINEAR RESPONSE-AND-PLATEAU MODEL

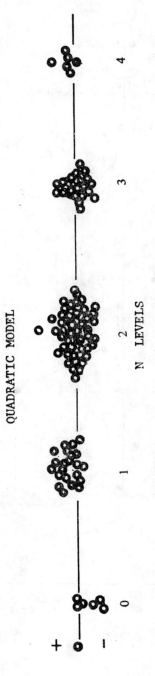

QUADRATIC MODEL

N LEVELS

Figure 3. Plots of regression residuals for the pool of six individual nitrogen experiments in soil-crop category II.

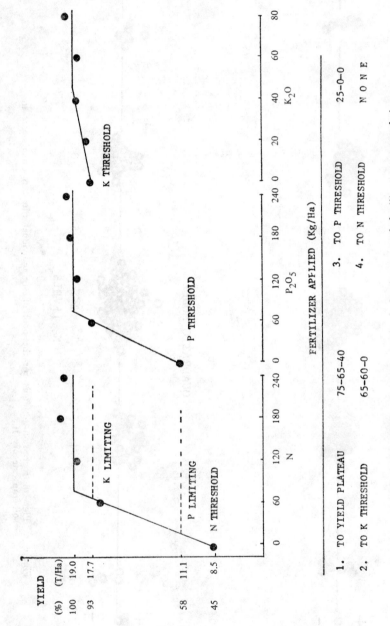

Figure 4. Multinutrient response interpretation and development of fertilizer recommendations using combined single-nutrient LRP models: Soil-crop Category I. (Potatoes).

Organize the single nutrient response data

Compute the mean of yield which correspond to the various application rates, i.e., level 0, level 1, level 2, etc. If the design contains more or less than five levels, a similar procedure may be followed, being careful to delete incomplete or inadequate nutrient combinations (those with 0-levels of the accompanying nutrients) in the means of the complete treatments being evaluated. Prepare a single nutrient plot of yield vs. nutrient application for each nutrient using the means of yield for each level. The best procedure to follow for a plot of this type is to arrange the plots for each nutrient side by side as shown in Figure 4. If the single-nutirent response plots are placed side by side, there will be a plateau yield common to all nutrients, providing more points through which the plateau yield line can more easily be plotted by sight alone.

Establish statistical significance in yield among treatment levels

Compute the Least Significant Differences (LSD's) among single-nutrient means. These least significant differences may be useful in determining which of the yield points are the same and, therefore, should be considered to be on the plateau.

Establish the yield plateau

Draw a best-fit horizontal line through all points which differ by no more than experimental error. If this plateau line includes the 0-level, then obviously there is no response for that nutrient. If the plateau line includes levels 1 through 4 (excluding only the 0), then the rate of nutrient application necessary to reach that yield is assumed to be the 1-level or less. If the plateau yield line includes only points at the 2-level or greater, a response (yield increase) slope must be established.

Establish the response slope

Draw a best-fit straight line through all points not already included in the yield plateau. If the 2-level applicatiion rate is already on the plateau line, the response line is established by connecting the yields at the 0-and 1-level up-ward with the same slope until it intersects with the yield plateau line. If the 2-level or 3-level is not on the plateau, the response line would be fitted through those points as well as the 0-and 1-levels.

Establish the yield inflection point

Drop a perpendicular line from the point of intersectiion of the two lines to the X axis to obtain the estimate of nutrient requirement.

Further observations on nutrient requirements

The results of this study showed that the curvilinear model predictions of nutrient requirement to reach maximum yield were high and varied widely between locations within a given soil-crop category. A striking example of the gross difference between the curvilinear and the linear response-and-plateau (LRP) models is depicted graphically in Figure 2. Where all models are likely to exhibit bias either on the high or low side of an ideal interpretation, the larger bias (always on the high side) appears to be associated with the quadratic model.

The use of the linear response-and-plateau (LRP) concept permits a tentative estimation of nutrient requirement even for response data based on only three nutrient levels. Figure 5 shows the three possible outcomes of such an interpretation of nutrient requirement: the 1-level or less, between levels 1 and 2, the 2-level or greater. In view of the enormous number of field trials that have been carried out with only three levels of nutrients applied (usually 3 x 3 x 3 factorials), some kind of response model other than the traditional quadratic is greatly needed.

Interaction between nutrients and single-nutrient response

A principal objective of experimental designs in the past has been that of measuring nutrient interaction. Experimental results will exhibit interaction in a number of ways, the most common occurring when more than one nutrient simultaneously contributes to a given response. In such cases, any one limiting nutrient will affect response to any other nutrient (Figure (1). Interactions between nutrients can be handled in the linear response-and-plateau approach by following the multinutrient graphing technique (Figure (4). The common yield plateau across all nutrients will readily show which nutrient is the most limiting, contributing to interactions aiding thereby in any subsequent correction of treatments to be used in computing treatment means of single-nutrient responses.

VII PREPARATION OF ECONOMICALLY-SOUND FERTILIZER RECOMMENDATIONS

Yields are very hard to predict because of the influence of numerous uncontrollable factors affecting them. This situation in practice can be shown graphically using as an example the soil-crop category I data (Figure 6). Of the eight separate experiments shown in Figure 6, all were conducted by the same agronomist the same year, in the same general locality, using improved varieties. Yet the absolute yields vary by nearly 150 percent. On the other hand, relative yields vary only about 40 percent, resulting in a reasonably predictable response. Stated another way, it is possible to predict with greater accuracy that a certain fertilizer application will increase yield by a certain relative amount than to predict what the absolute increase in yield will be. The economic evaluation of fertilizer recommendation options should take the limits of prediction into account.

Single-and multinutrient choices in making recommendations

The multinutrient interpretation of N, P, and K response for soil-crop categories I is illustrated in Figure 4. The plateau yield requires all three nutrients. Nitrogen is the most limiting nutrient in this soil-crop

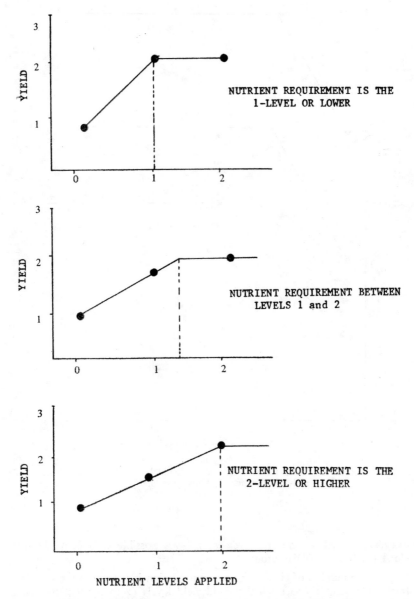

Figure 5. Estimation of nutrient requirement with Linear-Response-and-Plateau (LRP) model in experiments with only three nutrient levels applied.

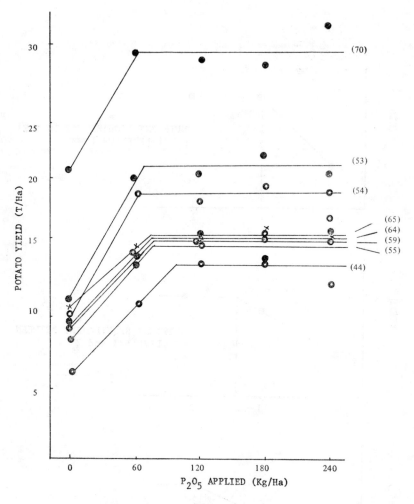

Figure 6. Yield variation among individual sités belonging to siol-crop Category I, Bolivian data.*

category, such that some improvement appears possible with N application alone for this particular group.

The number of choices for recommendation is limited to the fertilizer treatments necessary to reach threshold yield levels (zero for that nutrient) for each nutrient, and to reach the yield plateau when all responding are present. The number of choices will allways be one greater then the number of nutrients affecting yield, i.e., the extra choice will be the do-nothing option.

To increase yield to each successive threshold yield adds progressively to the cost because greater quantities and more nutrients are involved. When three nutrients are involved, with a resultant four choices (Figure 4), it is necessary to evaluate the step-wise economics of each option. This can be readily done by making a simple comparison between the additional crop value and additional fertilizer cost from each recommendation choice to the next one higher. Another technique, which may be particularly valuable when crop prices fluctuate greatly or are generally unknown, is that of comparing changes in relative cost and relative yield between each of the recommendation choices. With this latter technique the rule is: "apply the nutrient or fertilizer combination if the resultant percentage increase in cost does not exceed percentage increase in yield" (5). Its calculation and use is described below.

The percentage-increase-in-cost-and-yield approach

Cate *et al.* (5) point out that it is useful to differentiate between relative yield and percentage yield increase. Mathematically these two quantities are inversely related because they employ opposite bases of reference. Relative yield employs the plateau yild (complete treatment) as the divisor, whereas percentage increase in yield uses the threshold yield (yield limited by one nutrient) as the divisor. By way of illustration, a 50 percent relative yield means that the threshold yield was only half as much as the plateau yield, i.e., the application of a particular fertilizer nutrient doubled yield or produced a percentage increase of 100 percent.

The procedure for calculating percentage increases in yield and cost due to fertilizer use is illustrated in Table 4 using the Bolivian data. In soil-crop category I, each additional level of fertilization reduces the relative unit cost, and the percentage increase in yield is well above the percentage increase in cost. The correct recommendation, for a farmer with no constraints on fertilizer purchases, would be the complete treatment of 70-65-40. (N—P_2O_5—K_2O, kg/ha).

The calculations for potatoes in Table 4 are typical for an intensive crop where production costs are rather high even without fertilizer. Thus the percentage increase in yield is typically much higher than percentage increase in cost due to fertilization. Another way of interpreting this situation is that the producer already has considerable input investment to protect and, therefore, the relatively small added cost to fertilize to maximum yields is easily justified. However, in non-mechanized agriculture where cheap labor and available land can be substituted for fertilizer and other inputs, this may not be the case. Typically the percentage increase in cost under these conditions runs high when fertilizer is used, approaching or surpassing the predicted percentage increase in yield.

Table 4.—Economic evaluation of fertilizer recommendation. Calculation of percentage increases in yield and cost and the change in relative unit cost at each choice of fertilizer recommendation.[1]

Fertilizer recommendation choices	Yield data			Cost data				
	Relative yield at each nutrient threshold	Change from next lower recommendation choice		Fertilizer cost	Total Producción cost	Change from next lower recommendation choice		Relative unit cost[4]
		Increase in relative yield	Percentage increase in yield[2]			Increase in cost	Percentage increase in cost[3]	
			%	(U.S. $)	(U.S. $)	(U.S. $)	%	

SOIL CROP CATEGORY I. (From Figure 4).

Fertilizer recommendation choices	Relative yield	Increase in relative yield	%	Fertilizer cost (U.S. $)	Total Producción cost (U.S. $)	Increase in cost (U.S. $)	%	Relative unit cost
0- 0- 0	45	—	—	0	340	—	—	7.6
25- 0- 0	58	13	29	10	350	10	3	6.0
60-55- 0	93	35	60	40	380	30	9	4.1
70-65-40	100	7	8	60	400	20	5	4.0

1/ Based on potato and wheat production data with Bolivian cost estimates for seed, land, labor prior to harvest, pesticides, interest on borrowed money, all nutriends U.S. $0.35/Kg.

2/ Increase in relative yield/the relative yield, at each nutrient threshold, i.e., previous relative yield.

3/ Increase in cost/total production cost, for previous recommendation choice.

4/ Total production cost/relative yield, at each nutrient threshold.

VII SUMMARY

Interpretation of fertilizer response data from field trials was carried out by means of four response models, including three curvilinear models (quadratic, square root, and logarithmic) and a postulated Linear Response-and-Plateau (LRP) model based on Liebig's Law of the Minimum. The Linear Response and Plateau (LRP) model was found to give interpretation of data which, when evaluated both by regression R^2 for fit and by regression residuals, was reasonable and correct. A simple graphing technique was developed which permits a rapid interpretation of nutrient requirement based on single-or multi-nutrient responses.

Fertilizer recommendations which are developed directly from the multinutrient response functions of the Linear Response-and-Plateau model (LRP) are easily subjected to economic evaluation.

VIII REFERENCES

1. ANDERSON, R. L., and L. A., NELSON. 1971. Some problems in the estimation of single nutrients response functions. Inst. of Statistics. North Carolina State University, Reprint N° 244.

2. BARTHOLOMEW, W. V. 1972. Soil nitrogen - Supply processes and crop requirements. Tech. Bull. N° 6, ISFEI series, North Carolina State University, Raleigh, N. C.

3. BOYD, D. A. 1970. Some recent ideas on fertilizer response curves. Paper presented at Congress of Antibes on Role of Fertilization in the Intensification of Agricultural Production. Copyright: International Potash Institute, Berne, Switzerland.

4. CATE, R. B., J., and L. A. NELSON. 1965. A rapid method for correlatioin of soil test analyses with plant response data. Tech. Bull. N° 1, ISFEI series, North Carolina State University, Raleigh, N. C.

5. CATE, R. B., Jr., A. H. HUNTER., and J. W. FITTS. 1971. Economically sound fertilizer recommendations based on soil analyses. Proc. Int. Symp. on Soil Fert. Eval. New Delhi, 1:1065-1071.

6. SWANSON, E. R. 1963. The static theory of the firm and three laws of plant growth. Soil Sci. 95:338-343.

28 Adequate use of Fertilizers on Perennial and Annual Crops in Ecuador

WASHINGTON BEJARANO, JOSE LAINEZ C., and SAM PORTCH

I INTRODUCTION

Research on crop fertilization follows different approaches according to the country where it is conducted. In some countries, researchers rely heavily on the data obtained through chemical soil analysis as the basis for their recommendations (15); in others, this basic information is sought through field experimentation (5).

Both these approaches have only had a limited success in agricultural production, since they do noth always lead to making totally reliable recommendations; they do not take into account possible changes in climatic conditions, or the variability of soil characteristics, especially through the effects of their management. This situation has led to the search for new, more efficient research models, which will result in recommendations better fitted to specific farm characteristics as well as to the farmer's management capacity.

In order to appraise the fertility of soils, Fitts (10) advises going through the following stages: 1.—A good sampling, 2.—Accurate laboratory analyses, 3.—Establishment of nutrient fixation curves and correct interpretations of the data, 4.—Greenhouse-testing based on the conclusions drawn from laboratory results, 5.—Implementation of field experiments to verify the data obtained in the preceding steps, 6.—Correlation of the chemical analysis with the yield percentages obtained in the field experiments, 7.—Establishment of the optimum fertilizer dosage based on the fertilizer response curve under field conditions, and 8.—Formulation of the appropiate recommendations on the use of fertilizers, in accordance with the farmer's financial possibilities.

It must also be noted that the field tests must be carried out on the farmer's own land in each of the areas in production (17). A series of experiments is to be conducted in these areas where a favorable environment allows improvement of the crop yields.

The Instituto Nacional de Investigaciones Agro-Pecuarias (INIAP) in Ecuador, in collaboration with the International Soil Fertility Evaluation and Improvement (ISFEI) following Fitt's methods (10), has recently carried out several research projects. This paper presents only the results of five experiments with potatoes, three with coffee, and two with cacao.

II MATERIALS AND METHODS

For the selection of experimental sites INIAP conducts visits to the areas where the most important crops are grown, chooses twice as many potential sites as would be needed for the experiments. In each of these, a sketch of the plot is made, and five samples of the soil are taken. Composite samples are taken from strategic locations. Once the samples have been analyzed, the plots are chosen by reason of their homogeneity within a previously-established fertility range.

Using soil samples from the selected plots, fixation curves are worked out following the procedure designed by Hunter (14), and Palacios and Portch (19). These curves serve as the basis for deciding on the treatments to be used in greenhouse tests by adding the missing element to the soil from each plot. The method used for these tests was Hunter's (14) modified (19).

Stephenson and Shuster's method was formerly used in Pichilingue, with slight modifications (9). At present, Hunter's method (14) with Palacios and Portch's modifications (19) has been adopted. In this case, the nutritional deficiencies detected through greenhouse tests, were the basis for selecting the elements and levels to be studied in the field.

Potatoes

The experiments were conducted during the agricultural year 1972-1973, in the potato-producing southern areas of the Pichincha province, and the northern part of the Cotopaxi province, at an altitude of 3,000 to 3,500 m.a.s.l. The mean temperature of the area ranges from 10 to 14°C, and rainfall amounts from 900 to 1,400 mm/year.

A ramdonized block design with four replications, on a double-diamond arrangement was used. Thirteen treatments, 6 with N and P, plus two treatments with K giving a total of 15 treatments, were tested. The plots were 8 meters long by 6 meters wide and composed by 5 forrows with spacing of 1,20 meters.

The correlation helps to establish comparisons between laboratory data and the percentage yields in the field experiments (4).

The optimum economic fertilizer doses were estimated by obtaining the derivatives of the quadratic regression equations and establishing the ratio of the cost of inputs to the price of the product (2). The resulting data were arranged in tables as a basis for making recommendations on the appropriate use of fertilizers in accordance with the soil analysis.

Coffe and cacao

The chemical analysis of the leaves, by showing the nutritional condition of the plants, served as a test of the efficiency of the fertilization being used (3). For this purpose a sample of leaves was taken from each plot. In the case of coffee, the sampling was done following the indications of Chaverri, Bornemisza and Chavez (7); for cacao, as Boynton and Sands indicate (1). The samples were washed, dried, and ground conventionally. N digestion was realized using Kjeldhal's method, modified by Muller (18), and the digestion of other minerals was done using 5:1 mixture of nitric and perchloric acids. For the chemical analysis the methods were those of the Experimental Station in Pichilingue (16).

Fiel experiments: The fertilization experiments on coffee (Robusta variety) and cacao (colne EE-T-19) were carried out in Quevedo, in the central area of Ecuador's coast, at an altitude of 80 m. above sea level, an average temperature of 22 to 25°C and 1.900 mm. of annual rainfall.

Coffee: The soils used in the coffee experiments were of the lateritic regosol type, a group described by Frei (11). The first experiment was a factorial test, with two levels of N, P, and K. In the second one, 5 levels of N were used, combined with three levels of K. In both cases a randomized block design was used, with five replications and nine plants per plot, with a spacing of 3x3 m.

In a third experiment different times of application and N levels were tested, together with levels of irrigation; a spit plot design with three replications, five plants per sub-plot, at 3x2.5 m. spacing, was used.

In the first two tests, half the N (urea) and K was applied at the beginning of the rainy season, together with the total amount of P; the remaining half of the N and K was applied at the end of the season. In the third case, the fertilizer treatments were fractioned into two or three applications.

Cacao: The tests were done on characteristic soils from the recent alluvial formation of the Quevedo River. The first one was a complete factorial test with three levels of N, P, and K, and with a block design at random with five replications, six plants per plot, at 3x4 m. spacing. In the second one the object was to study the levels of N and of other nutrients shown to be deficient in greenhouse tests. The design was again randomzed blocks, with five plants of the same clone per plot.

In the first case, half the N (urea) and K, with the total amount of P were applied at the beginning of the rainy season, and the remainder at the end of the season. In the second test, the N, also applied as described above, was Ammonium Sulphate. The nutri-leaf 60 was distributed every two months by means of a motor pump, one liter of 1.4% solution per plant.

III RESULTS AND DISCUSSION

Potatoes

Soil analysis: In all five sites of the potato experiments, the soils were analyzed following Olsen's modified method (13). The results indicated that in all five cases the N contents were medium, with low levels of P, and medium to high contents of K (Tables 1 and 2). Due to the lack of sufficiente correlation data, the critical levels suggested by Hunter (13) were used as a first approximation to interpretation.

Fixation curves: Fixation curves of the soils samples were determined (Table 3). Only nutrients showing less-than high contents were included.

The data show all soils to have P-fixing capacity. This can be explained by the probable presence of amorphous materials, in the soils derived from volcanic ashes, (Andept sub-order), in the experimental areas.

Table 1.—Chemical analyses of the Potatoes experimental soils.[1]

Site	pH	Al + H	N	P	K	Ca	Mg	Zn	Cu	Fe	Mn
		meq/100 ml.			ug/ml.						
Santa Rosa	6.1	0.2	34	9	124	920	105	4.9	2.7	64.5	1.5
Umbría	6.2	0.3	58	8	147	1556	140	5.6	4.0	120.0	19.0
Santa Catalina	5.5	0.5	41	14	155	985	90	5.2	6.4	212.0	1.8
El Retiro	6.7	0.4	50	6	240	1880	401	14.5	4.8	256.0	1.5
Aychapicho	6.3	0.3	41	4	174	1750	155	6.0	5.8	100.0	16.5

Table 2.—Soil analyses interpretation.[1]

Site	pH	Al + H	N	P	K	Ca	Mg	Zn	Cu	Fe	Mn
Santa Rosa	med. acid	low	medium	low	medium	high	high	medium	medium	high	low
Umbría	med. acid	low	medium	low	medium	high	high	medium	medium	high	medium
Santa Catalina	med. acid	low	medium	low	high	high	high	medium	high	high	low
El Retiro	sligt. acid	low	medium	low	high	high	high	high	high	high	low
Aychapicho	med. acid	low	medium	low	high	high	high	medium	high	high	medium

1/ Five samples average.

Greenhouse tests: In these tests, a significant decrease in yields was registered when P was the missing element, in contrast to the results of using a full treatment. This was in agreement wit hthe soil analyses showing low amounts of available P (Table 1).

Table 3.—Nutrient fixation in the soils.

Locality	P	K	Zn	Cu	Mn
			mg/ml		
Santa Rosa	132	84	11.75	3.50	45
Umbría	108	130	11.50	0.25	40
Santa Catalina	167	—	11.50	—	40
Aychapicho	75	7	—	—	33

Three of the four soils tested showed significant responses to the addition of sulphur, which suggests that Hunter's method (14) recommending the omission of S in full treatments is not adequate in this case. Consequently, sulphur was applied in all treatments in subsequent tests.

In two of the four soils significant responses were shown to applications of Ca. This was not in agreement with the interpretations of the soil analyses (Table 2). Further research into Ca performance is therefore in order.

One of the soils presented significant response to the B application. The rest of the 12 elements tested did not indicate any response.

Field experiments: The yield levels obtained appear in Table 4. Table 5 shows the statistical analyses of the yields.

The chemical analysis indicated that the soils had medium nitrogen and potassium contents, and low levels of phosphorus.

The phosphorous fixation curves showed capacity to fix this element in all soils. In one case, Umbría, this was true of potassium also. At the same time, greenhouse tests indicated deficiencies in phosphorous, but not in nitrogen. As expected, (Table 5), there were quadratic effects, for N as well as P, in the yields of all soils. A K significant effect for the Umbría soil, with medium available K content, was obtained.

These effects, represented as response curves through quadratic regression equations, can be observed in Figs. 1, 2, 3, 4, and 5. As an analysis of the curves can indicate, the low levels of phosphorus in the soils make this the critical element. In all four cases, the yield percentages increased in greater proportion after adding P that after N additions (medium contents). In "El Retiro" the effect of phosphorus was linear.

Table 4.—Potatoes average yields (Ton/ha).

Treatment Nº	Treatments Kg/ha N—P₂O₅—K₂O	Locality				
		Santa Rosa	Umbría	Sta. Catalina	El Retiro	Aychapicho
1	0- 0- 0	7.217	9.926	7.490	10.243	8.130
2	0-200- 0	12.161	18.896	12.135	13.225	23.500
3	50-200- 0	22.801	34.910	20.971	22.960	33.066
4	100-200- 0	28.672	42.263	21.220	26.728	40.032
5	150-200- 0	28.159	47.414	22.860	27.586	44.398
6	200-200- 0	28.955	41.783	22.472	24.379	42.545
7	100- 0- 0	6.264	9.232	6.222	14.746	6.430
8	100-100- 0	24.410	37.523	16.231	25.471	30.214
9	100-200- 0	27.189	45.744	23.652	This treatment was not used.	38.505
10	100-300- 0	28.336	47.238	20.680	27.694	44.035
11	100-400- 0	28.786	45.731	25.141	27.269	47.149
12	200- 0- 0	5.188	6.997	6.483	13.058	5.290
13	0-400- 0	16.947	22.940	13.543	14.954	27.149
14	200-400- 0	34.847	45.571	30.975	28.107	47.612
15	100-200-100	29.821	45.121	23.118	25.914	42.864

Table 5.—Mean squares for the potato yields at five experimental sites.

Sources of variation	D.F.	Santa Rosa	Umbría	Sta. Catalina	El Retiro	Aychapicho
Total	59	—	—	—	—	—
Repetitions	3	88.8**	22.0	32.0	76.7*	34.5*
Treatments	14	385.0**	942.2	224.5**	178.5**	898.8**
Blanck vs. Treatments	1	934.5**	2365.4**	506.6**	555.1**	2459.9**
K_0 vs. K_1	1	9.5	2855.4*	1.2**	1.3	34.4
N_1	1	606.7**	1358.5*	203.6**	290.1**	961.2**
Np	1	194.2**	591.2**	83.1**	236.8**	190.7**
Pe	1	959.2**	2736.4**	715.2*	297.4**	3629.8**
Pp	1	365.5**	1256.7**	131.9**		555.6**
Deviation	8	2321.2	2027.5	1502.15	939.5	571.2
Error	42	10.0	7.4	10.2	12.4	6.22
V.C.(%)		14.43	8.16	17.60	17.49	7.77

* 5% Significance.
** 1% Significance.

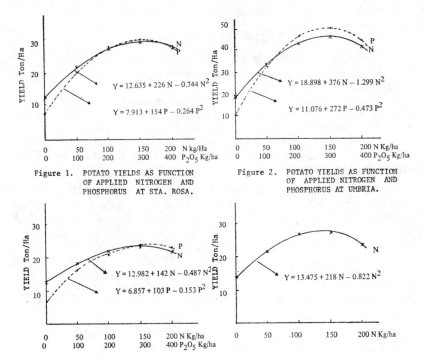

Figure 1. POTATO YIELDS AS FUNCTION OF APPLIED NITROGEN AND PHOSPHORUS AT STA. ROSA.

Figure 2. POTATO YIELDS AS FUNCTION OF APPLIED NITROGEN AND PHOSPHORUS AT UMBRIA.

Figure 3. POTATO YIELDS AS FUNCTION OF APPLIED NITROGEN AND PHOSPHORUS AT STA. CATALINA.

Figure 4. POTATO YIELDS AS FUNCTION OF APPLIED NITROGEN AND PHOSPHORUS AT EL RETIRO.

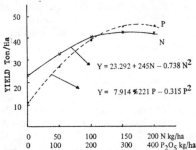

Figure 5. POTATO YIELDS AS FUNCTION OF APPLIED NITROGEN AND PHOSPHORUS AT AYCHAPICHO.

Correlation with chemical analysis: For this purpose, the yield percentages in each of the replication of the field experiments were calculated by means of this formula:

$$\frac{\text{Yield of the full treatment minus the nutrient}}{\text{Yield of the full treatment}} \times 100$$

Then, using Waugh and Fitts' technique (21), the data were correlated with the results if the phosphorus analysis, on the one hand, and of the potassium analysis on the other.

In order to determine the critical levels in this system, it is necessary to work with soils having high, medium and low contents of the element. Since this fertility range was not used in this case, all phosphorus points were placed on the positive, left quadrant, and all the potassium points on the positive right quadrant. This did not allow the obtention of the critical level of the analysis.

Optimum economic doses: By means of the derivatives of the quadratic regression equations (see Figs. 1, 2, 3, 4, and 5) the optimum economic fertilizer doses were obtained individually for nitrogen and phosphorous. The same doses were arrived at by establishing variables for the price of the product as well as the cost of the kilogram of N and P in sucres: 0.55, 1.10, 1.65 for the product; 8.00, 9.33 and 10.00 for N, and 8.00, 9.33 and 10.67 for P (Table 6). In this way it was established that the doses vary from 121 to 163 kg/ha of N and from 254 to 343 kg/ha of P. These doses, in Umbría, for example, produce as much as 50 tons of potatoes.

Coffee and cacao

Chemical analysis of the soil: The results (Table 7) show high supplies of cations of and phosphorus the soils, as well as low nitrogen availability. These results agree with those obtained by Colmet-Daage (8) and Hardy (12). They have analyzed samples of these same soils, and their conclusions on the availability of the nutrients are the same as those drawn from both the greenhouse and field tests. The results of these are shown further on.

Greenhouse tests: As in the case of the chemical analyses, these tests indicated high cation and low nitrogen availability. The greenhouse experiments further indicated that the cation contents were so high that their exclusion from the nutritional solutions caused increases in dry matter synthesis especially in the case of the Regosols. In the alluvial soil, the tests detected boron and sulphur as well as nitrogen deficiencies.

Coffee

Field experiments: Table 8 shows the effects of the nitrogen and potassium treatments on the leaves of the plants in the lateritic regosol and Table 9 shows the results obtained unith nitrogen, phosphorous and potassium fertilization on the coffee production in the same test.

Table 6.—Optimum economic doses in kg/ha of nitrogen and phosphorus for potato fertilization.

Locality	Potato prices S/kg.	Nitrogen Doses Prices per kg. of N in Sucres			Phosphorus Doses Prices per kg. of P in Sucres		
		7.39	8.70	10.00	8.00	9.33	10.00
Santa Rosa	0.55	145	141	139	264	259	254
	1.10	147	146	145	277	275	273
	1.65	148	148	147	282	281	279
Umbría	0.55	139	138	137	272	269	267
	1.10	142	141	141	279	278	277
	1.65	143	142	142	282	281	288
Santa Catalina	0.55	132	129	127	289	281	273
	1.10	138	137	136	312	308	304
	1.65	141	140	139	320	318	315
Aychapicho	0.55	157	155	153	327	323	320
	1.10	161	160	159	339	337	335
	1.65	163	162	162	343	341	340
El Retiro	0.55	124	123	121	—	—	—
	1.10	128	127	127	—	—	—
	1.65	129	129	128	—	—	—

The data on Table 10, corresponding to the results of the second experiment, show the positive influence of nitrogen, when applied in doses no greater than 408 grams per plant, and the negative effects of potassium fertilization.

Table 11 shows the high yields obtained when nitrogen fertilization was combined with irrigation. This is explained by the low humidity levels in the area during the dry season.

The results of the cacao tests, in which N, P, and K were tested, show that cacao clearly benefits, as much as coffee, from nitrogen additions, whereas no positive effects appeared from the use of P or K (Table 12).

Table 7.—Results and interpretation of the chemical analyses of the soils used in field experiments.

Soil	pH	N. Tot.	Po	Ca	Mg	K
	—	%	—	meq./100	grams	
Pichilingue Alluvial	6.44	0.14	0.17	17.22	5.15	1.12
Pichilingue Regosol	6.57	0.26	0.25	18.64	9.92	1.89
Café Robusta Regosol	6.93	0.36	0.30	27.15	10.65	1.86

INTERPRETATION

Soil	pH	N. Tot.	Po	Ca	Mg	K
Pichilingue Alluvial	medium	low	high	high	high	high
Café Robusta Regosol	medium	low	high	high	high	high
Pichilingue Regosol	medium	low	high	high	high	high

* These data are average, from six samples in the case of the alluvial soil; 40 samples in that of the Regosol Pichilingue, and 13 for the Regosol from the "Café Robusta" plantation.

Table 8.—Effects of nitrogen and potassium fertilization.

Treatment	N	P	K	Ca	Mg
N (204 g)	2.70**	0.13	1.63	1.76	0.36
Without N	2.27	0.14	1.58	1.78	0.38**
K20 (126 g)			1.67	1.63	0.36
Without K20			1.54	1.90	0.38**

** Significant at 1%.

Table 9.—Effects of Nitrogen, Phosphorus and Potassium fertilization on coffee production —in kgs. of washed coffee per ha.— in several annual crop cycles.

Treatments	1	2	3	4	5	6	7	8	Average
N (204 g/pl/yr)	114**	202**	701*	416**	2.689**	1.653**	857**	1.606**	1.030**
Without N	45	86	537	152	1.473	682	297	804	499
P_2O_5 (204 g/pl/yr)	72	154	591	248	2.237*	1.090	687*	1.110	765
Without P_2O_5	88	134	646	307	1.926	1.245	467	1.300	763
K_2O (136 g/pl/yr)	72	152	648	217	2.073	934	534	1.083	704
Without K20	88	135	590	349	2.089	1.400	620	2.411	825*

* Significant at 5%.
** Significant at 1%.

Table 10.—Production —in kgs. of washed coffee per ha.— and content of the leaves of coffee plants treated with variious doses of nitrogen and potassium.

Treatments	Crop Cycles					yied Average	Leaf content (%)
	1	2	3	4	5		
N_0 (without N)	357	497	169	996	1.148 b[1]	629 b	2.16[2]
N_1 (204 g/pl/yr)	264	653	292	1.130	1.947 a	857 ab	2.52[2]
N_2 (408 g/pl/yr)	415	763	296	1.461	2.263 a	1.039 a	2.69[2]
N_5 (1.020 g/pl/yr)	531	777	354	1.292	2.284 a	1.048 a	2.77[2]
N_4 (816 g/pl/yr)	581	778	294	1.571	2.207	1.087 a	2.81[2]
K_0 (Without K_2O)	415	790	331	1.285	2.175 a	999	1.41[3]
K_1 (136 g/pl/yr)	473	728	336	1.292	2.058 ab	977	1.47[3]
K_2 (272 g/pl/yr)	430	631	294	1.286	1.813 b	891	1.52[3]

1/ Those percentages followed by the same letters do not show differences at the 5% level of probabilities. D. B. Duncan Method.

2/ N in the leaves.

3/ K in the leaves.

Table 11.—Coffee production in the irrigation and fertilization experiment.

| Irrigation | Fertilization | | | | | | | Average Irrigation |
	1*	2	3	4	5	6	7	
R_0**	1.301	1.863	1.534	1.663	958	964	726	1.287 b
R_1	2.762	2.003	1.869	2.463	2.308	1.963	1.322	2.099 a
R_2	1.907	2.711	1.724	2.254	2.038	2.300	1.610	2.078 a
Average Fertilization	1.990	2.192	1.709	2.127	1.768	1.743	1.219	
	a***	a	ab	a	ab	ab	b	

* (1) 1 lb. urea in two applications; (2) 1 lb. urea in three applications; (3) 1½ lbs. urea in two applications; (4) 1½ lbs. urea in three applications; (5) 2 lbs. urea in two applications; (6) 2 lbs. in three applications; (7) control.

** (R_0) without irrigation; (R_1) one irrigation (R_2) two irrigations.

*** Percentages with the same letter show no difference at the 5% level of probabiilty. D. B. Duncan Method.

Table 12.—Influence of N, P, and K on cacao production in several crop cycles.

| Treatment | Crop Cycles | | | | | | Average |
	1	2	3	4	5	6	
			kg of dry cacao/ha				
N_0 (Without N)	1.412	2.605	1.354	2.211	1.364	0.809	1.626 b*
N_1 (204 g/pl/yr)	1.829	3.343	1.822	2.526	2.009	1.102	2.105 a
N_2 (408 g/pl/yr)	2.029	3.369	1.721	2.748	1.992	1.468	2.221 a
P_0 (Without P_2O_5)	1.774	3.235	1.639	2.506	1.750	1.164	2.011
P_1 (204 g/pl/yr)	1.688	3.023	1.483	2.551	1.741	1.039	1.921
P_2 (408 g/pl/yr)	1.808	3.059	1.775	2.429	1.874	1.200	2.024
K_0 (Without K_2O)	1.780	3.074	1.626	2.514	1.922	1.127	2.007
K_1 (106 g/pl/yr)	1.727	3.111	1.567	2.522	1.716	1.125	1.961
K_2 (272 g/pl/yr)	1.763	3.130	1.704	2.449	1.727	1.727	1.983

* Those percentages with the same letter do not differ statistically at the 5% significance level.

In the experiments studying the effects of fertilization with nitrogen and other nutrients shown to be deficient by the greenhouse tests, a significant increase in the crop was obtained, above that shown previously with nitrogen alone. In this experiment there also was an appreciable decrease of some disorders which seriously effect the crops (Table 13).

Table 13.—Production and incidence of some disorders on fertilized cacao on the basis of mineral deficiencies found in the soil.

Treatments	Kgs. dry cacao/ha.	Healthy fruits/plant	Monilia[1]/	Cherelle[2]/	Vegetative Broom sprouts[3]/
	kg/ha				
Control group	1.079	19,8	73,3	28	11,94
Fertilized	1.959	41,4	54,2	17	8,93

1/ Ears affected for each 100 reaching maturity.

2/ Observed on one branch pre-marked in each plant (per year).

3/ Average in one year in each 100 branches marked.

IV   SUMMARY

1) In general the procedure recommended by ISFEI, using the laboratory, greenhouse and field experiments, yielded acceptable results.

2) In view of the agreement between laboratory and greenhouse results, the data obtained should serve as the basis for designing fertilization treatments to be used in the field. Besides, they may serve as a first approximation to making fertilization recommendations, until field experiments yield their results.

3) The soil analyses can be used as an indicator to help in making fertilizer recommendations, when crop responses in the greenhouse and the field are known.

4) In the case of potatoes, for soils with characteristics similar to the ones studied, it is to be noted that:

   a) For low, medium and high nitrogen contents, applications of 180, 120 and 60 kg/ha of this nutrient, respectively, are recommended.

   b) For low, medium and high phosphorus contents, applications of 300, 150 and 50 kg/ha of this element, respectively, are recommended.

   c) For low, medium and high potassium contents, applications of 100, 50 and 0 kg/ha of this element, respectively, are recommended.

5) For coffee and cacao crops, when the soil shows low levels of nitrogen, as is the case in the central coastal areas, an application of 204 g. of this nutrient per plant per year is recommended.

V REFERENCES

1. BOYNTON, D., and SANDS, F. A. 1954. Survey of the fertility status of the cacao soils of Costa Rica, as determined by soil and leaf analysis and preliminary study of the relation of depth of rooting of cacao trees to soil drainage. 5ª Reunión del Comité Interamericano del Cacao, Vol. 1. 13 p. I.I.C.A. Costa Rica.

2. BROWN, E. L., HEAVY, E. O., and BLACKMORE, J. 1956. Economic analysis of fertilizer use data. The Iowa State College Press Ames, Iowa.

3. CACERES, J. 1973. Correlación y calibración de cinco métodos de análisis de fósforo asimilable, en suelos de la mesa central de México. Tesis de Maestro en Ciencias. Colegio de Postgraduados. Chapingo-México.

4. CATE, R. B., and NELSON, L. A. 1965. Un método rápido para correlación de análisis de suelo con ensayos de fertilizantes. Boletín Técnico Nº 1. ISFEI. N.C.S.U.

5. CIMMYT. 1969. El Proyecto Puebla 1967-1969. Avances de un Programa para aumentar rendimientos de maíz entre pequeños productores. Centro Internacional de Mejoramiento de Maíz y Trigo. México.

6. CIMMYT. 1967. International Maize and Wheat Improvement Center. 1966-1967. Report.

7. CHAVERRI, G., BORNEMISZA, E., and CHAVEZ, F. 1957. Resultados del análisis foliar del cafeto en Costa Rica. Información Técnica Nº 3. 39 p. Ministerio de Agricultura e Industria, Costa Rica.

8. COLMET-DAAGE, F. 1961. Estudios preliminares de los suelos de las regiones bananeras del Ecuador. Instituto Franco Ecuatoriano de Investigaciones Agronómicas. Guayaquil, Ecuador.

9. INSTITUTO NACIONAL DE INVESTIGACIONES AGROPECUARIAS. 1965. Estudios exploratorios de las condiciones nutricionales de algunos suelos agrícolas del Litoral ecuatoriano, por medio de pruebas en macetas. Departamento de Suelos, Pichilingue, INIAP, Ecuador.

10. FITTS, J. W. 1972. Filosofía de la Fertilidad y Fertilización del Suelo. Memoria I Reunión Internacional sobre Fertilidad y Fertilización del Suelo. Quito-Ecuador.

11. FREI, E. 1957. Informe al Gobierno del Ecuador sobre reconocimientos edafológicos exploratorios. Informe Nº 585. 47 pp. (Mimeografiado). FAO, Roma.

12. HARDY, F. H. 1960. Report on a visit to the Riverine belt of Ecuador. Inter-American Institute of Agricultural Science. Report Nº 37. Costa Rica.

13. HUNTER, A. H. 1968. Sugerencias para Estudios de Laboratorio e Invernadero para determinar las enmiendas del suelo requeridas para obtener el máximo crecimiento de la planta y el reconocimiento de los nutrimentos. Boletín Técnico. (In preparation). ISFEI. N.C.S.U.

14. HUNTER, A. H. 1968. Procedimiento analítico del suelo usando la solución extractante modificada de NaHCO₃. Boletín Técnico. (In preparation). ISFEI. N.C.S.U.

15. INSTITUTO COLOMBIANO AGROPECUARIO. 1971. Generalidades sobre la fertilidad de los suelos colombianos. Boletín N° 11. I.C.A. Ministerio de Agricultura. Colombia.

16. LAINEZ, J. A. 1972. Nutrición de Café Robusta en la zona de Quevedo, Ecuador. Boletín Técnico N° 1. 32 p. INIAP, Quito-Ecuador.

17. LAIRD, R. J. 1971. Evaluación de las prácticas de manejo de suelos en los Programas Regionales de Producción de Cultivos. Primer Seminario Latinoamericano FAO/PNUD sobre la Evaluación Sistemática de Recursos de Tierras y Aguas. México.

18. MULLER, L. 1961. Un aparato micro Kjeldahl simple para análisis rutinarios rápidos de materias vegetales. Turrialba 11(1):17-25.

19. PALACIOS, J. A., and PORTCH, S. 1973. El uso de curvas de fijación como base para seleccionar los niveles de tratamientos de fertilizantes. Sección Suelos. Ministerio de Agricultura y Ganadería. Panamá.

20. VANDECAVEYE, S. C. 1948. Biological Methods of determing nutrients in soil. In Bear, F. E. et al. Diagnostic Techniques for Soils and Crops. The Amer. Potash. Inst. Washington. 199-230.

21. WAUGH, D. L., and FITTS, J. W. 1966. Estudios de Interpretación de Análisis de Suelo: Laboratorios y Macetas, Boletín Técnico N° 3. ISFEI. N.C.S.U.

29 A Calibration Program for Corn and Rice Fertilization and Soil Test Data in Costa Rica

ALVARO CORDERO V. and GORDON S. MINER

I INTRODUCTION

Fitts and Bartholomew (5) list five phases of a soil fertility evaluation and improvement program:

1. Laboratory analysis.

2. Obtaining representative samples.

3. Interpretation of results of the analysis in both biological and economic terms.

4. Recommendations on fitting informatiion into farming practices.

5. Communication of information and getting it into use.

Information and knowledge exist for all phases except phase three although one or more of these phases may be a weak link in the fertility evaluation program of a given country. Most countries, including the United States, lack good correlation data that relate soil test analytical data to a predicted crop response to fertilizer applied in the field.

Various reasons exist for the lack of soil test correlation data. Some of these are.

1. Most field fertilizer trials conducted in the past did not include soil analysis.

2. Field correlation studies require a series of experiments covering a range of soil fertility levels.

3. It is difficult to evaluate more than three nutrients in a given experiment. Most studies have concentrated on N, P, and K and data is lacking on secondary and microelements.

4. Installation and maintenance of a group of experiments for soil test correlation is expensive and requires considerable labor.

5. The need for a range in soil fertility levels means that experiments have to be carried out on farmer's fields as well as on experiment stations. This increases the cost of experiments and increases the risk of lower precision.

— 518 —

Most studies have consisted of correlating relative yield to soil test values obtained from different extractants in greenhouse studies.

Linear and curvilinear correlation coefficients are computed to describe the relationship. A point on the curve below which there is a high probability of economic response to applied fertilizer and above which there is a low probability of economic response is chosen as the soil test critical level.

Cate and Nelson (4) have developed a rapid method of correlating soil test analysis with plant response data. It consists of assuming the points on the scatter diagram fall into two distinct groups. A line separating these two groups represents the critical level. This procedure has greatly simplified the process and made it possible for people with limited statistical training and experience to carry out correlation studies.

The critical level concept has been determined most frequently by greenhouse studies. The main advantages of greenhouse work are:

1. Can control variables to a much greater degree.

2. Can rapidly survey extractants to determine the most appropriate one.

3. Determine preliminary critical levels rapidly when no information exists in new programs.

4. Can include soil from many sites in study.

5. Is easier to study minor element critical levels.

The main criticism of greenhouse determined critical levels is that they are not necessarily representative of field conditions. They serve as starting points in a new soil fertility evaluation program but must be refined with field calibration studies for various crops.

II RESOURCES AVAILABLE FOR FIELD WORK

A small country like Costa Rica has a limited number of agronomists, and they can not devote their time solely to field calibration studies. Usually, they have the responsibility for conducting all agronomic studies for a particular crop and, therefore, calibration data is generally lacking.

To overcome this deficiency, a program was initiated between the Ministry of Agriculture (MAG) and the Peace Corps to provide eight volunteers to manage experiments in the field. The International Soil Fertility Project was requested to assist in a plannig and supervisory capacity.

The volunteers conducted 25 experiments in rice and corn in 1973 and required full-time supervision from one agronomist in the Ministry of Agriculture. Volunteers at five locations had accecss to technical assistance from MAG agronomists assigned to those locations.

The MAG furnished each volunteer a basic set of equipment including detailed field plans and instructions. A return of about 80% was realized on these experiments and additional experiments in sorghum, yucca, and soybeans were in the field at the end of the year.

Boyd (3) and Waugh *et al.* (7) have recently indicated that many response curves are better represented by two straight lines than by a quadratic equation. Boyd (3) also suggests that there is little practical value in conducting experiments on only one site in one year. To describe the rectilinear (two-line) relationship, Boyd (2) advocates using at least five or more levels of applied nutrient.

We have instituted multi-level type experiments consisting of seven levels of N, P, and K. The code for treatment combinations are given in Table 1.

Table 1.—The 27 treatments used for the Guadalupe design.

Treatment	N	P	K	Group	Treatment	N	P	K	Group
1	0	3	3	a	14	3	3	1	a
2	1	3	3	a	15	3	3	2	a
3	2	3	3	a	16	3	3	4	a
4	4	3	3	a	17	3	3	5	a
5	5	3	3	a	18	3	3	6	a
6	6	3	3	a	19	3	3	3	b
7	3	0	3	a	20	0	0	0	c
8	3	1	3	a	21	6	0	0	c
9	3	2	3	a	22	0	6	0	c
10	3	4	3	a	23	0	0	6	c
11	3	5	3	a	24	6	6	0	c
12	3	6	3	a	25	6	0	6	c
13	3	3	0	a	26	0	6	6	c
					27	6	6	6	c

Treatment 1 thru 18 (group a) correspond to increasing levels of N, P, and K while treatment 19 (group b) is a base level common to all three elements. The check plot is number 20. Treatments 20 thru 27 (group c) are all possible combinations of low and high levels of each nutrient and can be used to measure interaction. The geometrical configuration of the design is shown in Figure 1. It has been suggested that the extremes are not the best levels to use for interactions and that combinations of levels 1 and 5 would be more meaningful.

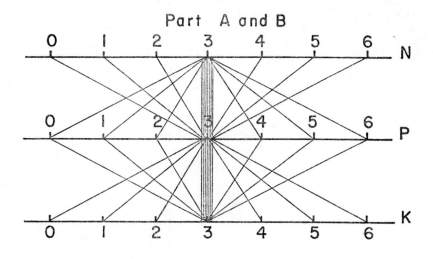

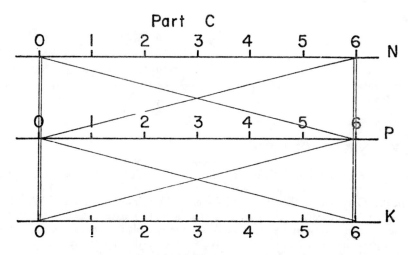

Figure 1. Geometric configuration of the design used in field experiments.

The design is versalite in that other treatments can be added or one nutrient can be eliminated if it is reasonably sure that soil levels are high. On some soils high in K we have applied K as a base dressing and added an additional treatment consisting of the base levels of N and P without K. This provides a check of K needs and reduces the number of treatments to 18 as is shown on Table 2.

Table 2.—The 18 treatments used in the simplified (—K) Guadalupe design.

Treatment	N	P	K
1	0	3	+K
2	1	3	+K
3	2	3	+K
4	4	3	+K
5	5	3	+K
6	6	3	+K
7	3	0	+K
8	3	1	+K
9	3	2	+K
10	3	4	+K
11	3	3	+K
12	3	6	+K
13	3	3	+K
14	0	0	+K
15	0	6	+K
16	6	0	+K
17	6	6	+K
18	3	3	—K

IV ANALYSIS OF DATA

A standard analysis of variance was determined for each experiment and treatment sum of squares was broken down into its N, P, and K components. Graphs were then prepared for each site using the criteria of Waugh et al. (7). Since Waugh et al. (7) and Boyd (2) have demonstrated that the linear response-and-plateau models represent plant response as well as, or better than other models, we have used only this model at the present time. The data will be evaluated by other models later.

Other graphs relating relative response to soil test levels of P and K were prepared also. Relative yield represented by the check plot dividd by the highest yield at each site allows a comparison of critical levels determined in the greenhouse and field. Data from sufficient field sites allow the refining of soil test critical levels for different crops.

V FIELD APPROACH

Boyd (3) suggests that a series of experiments are important to determine the relaitonship of crop fertilizer needs to kind of soil, crop rotation, etc. We have conducted experiments over a range of climatic and soil fertility conditions and have tried to represent the fertility conditions by soil test data. Once soil test critical levels are established then soils can be grouped to determine the response expected to various levels of applied fertilizer in each category.

The approach consisted basically of the following steps:

1. Each volunteer contacted ten prospective cooperators before sowing time.

2. Each prospective site was sampled to determine if there were fertility gradients and experiments were arranged accordingly.

3. Samples were sent to the laboratory for analysis and sites were chosen based on the following criteria:

    a. To have a range from low to high in P. (K was considered also but generally soils of Costa Rica are high in K).

    b. The farmers willingness to cooperate by assisting in preparation of land, providing labor and protection of experiments.

    c. Accessibility to volunteer's' site.

4. Materials, field plans, etc. needed to establish the field experiments were sent out and coordinating personnel assisted as much as possible in the establishment and harvest of at least one experiment per site.

5. Volunteers managed the experiments and agronomic and harvest data was sent to the central office for analysis.

VI REFINEMENT OF SOIL TEST CRITICAL LEVELS AND FIELD RESPONSE

Critical soil test levels for P and K were determined in greenhouse studies for various extractants.* The North Carolina extractant had been in use in Costa Rica and Nicaragua for many years but Balerdi et al. (1) had conducted studies that indicated Olsen's sodium bicarbonate extractant was superior.

The method of Cate and Nelson (4) was used to correlate soil P and relative yield. The relationships for $0.05N$ HCl and $0.025N$ H_5SO_4 (North Carolina) and $0.5N$ $NaHCO_3$ + $0.01M$ EDTA + 0.5 gm superfloc 127 per 10 liters at pH 8.5** extractants are presented in Figure 2. Only P

---

* Ing. Ramiro Montes, Centro de Enseñanzas, Investigaciones y Extensión Agropecuaria, Managua, Nicaragua, furnished data for a P correlation study with 36 soils and a K correlation study with 15 soils. P data are included in Figure 2.

** Hunter, A., Personal communication.

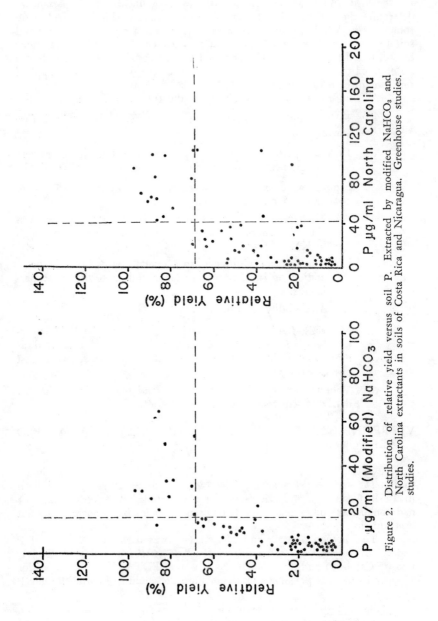

Figure 2. Distribution of relative yield versus soil P. Extracted by modified $NaHCO_3$ and North Carolina extractants in soils of Costa Rica and Nicaragua. Greenhouse studies.

data for modified $NaHCO_3$ and North Carolina extractants are presented because modified $NaHCO_3$ gave the best correlation of all extractants and the North Carolina extractant was being used in the soil laboratory. The K correlation study was not adequate to determine a K critical level because only two of 15 soils studies responded to applied K. These two soils tested less than 0.25 meq K/100 ml soil while the remainder tested greater than 0.25 meq K/100 ml. soil.

The modified $NaHCO_3$ gave a much better correlation than the North Carolina extractant. Many soils testing high for North Carolina still gave a good response to applied P. These same soils tested much lower by modified $NaHCO_3$. A critical level of 15 μg/ml soil was obtained with modified $NaHCO_3$. The 71 soils chosen represent a wide range of soil conditions in Costa Rica and Nicaragua but the modified $NaHCO_3$ still correlated very well.

The critical P levels obtained from two years of field calibration studies for corn and upland rice can be seen in Figure 3. The field studies for corn gave a distribution very similar to the greenhouse study. The field critical level for corn is about 10 μg/ml.

The field critical level for P with upland rice is extremely different than that obtained in the greenhouse. Corn on those soils testing low in P would have responded to applied P but there was little or no response in rice on soils testing as low as 4 μg/ml. Naphade (6) also found a P critical level of 3 ppm for rice when extracted with Olsen's extractant. Most of the rice areas are located in zones of higher rainfall and in many cases soils are saturated for several days at a time. Reducing conditions probably results in greater release and availability of P and since these soils never dry extensively, the P remains available.

The field critical level for K in rice and corn could not be established because all sites tested greater than 0.2 meq K/100 ml and there was no response to applied K as shown in Figure 4. It falls somewhere between 0 and 0.2 meq/100 ml. Most soils of Costa Rica contain more than 0.2 meq K/100 ml and consequently, K is not a problem in basic grains.

The average response to N, P_2O_5 and K_2O averaged over all sites for 1972 and 1973 are presented in Figures 5, 6, and 7. There was a response to 130 kg N/ha for hybrid corn and to only 60 kg/ha for rice in 1973. The response to only 80 kg N/ha in corn in 1972 included both hybrid and local varieties. Rice had a much smaller response to N in 1973 as compared to 1972. The lower N response was probably due to less solar radiation in 1973 which was a year characterized by excessive rains and cloudiness. The year 1972 was a drought year in much of Costa Rica and with considerable less rain and more solar radiation in rice growing areas.

There was no response to P or K in rice either year but corn responded to a level of 60 kg P_2O_5/ha both years when soils were deficient in P. In general, soils testing less than 10 μg/ml P responded to P applications while those testing higher did not respond. There was no response to K in corn in either year.

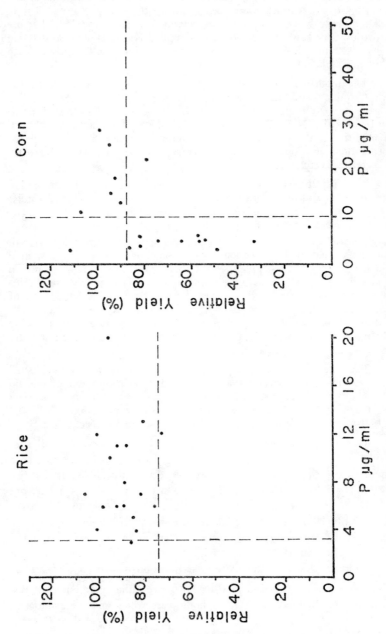

Figure 3. Distribution of relative yield versus soil P. Extracted with modified NaHCO₃ for corn and rice in Costa Rica soils. Field studies.

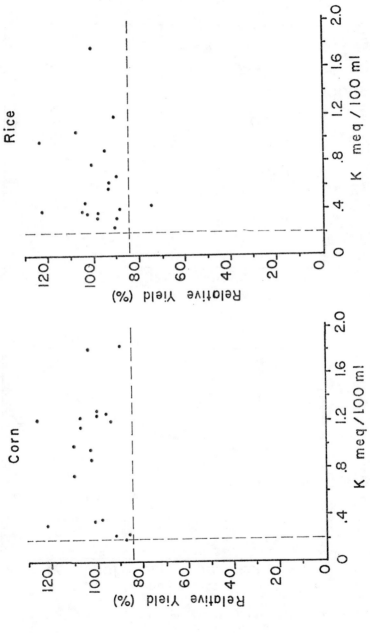

Figure 4. Distribution of relative yield versus soil K. Extracted by modified NaHCO₃ for corn and rice in Costa Rica soils. Field studies.

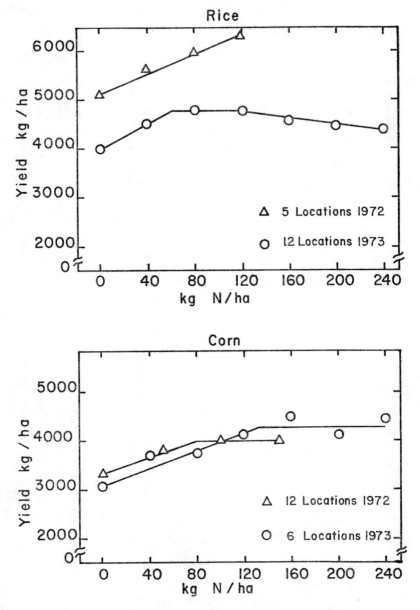

Figure 5. Response of rice and corn to different levels of N in Costa Rica in 1972 and 1973.

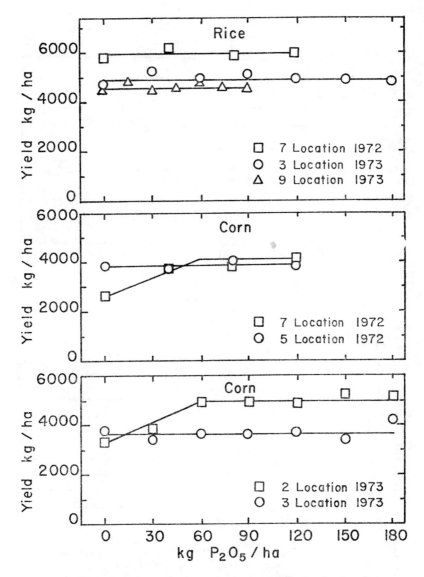

Figure 6. Response of rice and corn to different levels of P₂O₅ in Costa Rica in 1972 and 1973.

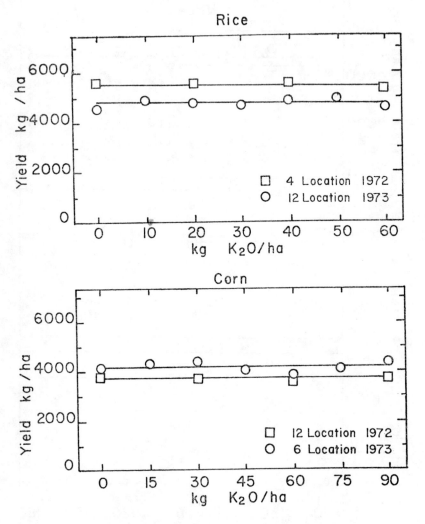

Figure 7. Response of rice and corn to different levels of
K₂O in Costa Rica in 1972 and 1973.

VII ACKNOWLEDGEMENTS

The authors want to thank Ingenieros Agrónomos Nevío Bonilla, José I. Murillo, Arnoldo Romero, Rolando González, Rafael Alvarado, Jorge Ulate, Carlos González, and Rafael Salazar for their support of the field work carried out in their respective agriculture zones.

A special thanks is extended to Peace Corps Volunteers Allen Yale, Brian Sullivan, Paul Halloroin, Thomas Eule, Neal Byrd, John Hollingsworth, Francis Burns and Fred Binder for their interest and dedicated efforts to carry out the field experiments.

VIII SUMMARY

Field studies consisting of 19 and 18 fertilizer trials in upland rice and corn respectively were carried out in 1972 and 1973 in Costa Rica. These studies demonstrated that rice and corn do not respond to K in soils containing more than 0.2 meq K/100 ml and that rice gave no response to P in soils testing as low as 4 μg/ml P. Corn responded to P when soil levels were below about 10 μg/ml and about 60 kg/ha P_2O_5 was sufficient for maximum response.

The N requirement of rice is usually about 100-120 kg/ha. In years of excess rainfall and low solar radiation, less N may be needed as production is limited. Corn responded to about 80 kg N/ha in 1972 and to about 130 kg N/ha in 1973.

A modified $NaHCO_3$ extractant was superior to the North Carolina extractant in predicting to P.

A field design consisting of seven levels of each nutrient in question provides sufficient points to interpret results by the linear response- plateau model. This model is easily interpreted and does not require much statistical knowledge.

IX REFERENCES

1. BALERDI, F., MULLER, L., and FASSBENDER, H. W. 1968. Estudio del fósforo en suelos de América Central. III. Comparación de Cinco Métodos Químicos de Análisis de F ósforo Disponible. Turrialba 18(4):348-360.

2. BOYD, D. A. 1970. Some recent ideas on fertilizer response curves. Presented at the Congress of Antibes, Role of Fertilization in the Intensification of Agricultural Production, Internacional Potash Institute/Berne - Switzerland.

3. BOYD, D. A. 1973. Developments in field experimentation with fertilizers Phosphorus in Agriculture, N° 61.

4. CATE, R. B., Jr., and NELSON, L. A. 1965. A rapid method for correlation of soil test analysis with plant response data. Tech. Bul. N° 1, International soil fertility proyect, North Carolina State University.

5. FITTS, J. W., and BARTHOLOMEW, W. V. 1970. A soil fertility evaluation and improvement program in Latin America. Presented at the American Society of Agronomy Meeting, Tucson, Arizona.

6. NAPHADE, J. D. 1973. Correlation of soil test with the response of rice to phosphate application. Il Riso. Anna. 22(1):69-72.

7. WAUGH, D. L., CATE, R. B., Jr., and NELSON, L. A. 1973. Discontinuous models for rapid correlation interpretation and utilization of soil analyisis and fertilizer response data. Tech. Bul. N° 7, International Soil Fertility Project, North Carolina State University.

SECTION VII

APPROACH AND COORDINATION OF SOILS
RESEARCH FOR DEVELOPMENT

30 The Role of Soil Science in Development of the American Tropics

A. COLIN McCLUNG

I SOIL SCIENCE - BASIC TO DEVELOPMENT

I should like to state the proposition that soil science is the critical agricultural discipline in the development of the American tropics. No other field of study is of equal importance. Improved and sustained agricultural production in tropical America does not depende upon breakthroughs in varietal improvement. For many species, varieties capable of yields several times those now commonly obtained are already available to farmers. Because of inadequate knowledge of how to deal with difficult soil conditions, literally millions of hectares are uncropped even though topography and climate are favorable. A green revolution in the American tropics awaits a better understanding of tropical soils and how to manage them.

In making these statements I am not taking issue with plant breeders as a group. I do not wish to minimize the importance of varieties with greater yield potential, higher quality and better insect and disease resistance. The fact is that by design, or by good fortune, the plant breeders are ahead of us. Some of the most knowledgeable breeders have for years been trying to tell us how critical our field is. I recall clearly a visit with Norman Borlaug early in 1960. I had just joined the staff of the Colombian Departamento de Investigaciones Agropecuarias and was headquartered at Tibaitata, as leader of the Soils Program. Borlaug came to my office and said, "Look, I want to talk to you about a soils program that will break the ceiling we are up against on wheat yields. We've gone as far as we can with breeding. Unless better fertilization and soil management practices are developed, we can't increase yields further".

Some of you present at this symposium may recall similar remarks Borlaug made at the Buenos Aires meetings of the Latin American Plant Science Society later that year. The meetings were divided into several concurrent sessions and Borlaug spent most of his time with the breeders and pathologists. But he joined the soils group at one point and during the discussion period asked if he might make a few remarks. As I remember it, the remarks had rather little to do with the subject we had been discussing. Instead they amounted to a thorough blistering of soil science for failing to provide the information needed to break yield barriers. He accused us of spending our time in laboratories or looking at soil profiles and not studying soil as a medium for plant growth under field conditions.

I think the tactics he proposed were wrong. Without a better knowledge of the fundamentals of soil classification, soil chemistry and other basics, the field investigator is flying blind. It doesn't do a whole lot of good to know everything there is to know about growing crops at site "A" if you can't characterize site "A" in relatioin to other places as well. I remember when I first reported for duty in the interior of Sao Paulo, Brazil, how anxious I was to talk with a good pedologist and to get my bearings on these questions. I suddenly realized how much I had relied on my colleagues in this field and wished that I knew a lot more geology and had spent more time studying soil profiles. Several of our Brazilian colleagues were kind enough to go on some long field trips with me and Reeshon Fuer's explanations of the geomorphology of Central Brazil were extremely helpful.

No, the answer wasn't to hold back on these studies, but rather to undertake additional ones designed to determine how existing soil conditions can be modified to achieve improved production on an economic basis. And to do this, a better understanding is needed of clay mineralogy, soil microbiology and other basic fields.

But Borloug's basic criticisms were right. Soil science did (and does) need to be strengthened and to take a place of leadership in agricultural development. It needs to get off of the experiment stations and to deal directly with farm conditions. Previous work in the tropics has often been unrelated to field problems and too little has been known about the actual conditions that farmers face.

Also, we have all too often tended to compartmentalize. "Crop Improvement" until relatively recently was taken to mean varietal improvement and was largely independent of soil science, entomology and other fields. In recent years we have learned a lot about the value of interdisciplinary teams to deal with production problems on a crop basis.

I think we are slowly coming to the realization that even integrated team effort on a crop-by-crop basis is not enough. Certainly great strides have been made by dealing with an individual crop in all its aspects, and we need to continue the use of this important approach through commodity-centered teams. But commodities interact with one another. We need to gain a better understanding of these interactions and to develop farming systems that are capable of getting the most out of a given environment and of providing the farmer with a better income, however that may be defined.

No matter how the research is organized, soil science comes out as one of the key elements. The soils of the American tropics are predominantly acid and highly leached, particularly in those areas which are sufficiently well drained for upland crops and which have favorable topography for cultivation. Nutrient deficiencies are so acute in some soils that major outlays for lime and fertilizer are needed from the outset. On all but a very few, the reserves are rapidly depleted under cultivation and within a relatively few years significant inputs are required if production is to be maintained.

Cropping systems are needed which will preserve inherent productivity to the extent possible and that will maximize the effectiveness of costly inputs. The agricultural research community must be highly innovative in developing these systems. They should draw on Asian and African experiences and not simply attempt to introduce systems that have been successful in North America and Europe. The soil scientists must determine how basic principles are expressed under a variety of tropical conditions and develop farming systems accordingly.

In emphasizing the important role of soil science I would not wish to divert attention from a promising sort of collaboration which is now developing between soil scientists and plant breeders. I refer to work underway to select genetic strains which will tolerate adverse soil conditions. I recall years ago some work done here at the Palmira Station of ICA which showed that certain varieties of alfalfa were more tolerant of low soil boron than others. When the history of the varieties in these tests was examined it was found that the more tolerant ones had been developed in parts of the world where boron deficiency was common. Unknowingly, the plant breeder had selected strains better suited to these adverse conditions. Now we find plant breeders and soil scientists working together to pinpoint genetic sources which are particularly adapted to specific problem soils and to developed high yielding varieties which require less of the expensive inputs. I applaud these endeavors and hope that they will be expanded.

II THE CURRENT STATUS OF AGRICULTURAL DEVELOPMENT

We are talking about the agricultural development of the American tropics and the role that soil science should play in this development. Here we find ourselves on a much larger stage than has usually been allotted to us. It means not merely assisting in the improvement of an agriculture whose nature and dimensions have largely been established, but in helping determine the course of events in huge areas that have never been used before. Appropriate technology is sought not only for the large commercial farm but for the small family unit as well. Until recently most of our efforts were limited to areas with an established agricultural and basically commercial farming systems.

A dozen years ago the soils group in Colombia was faced with a decision as to whether the available resources should be allocated to investigating areas of future potential or to working in established areas that had a range of urgent research needs. The decision strongly favored the urgent needs of the already established areas. For example, the Llanos Orientales would just have to wait and the Amazon forest area came in for one week-long visit by one soil scientist in the four years I was in the department. The situation in Colombia has changed since then and considerable effort is now being devoted by the soils group to these developing areas, but priority still lies with the established regions.

It is my contention that in the coming decade agricultural science can and must bend every effort to assist in the developmental problems of the underutilized areas. The continent is ready to develop its untapped resources and the scientific community will be expected to participate. As this effort gains impetus, major attention should be given to the small family unit. In light of this potential it might be well to examine the past course of development and the direction that events are now taking.

Throughout history agriculture in tropical America has been largely restricted to lands of intermediate and higher altitudes and to areas with soils of relatively recent origin. The fact is that it was only in those areas with more recent soils of better nutrient status that major permanent settlement was possible. Even now shifting agriculture is the predominant type in the Amazon basin and similar areas of high rainfall and highly leached soils.

Pre-Columbian agriculture was apparently quite well developed in many of the river valleys where flooding was only moderately severe and where soils were more fertile. Some of these more devloped areas were also found at lower altitudes and in places that came to be considered as having an unhealthy climate. Highest level of development came, of course, in relatively dry to arid places. The major civilizations of tropical America made significant use of irrigation just as did those of the old world, and in fact none of these thrived without it.

With the coming of European settlers agricultural development in the populated areas suffered a distinct setback. Significant regions of relatively intensified agriculture were converted to grassland and cattle production. Displaced population moved to steeper hillsides and started farming areas that were distinctly marginal. Thus some of the lands with best cultivation potential became centers of animal production while areas better suited for pasture were put to mixed cropping.

From this point onwards agriculture in tropical America developed along dual pathways. Subsistence agriculture continued to be the predominant way of life for the majority of farmers, but commercially-oriented agriculture appeared on the scene and came to be the type that received the greatest encouragement from governments. Larger scale enterprises were also the type that caught the attention of agricultural sciences including our own field of soils. The technology that was developed or adapted for tropical America had this orientation. If it happened to apply also for small farm units, it was more often by good fortune than by design.

In areas where there was no established pre-Colombian agriculture other than sparse shifting cultivation, the development pattern tended to be clear better forested areas, to emphasize crops that were suited to export and to continue farming a particular site only so long as its native fertility provided an adequate level of production. The move inland of the center of coffee production in Brazil is a classic example of this pattern.

So long as there were new lands to move to there was little pressure to search for ways of sustaining agriculture even on the more favored sites and none at all to develop the poorer soils. These were passed by for agriculture and used mostly for what natural grazing they afforded. Thus, some of the most desirable areas from the point of view of topography and climate have remained untouched almost to this day.

Only within the last two decades have conditions changed significantly from those prevailing since colonial times. Populations have grown rapidly throughout tropical America. Immigration as well as increases in life expectancy have been factors in population growth. The better lands have been largely cleared and brought under cultivation and those that remain undeveloped are remote from population centers.

The effect of this basic shift in land supply and demand is seen throughout the American tropics. The Cauca Valley of Colombia has long been a major center for beef production. It still is, but a sharp shift toward crop production is underway. Sugar, corn, cotton, soybeans and other crops are pushing out grazing lands. If it weren't for the susceptibility to flooding in certain areas the shift would be more rapid. The Sinu Valley and similar areas on the north coast of Colombia are experiencing an even more dramatic change. These have been the domain of the rancher since early times but wherever topography permits crops now have a place and their importance is rapidly increasing. The shift in some of these regions has been accelerated by major investments in drainage and irrigation.

In Brazil the development of frontier lands continues but is now balanced by a strong effort to rejuvenate older areas which have declined in productivity. I have been personally impressed by the activities in South Central Brazil where abandoned coffee land and mediocre grazing areas have given way to a highly productive mix of sugarcame, corn, soybeans, citrus and improved pastures. The "Campo Cerrados" are being increasingly used, first for upland rice, a tradiitonal crop for them, and then for soybeans and other more demanding and more profitable crops. Incidentally, my friends at the International Rice Research Institute could never really comprehend this role for rice. Rice as a crop that would give some production on soil too poor for most species just didn't fit the concept of rice in Asia. As a matter of fact it is used the same way in Asia where necessary, but the general view held is of rice as queen not as scullery maid.

The dramatic changes we now see in the development of agriculture in tropical America are largely based on economic changes which make it possible to utilize the technology that has been deemed to be questionable from an economic point of view. Fertilizer costs have been relatively favorable compared with the price of commodities and supplies have become increasingly available. The value of lime has been recognized and its use has increased rapidly. In the State of Sao Paulo, for example, less than 100,000 tons of agricultural lime was used in 1957. By 1970 usage amounted to almost one million tons.

Development is now also taking place in some of the more difficult areas such as the Amazon basin. Past experience in these locations has been based largely on shifting agriculture. To my knowledge no one has brought forth a reasonable substitute for this system which has been traditional not only in America but elsewhere in the world where high rainfall and highly leached soils occur in the tropics. Agricultural sciene hardly knows the dimensions of this problem let alone the solution.

Governments in tropical America have in recent years taken an unprecedented inetrest in agricultural development. Rising aspirations in all segments of the population and increasing total numbers of people have made it essential that food production be strongly increased. Further it has come to be generally recognized that the national economies of the region are basically agricultural and that agriculture must be improved if the overall economy of the country is to prosper. An improved level of life in rural areas is seen not only as desirable in itself, but also as means of slowing the migration to overtaxed urban centers. Population movement from overcrowded rural areas to underutilized lands is desirable both for improving rural standards of living and for increasing overall agricultural production.

Prospects for successful agricultural development in the American tropics are on balance overwhelmingly favorable. There are[a] however, large differences within the tropics. In some instances a major new technology will have to be developed, while in others a considerable background already exists. Soil science can serve an important role not only in establishing or improving the technology but in helping the governments determine areas of more probable success and in signaling pitfalls of attempting to develop marginal regions.

III A TEAM APPROACH

The traditional approach in agricultural research has been to divide the complex whole problem into what were deemed to be significant components and to study each of these independently. This method was considered necessary because of the intricate nature of most biological problems. The major disciplines which dealt with these principal components were often subdivided into smaller units for the same reason. This process has been as pronounced within the field of soils as in any other; perhaps more so than in most.

In the last decade or so we have seen something of a reversal of this basic procedure. Compartmentalization has been deliberately broken down in certain instances and a commodity-oriented team approach has been substituted. The results have generally been very gratifying both in terms of the speed with which specific problems have been "solved" and of the satisfaction which the system offers to the individual scientist. The best known of these team efforts in agriculture have been those that dealt with a single commodity such as rice. Excellent progress has made with a number of the major crops and animal species in developing packages of practices which have shown concrete results in increasing productiion of the commodity concerned. Unfortunately there have been some disappointments arising from the side effects of progress in the production of one particular commodity the so-called second generation problems. Only rarely can one commodity be markedly developed without having significant interactions with others. Such interactions are pronounced in the agriculture of the tropics and particularly so in the mixed agriculture as found in much of tropical America.

In recognition of these complexities several of the international centers are undertaking studies of cropping systems in addition to the better known commodity programs. The International Institute for Tropical Agriculture in Nigeria is placing a major portion of its resources of this type. Specifically, they are searching for alternatives to the shifting agriculture traditional to that area. The International Rice Research Institute is studying relay and interplanting as a means of increasing farm income and improving rural standards of living. CIAT's agricultural systems program intends to focus on developing a process for the identification and analysis of existing farming systems so as to facilitate the utilization of agricultural technology in the development of rural areas. These projects are of interest not only for the data they are developing but for the approach they are using.

This is by no means intended to say that all of us should be conducting field trials on fertilizers or cropping systems or such. Quite the contrary. Some very fundamental properties of soils are open to question and investigation. Every speciality in the field of soil science must be included. Each of us could make his own list of important problems which need attention and the presentations at this conference suggest others.

The whole question of soil organic matter needs careful attention and probably would be on anyones list of priority problems. Nitrogen, of course, is the element most likely to limit crop production in the tropics. In recent years the cost of fertilization relative to farm prices has tended to be quite favorable and there has been a tendency to look to the fertilizer bag to meet nitrogen needs. This is not necessarily going to continue to be true, and it behooves us to search for ways of making maximum use of native reserves of nitrogen in the soil and those arising through nitrogen fixation processes.

Many of our soils have major phosphorous problems and as was mentioned this morning the cost of phosphorous is rising rapidly. A better understanding of soil phosphorous relationships would add to our overall body of knowledge of soils and could contribute significantly to the development of the tropical regions.

Mineralogical studies of tropical soils are urgently needed. In these areas, too, we have had to rely primarily on data obtained outside the tropics. The field investigator is more often than not working in an unknown environment as regards mineralogy. The situation is undoubtedly improving markedly, but there are still many instances where soils of distinctly different proporties are grouped together much to the chagrin of the scientist studying crop performance and response to fertilizer. Probably too much time has been spent on studying the extreme cases or unusual situations. What we need now is a more systematic characterizatiion of the mineral status of the soils of large areas which are available for agricultural development or are already in use but are performing poorly.

In attacking these and other problems, soil scientists must cooperate not only with one another in the establishment of research goals and in the development of the indicated research, but they must also join forces with other specialists in the whole range of scientific disciplines which bear on the complex problem of tropical agriculture. The opportunity to participate in major agricultural development is unprecedented. The role of soil science will be fundamental. A first approximation of factors limiting development will almost invariably include soils. In some places soil conditions are overwhelmingly important.

IV SOIL SCIENCE - RESOURCES AND NEEDS

I do not intend to review the history of soil science in Latin America over the recent past. I should simply like to call attention to the really remarkable expansion that has taken place over a relatively short period of time. Twenty years ago it was hard to find a soils man who had even visited the Amazon area. What we knew of tropical soils came mostly from studies made at the intermediate or higher elevations. Within these regions attention had been given primarily to the better soils on which commercial agriculture depended, and little account was taken of the extremely extensive areas which largely provided low-grade grazing.

In 1957 I gave a paper before the Brazilian Soil Science Society in which I reported on some preliminary studies of soils of the Campo Cerrados. I included about half a dozen literature citations. The procedure of the Society in those days was for each speaker to submit a copy of his paper to a review committee a few days ahead of time, and for the reviewers to give oral criticism immediately after his talk. My reviewers chastised me for overlooking a paper that dealt with my subject. Instead of six papers dealing with crop nutrition on the Campo Cerrados, there were perhaps seven papers prior to that time. And only one other person present at the meetings had carried out any studies on them at all. Some observers thought the soils in these areas were poor because they were so dry and because they had a hardpan under them. If no hardpan was found, then it was postulated that one would occur if the areas were plowed ,and especially that liming them would result in rapid destruction of soil structure, which would render the areas completely unusable.

These varied explanations of the Campo Cerrados reflect to a degree the dependence that was placed on the literature in interpreting soil phenomena in the American tropics — or for that matter in the tropics in general. Data collected in the temperate zone provided the basis for soil science. That which had been found to be true in the temperate zone was presumed to be true in general until proven otherwise. And when there was a demonstrable trend from north to south in the temperate zone, it was presumed that an extrapolation of the same curve into the tropics would serve as a basis for understanding tropical soils, or at least it would serve until proven erroneous. Of course, the weight of proof was heavy and particularly so if the giants in the field had established the principle in question. Not only was it hard, but the number of trained people was small and there were many demands on their time; furthermore, the funds available to them for research were limited.

Fortunately, over the years there has been a sprinkling of highly dedicated international scientists who were keenly interested in the tropics and who studied the soils of these regions whenever they had the opportunity, and who recorded their thoughts and findings. Fortunately and unfortunately, perhaps we should say, for all too often their writings were given more weight than the authors intended and more too, than was justified. Some of the comments I mentioned as common interpretations of the problems of the Campo Cerrados were, I believe, based primarily on observations made in savanna areas of Africa. Whether or not they were accurate in those regions I don't know to this day, but I don't believe that they were at all helpful in interpreting the savannas of tropical America, particularly as regards their future in agricultural development. So, if we have been misled about tropical soils, or if we have misled ourselves, it was as much due to our over dependence on others as it was to the fact that most of the data came from the non-tropics.

Soil science in tropical America has reached a level of maturity where its own membership now includes recognized world authority. I have the impression that this is particularly true in the area of pedology. Over Borlaug's objections, so to speak, our pedologists have gone ahead and studied their soil profiles, and related one profile with another and with what their colleagues have reported elsewhere. They are being increasingly heard from, and their observations given increasing weight on a world basis.

In spite of the progress that has been made, efforts are still highly diffuse. There is too little communication among scientists at the operating level and relatively little cooperation in research on problems of mutual interest. This is a matter of pressing importance and is, of course, one of the objectives of this meeting.

National programs in this part of the world would also benefit from periodic review and evaluation. There is a natural tendency to continue certain lines of investigation beyond the point of greatest reutrn. It would be helpful for scientists in various agencies or national programs to review their overall activities from time to time, perhaps inviting colleagues from other agencies and other countries to participate in such reviews.

Trained manpower is still woefully short and every effort should be made to recruit and train new scientific talent. Maximum use should be made of national training centers in the countries concerned, but qualified personnel should continue to be sent abroad for advanced training. Institutions elsewhere in the region and in Europe should be used for training as well as those in North America. To the extent possible, the student should plan to do his thesis research in his home country or elsewhere in the tropics. The major international institutes could be called upon to provide such training opportunities in connection with their soils programs. Centers in Africa and Asia as well as in tropical America should be utilized for this type of study.

Soil science is going to be called upon to make a major contribution to the development of the American tropics. This challenge is the greatest that has been offered to persons in our profession. You and your colleagues are the ones who must meet the challenge. I urge you to make every effort. Join forces and take action. You can count on a great deal of support from your colleagues abroad, but the leadership is yours.

V SUMMARY

The great importance of soil science in the past, present and future development of the tropical regions is presented. Emphasis is put on the need of team work, as actually practiced, different to the individual approach practiced in the early days of tropical soil science.

The need to work on the most significant and specific problems of the tropical areas is presented. These problems are which retard agricultural development and promote migration to the cities. It is believed that more emphasis is needed on the problems of tropical lowlands, as most research has been directed toward the problems of medium and high elevations.

31 A Need for an International Network in Tropical Soils

OMER J. KELLEY

I INTRODUCTION

The Office of Agriculture, Technical Assistance Bureau (TA/AGR), is responsible within the Agency for fostering the build-up of global networks of mutually supporting research, information, and technical assistance activities in priority areas of agricultural development. These activities provide operating linkages between three sets of institutions: the national research systems of the LDCs, selected research organizations of the more developed countries that have particularly strong capabilities to contribute to the problems being addressed, and selected international or regional research centers. While network building is most advanced for the primary food —grains rice, wheat and maize— it is also being rapidly developed for other major food crops such as sorghum, millet, barley, potatoes, cassava, yams, sweet potatoes, beans, cowpeas, soybeans, mungbeans, pigeon peas, and chickpeas and also for selected areas of ruminant livestock; also, need exists in soils, water and possibly other areas.

Agency policy is to encourage and support research linkages and network building with special efforts to link the least developed countries into the networks.[1] Emphasis also is being placed on regional research networks such as the East and West Africa Cereals Projects. This overall policy emphasis on networks reflects the following three sets of facts:

— Agricultural research can be expensive, in use of scarce talent and money, and resources required to achieve significant break-throughs often exceed by far what individual LDCs can muster;

— knowledge building on common problems can proceed at widely separated locations in mutually reinforcing fashion, when supported by suitable information exchange and coordination;

— a great bulk of research facilities and capabilities exists in the developed countries, especially in the U.S.; these can be utilized, through cooperative networking arrangements, to assist LDCs work on their problems and to accelerate development of their own national research capabilities; widespread LDC participation, in turn, brings faster and more effective research results.

1/ Much of the material of this paper is taken from staff papers prepared by some or all of the staff of TA/AGR. Especially helpful have been papers prepared by Dr. Samuel C. Litzenberger, Dr. Guy B. Baird and Dr. Tejpal S. Gill.

II MAIZE RESEARCH NETWORK

The maize network is probably the most complete as of now even though others are rapidly developing. It therefore can be used as a good example of what may need to be done in soils. The maize network is made up of a number of components —the participating research institutions— and the tie-ins or linkages between them, e.g., joint research, training, advisory services, information and material exchanges. Figure 1 shows the major linkages and the sources of funds provided by donors in support of the international research network for maize. All linkages are not shown or may be shown somewhat inadequately. This is particularly true with reference to links to and within individual countries. Morover, since this is a dynamic system, changes can be expected in the network over time, resulting in new components being added which may require different linkages. Internal linkages within LDCs are not dealt with at all.

The basic information on the maize network usually needed by operational personnel is presented in descriptive form in Table I. The "Components" column refers to the individual research institutions or systems which are working towards development of the technology needed for utilization by LDCs. CIMMYT is the hub of the maize network; other international centers —CIAT and IITA, the regional Inter-Asian Corn Program (IACP), and other regional organizations such as EAAFRO, STRC, and SEARCA make up additional components. Maize research institutions or programs in both the developed and less developed countries constitute other integral components in the network. Other columns show: the "Functions" performed at each unit in the network; "Services Available" from each; and how each unit is financed. Other financing sources may be sought for particular LDC linkages now lacking that may be deemed essential.

III SOYBEANS RESEARCH NETWORK

As indicated earlier, I thought it might be of interest to this group to take a look at what is happening in soybeans. The International Soybean Research Base (INTSOY) which represents a different approach to an international research network on an important food crop. While the Consultative Group on International Agricultural Research (CGIAR) has focused on building such networks through the Centers such as CIMMYT and IRRI, increasing attention is being given alternate mechanisms. In particular, it is felt by both the CGIAR and its Technical Advisory Committee (TAC) that greater efforts must be made to tap the resources of strong national (or state) research institutions that are particularly well-suited to contribute to the agricultural research needs of the LDCs.

It is in this context that TAC, in considering means to develop international research programs on the food legumes, asked about the feasibility of tapping the preeminent U.S. resource base in soybean production and utilization research. Particular reference was made to the University of Illinois. Encouraged by TAC, A.I.D. explored with Illinois the feasibility of developing a proposal which would call for the establishment of an international soybean research network directed primarily to the needs

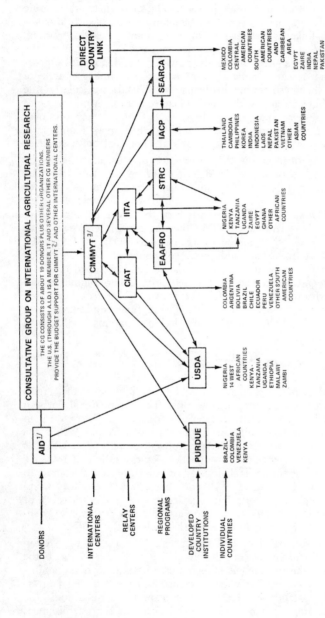

Figure 1. Consultative group on international agricultural research and its connection with cooperating groups.

Table 1.—International Maize Research Network.

Components	Functions	Services available	Source of funds
CIMMYT - INTERNATIONAL CENTER MAIZE AND WHEAT IMPROVEMENT, El Batan, Mexico	Serves as hub of international network; multidisciplinary production-oriented core research; outreach to national research and production programs; training; consultation.	Source of improved seed; technical information; consultant services; training, also, support in national research and production programs; and, assistance with workshops and seminars.	Consultative Group for core (operating) budget; bilateral arrangements for outreach and special projects.
CIAT - INTERNATIONAL CENTER FOR TROPICAL AGRICULTURE, Cali, Colombia	Serves as maize relay center to CIMMYT for Latin America; has limited maize research program; provides some training and consultation.	Basically the same as from CIMMYT, but more restricted. Requests, if not handled directly, would be referred to CIMMYT. Services limited to Latin American countries.	— do —
IITA - INTERNATIONAL INSTITUTE FOR TROPICAL AGRICULTURE, Ibadan, Nigeria	Serves as maize relay center to CIMMYT for Africa, has limited maize research program and facilities for training and consultation.	Basically the same as from CIMMYT, but more restricted. Requests, if not handled directly, would be referred to CIMMYT. Services limited to African countries.	— do —
IACP - INTER-ASIAN CORN PROGRAM, Bangkok, Thailand	Serves as maize relay center to CIMMYT for South and Southeast Asia; has limited maize research program and facilities for training and consultation.	Basically the same as from CIMMYT. Requests, if not handled directly, would be referred to CIMMYT. Services limited to South and Southeast Asia.	Rockefeller Foundation; Thailand.

TABLE 1.—International Maize (Continuation).

Components	Functions	Services available	Source of funds
EAAFRO - EAST AFRICAN AGRICULTURE AND FORESTRY RESEARCH ORGANIZATION, Nairobi, Kenya	Addresses research needs of the East African community nations; strengthens national research programs.	Technical support based on research conducted; arrangements for coordinated research; good library facilities.	Member countries, and outside donors - primarily U.S. and U.K.
STRC - SCIENTIFIC, TECHNICAL AND RESEARCH COMMISSION, OAS, Lagos, Nigeria	Encourages and sponsors research on important problems of participating countries, including agriculture.	Assistance for research on major cereals, including maize, and for complementary areas; technical information; sponsorship of seminars; assistance in selection of candidates for training; publishing reports.	OAS budget derived from contributions by participating countries; support for specific projects by outreach donors, including U.S, France and U.K.
SEARCA - SOUTHEAST ASIAN REGIONAL CENTER FOR GRADUATE STUDY AND RESEARCH IN AGRICULTURE, Las Banos, Philippines	Research, training and consultation; support to research and production programs, and agri-business development.	Consultant services, training, assistance with workshops and seminars.	AID, Philippines.
PURDUE UNIVERSITY, Lafayette, Indiana (Discoverer of value of opaque-2 in improvement of protein)	Research directed toward increased level and improvement in quality of protein in the grain; nutritive evaluation of grain; training; consultation.	Assistance in research, production as related to protein level and quality in the grain; source of improved germoplasm, information; advanced research training to the Ph.D. degree.	State Appropriations; AID.

TABLE 1.—International Maize (Continuation).

Components	Functions	Services available	Source of funds
AGRICULTURAL RESEARCH SERVICE (USDA), Beltsville, Maryland and Cooperative State Research Programs (primarily at Land Grant Universities)	Maintenance of germoplasm; multidisciplinary research to meet U.S. needs in production, handling, storage, and utilization; cooperative USDA State research programs.	Source of germoplasm, technical information, consultant services, training for advanced degrees.	Federal and State appropriations; AID.
LESS DEVELOPED COUNTRY AND OTHER DEVELOPED COUNTRY RESEARCH INSTITUTIONS AND PROGRAMS:	Development of technology required by the country concerned, training, liaison with extension.	Source of germoplasm, technical information, consultant services; training and management.	Country appropriations; support for LDC programs from outside donors such as AID, UNDP, FAO, IBRD, Ford and Rockefeller Foundations, etc.

Notably:

India, Pakistan, The Philippines, Thailand, Nepal, Indonesia, Nigeria, Kenya, Tanzania, Zaire, Egypt, Mexico, Colombia, Argentina, Brazil, Chile, Peru, Venezuela and the Central American countries.

of the LDCs of the tropics and sub-tropics. While Illinois was not envisaged as becoming the soybean equivalent of IRRI —e.g., an autonomous, CGIAR-supported international center— the assumption was made that it could be the focal point of an international research network and serve as a resource base for it.

A proposal has been developed which calls for establishment of INTSOY making use of the resources of the University of Illinois and the University of Puerto Rico to serve as the hub of an international soybean research network. The proposal was submitted to CGIAR and referred to TAC. While it was not approved at the last meeting for any CGIAR funding (primarily because of considerations associated with the base or center being located in the U.S. —a developed country), discussion is continuing to find ways to modify the proposal so that it can come under the aegis of the CGIAR.

A.I.D. has, however, had a contract with the University of Illinois and has more recently given grants to the University of Illinois and the University of Puerto Rico for development of INTSOY. It is expected that U.S. funding will be primarily for activities carried out on U.S. soil, that the outreach, the relay activities at other international centers and the training components usually associated with international networks will be bilaterally funded by various interested donors. To date, however, a number of field locations have already been developed and are actively cooperating with INTSOY and the beginnings of a true international network is underway. Figure 2 depicts the University of Illinois and the University of Puerto Rico as the nerve center of this international network and identifies the present outreach locations.

I have given you a brief sketch of our concept of the International Agricultural Research Networks and our feelings regarding a need for a network for tropical soils research. We are hopeful that this talk will stimulate discussion among the distinguished participants to this Conference and will generate ideas that will ultimately create an appropriate network in this very important field. Our Agency, and particularly our staff from TAB, would be very happy to cooperate with you in this respect.

IV NEEDS FOR TROPICAL SOILS RESEARCH

Improved management of tropical soils is a prerequisite to improved agricultural development in the tropics. There is ample evidence that good soil management and fertility practices so successful in the temperate regions generally cannot be applied directly in the tropics. The President's Science Advisory Committee (PSAC) Report[1] amply demonstrated the general lack of knowledge of the characteristics and management requirements of tropical soils.

Networks have been encouraged to achieve "critical massing" of resources that are required to gain breakthroughs on the important agricultural problems of LDCs. The need for coordinating and integrating all related international research efforts concerning specific crops, crop diseases,

---

1/ The World Food Problem. A Report of the President's Science Advisory Committee. Volume II (U.S.A.) 1967.

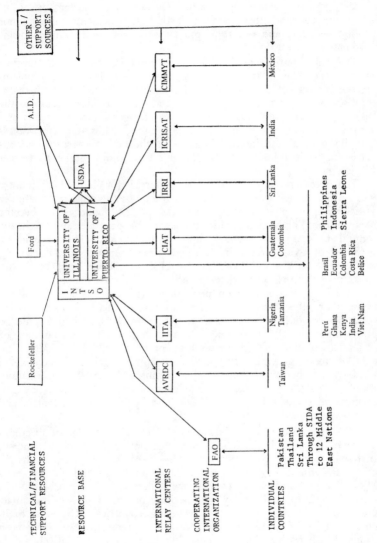

Figure 2. Proposed international research network for soybeans.

pests, weeds, soils, animals, etc., led to A.I.D.'s program stress on strengthening worldwide research networks and research linkages with emphasis on production, quality and income distribution. Maximum research productivity and avoidance of duplicative efforts, as well as maximum support for expansion of the LDC's own research capabilities, are the goals of this worldwide research network approach. The extreme shortage of LDC skilled manpower and their limited institutional capacity make donor cooperation necessary and call for rapid expansion of existing mechanisms of coordination.

The central purpose of the research networks is, of course, to improve the situations of the mass of LDC farmers. Thus the global problem-solving systems are not complete without effective internal linkages between the LDCs national research institutions and their farmers, causing the available worldwide knowledge to be adapted for local farming needs and actually used on the bulk of each country's farms. Thus the effectiveness of both the external and internal linkages of the national research organizations is critical in transforming world-wide capabilities into LDC farmer capabilities.

The international networks are resources for individual country programs which enable worldwide relevant technology to flow systematically to participating countries. These networks permit countries to become partners in coordinated worldwide endeavors to generate and exchange agricultural technology of mutual interest and value. They provide a powerful set of tools for use in assistance programming. A.I.D. (among other donnors) can assist LDCs to establish operating linkages within particular networks, as appropriate to each case, by such measures as good offices, providing information on network activities, financing of training or advisory or other assistance services within the network, participation in workshops or conferences, or of exposure visits. Such activities could be integral components of larger projects to assist individual LDCs building of particular agricultural research capabilities, or they could be discrete components of more general efforts to assist agricultural expansion (e.g., financial from technical support or other "umbrella" funds). Information, in the form of reports pertinent to establishment of the described linkages, is disseminated periodically by TA/AGR, and by international centers and other institutions in the research networks,

Within the last decade, however, a substantial amount of meaningful research has been initiated and is being continued by many national, international and regional institutions. This research has given us insight into the many troublesome problems of the tropical soils and has led many to believe that vast areas of the tropics now under cultivation can be brought into a high state of productivity within the economic framework of practices that can be adapted in the developing countries. The new high-yielding varieties of wheat and rice, and more recently corn, have been relevant only where these introductions have been made on relatively fertile soils with adequate water or where improved soil fertilization and soil management practices have also been employed. These experiences have been instrumental in triggering a significant increase in practical research (and to a lesser degree fundamental studies) on tropical soil management. Many national organizations have active and realistic research and utilization programs in operation. Expanded soil surveys into new areas and the correlation and interpretation of soil properties under one common system, such as the FAO-UNESCO soil map of the world, have greatly expanded the knowledge and the management practices required for some of the tropical soils.

Some of the international institutes, particularly IITA, CIAT and IRRI have impressive soil research programs dealing with shifting cultivation, management of savannah, rice production, etc. Many of the bilateral and regional programs have made substantial contributions during recent years.

These diverse and varied efforts increase the immediate need for better coordination and communication in increasing the output and effective use of the efforts that are now going into these activities. While there is at the present time the beginning of a network for tropical soils, there is a great need to consolidate this activity and particularly to identify and focus upon a "nerve center" which can carry out or facilitate many of the functions referred to earlier as being handled by the international research center. It is not my belief that all international networks require the same kind of organization or structure. It is important, however, that the functions and *modus operandi* be available to institutions and scientists —whether they be in the developed or developing countries, whether they be national, international or regional centers— to facilitate linkages into the network to be able to contribute to and to be able to draw from the ever-increasing world knowledge of the total network activity.

The Agency for International Development in 1971 agreed to fund a U.S. University Consortium on soils of the tropics. This Consortium includes Cornell University, North Carolina State University, Prairie View A & M University, University of Hawaii and the University of Puerto Rico.

This agreement was in terms of a five-year grant. The objectives were to strengthen the competency of these Universities in various areas of the field of tropical soils. These five Universities have accumulated substantial expertise not only in academically-oriented issues but in the practical aspects relating to the characterization and management of tropical soils. Further, A.I.D. has provided research contracts to two of these Universities, with a third one working under a sub-contract of one of the Universities. These contracts are related directly to the highly-leached, highly-acid, well-drained, deep tropical soils.

These are typified by the vast areas of the soils of the Campo Cerrado and the Llanos. In addition, A.I.D. has financed over the years a long history of soil research activities in the tropics with North Carolina State University. A.I.D. has under consideration research proposals with two other institutions of the Consortium for furthering work and understanding of tropical soils.

These projects, the ones financed by A.I.D. and those of the International Centers are only a small part of the overall effort on tropical soils research when one considlers the total effort by the various research institutions in the many developing countries and the other developed countries of Western Europe, Japan, etc. We have tried to develop a Fig. 3 that would include (as we now see it) the relationship between the research activities and institutions that I have mentioned above (See Ap-

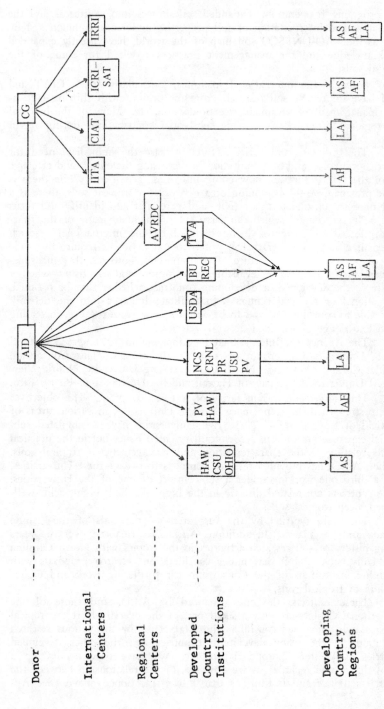

Figure 3. Proposed international soil research network.

pendix). This chart does not include research inputs of the Western European countries or Japan, nor does it go into detail on the possible institution relationships of the institutions in the developing countries or their relationships with one another. The main reason that it does not is because these linkages have not been adequately developed today. In many cases there probably is not even an informal linkage— let alone a formal one. It therefore becomes quite evident that there is a great need for the scientists working on tropical soils to find ways and means of creating a true international tropical soils research network. This should include all of the institutions that have an interest in and are working on tropical soils or related soils activity that would benefit from, or contribute to, the solution of tropical soils problems or add to the knowledge of this great (and as yet not fully developed) research area.

Appendix 1.—International Tropical Soils Research Network (U.S. - INPUT) *U.S. Aid Funded*

TA/AGR Supported Projects:

Research

1. Agro-economic Research on Tropical Soils - North Carolina State University.

2. Soil Fertility Requirements to Attain Efficient Production on Extensive, Deep Well-drained, but Relatively Infertile Soils of the Humid Tropics - Cornell University.

3. Improved Fertilizers for Developing Countries - TVA.

*4. Crop Production and Land Capabilities of a Network of Tropical Soil Families (Asia and Africa) - University of Hawaii.

*5. Crop Production and Land Potential of Benchmark Soils of Latin America - University of Puerto Rico.

6. Water Management Research in Arid and Sub-Humid Lands (LA) - Utah State University.

7. Water Management Research in Arid and Sub-Humid Lands (Asia) - Colorado State University.

8. Control of Weeds - Oregon State University.

9. Management of Heavy Clayey Delta Soils - Colorado State University.

10. Water Management Research in Arid and Sub-Humid Lands of LDC (Latin America) - Utah State University.

11. Water Management Research in Arid and Sub-Humid Lands of LDC (Asia) - Colorado State University.

---

* Projects expected to be funded in the near future.

Competency Buiding

1. Cultural Systems for Tropical Soils - Cornell University.

2. Biology-Mineralogy of Tropical Soils - University of Hawaii.

3. Soil Fertility Relating Plant Nutrition to the Physical and Chemical Properties of Tropical Soils - North Carolina State University.

4. Soil Fertility Problems Under Savanna - Prairie Ecology - Prairie View A & M University.

5. Conservation and Protection of Tropical Soils - University of Puerto Rico.

B. Council of U.S. Universities for Soil and Water Development in Arid and Sub-Humid Areas:

1. Watershed Management - University of Arizona.

2. Water Delivery, Removal Systems - Colorado State University.

3. On-Farm Management of Water - Utah State University.

*4. Dryland Moisture Utilization (Mediterranean type climate) - Oregon State University.

*5. Dryland Moisture Utilization (Tropical Wet/Dry to Semi-Desert Climates) - University of California, Riverside.

C. Council of U.S. Universities for Rural and Agricultural Development in India.**

1. Soil Fertility - Ohio State University.

General Technical Assistance

1. Fertilizers - TVA.

2. Soil Fertility in Relation to Corn and Wheat - CIMMYT.***

3. Soil Fertility in Relation to Sorghum, Millets, Chickpeas, and Pidgeon Peas - ICRISAT.***

4. Determining Research Needs of the Soils of the Humid Tropics - National Academy of Science (completed).

---

* Planned.
** Funded 1968-73.

Regional Bureau Supported Projects

Latin America

1. Soil Fertility Studies in Relation to Cassava, Beans, and Pasture - CIAT.***

2. Soil Testing and Fertilizer Response - North Carolina State University (over a dozen cooperating countries in L. A.).

Africa

1. Soil Fertility Studies in Relation to Farming Systems, Cereals, Grain Legume, Root and Tuber Improvement - IITA.***

Asia

1. Soil Fertility Studies in Relation to Rice Production - IRRI.***

Supporting Assistance

1. Management of Heavy Clayey Delta Soils, S. Vietnam - Colorado State University.

2. Soil Fertility and Water Management for Vegetable Crops - AVRDC.***

U.S. and State Funded

Some of the U.S. Federal and Land Grant College soils research has direct application to problems of the tropics and much has indirect relevance.

ACRONYMS

AF	Africa Bureau (AID).
AID	Agency for International Development
AS	Asia Bureau (AID)
AVRDC	Asian Vegetable Research and Development Center
BUREC	Bureau of Reclamation (Dept. of Interior)
CIAT	International Center for Tropical Agriculture
CG	Consultative Group (International Advisory Group)

*** Partially funded by AID.

CIMMYT	International Center for the Development of Wheat and Maize
CRNL	Cornell University
CSU	Colorado State University
HAW	University of Hawaii
ICRISAT	International Crop Research Institute for Semi-Arid Tropics
IRRI	International Rice Research Institute
IITA	International Institute for Tropical Agriculture
LA	Latin America Bureau (AID)
LDC	Less Developed Countries (Developing Countries)
NC	North Carolina State University
OHIO	Ohio State University
PR	Universityl of Puerto Rico
PV	Prairie View A & M University
TVA	Tennessee Valley Authority - Fertilizer Center
USU	Utah State University

32 What do National Governments expect from soil scientists in Latin America

NELSON DE BARROS B.

I INTRODUCTION

Even though there is not much literature prepared in relation to this subject, I would like to present the experience I have gathered after analyzing the situation in various developing countries I have visited and whose experience in agricultural development programs I have been able to discuss. Nevertheless, I must emphasize that I will refer to the subject keeping in mind the experiences of my country, Paraguay.

I will approach the problems related to the possible contribution that soil specialists can give in facing the problematic of agricultural development in his country.

In this context, the specialist should be prepared to analyze and solve problems referring to three main areas:

a) Soil science.

b) Administrative problems.

c) Situations related to the economic and/or financial results of the practices recommended.

Even though it is difficult to separate these three aspects, due to the close interrelationship existing between them, I have dared to separate them trying to indicate the most outstanding aspects of each one of these three orientations that are crucial to help soil scientists to perform as effective a task as possible.

In turn, we will keep briefly in mind the training a scientist should have to successfully face such situations.

II DEVELOPMENT

Technical preparation in soil science

In general, developing countries do not have the required number of soil scientists, trained in the different aspects of soil science, that are needed to develop agricultural programs. So it is necessary to have, in the first stage, professionals that have a complete knowledge of the factors involved in the use, handling and conservation of tropical soils, so that they can evaluate complex situations under conditions where there are no soil maps at a level higher than reconaissance, nor research work that demonstrate practices with a proven positive effect.

It is expected that this specialist be prepared to recognize the restrictions, as well as the potential, of the different soils that can be found in the country; what practices may be used under wet tropical conditions with the intensification of its exploitation, keeping in mind that now we cannot think of simple practices such as the effects of the use of fire, among others, but we can think of multiple crops, ammendments, rotations, fertilizers, pest control, etc., known as packages of cultural practices, basis of development or the expansion of new agricultural horizons of the world.

It is necessary to keep in mind that, when the greater part of governmental funds are being invested in building the neecssary infra-structure for social and economic development, very limited funds are left for basic research, since the national governments are generally concerned about the problems of the moment, and they cannot distract the necessary funds for that research. This means that soil scientists must be prepared to orient research towards practical applications that can give concrete results in an immediate manner. In that form he can develop an awareness and also prove that with research, future problems can be solved, and at a given moment, be prepared to go along with the technological changes that the development of the world demands, and avoid the failure of national programs for economic development that may be well oriented but techni-cally not too solid.

The soil specialist must be physically and mentally prepared to work in an interdisciplinary team, to be able to solve the complex problems of modern agriculture. In most developing countries, they must learn to work in close collaboration with agronomists, animal scientists, entomologists, plant pathologists, and agricultural economists among others. He must also know the complex interrelationships of the pH, the use of lime, avail-ability of N-P-K and microelements, the relationships between soil moisture and structure, its influence on agronomic and economic yields and the sustained use of these means as part of the technological modernization and intensification of agricultural production in the wet tropics. The influence of the slope, the texture and organic matter, that normally must be managed under different limits than those used in developed countries where soil science is more advanced and ecological conditions are different. He must be prepared to make specific recommendations as to what types of soils, within its ecological environment must be restricted to forestry uses or what lands can be dedicated without danger to crop systems that require the use of machinery, and what land cannot be used for subsistance crops or in small, modern, high efficiency farms.

Developing countries build roads in order to, unite the country and not necessarily open new areas for spontaneous or private settlement. Nevertheless we know that the landless farmers follow the opening of succh roads, and without the orientation from soil scientists, land may be used for settling when its most adequate ecological exploitation would have been to leave them with natural vegetation, the climax of which they have reached by natural evolution through time. National governments need these guides to be able to regulate the use of the land and to be able to organize settlements in places with a greater potential for development and where the settlers can have greater possibilities of success. They must also be capable of adapting basic research available from more advanced countries, to our conditions of countries with limited funds that cannot carry out this type of work.

The soil specialists must be able to read and understand scientific publications and magazines of an adequate technical level that keep him up to date in the technological development of soil science, and not expect to obtain his knowledge by merely attending international meetings that are costly both in time and money.

National governments also expect that high level soil scientists belonging to institutions such as CIAT, IRRI, CIMMYT, etc., prepare their publications in a language that is accessible to field professionals, thus permitting them to go along with the new technological advances of soil science and to be more effective in their propagation of knowledge pertinent to the process of development.

Administrative aspects

I consider the administrative aspect as one of the singularly important aspects to which normally no value is given, and that can mean the difference between the success or the failure the soil scientist's work.

It is generally considered that a well trained person can be a good program or project director, so when persons return from a advanced training, the professional is often placed in an administrative post, not having, in most cases, been exposed to training in the different aspects he will face, such as: office organization, handling of personnel, budget preparation, management by objectives, allocation of resources; in other words, all the administrative aspects that he will have to face so that his work may have the desired impact.

Basic knowledge in this area will permit the professional to adapt himself in the daily problem that will permit him to carry out an adequate technical work with the limited funds he disposes of, and without the facilities of equipment, personnel and elements he may have had during his years of study.

He will have to use his resourcefulness to be able to obtain the best use of the resources at his reach, such as assistants with limited technical knowledge, low salaries, difficulties to move, low or unexistent perdiems, political problems, etc. In other words, the sum of all the factors or limitations that keep our countries on the road to development, and that only with technically and mentally prepared persons, can such limitations be overcome.

The soil specialist must be willing to share his technical knowledge, information and technical publications with his colleagues, distribute the training possibilities among all, so as to form homogeneous working teams where group action is more important than the individual desire to stand out.

In developing countries it is quite common that many of the decisions are taken erroneously, not only due to technical flaws but also due to lack of knowledge of managerial organization and a lack of planning and programming with everybody dedicated to solving the problems of the moment, thus acting expediently and without concern for the problems of the future.

That can be probably due to the fact that our systems give credit to persons that solve or postpone problems in times of crisis and that the financial conditions are such that they do not permit foreseeing problems that might arise in a near future.

The problems are so many and so urgent that it is of primary importance that the soil scientist be able to establish real priorities among his own work projects, and also between his projects compared to other governmental projects.

Economic Aspects

The participation of the soil specialist is of vital importance to agricultural development, since his contribution can help to define new areas to be open to crops, the forms of improving the efficiency of agricultural production, the crops that can be considered in the new development plans, etc. For this reason it is essential that the soil specialists, whatever the area of soil science in which they are specialized, have in this stage of development, basic knowledge of economics to be able to orient their work with said criterium.

A soil specialist must fully know the factors limiting agricultural development, so that his efforts are not oriented towards practices or study pdojects that may have no bearing or cannot be applied by the rural producer.

It is much more important for a rural producer to know what he can obtain from the natural fertility of his soil, with which he can then generate the necessary capital to allow him to later on use fertilizers to obtain a better production; instead of using these fertilizers indiscriminately from the very beginning, in conditions where its response is not fully determined and where the contraction of debts in the purchase of inputs or services, apart from those generated by his own effort, can cause his financiae bankruptcy by not obtaining the expected benefits.

It is not necessary for a soil specialist to be an expert in agricultural economics too, but it is necessary that he knows, the rudiments of agricultural economics to know his limitations in that field and request the help of said specialists in the evaluation of the recommendations that he himself may give. It is well known that technologically speaking there are very few conditions under which crops cannot be raised, but where the possibility of economic success of the practice recommended may be the limiting factor.

The soil specialist must know the long term as well as the short-term effects of annual or multiple crops versus permanent crops such as pastures or trees and be able to orient the national governments in the determination of areas, either to be used by small rural producers or for managerial agriculture, depending on the policy to develop circumstances they may wish to promote. For example, can a successful exploitation be effected with families possessing 5, 20, 50 or 100 hectares of crop, or is it that the investment capital in equipment, machinery, facilities and administration will not allow it? These problems will require the best efforts and creative imagination on the part of the soil scientists working in inter-disciplinary teams.

III CONCLUSION

The author has tried to describe the problems with which the soil scientist is normally faced, and the training requirements he should have to be able to overcome these successfully. These aspects refer to three main areas: a) Soil science: a brief description is made of the technical problems related to the specialty; b) Administrative problems: it starts from the basis that sooner or later the professional will be placed in administrative posts, for which he should have some preparation in that field, and c) Economic aspects: a brief description is made of the need for the soil specialist to have a basic knowledge of economics due to the importance that his decisions may have in the economic and social development of a country.

33 What International Development Agencies expect of soil scientists in Latin America

JAMES E. HAWES

The international development agencies' expectations of soil scientists working in developing country agriculture programs are high. Whether these scientists are from national research institutions or other agencies working in developing countries under contract with or supported by AID, I look to them to make the necessary inputs to the field of soil technology as these inputs fit into the overall perspective and activities of agricultural development, in general. We hope that these efforts will be realistic, simplistic and adaptable to the situation in less developed countrie, particularly the situation of the small and intermediate size farmers.

I recognize that soil fertility problems in most Latin American countries may be limiting factors for increasing production and improving the income situation of the target group of farmers. With changing situations regarding fertilizer availabilities and prices and the rising prices and worldwide shortages of basic foods, new concepts and problems in the economies of agricultural production are upon us. Soil and fertiiity research in crops must guide the way with economic components of the agronomic research to make recommendations that will promote changes on the part of the small farmer from traditional agriculture to commercialized agriculture.

We suspect that the increasing demand for fertilizers and their limited supplies due to the worldwide energy situation must change our philosophies of fertilizer use. Instead of aiming for optimum yields with optimum fertilizer levels, it might be more prudent to make recommendations that provide for the greatest efficiency of total fertilizer use —for example, fertilizer applications in the lower level but steeper portion of the sigmoid response curve. Such recommendations would maximize profits to the small farmer and would maximize production per unit of fertilizer used. Such recommendations, of course, would vary according to soil type and to other ecological conditions. I envisage that recommendations proposed should be as simplistic and realistic as possible. The reduced availabilities of a wide variety of mixed composition fertilizers may require that scientists' recommendations be such that use is made of those fertilizers readily available or in stock. Recommendations made should be as simple as possible so that the inexperienced, untrained and unsophisticated small farmer or agricultural technician can understand the methodology involved. A small farmer certainly needs to be trained in simple calculations on which he will make his own decisions on fertilizer use.

I foresee also that recommendations might best be made to confine fertilizer use on a priority basis to food crops rather than other less important uses. This would most likely assure that fertilizer would be used for the immediate short term requirements to increase lower cost caloric and protein foods, but this too could change with the specific needs of the community at any one time.

Such a course is particularly relevant because he is operating at or very near the subsistence level. These farmers have very limited cash resources and they make their decisions on the basis of real costs, and the level of risk they are taking. Fertilizer use recommendations which are at a level which minimizes costs of inputs yet gives an opportunity for a very high rate of return on investment can do much toward assisting these farmers.

Finally, I urge all soil scientists to be assured in their own minds that their efforts of providing technological inputs to agricultural programs meet the needs of the program and the desire of the host governments. This may require getting out of an ivory tower of philosophical patterns of thinking and acting. It may require real innovative thinking and selfless action on the part of the scientists to assure that their work is a real part of the work of others working on related production problems. In view of the magnitude of the world's problems of food shortages, poverty, malnu-trition and ignorance —all of which can be relieved to some extent by your work— I urge you to adapt your work to the changing needs of the world in the spirit of dedication required to solve these serious problems.

Impreso en Costa Rica, por Litografía e Imprenta LIL, S. A.

— Apartado 75 - Tibás, Costa Rica —